THEORETICAL AND MATHEMATICAL BIOLOGY

A Blaisdell Book in the Pure and Applied Sciences

PAUL R. GROSS, *Consulting Editor*
BROWN UNIVERSITY

THEORETICAL AND
MATHEMATICAL BIOLOGY

EDITED BY

TALBOT H. WATERMAN

AND

HAROLD J. MOROWITZ

YALE UNIVERSITY

BLAISDELL PUBLISHING COMPANY

NEW YORK · TORONTO · LONDON

A Division of Ginn and Company

*Chapter **6**, by Kenneth S. Cole, was prepared at Bethesda, Maryland, with sponsorship of the National Institutes of Health. No part of this chapter may be reproduced in any form, by photostat, microfilm, or by any other means, without written permission from the publishers. Reproduction for the purpose of the United States government is permitted.*

238151

CONTRIBUTORS

M. S. BARTLETT, Department of Statistics, University College, London, England

GEORG VON BÉKÉSY, Psycho-Acoustic Laboratory, Harvard University, Cambridge, Massachusetts

J. D. BERNAL, Department of Physics, Birkbeck College, London, England

ROBERT E. BLACKITH, Zoology Department, University of Melbourne, Victoria, Australia

BRITTON CHANCE, Department of Biophysics and Physical Chemistry, University of Pennsylvania, Philadelphia, Pennsylvania

KENNETH S. COLE, Laboratory of Biophysics, National Institutes of Health, Bethesda, Maryland

HENRY EYRING, Department of Chemistry, University of Utah, Salt Lake City, Utah

DAVID GARFINKEL, Department of Biophysics and Physical Chemistry, University of Pennsylvania, Philadelphia, Pennsylvania

ROBERT S. LEDLEY, National Biomedical Research Foundation, Silver Spring, Maryland

RICHARD LEVINS, Department of Biology, University of Puerto Rico, Rio Piedras, Puerto Rico

ROBERT H. MAC ARTHUR, Department of Biology, University of Pennsylvania, Philadelphia, Pennsylvania

HAROLD J. MOROWITZ, Department of Molecular Biology and Biophysics, Yale University, New Haven, Connecticut

HENRY QUASTLER, late of the Department of Biology, Brookhaven National Laboratory, Upton, L.I., New York

N. RASHEVSKY, Committee on Mathematical Biology, The University of Chicago, Chicago, Illinois

WERNER REICHARDT, Max-Planck-Institut für Biologie, Tübingen, Germany

DAN W. URRY, Department of Chemistry, University of Utah, Salt Lake City, Utah

TALBOT H. WATERMAN, Department of Biology, Yale University, New Haven, Connecticut

PREFACE

This book evolved from a course of lectures and discussions on theoretical and mathematical biology given in the Zoology Department of Yale University in the spring of 1962. In turn the course itself had developed from the conviction that much of biology has great potentialities for progress which is blocked, in part at least, by problems of training and attitude among workers in the field. Both the course and the book were intended to outline these problems and to suggest possible means of their solution.

The basic plan was to present a series of case histories demonstrating how special attention to adequate conceptual and quantitative methods has promoted substantial advances in many parts of the life sciences. From such particular examples the general conclusion may be drawn that this kind of approach offers much to biologists of all sorts, provided that their education and motivation permit them to exploit its resources.

For a number of reasons complete coverage and a strictly unified point of view have not been achieved. To begin with, theoretical and mathematical biology is not yet so well defined or well developed that it is a universally recognized, strongly interconnected, coherent area of science. Comparison of the first two chapters shows that even the editors are not in precise agreement about its nature and function.

Consequently, choices of inclusion and emphasis both by the editors and by the authors reflect this somewhat unsettled and controversial character of the subject. In addition, the availability of competent coworkers willing to participate in the course and book, as well as problems of scheduling the original course, have inevitably forced further boundary conditions on our work.

Of the book's seventeen chapters, numbers three to sixteen were written as the direct outcome of the 1962 course; the first two and the last chapters were added in an effort to provide the perspective and generality which most multiple-author works may otherwise lack. The material covered in the individual chapters can be grouped for convenience into six sections as shown in the table of contents. Again to provide greater coherence and more explicit relevance to the book's over-all purpose, the editors have provided brief introductory passages to three major divisions of the work: 1) physical and chemical analysis (Section II), 2) quantitative biology (Sections III and IV), and 3) systems analysis (Section V).

The editors are much indebted to many people and institutions whose help and advice were essential. The National Science Foundation, by providing a substantial grant to

Yale, made it possible for the senior editor to organize the original course; Yale University, by supporting the program in many ways, including a grant from the Higgins Fund, has played a key part, too. One of us (T. H. W.) is grateful also to the Guggenheim Memorial Foundation for a fellowship which, among other things, provided him opportunity for some of the editing. In addition to our coauthors, a number of colleagues and friends should be thanked for their help and encouragement: Dr. Martynas Yčas and Dr. Paul Weiss, who participated in the teaching of the course but did not contribute to the book; Dr. Hilary L. Seal, Dr. Thomas L. Lincoln, and Dr. R. Bruce Nicklas. Particular thanks should also go to Elizabeth A. Livingston whose loyal and capable assistance in running the course and in editing the book has been invaluable. For editorial help we are also grateful to Barbara Folsom, Mabelita Campbell, and Mary Wheeler.

In July, 1963, the scientific community was shocked by the death of Dr. Henry Quastler whose personal and intellectual influence on theoretical biology has been far-reaching and important. His loss is a grievous one, but we are lucky in having his valuable chapter on the general principles of systems analysis in this volume. In addition, Yale was particularly fortunate that in the spring term of 1963 Dr. Quastler was appointed Visiting Professor of Theoretical Biology and offered a graduate course in this field. The National Science Foundation Advanced Training Grant which made possible the 1962 program also supported this second one. Fortunately the notes which Dr. Quastler prepared for this later course have now been published.* In a modest way these may serve as a fitting memorial to his deep insight into biological problems.

TALBOT H. WATERMAN
HAROLD J. MOROWITZ
Yale University

---

* Quastler, H. 1964. "The Emergence of Biological Organization," 83 pp. Yale University Press, New Haven.

CONTENTS

SECTION I

Introduction

[1]

THE PROBLEM*

Talbot H. Waterman

Biology is approaching an important crossroad. From one direction traditional zoologists and botanists travel a well-worn path which steadily becomes less rewarding as well as more repetitious because they have largely failed to be both rigorous and intellectually creative. As a result their work has been branded by its paucity of quantitative data and lack of conceptual strength.

From another direction the new biologists, biophysicists, biostatisticians, molecular biologists, biomathematicians, and systems analysts approach along a different path with its origins in mathematics, physics, chemistry, and engineering which have themselves often been elegantly rigorous and conceptually powerful. But despite its surface glitter and areas of brilliant achievement, the work of this second group is often crippled by ignorance or even scorn of the detailed facts about cells, organisms, and populations as well as of their complex integrations in space and time. Both avenues for approaching the study of life may alone fail to reach their goal of broad scientific understanding.

Yet there are some signs that an intersection of these different approaches to biology need not inevitably be followed by further divergence. Indeed if the traditionalists could learn to become more mathematical and theoretical, and if the new school could become more biological, an effective collaboration with potentially great revolutionary consequences seems quite possible.

Naturally a multitude of approaches may be valid in biology, and scientists of many temperaments can be fruitfully engaged in this field. Yet the deliberate cultivation of adequate quantitative analytical techniques now available combined with the newer, powerful, synthetic, deductive methods modeled after those of the physical sciences seems particularly promising for the future. May not the dissatisfaction among the traditional biologists[34,75,85] and the lively ferment of the new biology[13] effect a breakthrough to a new level of understanding?

I. THE NATURE OF BIOLOGY

Although some of biology's shortcomings as a quantitative highly conceptual science are due to deficiencies of biologists and their training, others clearly depend on the nature of the

* This chapter was published in slightly different form as "Revolution for Biology" in *American Scientist*, Vol. 50, pp. 548–569, 1962.

subject. Living organisms are multicomponent open chain systems which combine a remarkable stability with an exquisite sensitivity to change.[40] Such systems, whose important characteristics arise from just this presence of many strongly interdependent variables, are difficult even to describe and require a high level of sophistication to analyze effectively. Without mathematics one can hardly even begin to think about entities with more than two or three variables. Yet the internal variables or organisms along with the relevant environmental parameters number in the hundreds or thousands. To select which of these must be studied and to determine how few of them are adequate to explain the system's behavior make up the biologist's central task.

Thus the initial collection of data and just their descriptive ordering are formidable tasks even when attention is focused on some restricted aspect of the whole system. For this reason biology has frequently become bogged down in collecting data and has ignored or even despised the need for doing more than this. Yet in any well-developed science primary facts, or sensory data, are the mere beginnings.

Once obtained, facts must serve as the basis for developing an interconnected field of statements, propositions, and constructs which may ultimately give rise to inductive generalizations, hypotheses, and laws. Such higher order inductions to be considered valuable must meet certain metaphysical requirements[64] which are taken for granted, such as logical fertility, extensibility, sensibility, elegance, and causality.* Furthermore, these constructs to be of any use must permit deductive predictions and subsequent empirical verification. Hence a circularity is inherent in the methodology of science since one must proceed from data to construct or model and thence back to new data, or from model to data and back to model again.[5] In a well-developed science a multiplicity of such intersecting closed pathways form a coherent system of consistent relations.

It should be noted that this essential circularity of science ultimately interconnects a black box and a white box, to use Wiener's terminology.[107] The black box is the system under study, and hence in Margenau's phrase a configuration in the data plane; the white box is the model, construct, or law which explains the working of the black box. Science may start empirically with either qualitative or quantitative data relating the input of a black box to its output and proceed inductively to a corresponding white box. Or it may start theoretically with a construct and proceed deductively to the data plane in order to determine what validity this white box may have. This interpretation of the basic nature of science is considered further from a systems analysis point of view in Chapter 12.

In these terms biology, to become a mature science, must have white boxes to explain its facts. Each white box, if not achieved by intuition or creative insight, must be induced from data. Although simple qualitative information may suffice, multivariate relational and metric facts are quite likely required and may in fact be the only basis for understanding. It is in this connection that the recent emergence of appropriate statistical (Chapters 8 and 9) and electronic computer techniques (Chapters 10 and 11) has so much inherent interest and promise for biology.

The goal of an exact science is to develop a strong system of basic constructs with such depth and breadth that particular parts of the whole field can be explained deductively as logical consequences of a small number of more fundamental principles. Thus the retinal

---

* Such causality may seem to be deterministic, as in Newtonian mechanics, but both the nature of living systems and the means of obtaining data about them may indicate probabilistic stochastic causal relationships (for instance, references[8,9,65,89]).

absorption of photons by rhodopsin in the primary events of vision can be explained in the more inclusive terms of photochemistry in general.

In the biological sciences hypotheses and theories fall into two major categories. In one, as in the rhodopsin case, the data are explained in terms of underlying physical and chemical laws. Thus hemodynamics may be shown subject to Poiseuille's law, the diffusion of oxygen in tracheae to Fick's law, the activity of enzymes to the laws of catalysis, or the reactions of metabolism to the laws of irreversible thermodynamics and chemical kinetics. In the other major category the explanations provided are biological and hence couched in terms of the underlying principles of organic adaptation, development, heredity, or evolution.[102]

Further development and emphasis on deductive explanations are crucial if biology is to progress from its present weak state as a primarily descriptive correlational subject to that of a rigorous deductive science capable of accounting for much of its content in terms of broad elegant generalizations.

Undoubtedly the physical and chemical components of organisms are the elements of biology, but the molecular and submolecular bits and pieces become biologically meaningful only when they are put back together again in the highly organized context of the living system.[75] A clear demonstration of this was given by Anfinsen's stimulating essay at explaining molecular biological data in terms of evolution.[4] Nevertheless biophysicists and molecular biologists often seem to believe that physical and chemical explanations of life are the final goal of biology. One may as well say that Fourier analysis as such can provide *the* explanation of a Bartok quartet! The ultimate scientific explanation of life must indeed be biological. Both historically and functionally live organisms share a number of basic organizational and behavioral properties not known in the nonliving world.[74]

The special nature of biological systems centers around their immediate adaptedness and consequent persistence. Hence living systems as well as their environments must be so constituted and organized that life can survive and does in fact do so with a premium on a minimum over-all "cost" to the organism.[40] Life on earth has presumably persisted from its original inception at least two or three billion years ago.

A very large part of biology can be explained by hypotheses derived from concepts of adaptedness or fitness which measure contributions to survival. Depending on the time scale considered, adaptedness relates to physiology and ecology for short intervals, to genetics and development for longer periods, and to evolution and phylogeny for a far-extended temporal scale. This is not to say, of course, that all the underlying relevant processes are not occurring continuously, but merely that the time intervals in which the various series of events become significant, as well as the pathways through which they act, are characteristic of the different kinds of explanation associated with these areas of biology.[102] Adaptation is obviously related to the principle of adequate design considered in Chapter 3 and to the concepts of fitness discussed from genetic and ecological points of view in Chapters 15 and 16.

II. A POSSIBLE SOLUTION

In view of the nature of life and the current strong dichotomy among practicing biologists,[21,72] prospects for the early development of an exact science of biology may seem rather problematical. Yet a solution for these difficulties may well lie in the effective fusion of the two biologies characterized above and in the conscientious application of mathematical and theoretical methodology throughout the whole discipline. Not only should bio-physics and biochemistry be strengthened biologically, but systematics, zoogeography, and the study of evolution should also be quantified and more explicitly conceptualized. Embryology, too, would benefit from the same treatment.

Such reforms if effected would frankly acknowledge the real difficulties of biology and reduce the lack of balanced training and viewpoint shown by most biologists, as well as offer real promise of improving the field and raising it to a state worthy of its importance to man. To give substance to such hopeful generalities, some particular cases will be cited in illustration.

A.   Descriptions

Although adequate description of the many components and interconnections of biolog-ical systems is a difficult task, such basic facts clearly must be available before generaliza-tions or hypotheses can be induced and empirically tested.[73] Several aspects of the situation contribute to the difficulty. From a metric and technical point of view, the problem of measuring a large number of the living system's dimensions is a formidable one. From a relational point of view, too, the detection and evaluation of multiple interdependencies present considerable difficulties. Although the ultimate understanding of such systems may indeed be provided by the discovery of a few simple dimensions or relations, our faith in such a parsimonious outcome surely should not be sustained only by our inability to deal effectively with complex information.[77,80]

One general deterrent to achieving adequate biological description lies in our own perceptual capabilities. Two-dimensional comparisons are easy on a sheet of paper, three-dimensional comparisons are quite possible but more difficult, whereas multi-dimensional representations are practically impossible on an intuitively comprehensible level.

B.   Graphical Representation

Graphs may be effectively utilized in solving some of these problems. The basic situation is epitomized by the familiar attempt to represent phylogenies in a two- or three-dimensional illustration.[1] Quite aside from their frequently nonquantitative, conjectural nature, family trees of groups of organisms present the difficulty that they must, by the pattern of branching at least, indicate the degrees of similarity and difference between the subgroups involved.[91] Hence assigning to particular branches group names symbolic of a great number of metric and relational characters already includes a large degree of simplification. Such diagrams also frequently attempt to include a geological time dimension and perhaps some indication of the different numerical importance of the various taxa included (Figure 1). Even when more quantitative data are explicitly utilized and more sophisticated multi-dimensional analysis is employed, the representation of the results remains imperfect.[15,19,52,56,87,88,90a,90b]

If there are only three critical dimensions involved, quite adequate representations can be made with topographic models in which elevated and depressed values of a z-coordinate are represented by isolines on a terrain. These may be simply three-dimensional graphs (for example, in reference[60]), or they may be more like landscape analogs over which com-ponents are postulated to move through passes, climb peaks, or seek the lowest valleys. Such analogs have been used effectively by Eyring in developing the theory of reaction rates (Chap-ter 4 and Figure 1.4 in reference[46]) and have several interesting biological applications.

For example, in dealing with genetic drift in populations, Sewall Wright and others have visualized a landscape in which x and y represent dimensions of genotypic variation in a

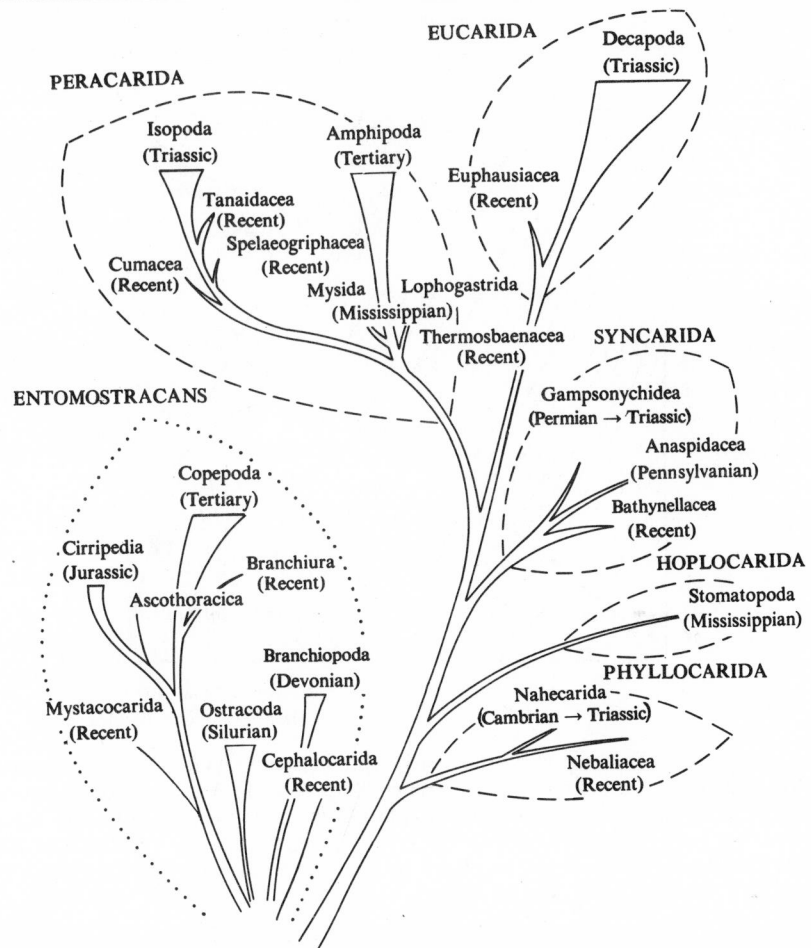

FIGURE 1. Proposed phylogenetic tree for the Class Crustacea. In diagrams of this sort a large number of parameters are compressed into a two-dimensional representation. Thus distance along a branch in the direction from root to crown is related, both to the evolutionary concept of transition from primitive to advanced groups, and to the geological time vector. The branching pattern represents direct relationships hypothesized, and the distance between two groups in the plane is inversely related to their degree of similarity and inferred relationship. In addition the approximate number of species in Recent Forms is indicated by the width of the branch they terminate. (From Waterman.[102])

polymorphic population, and z graphs the adaptedness of any particular combination of these: peaks being highly adapted, valleys relatively maladapted genotypes (Figure 2). In such a terrain natural selection* would force a population with a particular gene frequency not on a peak to move upward towards higher levels along paths like those in Figure 2.[59]

An analogous biological application[86] has been made in relation to interspecific competition where the numbers of individuals of two species competing in a restricted ecological space are represented by x and y, while z is a measure of their effective interaction determined

---

* Genetics and natural selection are discussed in detail in Chapter 15.

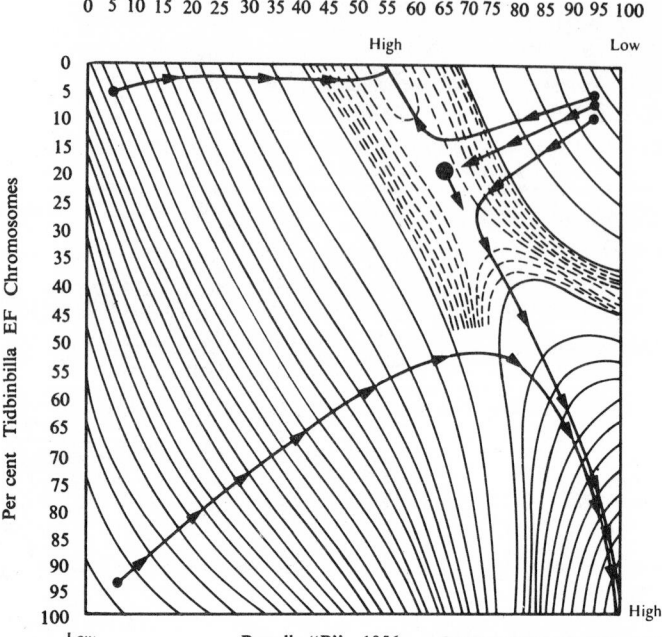

Per cent Blundell CD Chromosomes

FIGURE 2.   Topographic chart depicting the relationship between two dimensions of genetic variation in a polymorphic population of the grasshopper *Moraba*, and the calculated adaptiveness of a
particular combination of chromosome inversions plotted as isoadaptive contours of a *z*-coordinate.
It is postulated that genetic drift would tend to carry any given population over the resulting terrain
toward peaks of maximal adaptedness, as shown by the trajectories with arrows. (From Lewontin
and White.[59])

by the saturation values for the two species and their competition coefficients (Figure 3).
In such a model any momentary competitive position, defined by the numerical ratio of the
two organisms, would be forced by the ecological relationships assumed to move downhill toward the sinks where competitive interaction is at a minimum.*

Note that while the *x*-*y* coordinates of these analogs display relationships between directly
measurable dimensions (genotypes and numbers of individuals), the *z*-axis and the proposed
oriented movements of populations over the surface thus generated involve rather extensive
use of constructs and hypotheses. This emphasizes the care required in deciding to what
degree a graph or a mathematical expression is "just" a description of data and to what
degree it is a model or an explanation in the sense defined above. Even the simplest
cartesian graph ordinarily involves interpolative and extrapolative predictions which go
beyond the actual observations.

But to return to the fundamental problem of describing multi-dimensional data, one
important means of considerably exceeding the usual graphic limitations of two to three
dimensions is the use of nomograms.[57] These alignment charts are in effect graphic tabula-
tions that permit an unlimited number of variables to be plotted simultaneously on a plane
surface. In such graphs a great many variables could become unwieldy, but as many as ten

* Ecology and evolution are dealt with *in extenso* in Chapter 16.

can represent highly informative descriptive correlations in which quantitative coordinate values may be obtained simply by placing a straight edge on the chart and reading off the resulting intercept value for any coordinate. Obviously, in such a graph measurements of any two variables will determine all the rest by this means.

One of the most fruitful applications of this technique (which has been infrequently used by biologists) was made by L. J. Henderson in his important but neglected book, "Blood. A Study in General Physiology."[41] To describe blood adequately as a physicochemical system Henderson showed that at least eight to ten variables had to be taken into account. Obviously many more are pertinent and were in fact measured, but these can be rather simply derived from the particular eight to ten selected.

Thus, the over-all functional relations of human blood, as studied by Henderson and his co-workers, are summarized in a single ten-coordinate nomogram for a particular individual man at rest (Figure 4). In such a multi-dimensional graph, if a ruler is aligned with a specific measurement of blood pO_2 and with a second point for the concurrent pCO_2 measurement, all the correlated values for serum pH, volumes per cent oxyhemoglobin, cell pH, and so on, will lie directly on the same straight line. Two such intercepts of particular interest are the lines defining the equilibrium states for arterial and venous blood.

Evidently, graphing of this sort permits systems of moderate complexity to be well presented and compared. Thus nomograms of different physiological or pathological

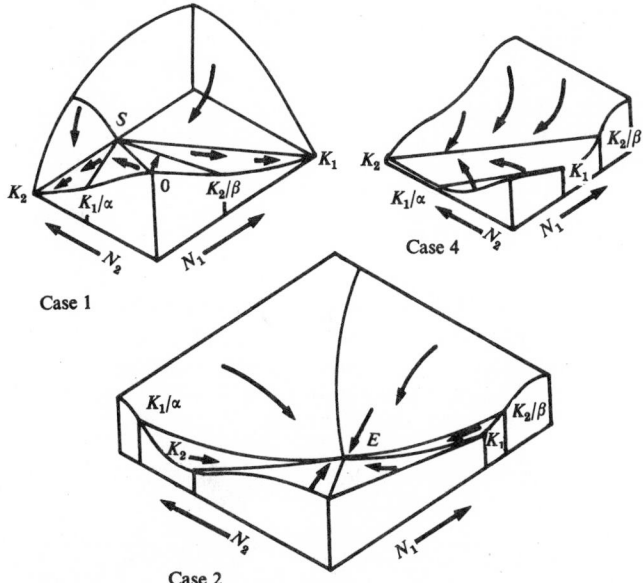

FIGURE 3. Topographic model for interspecific competition in which the numbers (N_1, N_2) of two species are plotted against a z-axis whose elevation represents their effective interaction as determined by the respective saturation values (K_1, K_2) and competition coefficients (α, β). The cases plotted assume particular numerical relations between the saturation and competition coefficients such that (a) either species may survive depending on the initial N_1, N_2 (Case 1), (b) both species will survive (Case 2), and (c) only Species 2 will survive (Case 4). Note that in contrast to the adaptive model of Figure 2, the populations in Figure 3 are postulated to move downhill to the lowest points in the landscape, specific paths being determined by the starting positions as indicated by the arrows. (From Slobodkin.[86])

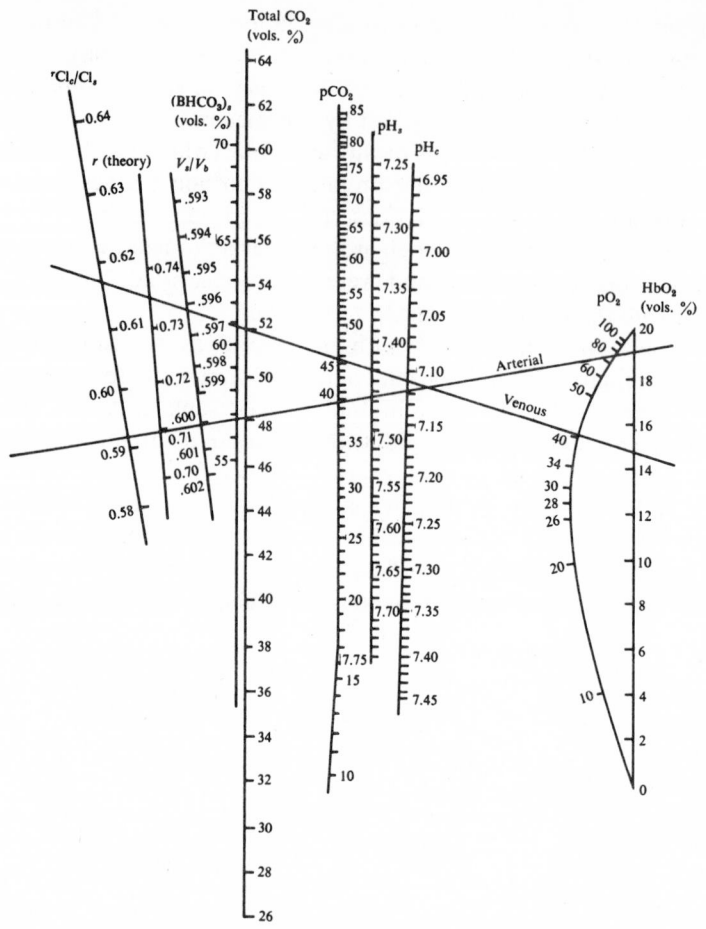

FIGURE 4. Nomogram indicating the relationships between ten physical chemical parameters of the blood of a man at rest. A straight line laid across all of the coordinates will determine the simultaneous values of each of the ten variables. The normal limiting cases for the arterial and venous equilibria are shown. The subscripts in the coordinate labels have the following meaning: b, whole blood; s, serum fraction; and c, cell fraction. (From Henderson.[41])

states may be quite distinct (Figures 5 and 6), and the blood of various species yields characteristic configurations.

Henderson himself felt that such a nomogram was the Law of the Blood and hence, in the sense of providing intellectual satisfaction, explanatory. However, opinions would obviously differ here on the extent to which such a representation significantly makes use of deductions from broad general principles. As pointed out above, the distinction between description and explanation must be made carefully and in certain areas at least is only relative. For example, none of the coordinates in the blood nomograms are as far abstracted from the measured variables as was the z-axis in the genetic and ecological topographic models cited above. In fact, the nomograph coordinates as used by Henderson appear to comprise direct descriptive representation rather than generalized constructs or explanatory mechanisms. If so, this representation is clearly a contribution to quantitative but not to theoretical biology.

So far the graphic methods mentioned have mainly been metric in nature, even though a strong degree of interdependence is characteristic of biological system components. Therefore, the importance of oriented graphs should not be overlooked since these can explicitly represent the relational features of a multi-dimensional organization (Chapter 3 and references[12,77]). A genetic chart showing genotypic and phenotypic ratios in successive generations is a simple case in point; a more complex example is the flow chart for metabolic reactions in glycolysis (Figure 7).

Here the interrelations between numerous reactants, products, enzymes, and cofactors in the many phases of the total phenomenon cannot be presented more simply than in an elaborate diagram which is essentially a multi-dimensional oriented graph. A comparable situation exists for representations of pathways and functional interrelations in the nervous system of animals.

Since certain of the graphic methods discussed above (topographic models and flow charts) come close to being physical models or analogs[10] of biological systems, the latter methodological tools should be mentioned more directly. These white boxes, noted above, are of many sorts and their discussion is not simplified by the numerous distinct definitions given to the words "model" and "analog" themselves. Thus a physical model may be rather literal in imitating selected properties of the organism, like a mechanical model demonstrating how an insect flaps its wings,[76] or it may operate in quite another energy

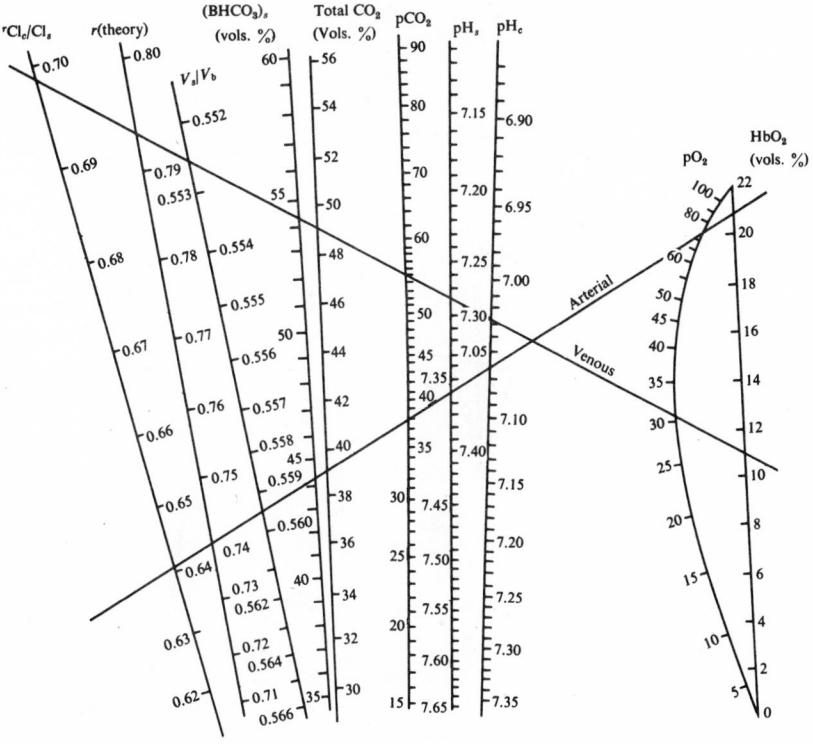

FIGURE 5. Human blood nomogram like that of Figure 4, except that here the subject's metabolic rate was augmented nine times by muscular work. Note that the relative positions and significant ranges of the ten coordinates have changed from the rest condition and that the differences between the arterial and venous equilibria have widened considerably. (From Henderson.[41])

sphere as an electrical network modeling some hemodynamic properties of the circulatory system.

Note that as above, the distinction between a model's function in description and explanation will become blurred when the known general principles on which the model works are broad enough to include the living system as a special case. Thus a mechanical or electrical analog may be used merely as a computer to interpolate or extrapolate responses which have not yet been measured in the organism, or it may go far beyond that to demonstrate in an explanatory way the principles on which a given living system works. In this connection recall that the broadest definitions of a model (the white box) would also include propositions or equations which deal with certain system parameters in symbolic rather than physical ways.[47] Both analog and digital computers may be used to run computer "experiments" on such mathematical or logical models, as discussed below, and in Chapters 10 and 11.

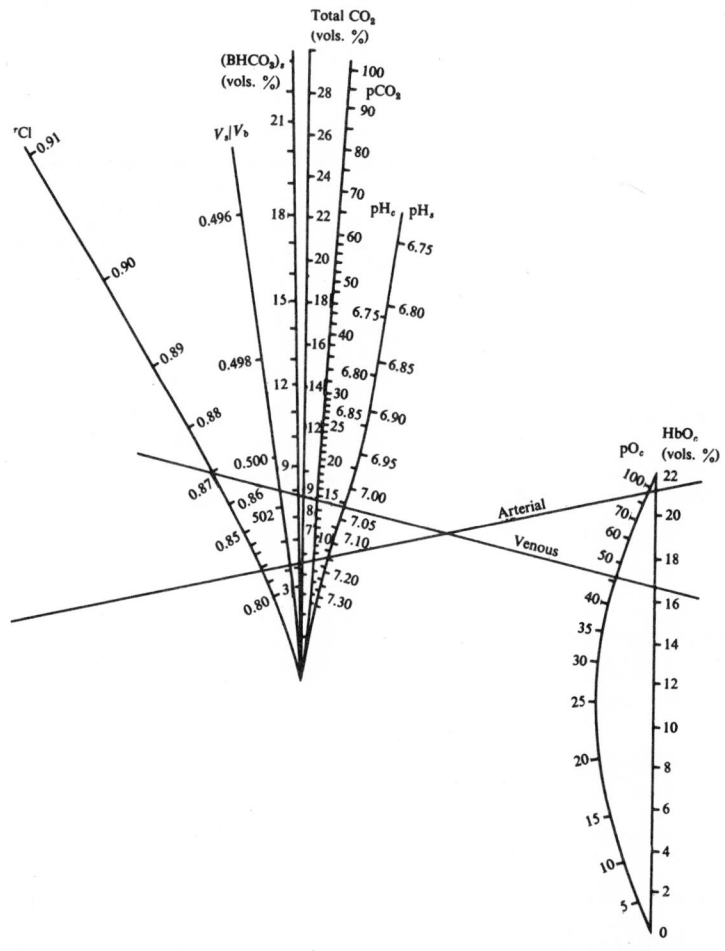

FIGURE 6.   Human blood nomogram like that of Figure 4, except that the pathological condition in diabetic coma is depicted instead of a normal state. Marked differences are notable in the positions and scales of a number of the coordinates. (From Henderson.[41])

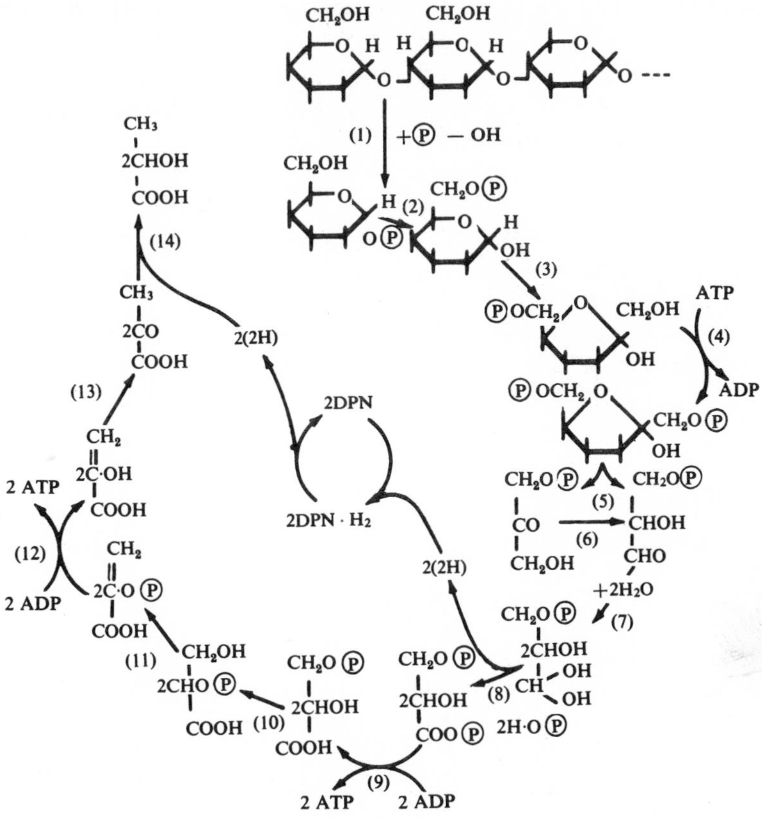

FIGURE 7. Flow chart summarizing the metabolic reactions in glycolysis from the phosphorylation of glycogen (Reaction 1) to the formation of lactic acid from pyruvic (Reaction 14). In the process one high-energy phosphate bond is used up (Reaction 4), and four are generated (Reactions 9 and 12). This familiar type of diagram illustrates the effectiveness of an oriented graph in modeling some aspects of multicomponent biological systems. (From Baldwin.[6])

C. Equations

Mathematical ways of describing biological systems have often been utilized in cases where adequate quantitative data were available. In a number of interesting examples these take the form of exponential equations of the form $y = ax^b$. Such diverse biological functions as relative growth, relation between oxygen uptake and body weight,[99,102] and the effect of stimulus magnitude on the resultant sensations[95] (Figure 8) are well described by equations of this form.[23] These may be derived from data plots by curve fitting, in which case their variables and coefficients may be obtained by a complex series of inductive and deductive steps that permit operational definitions and biological significance to be given to the elements in the equation.[36]

One general area where considerable success has accrued from such procedures is the field of animal locomotion. Here, following the pioneer contribution of Borelli,[17] quantitative applications of mechanics, hydrodynamics, and aerodynamics have led to particularly interesting analyses of walking, swimming, and flying.[33,76,105]

Following the lead of classical physics, the most elegant way of describing a natural

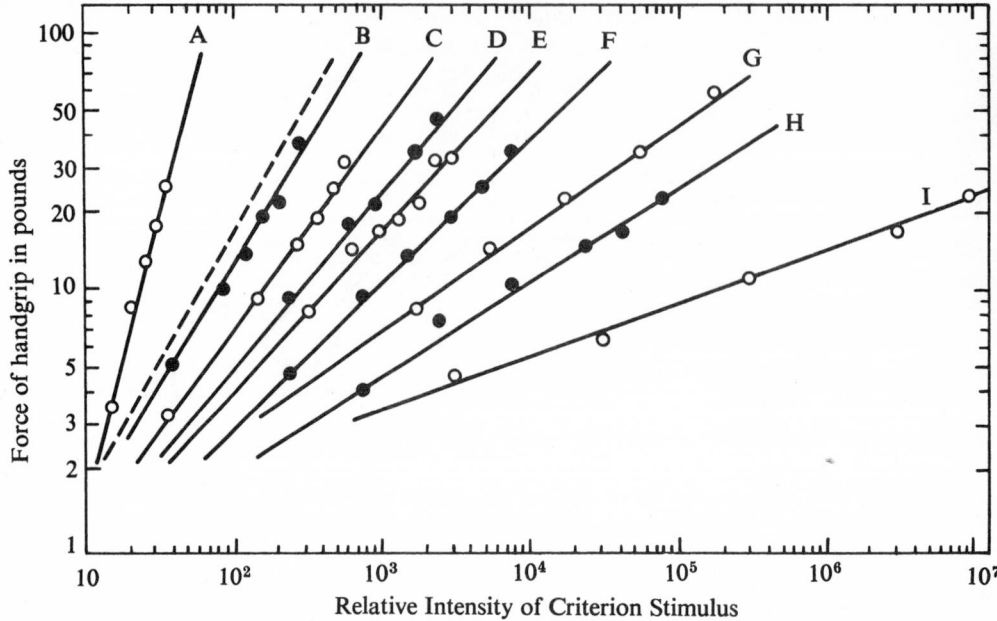

FIGURE 8. Exponential relationship between stimulus intensity and psychophysical response confirmed for nine different kinds of sensory stimulation by matching their apparent intensity to force exerted on a hand grip. Points are averages for at least ten observers. The slopes of these power functions show a remarkably good correlation with those predicted on the basis of magnitude estimation for the individual modalities. A = electric shock −60∼; B = warmth; C = lifted weights; D = pressure on palm; E = cold; F = vibration −60∼; G = white noise; H = 1000 ∼ tone; I = white light. (From Stevens.[95])

system is to formulate one or more differential equations which express the relations between the key variables. For example, the exponential equation for the relative growth curve cited above can be deductively obtained by integrating the differential equation:[99]

$$\frac{1}{y}\frac{dy}{dt} = b\,\frac{1}{x}\frac{dx}{dt}$$

This is a generalized hypothesis for the growth rates of two dimensions (x, y) of an organism, based on the assumptions that the growth of one dimension, say y, is simply proportional to the amount of y already present and that the ratio between the specific growth rates for the two dimensions can be expressed by a coefficient b which is assumed constant within certain boundary limitations. On this basis the a of the exponential form of the relative growth equation is seen to be just an integration constant.

Differential equations have been similarly applied to membrane potentials and nerve conduction,[42,77] population growth and competition,[51,86] the metabolic application of reaction rate theory,[20,46] and a variety of other biological systems.[23] When more than two or three simultaneous equations relate to a given case, the mathematics become difficult to deal with, but the use of computers has permitted quite complex systems to be handled quantitatively (for example, the work of Chance and his colleagues mentioned below and considered in detail in Chapters 10 and 11).

Note that although ordinary first order linear differential equations with constant coefficients can be treated mathematically in a satisfactory way, higher order variables, variable coefficients, and nonlinearity greatly increase their difficulty. Although natural systems often are nonlinear and involve time-dependent coefficients, their approximate treatment as linear systems has been highly fruitful.[97] In addition to such classical methods of the physical sciences, it seems quite certain that the application and further pertinent development of set theory,[32] dimensional analysis,[92,93] and multivariate analysis[3,50] (Chapters 8 and 9) will play important parts in the further development of mathematical biology.

D. Systems Analysis

In order that inductive generalizations as well as deductive predictions and their empirical verification can be generated in biology, information for a large number of components and their interrelationships must be available in the form of graphs, models, or equations as suggested above. In addition, some over-all organizational scheme must be postulated to provide a framework within which all the numerous parts may be ordered. Although it is true that such basic organization would be self-evident if all details were known, biological knowledge is far from that state. Hence hypotheses and generalizations about the organization of living things are an important part of methodology.[35]

The traditional biologists have long been aware of the importance of underlying organization and have in a number of instances greatly advanced our understanding by emphasizing its quantitative functional significance. For example, William Harvey's demonstration of the circulation of blood, Claude Bernard's attention to stabilization of the "milieu intérieur," and Walter Cannon's analysis of the homeostatic functions of the autonomic nervous system derived their great strength from what nowadays would be considered a kind of systems analysis. In the past 20 years the new biologists have been applying and developing more formally derived methods to achieve such understanding. Information theory, cybernetics, game theory, and decision theory have been the main contributors to this movement. All of these have provided insight into possible organizational properties of living systems and have at the same time suggested ways of analyzing biological data which take into account such interrelations (see particularly Chapter 12).

Although this approach has been widely hailed and does in fact offer important potentialities, relatively few significant new applications have materialized. One interesting theoretical development from cybernetics was the Reafferenzprinzip of von Holst and Mittelstaedt[101] (Figure 9). This postulates a general mechanism whereby the central nervous system (CNS) can discriminate real from self-induced apparent changes in an animal's environment by comparing the actual sensory input at any given moment with that expected on the basis of the animal's own activity. In a few experimental situations applications of systems analysis to relatively simple reflex mechanisms have also been rewarding (for instance, references[66,67,94] and Figure 10), as they have, too, for some more complex general systems.[35] Yet the effective exploitation of this general field lies largely in the future and undoubtedly depends on a real fusion of the traditional and the new biology.

Clearly one of the most challenging problems in nature is embodied in the integrative mechanisms which give rise to the behavior of animals. These ultimately include perception, thinking, consciousness, creativity, and other higher functions of the human central nervous system. Since all awareness of ourselves and the world around us as well as all our overt and covert responses (including science) are dependent on these biological processes, their

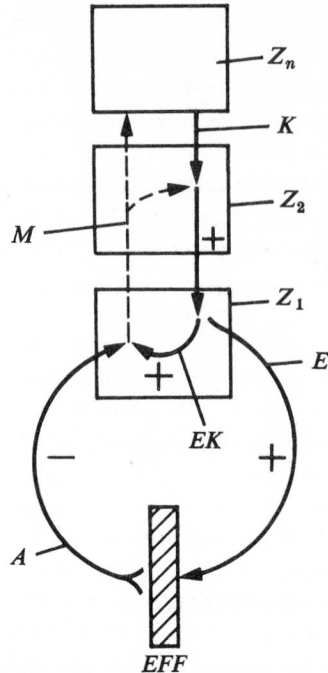

FIGURE 9.   The Reafferenzprinzip proposed to account for the usual absence of reaction by animals to apparent movements generated by their own voluntary displacement. In this model a higher nervous center (Z_n) sends out a command (K) relayed through two lower centers (Z_2 and Z_1). In the latter this command is sent out as an efferent motor message (E), and a duplicate of the efferent signal (EK) is sent to another part of Z_1 where it is compared with the afferent sensory message (A) resulting from the movement evoked by E. Any discrepancy between the sensed displacement and that expected on the basis of K is fed back (M) to Z_2 or Z_n where appropriate adjustments may be made. If EK and A correlate perfectly, there will be no response to the apparent movement. (From von Holst and Mittelstaedt.[101])

crucial importance can scarcely be overemphasized. Because of the complexities of the functional mechanisms involved and the difficulties of their adequate study, systems analysis and other theoretical and mathematical methods have been applied in a variety of ways at different levels.

One important area for such research has been the exploration of the properties of aggregates of neuron-like elements interacting in networks. In some cases the models have been mathematical as in the basic contribution of McCulloch and Pitts[63] where Boolean algebra was applied to greatly simplified neural networks made up of all-or-none binary units. Quite complex and interesting properties have been demonstrated in such logical nets.[14,27,43,61]

Application of the concepts of information theory (see Chapter 12) has also provided insight into the basic problem of data handling in neuron aggregates as well as the processing of their sensory input.[11,78,82,96,108] Questions of channel capacity, redundancy, efficiency of transmission, and storage which can all be quantitatively specified by this approach are obviously highly relevant to CNS function (for example, references[7,22,62,81]).

In other cases the models simulating neural network behavior have been hardware systems in the form of digital computers[31] or analog devices which quite closely mimic certain functional properties of neurons.[27,38,39,55,58,98] Quite another widely used computer approach has been the modeling of behavioral output of the whole organism often for cognitive human behavior such as learning, problem solving, or composing music.[69] Simple behavior of a basic sort has also been extensively analyzed by more direct quantitative methods, particularly in arthropods.[45,68,83,84,103]

While recognizing the stimulating power of such modeling of CNS functions and behavior one cannot lose sight of the far-reaching simplifications and transformations involved in establishing the white boxes.

Thus the neuron and the synapse are usually far from all-or-nothing unit transmitters[16,18,25] and excitatory as well as inhibitory interactions of nerve cells in aggregates undoubtedly take place in several complex ways.[29,44,53,104] Inhibitory feedback seems to be a particularly important factor here.[2,24,26] Also one must remember that quite complex peripheral differentiation and integration may already have taken place in an organism's sensory input long before the resultant spike information reaches the CNS proper[28,37,54,79,100] (see also Chapters 7 and 14), so that purely central simulation of such processes may be quite unrealistic. Finally, in the computer simulation of complex human behavior, one must remember that the functional context of human perception and the like is of a quite different order of magnitude from the kinds of programs one can now write for computers.[71]

These caveats are mentioned not to discount the importance and excitement of the theoretical and mathematical study of neuron integration but to reemphasize the point that science consists of a circular system connecting its black and its white boxes (pp. 4, 11, 12 and Chapter 12). Only when one proceeds effectively and repeatedly from data to model to data, and when both methods and problems (means and ends[69,70]) are brilliantly conceived, is sound scientific progress possible.

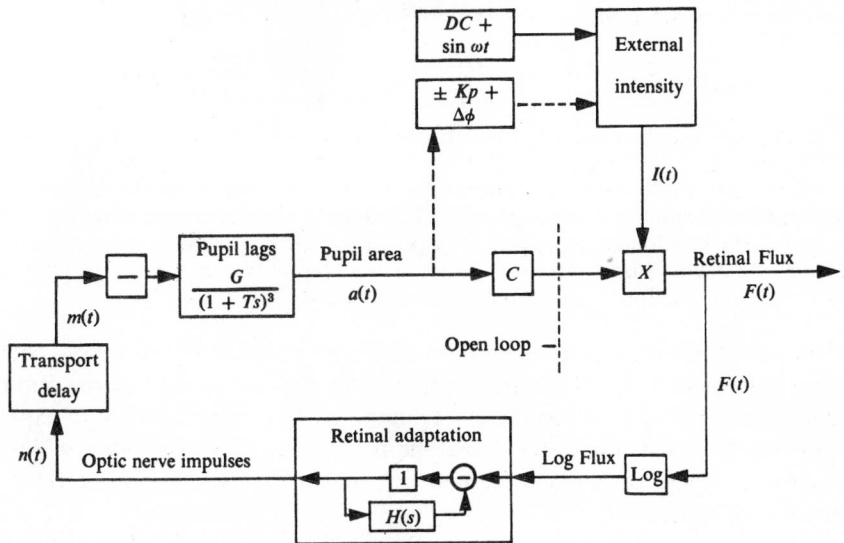

FIGURE 10. Cybernetic model for system regulating pupillary aperture in the human eye. I, external intensity; F, retinal flux; $H(s)$, the transfer function of the control system; $DC + \sin \omega t$ is sinusoidal light source; $\pm Kp + \Delta\varphi$, electronic feedback control of light intensity; G, pupillary gain; T, time constant; C, point where pupil edge regulates amount of light reaching the retina. (From Stark.[94])

Perhaps the most impressive applications of theoretical and mathematical techniques to living things have been cases in which differential equations were set up to describe the various rate processes in the system, where these have been programmed into a computer which has carried out various experimental solutions of the simultaneous equations involved, and where the predictions of such specific quantitative models were directly compared with the outcome of actual empirical tests. Four particularly interesting instances may be cited.

One example comes from the area of developmental biology in which Weiss and Kavanau have proposed a specific mathematical model for growth and differentiation, the predictions from which have undergone some empirical verification.[48,49,106] The model combines three differential equations representing processes which include a closed loop permitting negative feedback ultimately to regulate development in the adult steady state. These equations define the rates of change in generative mass, in differentiated mass, and in an inhibitory component which is postulated to account for the ultimate slowing and stabilization of growth and differentiation. Although the equations for these processes are quite complex in the general case (equations in Figure 11), they can be considerably simplified if over-all growth is assumed to be essentially complete and only regenerative growth in the adult organism is considered.

$$dG = G\left[\left[1 - \frac{b(I/I_e)^x}{(V/V_e)^x}\right]\log 2 - k_2 - k_1\left[1 - \frac{(I/I_e)^x}{(V/V_e)^x}\right]\right]dt,$$

$$dD = \left[k_2G + k_1G\left[1 - \frac{(I/I_e)^x}{(V/V_e)^x}\right] - k_3D\right]dt,$$

$$dI = k_5I_e[[(G/G_e); (D/D_e)] - I/I_e]\,dt.$$

restrictions: $\left[1 - \dfrac{b(I/I_e)^x}{(V/V_e)^x}\right] \geq 0, \quad \left[1 - \dfrac{(I/I_e)^x}{(V/V_e)^x}\right] \geq 0.$

FIGURE 11. System of differential equations hypothesized to model growth and growth control. The first equation relates to change in the generative mass G, the second to change in the differentiated mass D, and the third to change in an inhibitory factor I (antitemplate molecules). The k's are rate constants; b, ratio of equilibrium negative feedback to complete inhibition; subscript e, terminal value; x, number of antitemplate molecules required to inactivate one template; V, volume of dilution pool. At equilibrium (maturity) these equations simplify considerably so that computer solutions become feasible for regeneration. (From Kavanau.[48])

Based on available data, appropriate values have been assumed for the various coefficients of these equations and a digital computer program carried out to explore the implications of the mathematical model. When these are compared with empirical data of experiments on compensatory growth, the systems analysis predictions show a number of interesting correlations and suggest certain specific new experiments to provide a more rigorous test of the underlying hypothesis.

A somewhat more complicated mathematical model has been proposed and quantitatively compared with experimental data relating to photosynthesis by the red alga *Porphyridium*.[30] Here a two-pigment photochemically driven model was established with a set of five differential rate equations. The properties of this hypothesized kinetic system were then shown by means of an analog computer to account for a considerable number of experimental findings on the living system.

An even more complex and far-reaching analysis of a basically similar sort is provided by the work of Britton Chance and his co-workers on metabolic regulation.[20] This is reviewed in detail in Chapters 11 and 13. Another interesting case relating to the respiratory and circulatory systems is considered in Chapter 10.

III. CONCLUSIONS

In the author's opinion, work of the sort illustrated by these several examples provides a cogent indication of the direction in which biology must move. Such multivariate quantitative and theoretical approaches need to be devised and applied not only in the study of photosynthesis, development, and biochemistry, but in all other areas of biology including systematics,[1] morphology, paleontology, and biogeography. Although it has not been specifically mentioned, these reforms must include, when appropriate, the explicit treatment of the statistical and stochastic aspects of living things.[8,9,15,50,65,89]

Only in this way can the dangers of a continuing schizoid biology be avoided. Only in this way can biology outgrow the stigma of being a mere descriptive science and rise to the level of a rigorous intellectual discipline. To do this, the methods not only of biology itself but also those of mathematics, physics, chemistry, and engineering are obviously required even though the examples cited above may only tentatively suggest the lines which will ultimately prove most fruitful. No doubt the required techniques and constructs in many instances still remain to be discovered and developed (Chapters 2, 3, and 7).

On the other hand, protoplasm, organisms, and populations must be considered holistically because their behavior cannot be adequately encompassed just by reduction to molecular or physical or chemical explanations. Hence biologists must be central participants in research on living things. Yet many of them must learn to work and think effectively in the other relevant scientific disciplines as well as to collaborate with scientists better trained in such fields than they can realistically hope to be. No other means is available to obtain the kind of data and to carry out the kind of analysis required to advance the biological sciences effectively.

If indeed such a synthesis of the new and the old biologies can be effected, it may not be too sanguine to predict that the present nuclear age of science will be succeeded by a spectacularly revolutionary biological age in which the understanding of life, of growth, of evolution, and of man and his behavior would far transcend any of the tentative beginnings we now know. However, one should not overlook the pitfalls and difficulties in such a revolutionary path. There is a challenging difference between the vague awareness of a problem and the energetic insight required to solve it. The forces of reaction are great; they are favored by inertia and the formidable difficulties of creative advance in any new or interdisciplinary area.

Nevertheless, the rewards of such an effort are so attractive and the satisfaction to be derived from its success so great that it is surely worth a more serious try than has yet been made!

REFERENCES

1. Alston, R. E., and Turner, B. L. 1963. "Biochemical Systematics," 404 pp. Prentice-Hall, Englewood Cliffs, N.J.

2. Anderson, P., Eccles, J. C., and Løyning, Y. 1963. Recurrent inhibition in the hippocampus with identification of the inhibitory cell and its synapses. *Nature* **198:** 540–542.

3. Anderson, T. W. 1958. "An Introduction to Multivariate Statistical Analysis," 874 pp. Wiley, New York.

4. Anfinsen, C. B. 1959. "The Molecular Basis of Evolution," 230 pp. Wiley, New York.

5. Aronow, S. 1959. A theory of analogs. *In:* "Proc. Natl. Biophys. Conf., 1st, Columbus, Ohio, 1957," (H. Quastler and H. J. Morowitz, eds.), pp. 27–34. Yale Univ. Press, New Haven.

6. Baldwin, E. 1957. "Dynamic Aspects of Biochemistry," 3rd ed., 526 pp. Cambridge Univ. Press, London.

7. Barlow, H. B. 1959. Sensory mechanisms, the reduction of redundancy and intelligence. *In:* "Mechanization of Thought Processes," *Natl. Phys. Lab. G.Brit. Proc. Symp.* **10,** Vol. II, pp. 535–559.

8. Bartlett, M. S. 1951. The goodness of fit of a single hypothetical discriminant function in the case of several groups. *Ann. Eugen. London* **16:** 199–214.

9. Bartlett, M. S. 1960. "Stochastic Population Models in Ecology and Epidemiology," 90 pp. Methuen, London; Wiley, New York.

10. Beament, J. W. L., ed. 1960. "Models and Analogues in Biology," *Symp. Soc. Exptl. Biol.* **14,** 255 pp.

11. Beament, J. W. L., ed. 1962. "Biological Receptor Mechanisms," *Symp. Soc. Exptl. Biol.* **16,** 372 pp.

12. Berge, C. 1958. "Théories des Graphes et ses Applications," 275 pp. Dunod, Paris.

13. Bernal, J. D. 1958. Some reflections on structure and function in the evolution of life. *Trans. Bose Res. Inst. Calcutta* **22:** 101–110.

14. Beurle, R. L. 1956. Properties of a mass of cells capable of regenerating pulses. *Phil. Trans. Roy. Soc. London* **B240:** 55–94.

15. Blackith, R. E. 1960. A synthesis of multivariate techniques to distinguish patterns of growth in grasshoppers. *Biometrics* **16:** 28–40.

16. Bodian, D. 1962. The generalized vertebrate neuron. *Science* **137:** 323–326.

17. Borelli, G. A. 1680/81. "De Motu Animalium," Vol. I, 387 pp.; Vol. II, 520 pp. Bernabò, Rome.

18. Bullock, T. H. 1959. Neuron doctrine and electrophysiology. *Science* **129:** 997–1002.

19. Cain, A. J. 1962. The evolution of taxonomic principles. *In:* "Microbial Classification," (G. C. Ainsworth and P. H. A. Sneath, eds.), pp. 1–13. Cambridge Univ. Press, London.

20. Chance, B., Garfinkel, D., Higgins, J., and Hess, B. 1960. Metabolic control mechanisms. V. A solution for the equations representing interaction between glycolysis and respiration in ascites tumor cells. *J. Biol. Chem.* **235:** 2426–2439.

21. Commoner, B. 1961. In defense of biology. *Science* **133:** 1745–1748.

22. Cowan, J. D. 1963. The engineering approach to the problem of biological integration. *In:* "Nerve, Brain and Memory Models," (N. Wiener and J. P. Schadé, eds.), pp. 22–29. Elsevier, Amsterdam.

23. Defares, J. G., and Sneddon, I. N. 1961. "An Introduction to the Mathematics of Medicine and Biology," 663 pp. Year Book, Chicago.

24. Desmedt, J. E. 1960. Neurophysiological mechanisms controlling acoustic input. *In:* "Neural Mechanisms of the Auditory and Vestibular Systems," (G. L. Rasmussen and W. F. Windle, eds.), pp. 152–164. Thomas, Springfield, Ill.

25. Eccles, J. C. 1964. "The Physiology of Synapses," 316 pp. Academic, New York.

26. Engström, H. 1960. Electron micrographic studies of the receptor cells of the organ of Corti. *In:* "Neural Mechanisms of the Auditory and Vestibular Systems," (G. L. Rasmussen and W. F. Windle, eds.), pp. 48–64. Thomas, Springfield, Ill.

27. Farley, B. G. 1962. Some results of computer simulation of neuron-like nets. *Federation Proc.* **21:** 92–96.

28. Fex, J. 1962. Auditory activity in centrifugal and centripetal cochlear fibres in the cat. A study of a feedback system. *Acta Physiol. Scand.* **55,** *Suppl.* **189:** 1–68.

29. Florey, E., ed. 1962. "Nervous Inhibition," 490 pp. Pergamon, Oxford.

30. French, C. S., and Fork, D. C. 1961. Computer solutions for photosynthesis rates from a two pigment model. *Biophys. J.* **1:** 669–681.

31. George, F. H. 1961. "The Brain as a Computer," 413 pp. Pergamon, Oxford.

32. Goldberg, S. 1960. "Probability," 322 pp. Prentice-Hall, Englewood Cliffs, N.J.

33. Gray, J. 1955. The movement of sea-urchin spermatozoa. *J. Exptl. Biol.* **32:** 775–801.

34. Grobstein, C. 1962. Levels and ontogeny. *Am. Scientist* **50:** 46–58.

35. Grodins, F. S. 1963. "Control Theory and Biological Systems," 205 pp. Columbia Univ. Press, New York.

36. Guest, P. G. 1961. "Numerical Methods of Curve Fitting," 422 pp. Cambridge Univ. Press, London.

37. Hagbarth, K.-E. 1960. Centrifugal mechanisms of sensory control. *Ergeb. Biol.* **22:** 47–66.

38. Harmon, L. D. 1961. Studies with artificial neurons, I: Properties and functions of an artificial neuron. *Kybernetik* **1:** 89–101.

39. Harmon, L. D. 1964. Artificial neuron studies. *In:* "Information Processing in the Nervous System," (R. W. Gerard, ed.), pp. 117–124. Excerpta Medica Foundation, Amsterdam.

40. Henderson, L. J. 1913. "The Fitness of the Environment: An Inquiry into the Biological Significance of the Properties of Matter," 317 pp. Macmillan, New York.

41. Henderson, L. J. 1928. "Blood. A Study in General Physiology," 397 pp. Yale Univ. Press, New Haven.

42. Hodgkin, A. L., and Huxley, A. F. 1952. A quantitative description of membrane current and its application to conduction and excitation in nerve. *J. Physiol. (London)* **117:** 500–544.

43. Householder, A. S., and Landahl, H. D. 1945. "Mathematical Biophysics of the Central Nervous System," 124 pp. Principia, Bloomington, Ind.

44. Hubel, D. H., and Wiesel, T. N. 1962. Receptive fields, binocular interaction and functional architecture in the cat's visual cortex. *J. Physiol. (London)* **160:** 106–154.

45. Jander, R. 1963. Insect orientation. *Ann. Rev. Entomol.* **8:** 95–114.

46. Johnson, F. H., Eyring, H., and Polissar, M. J. 1954. "The Kinetic Basis of Molecular Biology," 874 pp. Wiley, New York.

47. Kacser, J. 1960. Kinetic models of development and heredity. *In:* "Models and Analogues in Biology," (J. W. L. Beament, ed.), *Symp. Soc. Exptl. Biol.* **14:** 13–27.

48. Kavanau, J. L. 1960. A model of growth and growth control in mathematical terms, II. Compensatory organ growth in the adult. *Proc. Natl. Acad. Sci. U.S.* **46:** 1658–1673.

49. Kavanau, J. L. 1961. Predictions of the growth model for normal chicken growth. *Science* **134:** 1627–1628.

50. Kendall, M. G. 1957. "A Course in Multivariate Analysis," 185 pp. Griffin, London; Hafner, New York.

51. Kerner, E. 1961. On the Volterra-Lotka principle. *Bull. Math. Biophys.* **23:** 141–157.

52. Kubo, K. 1961. Studies on the serology of sea-stars, V. *Japan. J. Zool.* **13(1):** 15–37.

53. Kuffler, S. W. 1953. Discharge patterns and functional organization of mammalian retina. *J. Neurophysiol.* **16:** 37–68.

54. Kuffler, S. W., and Eyzaguirre, C. 1955. Synaptic inhibition in an isolated nerve cell. *J. Gen. Physiol.* **39:** 155–184.

55. Küpfmüller, K., and Jenik, F. 1961. Über die Nachrichtenverarbeitung in der Nervenzelle. *Kybernetik* **1:** 1–6.

56. Leone, C. A. 1954. Further serological data on the relationships of some decapod Crustacea. *Evolution* **8:** 192–205.

57. Levens, A. S. 1959. "Nomography," 2nd ed., 296 pp. Wiley, New York.

58. Levinson, J., and Harmon, L. D. 1961. Studies with artificial neurons, III: Mechanisms of flicker-fusion. *Kybernetik* **1**: 107–117.

59. Lewontin, R. C., and White, M. J. D. 1960. Interaction between inversion polymorphisms of two chromosome pairs in the grasshopper, *Moraba scurra*. *Evolution* **14**: 116–129

60. Licklider, J. C. R. 1951. Basic correlates of the auditory stimulus. *In:* "Handbook of Experimental Psychology," (S. S. Stevens, ed.), pp. 985–1039. Wiley, New York; Chapman and Hall, London.

61. McCulloch, W. S. 1959. Agathe Tyche: Of nervous nets—the lucky reckoners. *In:* "Mechanization of Thought Processes," *Natl. Phys. Lab. Gt. Brit. Proc. Symp.* **10**, Vol. II, pp. 611–625.

62. McCulloch, W. S. 1960. The reliability of biological systems. *In:* "Self-Organizing Systems," (M. C. Yovits and S. Cameron, eds.), pp. 264–279. Pergamon, Oxford.

63. McCulloch, W. S., and Pitts, W. H. 1943. A logical calculus of the ideas immanent in nervous activity. *Bull. Math. Biophys.* **5**: 115–133.

64. Margenau, H. 1961. "Open Vistas," 256 pp. Yale Univ. Press, New Haven.

65. Martin, L. 1961. Stochastic processes in physiology. *In:* "Proc. 4th Berkeley Symp. Mathematical Statistics and Probability," Vol. IV, pp. 307–320. Univ. California Press, Berkeley.

66. Mittelstaedt, H. 1961. Die Regelungstheorie als methodisches Werkzeug der Verhaltensanalyse. *Naturwiss.* **48**: 246–254.

67. Mittelstaedt, H. 1962. Control systems of orientation in insects. *Ann. Rev. Entomol.* **7**: 177–198.

68. Mittelstaedt, H. 1963. Bikomponenten-Theorie der Orientierung. *Ergeb. Biol.* **26**: 253–258.

69. Newell, A., and Simon, H. A. 1961a. Computer simulation of human thinking. *Science* **134**: 2011–2017.

70. Newell, A., and Simon, H. A. 1961b. The simulation of human thought. *In:* "Current Trends in Psychological Theory," (W. Dennis, ed.), pp. 152–179. Univ. Pittsburgh Press.

71. Niesser, U. 1963. The imitation of man by machine. *Science* **139**: 193–197.

72. Northrop, J. H. 1961. Biochemists, biologists and William of Occam. *Ann. Rev. Biochem.* **30**: 1–10.

73. Oliver, W. D. 1951. "Theory of Order," 345 pp. Antioch Press, Yellow Springs, Ohio.

74. Oparin, A. I. 1961. "Life, Its Nature, Origin and Development," 207 pp. Academic, New York.

75. Picken, L. E. R. 1961. Molecular biology and the future of zoology. *In:* "The Cell and the Organism," (J. A. Ramsay and V. B. Wigglesworth, eds.), pp. 90–102. Cambridge Univ. Press, London.

76. Pringle, J. W. S. 1957. "Insect Flight," 132 pp. Cambridge Univ. Press, London.

77. Rashevsky, N. 1960. "Mathematical Biophysics," 3rd rev. ed., Vol. I, 488 pp.; Vol. II, 462 pp. Dover Publications, New York.

78. Rasmussen, G. L., and Windle, W. F., eds. 1960. "Neural Mechanisms of the Auditory and Vestibular Systems," 422 pp. Thomas, Springfield, Ill.

79. Ratliff, F., and Hartline, H. K. 1957. Fields of inhibitory influence of single receptor units in the lateral eye of *Limulus*. *Science* **126**: 1234.

80. Remane, A. 1956. "Die Grundlagen des Natürlichen Systems, der Vergleichenden Anatomie und der Phylogenetik," 364 pp. Akademische Verlagsges., Leipzig.

81. Rosenblatt, F. 1960. Perceptual generalization over transformation groups. *In:* "Self-Organizing Systems," (M. C. Yovits and S. Cameron, eds.), pp. 63–96. Pergamon, Oxford.

82. Rosenblith, W. A., ed. 1961. "Sensory Communication," 844 pp. M.I.T. Press, Wiley, New York.

83. Schöne, H. 1959. Die Lageorientierung mit Statolithenorganen und Augen. *Ergeb. Biol.* **21**: 161–209.

84. Schöne, H. 1961. Complex behavior. *In:* "The Physiology of Crustacea," (T. H. Waterman, ed.), Vol. II, pp. 465–520. Academic, New York.
85. Simpson, G. G. 1962. The status of the study of organisms. *Am. Scientist* **50:** 36–45.
86. Slobodkin, L. B. 1961. "Growth and Regulation of Animal Populations," 184 pp. Holt, Rinehart and Winston, New York.
87. Sneath, P. H. A. 1961. Recent developments in theoretical and quantitative taxonomy. *Systematic Zool.* **10:** 118–139.
88. Sneath, P. H. A. 1962. The construction of taxonomic groups. *In:* "Microbial Classification," (G. C. Ainsworth and P. H. A. Sneath, eds.), pp. 289–332. Cambridge Univ. Press, London.
89. Sneath, P. H. A., and Sokal, R. R. 1962. Numerical taxonomy. *Nature* **193:** 855–860.
90a. Sokal, R. R. 1961. Distance as a measure of taxonomic similarity. *Systematic Zool.* **10:** 70–79.
90b. Sokal, R. R., and Sneath, P. H. A. 1963. "Principles of Numerical Taxonomy," 359 pp. Freeman, San Francisco.
91. Sporne, K. R. 1956. The phylogenetic classification of the angiosperms. *Biol. Revs. Cambridge Phil. Soc.* **31:** 1–29.
92. Stahl, W. R. 1961. Dimensional analysis in mathematical biology. I. General discussion. *Bull. Math. Biophys.* **23:** 355–376.
93. Stahl, W. R. 1962. Dimensional analysis in mathematical biology. II. *Bull. Math. Biophys.* **24:** 81–108.
94. Stark, L. 1960. Vision: Servoanalysis of pupil reflex to light. *In:* "Medical Physics," (O. Glasser, ed.), Vol. III, pp. 702–719. Year Book, Chicago.
95. Stevens, S. S. 1961. The psychophysics of sensory function. *In:* "Sensory Communication," (W. A. Rosenblith, ed.), pp. 1–33. M.I.T. Press, Wiley, New York.
96. Thorpe, W. H., and Zangwill, O. L., eds. 1961. "Current Problems in Animal Behaviour," 424 pp. Cambridge Univ. Press, London.
97. Trimmer, J. D. 1950. "Response of Physical Systems," 268 pp. Wiley, New York.
98. van Bergeijk, W. A. 1961. Studies with artificial neurons, II: Analog of the external spiral innervation of the cochlea. *Kybernetik* **1:** 102–107.
99. von Bertalanffy, L. 1951. "Theoretische Biologie," 2nd ed., Vol. II, 418 pp. Francke, Bern.
100. von Holst, E. 1950. Quantitative Messung von Stimmungen im Verhalten der Fische. *In:* "Physiological Mechanisms in Animal Behaviour," *Symp. Soc. Exptl. Biol.* **4** (J. F. Danielli and R. Brown, eds.), pp. 143–172.
101. von Holst, E., and Mittelstaedt, H. 1950. Das Reafferenzprinzip. *Naturwiss.* **37:** 464–476.
102. Waterman, T. H. 1961. Comparative physiology. *In:* "The Physiology of Crustacea," (T. H. Waterman, ed.), Vol. II, pp. 521–593. Academic, New York.
103. Waterman, T. H. 1963. The analysis of spatial orientation. *Ergeb. Biol.* **26:** 98–117.
104. Waterman, T. H., Wiersma, C. A. G., and Bush, B. M. H. 1964. Afferent visual responses in the optic nerve of the crab, *Podophthalmus. J. Cellular Comp. Physiol.* **63:** 135–156.
105. Weis-Fogh, T. 1961. Power in flapping flight. *In:* "The Cell and the Organism," (J. A. Ramsay and V. B. Wigglesworth, eds.), pp. 283–300. Cambridge Univ. Press, London.
106. Weiss, P., and Kavanau, J. L. 1957. A model of growth and growth control in mathematical terms. *J. Gen. Physiol.* **41:** 1–47.
107. Wiener, N. 1961. "Cybernetics," 2nd ed., 212 pp. M.I.T. Press, Wiley, New York.
108. Yovits, M. C., and Cameron, S., eds. 1960. "Self-Organizing Systems," 322 pp. Pergamon, Oxford.

[2]

THE HISTORICAL BACKGROUND

Harold J. Morowitz

I. SCOPE OF THEORETICAL BIOLOGY

A. *General Nature*

Theoretical biology is a somewhat confusing term since biologists have always worked within a framework of postulates and heuristic hypotheses regarding the nature of the organic world. As William A. Locy noted many years ago, "In the rise of biology the facts have accumulated constantly, through observation and experiment, but the general truths have emerged slowly and periodically, whenever there has been granted to some mind an insight into the meanings of the facts. The detached facts are sometimes tedious, the interpretations always interesting."[11]

The insights of biology have tended to be verbal formulations whose validity rested on a number of generalized observations on living systems. It is of interest to note that certain branches of physics have also rested on such verbal formulations. The prime example of this is the second law of thermodynamics. As formulated by Lord Kelvin the statement is: a transformation whose only final result is to transform into work heat extracted from a source which is at the same temperature throughout is impossible. The verbal nature of thermodynamic theory has led Percy Bridgman to remark[3]: "It must be admitted I think that the laws of thermodynamics have a different feel from most of the other laws of the physicist. There is something more palpably verbal about them—they smell more of their human origin." This property of thermodynamics so vividly expressed in the preceding quotation is characteristic of much of biological theory.

However, theoretical physics has also developed in another direction, namely the formulation of laws in terms of precisely defined symbols and rules of operation with the symbols. By applying these rules it is possible to predict a wide range of experimental results. It is this type of theory which has imparted much of the power to physics. It is also this type of theory which has led some biologists to look at physics with envy and envision a theoretical biology which can be formulated with the compactness, elegance, and predictability of much of physical theory. Some grounds for this hope have been provided by one branch of biology which has been susceptible to this type of analysis.

Genetics from its inception has had the symbolic character found in mathematical physics. Because much of the mathematics involved has been elementary, many people have failed to realize the theoretical nature of genetic studies.

Gregor Mendel's original paper sets up a series of symbols, AaBbCc, which are precisely defined in terms of resulting phenotypes. He then presents rules for manipulating these symbols, such rules corresponding to different types of breeding experiments. He is able to state "that the constant characters which appear in the several varieties of a group of plants may be obtained in all associations which are possible according to the [mathematical] laws of combination, by means of repeated artificial fertilization."[13] Subsequent researchers have been able to formulate Mendelian genetics in terms of a few simple postulates and operational rules on the symbols (genes) Aa, et cetera. The results of these operations, then, predict the statistical distribution of progeny in a controlled breeding experiment. This approach is closely akin to the methods of theoretical physics. It provides the proof that symbolic theoretical biology is possible, at least in some areas.

There is little in physics and chemistry to compare with the striking success and broad sweep of genetic theory. The theory stands with the atomic hypothesis or Newton's laws as one of the great achievements of the human intellect. It must also stand as a rebuttal to those who maintain that biological phenomena are too complex to yield to theoretical analysis. One other feature of classical genetics must be noted. Prior to genetic theory, breeding experiments appeared to be almost hopelessly multivariate for the formulation of an analytical theory. The accomplishment of those who formulated genetics was the ability to select a few parameters which behaved in a regular manner and to develop constructs in terms of these parameters.

Chemistry provides another example of an area of science that looked extremely multivariate until theory demonstrated the underlying simplicity. Prior to the formulation of the periodic table, chemistry was a large mass of data related by a large number of empirical rules. With the discovery of the periodic table, much of the complexity vanished and the previous empirical rules were shown to be derivable from the theory. The subsequent rise of quantum mechanics has been able to provide an even more fundamental grasp of chemistry in terms of the most basic notions of the laws of interactions of particles.

In tracing the recent development of theoretical biology, we shall confine ourselves mostly to symbolic theoretical attempts to represent areas of biology within formalisms. The formalisms may be mathematical in the traditional sense or may be more general symbolic representations such as modern logic.

B. Main Subdivisions

For didactic reasons, current theoretical biology can be divided into three general areas: formal theory, physical theory, and systems theory. Modern formal theory utilizes the following approach. A given biological situation is examined and a postulate or set of postulates is formulated. These postulates are set forth as mathematical statements, which are often differential or integral equations. Subsequent manipulations are carried through with the equations to deduce the consequences of the postulates. These consequences are then, where possible, checked against experimental results. It is frequently the case that there are no experimental results in a form appropriate to check the theory. It is then necessary to perform the experiments. Unfortunately the experimentalists have often been so unimpressed by theory that the experiments have not been carried out. Theory then becomes a pure academic discipline untouched by the harsh contradictions of experimental reality. Formal theory has had considerable success in ecology, since theory and experiment in this field have been more closely allied than in other areas of biology. However, as previously stated, formal theory has had its maximum success in genetics. It is interesting to note that the constructs of formal theory do not have to be the constructs of physics and chemistry, but may be purely biological in nature.

The second area of theoretical biology, physical theory, is closely allied to the recent rise of molecular biology. In physical theory one starts with established ideas of molecular structure, molecular interactions, kinetics, statistical mechanics, thermodynamics, and a number of other formal disciplines of physics and chemistry and attempts to apply these ideas to biological situations. The ultimate in this point of view is to start out with Schrödinger's equation, formulated for the appropriate system and the necessary boundary conditions, and to predict from its solution observed properties of living systems. Needless to say, physical biology is very far from this goal. However, physical problems do exist. The detailed studies of membrane transport from the point of view of the Donnan equilibrium, the diffusion potential, Poiseuille's law, and irreversible thermodynamics are examples of physical theory applied to biology. Another example is the attempt to study enzymatic catalysis in terms of the quantum chemistry and spectroscopy of the enzyme-substrate complex.

The third area, systems theory, is a special case of a formal approach to biological problems. Because this theory has its own origins and its own "jargon," we treat it separately. This study is rooted in the modern development of information theory, game theory, operations research, network theory, analysis of servo-systems, and computer development. The type of question posed is in what way are the properties of a biological system the result of its being a complex array of interacting elements? Systems theory has been worked on in connection with neural networks and behavior of organisms, as well as such problems as homeostasis of intermediary metabolism of cells. Indeed, homeostasis problems have been the core of much of the biological work on systems theories.

A special word needs to be said about computers. At present both analog and digital techniques have been applied to biological problems. The results have not been spectacular nor has the impact on biology been very large to date, but it seems apparent that the power of computer techniques will open many facets of theoretical biology which have previously been impossible to approach. Clearly computers will play an ever larger part in theoretical biology. Chapters 10, 11, and 13 of this book give some interesting insights into the emerging role of computers.

Another discipline often associated with theoretical biology is biometry and the application of statistical techniques to data analysis. This forms the core of what is usually designated as quantitative biology. The aim of this type of analysis is to provide methods of systematically dealing with the numerical data which are obtained in many biological experiments. This area is now widely recognized and some training in statistics is included in the curriculum of many biology departments. Some of the most recent achievements of this field are discussed in Chapters 8 and 9.

II. DEVELOPMENT OF THE FIELD

A. *Early Efforts*

We have briefly outlined the approaches of theoretical biology, and it is now of interest to examine some of the major works of the past fifty years to gain some insight into the field from an historical point of view. Before looking at the modern period, a few landmarks in the early attempts to formulate aspects of biology in a mathematical or physical fashion will be considered. One of these was printed in Rome as early as 1680 and was written by Giovanni Alphonso Borelli. The work entitled "De Motu Animalium"[2] is an analysis

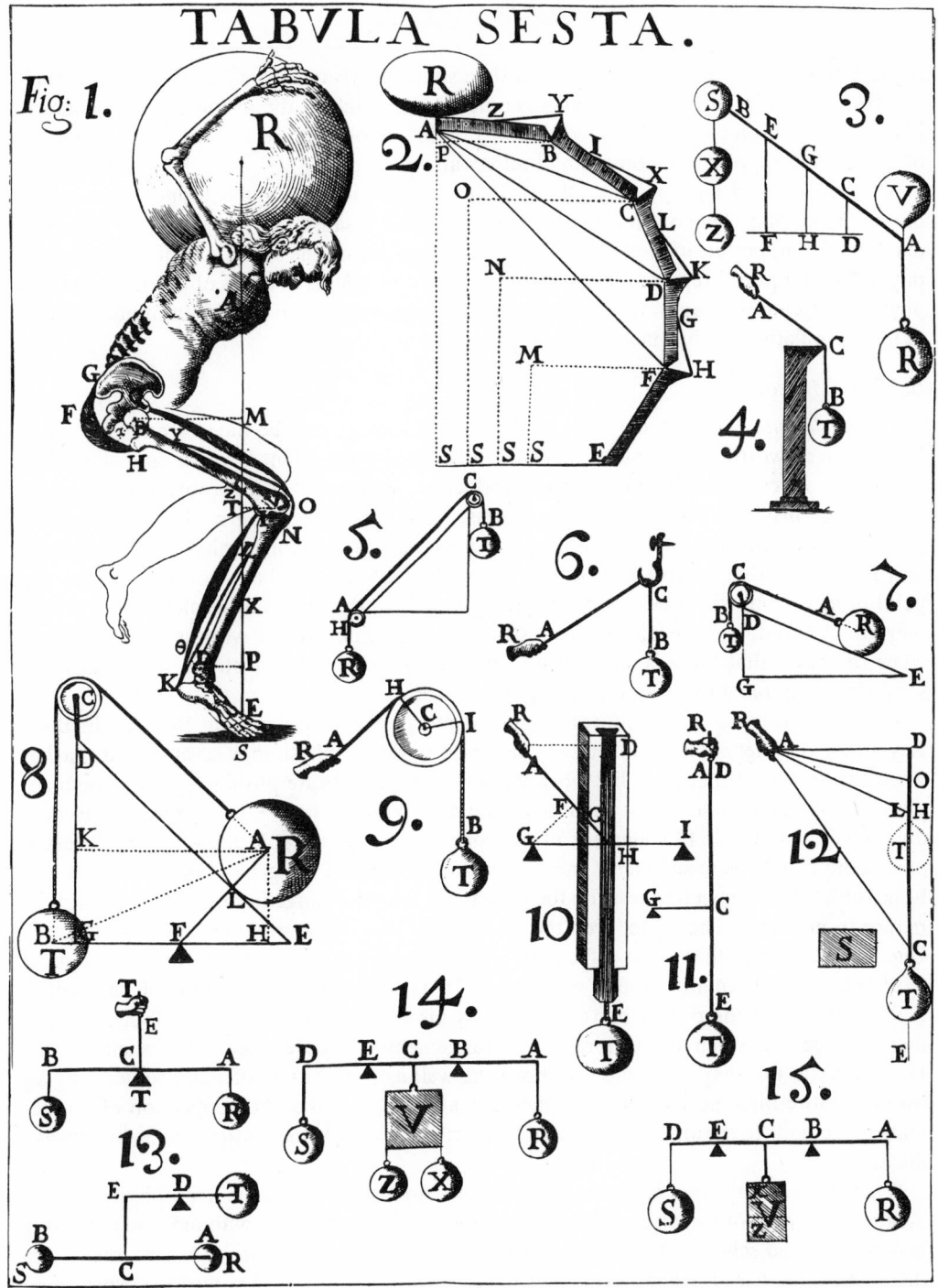

FIGURE 1.   Plate from Borelli's book "De Motu Animalium," published in 1680. This diagram indicates how, in terms of pre-Newtonian physics, Borelli attempted to solve problems about the mechanical motions and structural constraints of vertebrates. Proofs are worked out in terms of statics. Borelli's work is one of the earliest formal books on theoretical biology.[2]

of the mechanics of animal motion. Published some ten years before Newton's "Principia" it is formulated in terms of a strongly geometric approach to the problems of mechanics. Plate 6 from Volume I of the first edition of Borelli's book (Figure 1) gives some indication of his elegant approach to combining biology and physics.

Another series of high points in the history of theoretical biology is found in the works of von Helmholtz. One of the last of the scientific universalists, he was physicist, biologist, mathematician, physician, and philosopher. His treatises on the sensations of tone[22] and on physiological optics[23] represent analysis of biological problems in terms of the mathematical physics of Helmholtz' age. It is well to note that Helmholtz also played an important role in the formulation of that mathematical physics.

B. The Modern Era

1. *Foundations.*   The modern era in theoretical biology can be dated from 1917 when D'Arcy Wentworth Thompson published his epic work "On Growth and Form."[18] Thompson's creed, as embodied in his introduction, was that "Their problems of form are in the first instance mathematical problems, their problems of growth are essentially physical problems, and the morphologist is *ipso facto*, a student of physical science. He may learn from that comprehensive science, as the physiologists have not failed to do, the point of view from which her problems are approached, the quantitative methods by which they are attacked, and the wholesome restraints under which all her work is done. He may come to realize that there is no branch of mathematics, however abstract, which may not some day be applied to phenomena of the real world."

Thompson tried to do for morphology and morphogenesis what von Brücke, du Bois-Reymond, von Helmholtz, and Ludwig had tried to do for physiology seventy years earlier when they resolved that their life work would be to "constitute physiology on a chemico-physical foundation and give it equal scientific rank with physics."[4] It is interesting to note du Bois-Reymond's 1848 statement of his concept of theoretical biology, "nevertheless if our methods only were sufficient, an analytical mechanics of the general life process would be possible. This conviction rests on the insight . . . that all changes in the material world . . . reduce to motions. Therefore, even the life process cannot be anything but motions. . . . One sees, therefore, that if the difficulties of analysis did not exceed our ability, analytical mechanics fundamentally would reach even to the problem of freedom of the will."[4]

Returning to Thompson's book, he follows his introduction by over 700 elegant and literate pages in which he explores the arrangements of leaves, the spiral shells of the Foraminifera, the shapes of eggs and horns as well as a multitude of other topics ranging over the entire biological world. His theme is always the same, the application of mathematical methods to the analysis of growth and form. His mathematics are simple, but always illuminating.

When read today, the book seems curiously archaic, for Thompson's physics is the preatomic physics of the nineteenth century. Our present obsession with molecular biology makes the grand scheme of Thompson seem too large by comparison. Yet the insights are there and if they seem trivial at times it is because, as a result of Thompson's work, they have been impressed on us since elementary biology courses. Thompson must be reckoned as one of the forefathers of contemporary theoretical biology.

Another work of theoretical biology on a grand scale is "Elements of Physical Biology"[12] by Alfred J. Lotka, published in 1924. The theme of Lotka's work, as set forth by the author, is "The laws of chemical dynamics of a structured system of the kind described will be precisely those laws, or at least a very important section of those laws, which govern the evolution of a system comprising living organisms." Lotka's view is almost cosmological in scope. He sees biology as a special case of the unfolding of the universe, evolution as a special case of irreversible transformation, and life as a grandiose chemical process. To this end he is interested in biological systems rather than the life processes of individuals.

The mathematics of the book are largely differential equations, systems of simultaneous differential equations, and integral equations. The work is enormously ambitious in scope, encompassing everything from thermodynamics to the function of consciousness. In the end it emerges as much a grand work of philosophy as a scientific treatise. It has, however, provided much of the background for the development of theoretical biology which took place in the 1940's and 1950's.

One aspect of Lotka's work, the study of ecological relations, was pursued vigorously by a number of researchers. It is perhaps best known through the work of Volterra and his associates and the following three books are examples of the foundations of mathematical ecology: "Leçons sur la théorie mathématique de la lutte pour la vie"[19] by Vito Volterra, 1931, "Les associations biologiques au point de vue mathématique"[20] by Vito Volterra and Umberto D'Ancona, 1935, and "Biologie mathématique"[10] by V. A. Kostitzin, 1937. Kostitzin's book contains a note on the history of theoretical biology that is worth quoting in its entirety.

"Les sciences naturelles utilisent la méthode statistique depuis longtemps, mais c'est au grand savant anglais K. Pearson qu'on doit le renouvellement complet de cette méthode et la fondation d'une nouvelle science—la biométrie. L'équation fut donnée pour la première fois par Verhulst en 1845 dans l'hypothèse d'une population fermée. Depuis les mémoires de Verhulst, des problèmes biologiques particuliers furent de temps en temps traités par la méthode analytique, mais c'est à M. Lotka et indépendamment de lui à M. Volterra qu'appartient l'honneur d'avoir appliqué cette méthode aux problèmes plus généraux de façon systématique. L'ouvrage de M. Lotka sur la biologie physique a déclanché un mouvement biologo-mathématique dans les pays anglo-saxons. Les brillantes recherches de M. Volterra, si riches en suggestions mathématiques, ont déterminé un mouvement analogue dans l'Europe continentale. Les recherches mi-théoriques, mi-expérimentales de M. Pearl sur les lois de la croissance d'une population ont servi de base à la démographie moderne. Il faut mentionner d'autre part les contributions très importantes de M. J. B. S. Haldane à la théorie mathématique de la sélection."

The general procedure followed by the mathematical ecologists of the 1930's and to some extent subsequently, is to take a verbal statement regarding a population and how it varies under certain conditions, and to reformulate that verbal statement as an equation, usually a first order linear differential equation. On occasion, it is necessary to use nonlinear equations and higher order derivatives. A given problem is then formulated as a series of such simultaneous differential equations. The solutions, subject to given boundary conditions, constitute the treatment of the problem. The resulting functions can then be tested against experimental and observational data on populations. The most serious difficulty arises in the solution of the simultaneous equations particularly where nonlinear equations are present. Volterra evolved some interesting mathematical techniques for such equations. In this area it is likely that modern computer techniques will be of great value, and the approach is discussed in Chapters 10 and 11 of this work. There are few areas of biology where theoretical mathematical studies have had as much impact as they have had in ecology.

On a par with the ecological studies and closely related to them in many ways, have been the mathematical studies of populations and population genetics. Among the books on this subject are "A Mathematical Theory of Natural and Artificial Selection"[7] published by J. B. S. Haldane in 1924 and two works by R. A. Fisher published in 1930 and 1949:[5,6] "The Genetical Theory of Natural Selection" and "The Theory of Inbreeding." Also of great importance in this area have been the writings of Sewall Wright.[28] These authors have combined insights from genetics, statistics, and ecology to set up formal systems to represent evolving populations.

A novel and original approach to formal biology was described in 1937 by J. H. Woodger. He published a monograph called "The Axiomatic Method in Biology"[27] which attempts to utilize modern symbolic logic to formulate biological problems. The author's expressed purpose is "the application of the methods of the exact sciences to biology. . . . Another way of expressing the aim of this book is by saying that it is to provide an exact and perfectly controllable language by means of which biological knowledge may be ordered." Woodger constructs a biological calculus based on the methods developed by Whitehead and Russell in their "Principia Mathematica."[25] Although the influence of this work must yet await the test of time, Woodger has made a highly significant point for theoretical biology, namely, that at the moment we do not know which formal and mathematical methods will be useful in biology. We must not assume that the mathematical language of theoretical physics will automatically serve as an appropriate language for biology. Therefore other symbolic formalisms should be explored, and this Woodger has done in his discussion of axiomatic methods. We shall return to the problem of other formalisms in discussing the work of von Neumann.

2. *Mathematical biophysics.* One of the influential schools of modern theoretical biology has derived from the work of Nicolas Rashevsky and his students. Some recent aspects of their work are discussed in Chapter 3. Rashevsky's major work, "Mathematical Biophysics,"[15] was first published in 1938 and has subsequently gone through two editions and revisions. The author states his aim with clarity. "In this book we propose to lay down the foundations for a mathematical biology analogous in its methods to mathematical physics. Inasmuch as we shall not necessarily treat here biology as a science *sui generis*, but shall, wherever possible, look for physical interpretation, we propose the name 'mathematical biophysics.' "

Rashevsky's next paragraph presents his concept of the role of theoretical science and is of interest in this regard:

"In our study we should first start with the fundamental living unit, the cell. Following the fundamental method of physicomathematical sciences, we do not attempt a mathematical description of a concrete cell, in all its complexity. We start with a study of highly idealized systems, which at first may not have any counterpart in real nature. This point must be particularly emphasized. The objection may be raised against such an approach, because such systems have no connection with reality; and therefore any conclusions drawn about such idealized systems cannot be applied to real ones. Yet this is exactly what has been, and always is, done in physics. The physicist goes on studying mathematically, in detail, such nonreal things as 'material points,' 'absolutely rigid bodies,' 'ideal fluids,' and so on. *There are no such things as those in nature.* Yet the physicist not only studies them but applies his conclusions to *real things.* And behold! Such an application leads to practical results—at least within certain limits. This is because within these limits the real things have common properties with the fictitious idealized ones! Only a superman could grasp mathematically at once all the complexity of a real thing. We ordinary mortals must be more modest and approach reality asymptotically, by gradual approximation."

A good deal of the opposition to theoretical biology on the part of "Natural History" oriented biologists stems from differences over the points made in the last quotation. The biologist who has devoted great effort to examining some aspect of nature in all its richness and fullness often feels uncomfortable with the idealized system which fails to embody the details to which he has devoted so much effort. This type of tension is bound to exist with such different approaches to the same biological material. We may hope that proponents of both points of view will see the value of the contributions made from a different outlook and will devote the effort to attempting to understand approaches far from their own views of biology.

The original edition of Rashevsky's book covered biophysics of the cell, excitation phenomena, and the central nervous system. The later parts tend to fall more in the area of formal representation rather than in that of the direct application of physics to these phenomena. (For a discussion of nerve function from the more physical point of view, see Chapter 6.) In the subsequent years, Rashevsky's own work has tended more toward mathematical theories of biology with the physical representation assuming a secondary character. However, in the next chapter Professor Rashevsky speaks for himself.

The Chicago group under Professor Rashevsky founded *The Bulletin of Mathematical Biophysics* which has been a major means of communication in this field. Contributors to this journal have written on a very wide range of topics pertinent to theoretical biology.

In relation to *The Bulletin of Mathematical Biophysics* we might take note of other journals in this area. In 1935 the group at the Professor Jan van der Hoeven Foundation for Theoretical Biology of the University of Leiden founded *Acta Biotheoretica* which has been published continuously since that date. This journal deals primarily with the verbal type of theory in biology and is not primarily a mathematical publication. This same group publishes *Bibliographia Biotheoretica* which is a bibliography of wide scope, encompassing theoretical biology as well as some related areas. In 1961 a new periodical was started, the *Journal of Theoretical Biology*. This journal covers a wide range of theoretical topics.

Another school of theoretical biology is that associated with Ludwig von Bertalanffy. His major work, "Theoretische Biologie"[21] republished in 1951, is a treatment of a very broad range of biological problems, reminiscent in scope of Lotka's earlier work. It is a combination of both verbal and symbolic theory and a number of topics are treated by mathematical analysis.

3. *Physics and chemistry.* Erwin Schrödinger, one of the founders of quantum mechanics, later turned his attention to biology, among a number of other subjects. In 1943 he delivered a series of lectures at Trinity College, Dublin, which were later published under the title "What is Life?"[16] This remarkable little volume has had considerable influence on the development of theoretical biology. Schrödinger discusses, in a penetrating manner, the relation of quantum mechanics and statistical mechanics to the functioning of cells and to the problem of genetic transmission. He was one of the first to use the concept of coding in connection with genetic control of phenotype. The central question that Schrödinger raises is "How can the events *in space and time* which take place within the spatial boundary of a living organism be accounted for by physics and chemistry?" This is, of course, the main point in the formulation of theoretical biology based on theoretical physics. Furthermore, Schrödinger's book has been rather influential in interesting physicists in working on biological problems.

Chemical kinetics has been an important tool in the formulation of theoretical chemistry and a number of workers have attempted to examine various biological processes in these terms. An extended effort in this direction was made by C. N. Hinshelwood in his 1946 volume, "The Chemical Kinetics of the Bacterial Cell."[8] The author's description of this study is "Chemical reactions have long been studied in isolation: in a cell these reactions occur in a coordinated manner, and in particular the autosynthetic process assumes a dominant role. The question whether any of the modes of thought and work to which the chemist is accustomed in dealing with inanimate systems help in understanding the behavior of the living cell is one which must be asked unless the traditional method of proceeding from the known to the unknown is abandoned."

Hinshelwood's methods consist largely in formulating the differential equations of chemical kinetics for cellular processes and exploring the solutions of these equations. Again we are faced with simultaneous differential equations some of which are nonlinear. Such difficulties would seem almost to require the use of computers, and the work of Garfinkel and Chance (Chapters 11 and 13) indicates the logical extension of Hinshelwood's ideas supplemented with modern computer techniques.

A rather different approach to kinetics in biology was taken by Frank H. Johnson, Henry Eyring, and Milton J. Polissar in "The Kinetic Basis of Molecular Biology"[9] published in 1954. They set their goal as follows. "The chief purpose of this book is to apply modern molecular theory, in so far as it is now possible, to some representative biological processes." They do not start, as does Hinshelwood, with the phenomenological rate equations of chemistry but rather go back to the statistical and quantum mechanical foundation of reaction rate theory (see Chapter 4). They then apply the concepts of absolute reaction rate theory to a number of biological processes. These include bioluminescence, temperature effects, hydrostatic effects, membrane transport, cell irritability, and contractile processes. A wide variety of experimental results are collected and compared with the theoretical analysis.

4. *Cybernetics.*   So far we have had little to say about the problems of control and order in biological systems (Chapter 12). The general problems have long been of interest to neurophysiologists, engineers, mathematicians, and others. In 1948 two works appeared which have had considerable influence in establishing these fields within the framework of theoretical biology. The two works are "Cybernetics"[26] by Norbert Wiener and a journal article entitled "A Mathematical Theory of Communication" by C. E. Shannon. (Shannon's original journal article has been reprinted with another article in book form as "The Mathematical Theory of Communication"[17] by C. E. Shannon and W. Weaver. This volume includes a long essay by Weaver exploring some of the consequences of Shannon's original article.)

Shannon's work provided a formal basis for defining information and demonstrating the utility of the concept. Although it did not deal with biological systems *per se* it had an influential effect on a number of workers who began to explore biological systems in these terms.

Wiener's book develops many of the concepts of information and relates them to a number of fundamental ideas in physics and mathematics. From a biological point of view, Wiener stresses the importance of feedback, closed loop control; he presents numerous examples from normal and pathological processes to demonstrate the utility of these concepts in physiology. He discusses the relation between computing machines and the nervous system. He also considers broader aspects of the control problem in respect to psychology and sociology. Cybernetics, the word coined by Wiener to encompass the entire field of control and communication theory, has now passed into common English usage. Likewise many of the ideas formulated by Wiener have become a part of the intellectual equipment of those interested in biological control. Associated with Wiener in many of the early investigations were Arturo Rosenblueth and Julian H. Bigelow.

The informational aspect of the work of Shannon and Wiener has received particular emphasis in biology. Many of the applications are summed up in two books, "Information Theory in Biology"[14] edited by Henry Quastler, 1953, and "Symposium on Information Theory in Biology"[29] edited by Hubert P. Yockey, Robert Platzman, and Henry Quastler, 1958. In these publications a large number of contributors have applied information theory to such diverse problems as protein sequence, protein synthesis, organ regeneration, neural networks, membrane transport, antigenic specificity, psychological testing, radiation damage, aging, and mosaic receptors. Much of the work has gone into the concept of defining measures for various biological phenomena by means of the information formalisms. As noted in the 1953 book, "The cybernetics of biological function should ultimately contribute to the understanding of the nature of biological control systems. The first stage in the analysis is quantification: a *count* of control elements, a *measure* of the amount of control exercised. Most papers in this volume deal with counts and measures; only on a few occasions have steps beyond this stage been attempted." Many of the studies reported in these two volumes are actively continuing at the present time.

A different type of approach to the neural control problem was made by W. Ross Ashby in 1952. His book, "Design for a Brain,"[1] explores the problem of adaptive behavior from a theoretical point of view. Ashby states the problem he treats as follows: "We commence with the concept that the organism is mechanistic in action, that it is composed of parts, and that the behavior of the whole is the outcome of the compounded actions of the parts. Organisms change their behavior by learning and change it so that the later behavior is better adapted to their environment than the earlier. Our problem is first, to identify the nature of the change which shows as learning, and secondly, to find why such changes should tend to cause better adaptation for the whole organism." Ashby proceeds to model systems, mathematical representations of entirely mechanistic systems, and shows that they demonstrate what he has defined as adaptive behavior. He carries out a parallel development, both verbally and in terms of mathematical analysis. He has also constructed a machine which analogs the type of behavior he postulates.

The problem of the relationship of living organisms to automata has been treated by John von Neumann. Many of his ideas have never been formally published but were presented in lectures and reports. Some of these ideas are published in "The Computer and the Brain,"[24] although von Neumann's untimely death in 1957 prevented him from completing the analysis. He has explored the relationship between modern high speed computers and neural processes in living systems, and arrives at the somewhat startling result that the language of the brain is not the language of mathematics. Von Neumann notes that "whatever language the central nervous system is using, it is characterized by less logical and arithmetic depth than we are normally used to. . . . Thus logics and mathematics in the central nervous system when viewed as language, must structurally be essentially different from those languages to which our common experience refers. . . . However, the above remarks about reliability and logical and arithmetic depth prove that whatever the system is, it cannot fail to differ considerably from what we consciously and explicitly consider as mathematics."

Thus von Neumann has challenged theoretical biology to discover the natural formalism, the mathematics used by neural networks.

III. CONCLUSION

In this brief sketch of the last fifty years of theoretical biology, no attempt has been made to make this a complete treatment or to include the most recent work, much of which is covered in subsequent chapters. Instead, we have tried to summarize the points of view of some major works that have been landmarks in the development of theoretical biology. From an examination of these works a few general conclusions can be drawn. First, we note that although the formal theoretical approach has been of importance in a few areas of biology, the general impact on biology of mathematical approaches has not been very forceful. This is nowhere better seen than in the minimal amount of mathematics required in most college biology curricula. Second, we note that a relatively small number of researchers have made some imaginative starts in formulating theoretical approaches to biological problems. These approaches are instructive in their failures as well as in their successes, for they give some indications of what can and cannot be done in these fields.

Third, we see some inadequacies in present mathematics that indicate the possible need for constructing new mathematics for biological applications. These inadequacies are seen most vividly in the absence of an effective systems theory and in von Neumann's conclusion that at least one phase of biological function operates with a presently unknown type of mathematics. Computers present an approach to some of these problems but just how far this will take us is unknown.

Fourth, and finally, to end this chapter on an encouraging note, the structured nature of biology and the relation to physics and chemistry gives every promise that formal theory will be of great value in our understanding of living systems.

REFERENCES

1. Ashby, W. R. 1952. "Design for a Brain," 259 pp. Chapman and Hall, London.
2. Borelli, G. A. 1680/81. "De Motu Animalium," Vol. I, 387 pp.; Vol. II, 520 pp. Bernabò, Rome.
3. Bridgman, P. W. 1941. "The Nature of Thermodynamics," 229 pp. Harvard Univ. Press, Cambridge.
4. Cranefield, P. E. 1959. The nineteenth-century prelude to modern biophysics. *In:* "Proceedings of the First National Biophysics Conference," (H. Quastler and H. J. Morowitz, eds.), pp. 19–26. Yale Univ. Press, New Haven.
5. Fisher, R. A. 1930. "The Genetical Theory of Natural Selection," 272 pp. Clarendon, Oxford.
6. Fisher, R. A. 1949. "The Theory of Inbreeding," 120 pp. Oliver and Boyd, London and Edinburgh.
7. Haldane, J. B. S. 1924. "A Mathematical Theory of Natural and Artificial Selection," 55 pp. Univ. Press, Cambridge.
8. Hinshelwood, C. N. 1946. "The Chemical Kinetics of the Bacterial Cell," 284 pp. Clarendon, Oxford.
9. Johnson, F., Eyring, H., and Polissar, M. J. 1954. "The Kinetic Basis of Molecular Biology," 874 pp. Wiley, New York.

10. Kostitzin, V. A. 1937. "Biologie mathématique," 215 pp. Librairie Armand Colin, Paris.

11. Locy, W. A. 1951. "Biology and Its Makers," 469 pp. Holt, New York.

12. Lotka, A. J. 1925. "Elements of Physical Biology," 460 pp. Williams and Wilkins, Baltimore.

13. Mendel, G. 1950. Letters to Carl Nägeli. 1866–1873. *Genetics* **35** (*Suppl.*, "The Birth of Genetics"): 1–29.

14. Quastler, H., ed. 1953. "Essays on the Use of Information Theory in Biology," 273 pp. Univ. Illinois Press, Urbana.

15. Rashevsky, N. 1938. "Mathematical Biophysics," 340 pp. Univ. Chicago Press, Chicago.

16. Schrödinger, E. 1944. "What is Life?," 91 pp. Cambridge Univ. Press, London.

17. Shannon, C. E., and Weaver, W. 1949. "The Mathematical Theory of Communication," 117 pp. Univ. Illinois Press, Urbana.

18. Thompson, D'A. W. 1917. "On Growth and Form," 793 pp. Univ. Press, Cambridge.

19. Volterra, V. 1931. "Leçons sur la théorie mathématique de la lutte pour la vie," 214 pp. Gauthier-Villars, Paris.

20. Volterra, V., and D'Ancona, U. 1935. "Les associations biologiques au point de vue mathématique," 96 pp. Hermann, Paris.

21. von Bertalanffy, L. 1951. "Theoretische Biologie," 2nd ed., Vol. II, 418 pp. Francke, Bern.

22. von Helmholtz, H. L. F. 1863. "Die Lehre von den Tonempfindungen als Physiologische Grundlage für die Theorie der Musik," 600 pp. Vieweg, Braunschweig.

23. von Helmholtz, H. L. F. 1867. "Handbuch der Physiologischen Optik," 874 pp. Voss, Leipzig.

24. von Neumann, J. 1958. "The Computer and the Brain," 82 pp. Yale Univ. Press, New Haven.

25. Whitehead, A. N., and Russell, B. 1925/27. "Principia Mathematica," 2nd ed., Vol. I, 674 pp.; Vol. II, 742 pp.; Vol. III, 491 pp. Univ. Press, Cambridge.

26. Wiener, N. 1948. "Cybernetics," 1st ed., 194 pp. M.I.T. Press, Wiley, New York.

27. Woodger, J. H. 1937. "The Axiomatic Method in Biology," 174 pp. Univ. Press, Cambridge.

28. Wright, S. 1949. Adaptation and selection. *In:* "Genetics, Paleontology and Evolution," (G. L. Jepsen, G. G. Simpson, and E. Mayr, eds.), pp. 365–389. Princeton Univ. Press, Princeton.

29. Yockey, H. P., Platzman, R. L., and Quastler, H., eds. 1958. "Symposium on Information Theory in Biology," 418 pp. Pergamon, New York.

[3]

MODELS AND MATHEMATICAL PRINCIPLES IN BIOLOGY

N. Rashevsky

This chapter deals with the formulation of possible *general mathematical principles* in biology, as opposed to the construction of *mathematical models*. The relation between the two approaches is discussed first, after which two general principles of recent origin are suggested and their applications discussed. This paper gives a very general survey of a new field in which a large number of technical papers has been published. It is impossible to give details in such a bird's-eye view. Therefore, the reader may find some statements unjustified, or fail to see the manner in which the conclusions are reached. For a complete critical understanding of all such points the reader must refer to the original publications cited.

I. MATHEMATICAL MODELS AND GENERAL PRINCIPLES

From its earliest days, which may be traced as far back as Leonard Euler's[9] work on the mathematical theory of circulation of blood, the development of mathematical biology proceeded almost exclusively through the development of physicomathematical or purely formal mathematical models of various biological phenomena.* Thus Euler's[9] ideas, which were independently revived by O. Frank[11-15] much later, conceive a circulatory system approximately as consisting of an elastic reservoir, a peripheral resistance, and a pump—the heart. This is essentially a physical model, and, as all models, is intentionally oversimplified. The work of Fischer[10] and Braune (cited by Fischer) on the kinematics of human locomotion considered linked levers as a model of some parts of arms and legs. A. J. Lotka[34] and Vito Volterra[71] developed a theory of interaction of species that is based on oversimplified mathematical models of processes of competition for food or of predator-prey interactions.†

In 1934 a systematic development of mathematical biology began at The University of Chicago. This development aimed at the creation of a mathematical biology that would

---

* These and other historical aspects of the field are also discussed in Chapter 2.
† Theoretical ecology is also treated in Chapters 1, 2, 11, 15, and 16.

stand in the same relation to experimental biology as mathematical physics stands to experimental physics. It proceeded further largely by developments of mathematical models of different biological phenomena. Thus the early work of N. Rashevsky[40,54] on cell division is based on the model of a cell conceived as a metabolizing system with metabolites flowing in and out. These flows produce the so-called diffusion drag forces. It is shown mathematically that these forces will, under specified conditions, divide the system into two. This model cannot be considered as a successful one, and a good theory of cell division is still lacking. Nevertheless, even this crude model led to the prediction of a number of quantitative relations that were verified experimentally.[54] Moreover, the model leads to a theory of some aspects of cell respiration which has been verified experimentally, as well as to the theory of cell polarity and self-regulation in cells.[54]

More successful were the models of the peripheral and central nervous systems. The development of the models of the central nervous system is based on first postulating some simple laws of interaction between neurons, then constructing various possible neuronal circuits which, on the basis of the postulated laws of interaction, possess some properties of the central nervous system.[54] In this way, successful theories have been developed not only of such relatively simple phenomena as reaction times, psychophysical discrimination,[27] discrimination of intensities, but even of such phenomena as gestalt perception, gestalt transposition, perception of abstract relations, rational learning and thinking, and even esthetic perception.[54] The vast amount of work that has been done in other branches of mathematical biology, such as H. D. Landahl's[55] work on learning, R. Bush and F. Mosteller's[3] theory of learning, Landahl's[30–32] theory of vision, G. Karreman's theory of excitation[20] and his theory of pulse waves,[21–26] S. Roston's,[67] F. Cope's,[6] and J. R. Womersley's[72] work on circulation, J. Hearon's[18] work on diffusion in metabolizing systems, C. Patlak's[36,37] work on active transport, Landahl's,[28,29] Segre's,[70] Bellman, Jacquez, and Kalaba's[2,19] works on pharmacological phenomena, and Defares'[7] work on the pulmonary system, to mention only a few, are all essentially based on constructing physicomathematical models of various biological phenomena. Of the more than 600 papers published since 1939 in the *Bulletin of Mathematical Biophysics* alone, by numerous contributors both in this country and abroad, the majority may be classified as dealing with models.[32,33,*]

Mathematical models are not unknown to the mathematical physicist. We speak of the model of the atom, model of the solid state, et cetera. The physicist, however, does more than construct models. He discovers and formulates what may be called general mathematical principles. These are exemplified by the laws of Newton, the principles of thermodynamics, the principle of relativity, and the principles of quantum mechanics. A model is essentially of a transient nature. Bohr's model of the atom was eventually discarded and superseded by the Schrödinger model. A useful model, however, has some features that are retained in future models, even after the original model is discarded.

The laws of Newton, or the principle of relativity, can hardly be called models. According to H. Poincaré,[38] the laws of Newton and other general principles of physics are essentially useful conventions. Sometimes they may even be regarded as "hidden definitions." Whatever view we may accept on the nature of these general principles, one characteristic of such principles stands out clearly: taken *alone*, these principles do not lead to any *concrete* conclusions or predictions. Thus consider the second law of Newton, which in its

---

* A wide range of biological models is dealt with in a recent book edited by Beament,[1] as well as in various other chapters in this volume, such as Chapters 1 and 12.

mathematical form may be written

$$m \frac{d^2x}{dt^2} = F$$

where m is the mass, x the coordinate, t the time, and F the force. Unless we specify in a system the masses and their initial coordinates and velocities, as well as the forces acting between these masses, we cannot draw any conclusion from this equation as to the time course of the system. But once we have either a real or a conceptual system, then this formula can be applied to it and predict its behavior. But any conceptual system is essentially a model. Thus the general principle, Newton's second law, can be applied to any model and help us in determining its properties.

Thus, in physics, the models are based on a number of general mathematical principles. It is also important to notice that frequently a general principle in physics is stated in a verbal rather than in a mathematical form. The mathematical formulation enters only when the principle is applied either to a concrete situation or to a conceptual model. Thus the first and third laws of Newton are formulated verbally, as is the law of conservation of energy and the principle of relativity *as such*. Within the framework of a general principle we can thus build models. Hence the concept of a finite space-time universe is a model within the framework of the general principle of relativity.

We stated above that models are of a transient nature, being superseded in time by better models. One might be inclined to think the same holds for general principles, since, for example, Newton's mechanics has been superseded by relativistic mechanics. There is, however, a great difference between the two cases. When Bohr's model of the atom was superseded by the Schrödinger model, some features of Bohr's model were retained. However, in developing a quantum mechanical theory of some atoms, the physicist does *not* now use the simple mathematical machinery used by Bohr. It simply is not applicable any more.

When, on the other hand, relativistic mechanics was substituted for the Newtonian one, it was also found that classical mechanics is a limiting case of the relativistic one, for sufficiently small velocities. Within the range of small velocities it not only *can* be used, but actually *is* used in exactly its original form. More than half a century ago Henri Poincaré remarked that, no matter how great the progress of automobilism may be in the future, it will always be perfectly safe to teach the engineers classical Newtonian mechanics. This feature of greater permanency is characteristic of a general principle.

It may, however, happen that a general principle may be reduced to another one. Thus the principles of thermodynamics are reducible to those of statistical mechanics. The principles of optics become reducible to those of electromagnetism, et cetera, but this does not affect their usefulness. In any given concrete situation it may be more practical, and mathematically simpler, to use the principles of thermodynamics rather than the principles of statistical mechanics. It all depends on the problem.

For their relatively greater permanence the general principles in physics frequently pay the price of requiring a long time to be put into their final and precise formulation. Consider, for example, the principle of conservation of energy as formulated by H. von Helmholtz and by Robert Meyer, and compare it with modern precise and rigorous formulation in any modern textbook of physics. The difference is tremendous. Helmholtz spoke "über die Erhaltung der Kraft," that is, about "the conservation of force," a looseness of terminology that would not be tolerated today. Yet the basic idea of Helmholtz and of Meyer was correct, and it remained unchanged.

Consider again the present-day principles of quantum mechanics in their rigorous mathematical formulations, and compare them to Planck's early formulation in 1902 of his hypothesis of discontinuous emission. They are different—almost beyond recognition. Yet, again, the basic idea was already stated by Planck, and it is here to remain.

Again, take the formulation of the periodic law as given by Mendeleyeff, based on atomic weights, and compare it with the present-day formulation in terms of atomic numbers. The two "periodic tables," the original one and that of today, differ appreciably. Yet the basic idea remains the same.

II. GENERAL MATHEMATICAL PRINCIPLES IN BIOLOGY

As we stated above, most of mathematical biology proceeded by way of constructing mathematical models of different biological phenomena. But whereas in physics the models are based on general physical principles, in biology, with one exception to be mentioned presently, the models are based not on general biological principles but also on well-established physical principles. This in itself is not objectionable. So far there is every evidence that individual biological phenomena are basically reducible to physical ones. If so, then biological models should be based on physical principles. There is, however, the following difficulty. In dealing with even relatively complicated, but isolated and specific biological phenomena such as circulation, nerve excitation, et cetera, the approach via physicomathematical models has proven its worth. If, however, we tackle the problem of the organism as a whole, the problem of interrelations between the different biological phenomena, we come to situations where the application of the "model" method and of a *direct* reduction to physical principles becomes impractical.

Similar situations occur in physics. A physicist designing a system of lenses for a microscope uses the principles of classical optics and does not start by writing down Maxwell's equations—in spite of the fact that the principles of optics are reducible to Maxwell's equations. But the use of this reducibility would only complicate the problem. In biology, such situations are likely to occur more frequently because of the greater complexity of biological phenomena. A general biological principle may simplify the mathematical handling of a problem, even though eventually it may prove to be reducible to physical principles. Moreover, nothing assures us that biology will be reducible to present-day (1963) physics. It is not precluded that physics may have to be *extended* in order to include biological phenomena, just as it had to be extended to include more phenomena than classical physics could explain. Quantum mechanics is an extension of classical physics. Some physical phenomena reducible to quantum mechanics are not reducible to classical physics. A similar situation may occur with respect to biology. In that case, it is conceivable that a final, appropriate formulation of a biological principle may come to be considered as a sort of extension of physics. At present this is, however, pure speculation.

We mentioned above an exception to the apparent lack of general biological principles. The exception is the set of principles of genetics as formulated originally by Gregor Mendel. These principles are the foundations of a well-developed discipline—mathematical genetics, among the founders of which we find such illustrious names as Sewall Wright, J. B. S. Haldane, L. Hogben, and others. Mathematical genetics does form a part of mathematical biology. Its scope, however, is restricted compared with the scope of other branches of mathematical biology, such as those mentioned on page 37. Because mathematical genetics was already a well-developed science when other branches of mathematical biology began to develop, and because there is a vast literature on the subject, we shall not discuss it here.

We shall now briefly discuss two general principles in mathematical biology, which we have proposed and developed to some extent in the last two decades. In discussing these principles we must keep in mind what has been said in the last three paragraphs of Section I (pp. 38–39). It can hardly be expected that the first tentative formulation of a general principle would be sufficiently rigorous. The final formulation may come in the future. We shall, however, attempt to state some general ideas that we believe may grow eventually into rigorously formulated principles.

A. *The Principle of Adequate Design of Organisms*

Our search for a general principle began in 1943 in connection with our studies on the mathematical theory of organic form.[41–43] The problem of organic form is conceded to be a very difficult one. At first sight there seems to be no particular reason for pessimism. Analytical geometry teaches us that any particular geometric form, that of a surface or a volume, can be represented by an appropriate equation. Thus it would seem that the difficulty is purely a mathematical one. However, this is not so. Suppose that we succeed in representing mathematically, let us say, the profile of a particular dog. Not only are there no two dogs that are exactly alike, but the same dog will have a different profile depending on whether it stands or sits, or whether it holds its tail up or down. One could think of taking care of the different positions of the same dog, or of the differences between different dogs, by using the same equation containing a sufficient number of parameters. The number of parameters needed would, however, be so large that the impracticability of such an approach is evident.

One might perhaps think that from an appropriately developed mathematical biology of the cell, based perhaps on molecular dynamics, we could develop a theory of physical forces between cells and, on the basis of such a theory, calculate the shapes of multicellular organisms. Such an approach would amount to a kind of n-body problem with n of the order of magnitude of 10^{13} and with nonconservative forces to boot. Attempts in that direction have actually been made, but all one can hope in this case is to obtain some very general conclusions.[39,40]

An important factor in our problem is the fact mentioned above; namely, there are no two organisms *exactly* alike. Yet, in spite of the diversity of different dogs, different cats, or different horses, we do recognize a dog as a dog, a cat as a cat, and a horse as a horse. Obviously it is not the exact details of the geometrical form of an animal (or, for that matter, a plant) that are important. It is the *absolute* as well as the *relative* sizes of different parts of the body, for example, the trunk, the legs, the neck, and the head, that make us recognize an animal as belonging to a particular species. Where the absolute and relative dimensions are similar, a confusion may arise. Thus, in darkness, it is possible to mistake a very small dog for a large cat, or a hippopotamus for a rhinoceros. But under no conditions can we mistake an elephant for a deer, or a giraffe for a dog. In darkness we may mistake an oak for a maple, but not for a poplar or for a palm.

What determines the absolute and the relative sizes of the different parts of an organism? An organism, whether a unicellular or a multicellular one, performs a number of biophysical, biochemical, and other functions. Some functions may be purely mechanical, such as the need for the legs of a quadruped to be sufficiently strong to support the weight of the whole animal. Other functions may be of a mixed nature. For example, locomotion involves purely mechanical phenomena, as well as biochemical and biophysical phenomena involved in supplying the energy necessary for locomotion. Most of these biological functions have, among other things, a quantitative or numerical specification. In the above-mentioned examples these are the weight to be supported and the velocity of locomotion. The size of the organ, or of the part of the body that performs a given function, is largely determined by the quantitative specification of the function to be performed. Thus a leg *must* have a certain minimum thickness if it has to support a given weight. Legs that are too short will not permit a sufficiently high speed of running.

The same functions having the same intensities can, in general, be performed by several different structures. In 1943 a general principle was tentatively formulated[41,42] according to which that particular structure or design that actually is found in nature is the *simplest* one compatible with the performance of a given function or set of functions. To apply this principle in any particular case we consider different mechanisms that can perform the prescribed function or functions. In other words, we consider different possible models. Of these models we choose that which is the simplest possible one. Thus we apply the *principle of maximum simplicity* to different models. As a general principle, it must be applicable to any given situation or model.

Simplicity, however, is a rather vague concept. There is no unit in which simplicity could be measured in all cases. Something simple from one point of view may be complicated from another point of view. For mathematical applications the above formulation of the principle was found to be unsatisfactory, although the principle did lead to some interesting results in regard to the form of both plants and animals.[43] In 1954 D. L. Cohn[4,5] applied the general idea embodied in the above principle to the problem of structure of the arterial bed. He sharpened the formulation, however, by requiring that an organic structure necessary for the performance of a given function be *optimal* with respect to needed material and necessary energy expenditure. Thereafter it was spoken of as the *principle of optimal design*.[55] Optimality, however, is also a relative concept. It may turn out that a structure optimal with respect to needed material will not be optimal with respect to energy expenditure. Thus a certain vagueness is still inherent in the formulation. In the latest formulation of the principle, the notion of optimality is discarded and the principle is formulated in the following manner:[56] When a set of functions of an organism or of a single organ is prescribed, then, in order to find the shape and structure of the organ, the mathematical biologist must proceed just as an engineer proceeds in designing a structure or a machine for the performance of a prescribed function. The design must be *adequate* to the performance of the prescribed function under specified varying environmental conditions. This may be called the principle of adequate design of the organism.

The solution of the problem of form or structure is evidently not unique under the principle formulated above. But this is not an objection; it represents an asset. In the organic world we do find organisms and organs that perform essentially the same functions, but which are nevertheless different in their form. The converse, however, does not hold. Organisms performing different functions are different in their structure. The same situation is found in engineering. A racing car, a passenger car, and a truck look different because they perform different kinds of transportation functions. But, in designing a passenger car, different engineers may use slightly different designs that will all perform more or less the same functions. Passenger cars of different makes differ in their appearance. No one, however, will mistake a passenger car for a moving van, just as no one will mistake a dog for a camel.

In applying the principle of adequate design, the mathematical biologist should consider not only the functions to be performed but also the varying environmental conditions that an organism may meet in its life. In calculating the size of a branch, the mathematical biologist must take into account not only the necessity for the branch to be sufficiently strong mechanically so as not to break under its own weight, but must also consider the maximal possible strength of the winds that the branch must withstand in a given locality. This is again analogous to the engineering problem. The dimensions of the different parts of an automobile are not designed merely to operate on new, smooth highways. They must withstand the shocks of the most bumpy roads.

What type of mathematics is required in the application of the principle of adequate design? The type of mathematics and the method of general approach will differ from problem to problem. This is again analogous to engineering design. In the design of a space ship, mathematical problems occur that are different from those met in the design of a tractor.

As a rule, the mathematical biologist will first consider the most important functions and accordingly will make a general, rough layout of the structure of the organ or organism as a whole. He then will introduce the necessary modifications by considering other functions which may or may not be less essential to the organism. He will end with working out the details that are necessary for the performance of the least essential functions. An automotive engineer also begins with a general layout of a car and ends with details of the door handles, cigarette lighters, et cetera.

In a sense, the above is still largely a program. A detailed structure of an organism has not yet been worked out because of the tremendous complexity of the organisms. Some "rough layouts" have, however, been made and lead to interesting results. We shall now consider them briefly.

In the early stages of our research in this field, when we still used the concept of simplicity, some applications to actual cases were made.[43] The trunk of a quadruped is supported at its ends by the four extremities. If, for a given mass of the animal, the trunk were to be rather narrow and long, it would sag under its own weight. The belly of the animal would drag on the ground and impede the locomotion, unless locomotion is by creeping—as with a lizard. Very crude mathematical considerations show that the greater the mass of the quadruped, the greater should be the ratio of the "average width" of its body to its "average length." In fact, the body of a horse has a more "slender" shape than that of an elephant. The above-mentioned considerations lead to the conclusion that the width of the body must vary roughly as the 3/2 power of the length. Neither the length nor the width of a trunk of a quadruped is sharply defined. It is, however, interesting that using photographs by Muybridge[35,55] of a variety of animals on the background of a divided scale, and estimating approximately from these photographs the width and length of the trunk, we find that if we plot the width against the length on a logarithmic scale, the points cluster definitely around a straight line with a slope of 3/2, as required by the calculation. This 3/2 power law holds for different animals in the range from cat to ox.[41-43,55,56]

A somewhat more complicated application involves the function of the heart and of the lungs. Both must provide a sufficient amount of oxygen to the tissues. The mechanisms involved in the two cases are different and so are the mathematical arguments. The conclusions, however, prove to be similar. By assuming Rubner's law[69] to hold, we find that the heart rate, as well as the rate of respiration, should vary as the inverse cube root of the mass of the animal—*other conditions being equal*. The situation described by the italicized words, of course, never occurs. There are no two animals that would differ in mass but in nothing else. Rubner's law is also only a rather crude approximation. If Rubner's law applied exactly, and if the other conditions were equal, a plot of the heart rate or of the respiration rate against the mass on a logarithmic scale should yield a straight line with the slope −1/3. All that we may expect actually is that the points of such plots will cluster around a straight line of slope −1/3. This is found to be the case both for the heart rate and for the rate of respiration in a number of animals ranging from rat to horse.[55]

This inverse cube root relation was also derived by B. Günther and E. Guerra[17] in 1955 from a very different principle which they proposed, namely, the *principle of biological similarity*. This principle is based on considerations used in dimensional analysis. We cannot enter here into a discussion of this interesting work.

Somewhat better results were obtained by D. L. Cohn in his above-mentioned work on the arterial bed. Cohn begins by considering the size of the aorta.[4] The smaller the aorta the greater for a given rate of flow is the velocity of flow. From the point of view of economy of material, the aorta should be small. But this results in an increased velocity and increased Reynolds number, with ensuing turbulence. This, in its turn, results in a very great increase of the energy required to maintain the flow. Cohn, therefore, calculated the radius of the aorta from the requirement that it be the smallest possible without turbulence setting in.

Cohn considers further the arrangement of the branching system of the arteries from the point of view of the best and most economic way of supplying the necessary oxygen to tissues through diffusion from the capillaries. This leads to a relation between the radius of a vessel and that of its branches at points of bifurcation. The radius of the capillaries is also calculated.

Cohn made a comparison of his calculation with data supplied for the structure of the arterial bed of a dog studied by H. D. Green.[16] The following are the results of the comparison:

TABLE 1

	Calculated	Observed
Radius of the aorta	0.43 cm	0.5 cm
Ratio of radii of branches to that of original vessel at bifurcation	0.79	0.8
Diameter of capillaries	$2.2\,\mu$	$4.0\,\mu$

Recently[59] we have generalized this line of reasoning further and applied it to the estimation of the orders of magnitude of different important parameters in the cardiovascular system. Cohn's considerations lead directly to an expression for the peripheral resistance. Since the total rate of flow Q is given by the ratio of the average blood pressure P over the peripheral resistance R, we obtain P, therefore, from known Q and R. Considerations of design require that the aorta and the other major arteries be sufficiently elastic to store enough blood during diastole and to insure as constant a rate of flow as possible. If all the blood vessels were absolutely rigid, then the sudden stoppage of blood supply by the heart at the end of the systole would result in undue mechanical stresses and in a loss of efficiency of the whole system. The important parameter here is the so-called volume elasticity of the aorta, that is, the increase of the volume per unit increment of pressure. This is not a *material constant* like Young's modulus. The volume elasticity depends on the modulus of elasticity of the wall of the aorta, as well as on the thickness of the wall and the radius of the aorta. Thus by varying the thickness of the wall we can change the volume elasticity.

Considerations of design lead to relations between the volume elasticity and the variation of the pressure around its average value during the cardiac cycle. Similar considerations lead to expressions for the stroke volume of the heart and for the duration of the cardiac cycle. Because of the crudeness of the approximations made (this being the "gross" layout), only an agreement of the orders of magnitude can be expected. The results for an average human are as follows:

TABLE 2

Rate of flow Q	$\sim 10^2$ cm^3 sec^{-1}
Average blood pressure	$\sim 10^5$ dyne cm^{-2} = 100 mm Hg
Range of variation of blood pressure between systole and diastole	$\sim 0.5 \times 10^5$ dyne cm^{-2} = 50 mm Hg
Radius of aorta	~ 1.5 cm
Length of aorta	~ 15–20 cm
Cardiac period	~ 1 sec
Stroke volume	$\sim 10^2$ cm^3
Peripheral resistance	$\sim 10^3$ dyne sec cm^{-5}
Volume elasticity of the aorta	$\sim 10^3$ dyne cm^{-5}

The first six items are clearly of the correct order of magnitude. In regard to the last three, we may mention that the stroke volume, as estimated by indirect experiments, is of the same order of magnitude as the calculated one. As regards the peripheral resistance and volume elasticity, they are found[68] actually to vary within a wide range, but are also of the same order of magnitude as the calculated ones.

For immediate practical purposes such crude calculations as ours are of no use. They indicate, however, the general applicability of the principle of adequate design. Calculations from *indirect observation* of the volume elasticity of the aorta in intact humans have been attempted by several investigators. This knowledge is clearly of great potential clinical importance. The possibility of calculating this quantity from first principles is, therefore, likely to lead to important applications.

In our calculations we neglected, as a first approximation, the nonlinear nature of aortic elasticity, now well established. This, as well as other factors, will have to be taken into consideration in the next, better approximations.

An objection that might be raised against the principle of adequate design is that it is "teleological" in nature and, therefore, repugnant to a mechanistically minded scientist. To this we may reply that all variational principles in physics are "teleological," beginning with the principle of least action. They all involve both the beginning and the end point, that is, a "future" point of a process.

Another objection may be that the principle of adequate design seems to imply the existence of a special creative intelligence in nature. This, however, is not the case. The principle may possibly follow from natural selection, which preserves only adequately designed organisms. It may, however, turn out to be an independent principle. But even in this case we do not need any hypothesis of a "universal engineering mind" or the like.

Like other general scientific principles, the principle of adequate design offers us merely an operational prescription for the determination of organic form by calculation.

It may be added that what is now called "bionics" may perhaps eventually become merely an application of the principle of adequate design.*

B. The Principle of Biological Epimorphism

We shall now discuss a very different type of general principle,[44] proposed in 1954. Hitherto we have paid attention to the quantitative aspects of biology, both in constructing models and in discussing the principle of adequate design. To the layman, mathematics seems to be a purely quantitative science, dealing with numbers and quantities. This view is, however, already belied by elementary plane geometry. The theorem that the three bisectors of the angles of a triangle all intersect at the same point can be, and is, proven by rigorous mathematical reasoning. Yet there is nothing quantitative about it. It expresses a qualitative relation or, as we say, it is relational in its nature. True enough, quantitative theorems do appear in plane elementary geometry. But they are more an exception than a rule.

The relational aspects of geometry reach their culminating point in topology, which is relational geometry *par excellence*. There are, however, other branches of higher mathematics that are relational rather than quantitative in nature. To these belong the theory of groups, theory of sets, and theory of relations.

In biology, relational aspects are sometimes just as important, if not more important, than quantitative or, as we shall say, *metric* aspects. A *Paramecium*, when stimulated by an appropriate sensory stimulus, will move after another microorganism—its prey. It may eventually contact that prey, ingest it into its digestive vacuole, digest it, excrete the indigestible residue, and absorb and assimilate the rest. Or the *Paramecium* may follow and contact another *Paramecium*, conjugate with it, and thus perform what may be considered an elementary sexual act.

Now consider a bird stimulated by the sight of a flying insect. The bird will fly after the insect, catch it, swallow it, digest it, defecate the indigestible residue, and assimilate the rest. Or the bird may move toward another bird of opposite sex and mate with it. Analogous situations obtain for other higher or lower animals.

To the locomotion of the *Paramecium* there corresponds the locomotion (flight) of the bird. To the ingestion of food in the *Paramecium* there corresponds the swallowing of food in the bird. To the digestion in the digestive vacuole of the *Paramecium* there corresponds the digestion in the gastrointestinal tract of the bird. To the excretion of the indigestible residue in the *Paramecium* there corresponds the defecation in the bird. To the conjugation in the *Paramecium* there corresponds the copulation in the bird.

The corresponding processes in the two organisms are different not only *quantitatively*, that is, with respect to their intensities—they differ even in their mechanisms, in their physicochemical nature. Even though the molecular mechanism of contractility of a muscle fiber and of a cilium may have substantial features in common, the *mechanics* of ciliary locomotion of a *Paramecium* are quite different from that of the locomotion involved in the flight of a bird. The digestion in the *Paramecium* involves different biochemical processes than does the digestion in the bird. Even though all digestive processes may involve hydrolysis, the actual mechanism of hydrolysis may vary from case to case. The

* Fitness is a measure commonly used to express the adequacy of biological systems (see Chapters 15 and 16).

digestive enzymes of a man are, in general, different from those of a *Paramecium*. The excretion is different from the defecation. Yet, in spite of these essential differences, the relations between any processes in the bird are the same as the relation between the corresponding processes in the *Paramecium*. And this is true for any organism.

The relations between the different "biological properties" of an organism, such as sensation, locomotion, ingestion of food, excretion, assimilation, et cetera, characterize the organism *as a whole*. Those relations, as we have seen in the above example, remain the same, are *invariant*, for all organisms, no matter how different they may be in their physicochemical constitution.

Another important fact must be noticed. The corresponding processes, or biological properties, are much more complex in a higher organism than in a lower one. The movements of all the muscles of a bird in flight are kinematically more complex than the ciliary movements of a *Paramecium*. The process of visual perception in a bird is more complex than the simple sensory process in the *Paramecium*. A process in a higher organism, which corresponds to a given process in a lower one, contains many more elementary processes than that of the lower organism. Thus, we do have a correspondence between the processes, or biological properties, of a higher organism and those of a lower one. The nature of this correspondence is such that to an elementary process in the lower organism there correspond several elementary processes in the higher one.[44,55] Such a correspondence is called in mathematics a many-to-one mapping, or an *epimorphism*. We thus find that different organisms can be epimorphically mapped onto each other. In such epimorphic mapping, the basic relations that characterize the organism as a whole are preserved. This is the essence of the principle of biological epimorphism, which expresses an actual, well-known fact, a fact so well known, indeed, that we are likely to overlook its importance.

What do we do with the above mathematically? Since we are dealing here not with quantitative but with relational aspects, we must use some branch of relational mathematics. At first the suggestion was made to use topology. Mathematically, the above situation was formulated thus: to each organism there corresponds a topological complex or a topological space. To higher organisms correspond complexes or spaces of more complicated structure. The topological complexes or spaces that correspond to different organisms are obtained from each other by a universal rule of geometrical transformation and can be mapped on each other in a many-to-one manner with the preservation of certain basic relations.[55]

The universality of the transformation is basically the expression of the scientist's faith in the uniformity of nature. It is this uniformity that enables the scientist to establish generally valid laws and hence predictions. If the above-mentioned rule were not universal, but varied from case to case, then this would mean the abandonment of all hope of finding some general relations between different organisms and of speaking of the *organic world as a whole*.

As we stated in Section I (page 37), a general principle as such does not lead to any specific, concrete conclusions. It must be applied either to an actual situation or to a conceptual model. We must build models within the framework of a general principle. To do this in the present case we must first suggest a specific way of assigning to each organism a topological complex or a topological space. In the earlier attempts it was suggested assigning to each organism an *oriented graph*.[44–46,55] An oriented graph is a one-dimensional topological complex that consists of a set of points connected by lines to which directions are assigned by arrows. Biochemical systems give examples of oriented graphs in biology.[58] The reason for this choice is suggested by the circumstance that the word "organism" derives from the same root as the word "organization."

The relations within man-made organizations, such as corporations, societies, military establishments, et cetera, are described by organization charts. Those, as everyone knows, consist of boxes that stand for different parts of the organization (president, vice-presidents, managers, and so on), joined by lines that indicate the relations between the different parts. The circumstance that a manager of a given department takes orders from a given vice-president will be shown on the chart by providing an arrow on the line connecting the box "vice-president" to the box "manager" and directed from the former to the latter. If two parts of the organization are on equal footing and exchange information, the corresponding boxes will be connected by two lines with arrows in opposite directions. If points are substituted for the boxes, we then obtain an oriented graph. Thus the idea of representing an organism by an oriented graph is suggested. This is not new. In endocrinology, for example, the relations between different endocrine glands are frequently represented by what is essentially an oriented graph. Detailed further examples are given in Chapters 10–13.

A graph may be used in mathematics to represent binary relations. In organisms *n*-ary relations must be considered, and the graph may thus seem too simple a representation for an actual organism. However, even the representation of organisms by graphs reveals very great complexities.[59] Even more complex situations are obtained by a generalization of the graph-theoretical methods.[63,64]

The next step is to postulate the required universal transformation. Here we again may be led by well-known biological facts. The derivation of a higher organism from a lower proceeds through a process of specialization. *In abstracto* we may conceive this process as follows: In a group of originally identical cells, each of which performs all the biological functions necessary for its life, some cells lose some of their biological properties, specializing in fewer ones. Different cells lose different properties and correspondingly specialize in different ones. In terms of the oriented graphs that correspond to the original cells, this means that some graphs will lose some of their points. As we have seen, specialization in a higher organism is connected with an increase in complexity and in the number of elementary biological functions. In terms of a graph, this means that for each point lost several points are added.

The requirement of preservation of the basic relations between corresponding properties leads to definite requirements for the construction of the "derived," more complicated graph from the original, simple one. Those requirements do not, however, determine the transformation rules compatible with the known process of specialization. About a score of them has been studied.[47] Each mathematically possible rule corresponds to a different model within the framework of the principle of biological epimorphism. Each of these rules leads to different conclusions, which are experimentally verifiable.[48] But, of course, only one of them does correspond to reality. Thus we have a large number of "abstract biologies,"[45,64] one of which corresponds to what actually occurs in nature. The situation is not unlike that with non-Euclidean geometries. That the geometry of our space-time universe is non-Euclidean follows from the principle of the general theory of relativity. But the opinion as to which of the possible non-Euclidean geometries is actually realized in nature has been debated and changed several times in the past.

Later on it was found that it is advantageous to represent an organism not by a topological complex, but by a topological space[49,51] of a special type. The two methods of representation are actually equivalent and can be used interchangeably. In fact, we may free ourselves completely from topological considerations and consider an organism as represented by a set (of its biological properties) with prescribed relations on this set.[50,52] The space and the set approach lead immediately to conclusions that can be verified experimentally. These conclusions are, however, not of a quantitative form. They are of an *existential nature*. Thus the following conclusion, for example, is reached: In higher organisms, emotional disturbances are in some cases accompanied by gastrointestinal disturbances.[49,55] This is a well-known clinical fact. One can, of course, easily conceive a model of the nervous system that explains this without recourse to any general principle. But, in order to decide to make such a model, we must have the fact given. For a long time it has actually been given empirically. The important thing here is that we derive the existence of this phenomenon from general principles, regardless of its mechanism.

Another verified conclusion is that emotional disturbances, and more general external stimuli, produce changes in the cardiovascular functions. A still different conclusion is that there exist animals with glands whose secretion is used to catch food. The spider is a classical example. The marine worm *Urechis* is another.

We shall mention here only one more conclusion, which is still awaiting experimental confirmation but which may become of potential practical value. There must exist unicellular organisms that produce antibodies to given antigens.[49,55] Experimental evidence available in the literature is still inconclusive.

For other conclusions and for their derivation we must refer the interested reader to the existing literature.[53]

C. Relational Biology

The graph-theoretical approach, originally suggested by Rashevsky, has been taken up and developed by Robert Rosen[60-66] in a rather different connection. Rosen does not preoccupy himself with epimorphic mappings of one organism on another. Rather, he is interested in what general relational statements can be made about an organism by considering that an oriented graph can be associated with it. The representation of an organism by an oriented graph is interpreted by Rosen in a manner slightly different from the one made above. Rosen considers the points of the graph as representing not the biological properties of an organism, but the components of the organism, or organs, that are the carriers of those properties, that perform the corresponding functions. The directed lines leading to a point are then interpreted as inputs into the organ, whereas the directed lines leading away from the point are interpreted as the outputs of that organ. The nature of the inputs and outputs may vary from case to case.

Thus the input into the organ of vision is light of different wavelengths. The output is a pattern of nerve impulses in the optic nerve. The input into the digestive organ—the gastrointestinal tract—may be a set of proteins. The corresponding output will be a set of amino acids. We are not interested here in the mechanism but only in the relational aspects of the phenomenon. An organ may receive inputs from several other organs. In terms of the graph, a point may receive directed lines from several other points. If the normal functioning of an organ requires the integrity of all its inputs, then the damage or destruction of an organ that sends an input into a given one will result in the impairment of functions of the latter. In terms of a graph, the removal of a point A that sends a directed line to a point B will impair the function of the organ represented by B.

Organs are subject to accidental damage and destruction. In order for the organism to survive, there must exist mechanisms that repair a damaged organ or reestablish a lost one.

Whatever the physical mechanisms of the repair or reestablishment, this mechanism may itself be represented by a point on the graph. In order to function properly the mechanism must receive at least one input from some other component. If that other component that activates the reestablishing mechanism itself receives an input from the lost or damaged organ, then a loss of the organ cannot be reestablished, because its loss will impair the function of the component that activates the reestablishing mechanism.

Rosen[60] has proven an important theorem: If the normal functioning of a component of an organism requires all the inputs that it receives, then, regardless of the actual mechanism of reestablishment, it is impossible for all the components to be reestablishable.

This theorem is based on purely topological considerations, and is independent of any assumptions that we may make about the actual mechanism by means of which a component is reestablished.

Another interesting theorem demonstrated by Rosen[60] is that if in an organism a component M receiving inputs from the environment is nonreestablishable, while all others are, then the loss of that component M will result in a cessation of function, that is, in the death of the organism. The theorems hold, as we mentioned before, under certain restrictive conditions. Those conditions, although plausible, are not always realized in organisms. The second theorem cannot, therefore, be applied to such organs as, for example, eyes or legs. However, the important thing is that those theorems are, in principle, verifiable when their conditions are fulfilled. Topological considerations give us also a method for a theoretical discussion of the regeneration of organs in some higher organisms.[52,57]

That the above two theorems are verifiable in principle is evident. The implications of the two theorems are quite interesting.

The representation of an organism by a simple, oriented graph has serious shortcomings. If several directed lines (arrows) land from one point, there is no way of telling whether they represent the same output going to other different components, or different types of outputs. Biologically, however, the distinction is very important. Rosen, therefore, suggested a very ingenious change in the method of representation.[61] To a given set of inputs into an organ there corresponds a definite set of outputs. If we change some inputs, we shall change the outputs. A correspondence is called a mapping in mathematics.

Thus we may say that an organ maps a set of inputs onto a corresponding set of outputs. The whole organism thus becomes a collection or a set of mappings. If we have two collections of mappings, then it is sometimes possible to establish a correspondence between a mapping of one set and a mapping of another. We thus can speak of mappings of mappings. All this forms a part of the so-called theory of categories, developed by S. Eilenberg and S. MacLane in 1945.[8] Rosen[61,62] applied the theory to biological systems. To do this he proposed to change the hitherto usual representation of an organism by a graph to one in which the organs, which represent, as we have seen, mappings, are represented by arrows, while inputs and outputs are now represented by points. In this representation the above-mentioned difficulty disappears. An important result of this study is that the set of mappings that constitutes an organism contains the mapping that represents a replication of the organism.

These studies have also led Rosen to interesting conclusions regarding the effects on the organism of changing environmental conditions.[63] The problems as to how far certain mathematically possible mappings can actually be realized in nature have led Rosen to a profound study that bears on the problem of reducibility of biology to physics.[66]

We should also mention that, using topological considerations, Rosen[65] has given a rigorous mathematical representation of the fact found by D'Arcy W. Thompson that corresponding parts of the skeleton of different vertebrates can be transformed into each other by what is called homotopic deformation.

The reader may naturally wonder whether the discussion in this section has anything to do with the principle of biological epimorphism. Rosen's work seems to be more akin to the construction of models, though his models are of a topological or, more generally, relational type. The following must, however, be remarked. The formulation of the principle of biological epimorphism on page 46 contains, as a part, the statement: "To each organism there corresponds a topological complex or a topological space." This is followed by the statements of the other requirements of the principle. It is not obvious at all that a topological complex, such as a graph, can be associated with each organism. Therefore, possibly what we dealt with in Section B are really two separate principles: First, the principle of topological representation of organisms; and, second, the principle of epimorphism. The two seem to be logically independent. If so, Rosen's work can be naturally considered as the building of models within the framework of the principle of topological representation.

No principle of science is usually applied alone. It is, therefore, natural to combine in appropriate situations the principle of adequate design and the principle of topological representation, or the principle of epimorphism. By combining the first with the second, Rosen arrived at a very interesting conclusion, namely, that genetic material in the nucleus should be arranged in *linear* arrays.[62] By combining the first principle with the third, Rashevsky finds that the higher an organism, the weaker the regenerative ability for lost organs.[57]

REFERENCES

1. Beament, J. W. L., ed. 1960. "Models and Analogues in Biology," *Symp. Soc. Exptl. Biol.* **14:** 255 pp.
2. Bellman, R., Jacquez, J. A., and Kalaba, R., 1960. Some mathematical aspects of chemotherapy: I. One-organ models. *Bull. Math. Biophys.* **22:** 181–198.
3. Bush, R. R., and Mosteller, F. 1955. "Stochastic Models for Learning," 365 pp. Wiley, New York.
4. Cohn, D. L. 1954. Optimal systems: I. The vascular system. *Bull. Math. Biophys.* **16:** 59–74.
5. Cohn, D. L. 1955. Optimal systems: II. The vascular system. *Bull. Math. Biophys.* **17:** 219–227.
6. Cope, F. 1960. An elastic reservoir theory of the human systemic arterial system using current data on aortic elasticity. *Bull. Math. Biophys.* **22:** 19–40.
7. Defares, J. G. 1960. Cybernetic analysis of the respiratory chemostat. *In:* "Physicomathematical Aspects of Biology," (N. Rashevsky, ed.), pp. 196–239. Academic, New York.
8. Eilenberg, S., and MacLane, S. 1945. General theory of natural equivalences. *Trans. Am. Math. Soc.* **58:** 231–294.
9. Euler, L. 1862. Principia pro motu sanguinis per arterias determinando. *In:* "Opera Postuma, Mathematica et Physica," Vol. II, pp. 814–823. Eggers, St. Petersburg, Russia.
10. Fischer, O. 1906. "Theoretische Grundlagen für eine Mechanik der Lebenden Körper," 372 pp. Teubner, Leipzig and Berlin.
11. Frank, O. 1899. Die Grundform des arteriellen Pulses. *Z. Biol.* **37:** 483–526.
12. Frank, O. 1905. Der Puls in den Arterien. *Z. Biol.* **46:** 441–553.
13. Frank, O. 1920. Die Elasticität der Blutgefässe. *Z. Biol.* **71:** 255–272.

14. Frank, O. 1927. Die Theorie der Pulswellen. *Z. Biol.* **85:** 91–130.
15. Frank, O. 1928. Der Ablauf des Strömungsgeschwindigkeit in den Blutgefässen. *Z. Biol.* **88:** 249–263.
16. Green, H. D. 1950. Circulatory system: Physical principles. *In:* "Medical Physics," (O. Glasser, ed.), Vol. II, pp. 228–251. Year Book, Chicago.
17. Günther, B., and Guerra, E. 1955. Biological similarities. *Acta Physiol. Latinoam.* **5:** 169–186.
18. Hearon, J. Z. 1950. Some cellular diffusion problems based on Onsager's generalization of Fick's law. *Bull. Math. Biophys.* **12:** 135–159.
19. Jacquez, J. A., and Bellman, R. 1960. Some mathematical aspects of chemotherapy. II: The distribution of a drug in the body. *Bull. Math. Biophys.* **22:** 309–322.
20. Karreman, G. 1951. Contributions to the mathematical biology of excitation with particular emphasis on changes in membrane permeability and on threshold phenomena. *Bull. Math. Biophys.* **13:** 189–243.
21. Karreman, G. 1952. Some contributions to the mathematical biology of blood circulation. Reflections of pressure waves in the arterial system. *Bull. Math. Biophys.* **14:** 327–350.
22. Karreman, G. 1953a. Erratum. *Bull. Math. Biophys.* **15:** 109.
23. Karreman, G. 1953b. Contributions to the mathematical biophysics of the cardiovascular system. *Bull. Math. Biophys.* **15:** 185–195.
24. Karreman, G. 1953c. Blood flow in branching circulatory systems during rest and activity. *Bull. Math. Biophys.* **15:** 301–309.
25. Karreman, G. 1954a. On the velocity of propagation of pressure waves in an incompressible viscous fluid enclosed in a tube with an elastomeric wall. *Bull. Math. Biophys.* **16:** 103–109.
26. Karreman, G. 1954b. Contributions to the mathematical biophysics of branched circulatory systems. *Bull. Math. Biophys.* **16:** 111–116.
27. Landahl, H. D. 1938. A contribution to the mathematical biophysics of psychophysical discrimination. *Psychometrika* **3:** 107–125.
28. Landahl, H. D. 1946a. On the relationship between response time and dosage of a drug as a function of its mode of entry. *Bull. Math. Biophys.* **8:** 121–127.
29. Landahl, H. D. 1946b. The half-life of a drug in relation to its therapeutic index. *Bull. Math. Biophys.* **8:** 129–133.
30. Landahl, H. D. 1952. Mathematical biophysics of color vision. *Bull. Math. Biophys.* **14:** 317–325.
31. Landahl, H. D. 1956. Mathematical biophysics of color vision II: Theory of color changes induced by the alternation of colors at various frequencies. *Bull. Math. Biophys.* **18:** 137–149.
32. Landahl, H. D. 1957. On the interpretation of the effect of area on the critical flicker frequency. *Bull. Math. Biophys.* **19:** 157–162.
33. Landahl, H. D. 1958. Theoretical considerations on potentiation in drug interaction. *Bull. Math. Biophys.* **20:** 1–23.
34. Lotka, A. J. 1956. "Elements of Mathematical Biology," 465 pp. Dover, New York. (Originally published 1925 as "Elements of Physical Biology," 460 pp. Williams and Wilkins, Baltimore.)
35. Muybridge, E. 1887. "Animal Locomotion," 175 plates. Univ. of Pennsylvania, Philadelphia.
36. Patlak, C. S. 1956. Contributions to the theory of active transport. *Bull. Math. Biophys.* **18:** 271–315.
37. Patlak, C. S. 1957. Contributions to the theory of active transport: II. The gate type non-carrier mechanism and generalizations concerning tracer flow, efficiency, and measurement of energy expenditure. *Bull. Math. Biophys.* **19:** 209–235.
38. Poincaré, H. 1946. "The Foundations of Science," 553 pp. Science, Lancaster, Pa.
39. Rashevsky, N. 1933. The theoretical physics of the cell as a basis for a general physicomathematical theory of organic form. *Protoplasma,* **20:** 180–188.

40. Rashevsky, N. 1938. "Mathematical Biophysics," 1st ed., 340 pp. Univ. of Chicago Press, Chicago.
41. Rashevsky, N. 1943a. Outline of a new mathematical approach to general biology: I. *Bull. Math. Biophys.* **5**: 33–47.
42. Rashevsky, N. 1943b. Outline of a new mathematical approach to general biology: II. *Bull. Math. Biophys.* **5**: 49–73.
43. Rashevsky, N. 1944. Studies in the physicomathematical theory of organic form. *Bull. Math. Biophys.* **6**: 1–59.
44. Rashevsky, N. 1954. Topology and life: In search of general mathematical principles in biology and sociology. *Bull. Math. Biophys.* **16**: 317–348.
45. Rashevsky, N. 1955. Some remarks on topological biology. *Bull. Math. Biophys.* **17**: 207–218.
46. Rashevsky, N. 1956a. The geometrization of biology. *Bull. Math. Biophys.* **18**: 31–56.
47. Rashevsky, N. 1956b. Contributions to topological biology: Some considerations on the primordial graph and on some possible transformations. *Bull. Math. Biophys.* **18**: 113–128.
48. Rashevsky, N. 1956c. What type of empirically verifiable predictions can topological biology make? *Bull. Math. Biophys.* **18**: 173–188.
49. Rashevsky, N. 1958a. A contribution to the search of general mathematical principles in biology. *Bull. Math. Biophys.* **20**: 71–93.
50. Rashevsky, N. 1958b. A comparison of set-theoretical and graph-theoretical approaches in topological biology. *Bull. Math. Biophys.* **20**: 267–273.
51. Rashevsky, N. 1959a. A note on topological biology. *Bull. Math. Biophys.* **21**: 97–100.
52. Rashevsky, N. 1959b. A set-theoretical approach to biology. *Bull. Math. Biophys.* **21**: 101–106.
53. Rashevsky, N. 1959c. A note on the nature and origin of life. *Bull. Math. Biophys.* **21**: 185–193.
54. Rashevsky, N. 1960a. "Mathematical Biophysics," 3rd rev. ed., Vol. I, 488 pp. Dover, New York.
55. Rashevsky, N. 1960b. "Mathematical Biophysics," 3rd rev. ed., Vol. II, 462 pp. Dover, New York.
56. Rashevsky, N. 1961a. "Mathematical Principles in Biology and Their Applications," 128 pp. Thomas, Springfield, Ill.
57. Rashevsky, N. 1961b. Biological epimorphism, adequate design, and the problem of regeneration. *Bull. Math. Biophys.* **23**: 109–113.
58. Rashevsky, N. 1962. Some theoretical considerations on organization and homeostasis with possible reference to neoplastic growth. *In:* "Biological Interactions in Normal and Neoplastic Tissue," (M. S. Brennan and W. L. Simpson, eds.), pp. 519–532. Little, Brown, Boston.
59. Rashevsky, N. 1963. The principle of adequate design and the cardiovascular system. *Bull. Math. Biophys.* **25**: 59–74.
60. Rosen, R. 1958a. A relational theory of biological systems. *Bull. Math. Biophys.* **20**: 245–260.
61. Rosen, R. 1958b. The representation of biological systems from the standpoint of the theory of categories. *Bull. Math. Biophys.* **20**: 317–341.
62. Rosen, R. 1959. A relational theory of biological systems II. *Bull. Math. Biophys.* **21**: 109–128.
63. Rosen, R. 1961. A relational theory of the structural changes induced in biological systems by alterations in environment. *Bull. Math. Biophys.* **23**: 165–171.
64. Rosen, R. 1962a. A note on abstract relational biologies. *Bull. Math. Biophys.* **24**: 31–38.
65. Rosen, R. 1962b. The derivation of D'Arcy Thompson's theory of transformations from the theory of optimal design. *Bull. Math. Biophys.* **24**: 279–290.
66. Rosen, R. 1962c. Church's thesis and its relation to the concept of realizability in biology and physics. *Bull. Math. Biophys.* **24**: 375–393.
67. Roston, S. 1959. Mathematical formulation of cardiovascular dynamics by use of the Laplace transform. *Bull. Math. Biophys.* **21**: 1–11.

68. Roston, S., and Leight, L. 1959. A practical study of the air chamber model of the cardio-vascular system. *J. Clin. Invest.* **38:** 777–783.

69. Rubner, M. 1928. Körpermasse und Energieverbrauch. *In:* "Handbuch der Normalen und Pathologischen Physiologie," Vol. 5, pp. 163–166. Springer, Berlin.

70. Segre, G. 1962. Application of transfer function to pharmacology. *Ann. N.Y. Acad. Sci.* **96:** 913–938.

71. Volterra, V. 1931. "Leçons sur la Théorie Mathématique de la Lutte pour la Vie," 214 pp. Gauthier-Villars, Paris.

72. Womersley, J. R. 1957. "An Elastic Tube Theory of Pulse Transmission and Oscillatory Flow in Mammalian Arteries," 238 pp. Report TR 54-614, Wright Air Development Center. Wright-Patterson Air Force Base, Ohio.

$$\left[\quad \textbf{SECTION II} \quad \right]$$

Physical and Chemical Analysis

The four chapters in this section might appropriately be labeled theoretical biophysics because they describe the analysis of biological phenomena directly in terms of physical theory. Each chapter draws upon different branches of physics most appropriate to the biological questions that it raises. Thus the discussion by Eyring and Urry (Chapter 4) deals primarily with statistical mechanics and thermodynamics. The fundamental equations of reaction rate theory are derived and applications of the resulting formalism are then made to many areas of biology. Since reaction rates are involved in all biological processes, their possible range of relevance is almost limitless.

The foundation of Bernal's essay (Chapter 5) is the impressive knowledge of the molecular structure of biologically important compounds which has been acquired during the past thirty years. Much of this information has come from x-ray analysis. The author, starting with this background, discusses many of the most fundamental problems of modern biology, such as the origin of life and the mechanism of its development and evolution. The chapter on the nerve impulse (Chapter 6) exemplifies an approach to biology which has been close to physics both in instrumentation and in concept. Mainly from an historical analytical point of view, Cole outlines the electromagnetic properties of living systems, more specifically the axon. He reviews the kinds of experimental measurements that have been made and develops the contemporary theories of mechanisms underlying the nerve impulse.

Chapter 7, on cochlear mechanics, demonstrates the interaction between physical and physiological acoustics. Here again is an area in which a well-defined physical theory existed and important results emerged from applying this to the problems of hearing. Von Békésy reviews the experiments and analyses which have been done in applying acoustical theory to understanding the function of the cochlea.

The four problems covered in this section are of course just representative of the much wider areas of biology accessible to direct applications of physical theory. Among other projects of this sort being carried out are the application of mechanics to animal movement and locomotion, the use of optics and quantum chemistry in vision, and the application of thermodynamics to biological energy regulation (Chapters 11 and 13).

[4]

THERMODYNAMICS AND CHEMICAL KINETICS*

Henry Eyring and Dan W. Urry

I. INTRODUCTION

A biological organism is a unique collection of well-integrated enzyme systems. It is a nonequilibrium system whose existence is dependent upon a dynamic steady state of enzyme-directed reactions. Enzymes function to lower the required activation energies of chemical reactions so that under physiological conditions reactions, which would otherwise occur at imperceptible rates, will actually occur at the rates necessary in the living system. Thus a knowledge of reaction rate theory would appear fundamental to the understanding of life processes. But to acquire a useful familiarity with reaction rate theory a minimal background of statistical mechanics is necessary. The purpose of the first part of this chapter is to develop a minimum acquaintance with this field.

The two major factors controlling the velocity of chemical reactions are the concentrations of the reactants and the energy required to go from reactants to products. We wish to develop an understanding of these two factors. In particular, we are interested in the frequency of occurrence of a given energy state. The high energy state which occurs in passing from reactants to products, called the activated or transition state, controls the rate at which a reaction can occur. Also the reactants themselves represent a particular energy state, and we are interested in the relative frequency of occurrence of this state. Although the biological system is, as a whole, a nonequilibrium system, we are interested, too, in equilibria because they will give us relationships between concentrations.

The second part of this chapter deals with the application of reaction rate theory to particular biological problems. It points to some of the useful information and concepts that arise therefrom.

II. EQUILIBRIUM THEORY AND REACTION RATES

A. Derivation of the Boltzmann Equation of Statistical Mechanics

In order to understand more fully the complex and integrated series of reactions that comprise the biological organism, it is important to obtain a sort of understructure of the

* The material in this chapter, presented by Henry Eyring as part of the Yale course, was revised and prepared for publication by Dan W. Urry. The latter would like to thank the Corning Glass Works Foundation for support during the preparation of this manuscript.

elementary reaction. This is obtained in a short cut by deriving the barometric equation which treats molecules at different elevations, that is, in different energy states with respect to the gravitational field of the earth. One may think of a chemical reaction as molecules drifting across a mountain pass, and one thinks of there being more molecules in a cubic centimeter of air at sea level than in a cubic centimeter of air above the Rocky Mountains, simply because of the work required to lift molecules from one level to the other. So we will briefly derive the barometric equation and determine the number of molecules at different levels. But due to the objectionable use of the perfect gas restriction in deriving the barometric formula, statistical mechanics will be approached in greater generality by the method of compounding of systems.

1. *The barometric formula.* If one has a column of air with a square centimeter cross section, then there will be a difference of pressure between a lower level and some higher level because of the weight of molecules in between. Furthermore, the pressure difference in a given interval will be less as altitude increases, so that the pressure, in going from a given height, h, to one slightly higher, $h + dh$, is $p - dp$. And the change in pressure, $-dp$, is the number of molecules per unit volume, n/v, times the height increment, dh, multiplied by the gravitational force, mg.

$$-dp = n/v \, dh \, mg \tag{1}$$

By employing the perfect gas law for a molecule and substituting into Equation (1) we have

$$pv = nkT$$
$$n/v = p/kT \tag{2}$$
$$-dp = p/kT \, dh \, mg$$

By integrating one obtains

$$\int dp/p = -\int mg/kT \, dh + \ln c$$
$$\ln p = -mgh/kT + \ln c \tag{3}$$

where $\ln c$ is the constant of integration which may be evaluated at $h = 0$ to be $\ln p_0$, the pressure at sea level. The following result is obtained

$$p/p_0 = e^{-mgh/kT} \tag{4}$$

We then have the pressure at any level compared to the pressure perhaps at sea level or wherever the reference level might be taken. The product mgh is simply the energy difference between molecules at two different levels, those molecules at the higher altitude being in a higher energy state. Again utilizing the perfect gas law, we see that $p/p_0 = n/n_0$ for a given volume and temperature so that we may write

$$n/n_0 = e^{-(\epsilon - \epsilon_0)/kT} = e^{-\epsilon/kT}/e^{-\epsilon_0/kT} \tag{5}$$

Therefore the number of molecules, n, for example, in Salt Lake City divided by the number of molecules, n_0, in New Haven is equal to the ratios of the exponentials of minus their respective energies divided by kT, the average energy of an oscillator. The energy difference, $\epsilon - \epsilon_0$, is the work of taking a molecule from one elevation to another.

Equation (5) may also be written as

$$\frac{n}{e^{-\epsilon/kT}} = \frac{n_0}{e^{-\epsilon_0/kT}} = \lambda \tag{6}$$

where λ is called the absolute activity of the molecules in their respective energy states. This equation is true for any energy level or for any collection of energy levels; that is,

$$\lambda = \frac{n_0}{e^{-\epsilon_0/kT}} = \frac{n_1}{e^{-\epsilon_1/kT}} = \ldots = \frac{n_i}{e^{-\epsilon_i/kT}} = \ldots \tag{7}$$

However, by Equation (7) we have the set of equations

$$\lambda e^{-\epsilon_0/kT} = n_0, \quad \lambda e^{-\epsilon_1/kT} = n_1, \quad \lambda e^{-\epsilon_i/kT} = n_i, \text{ etc.} \tag{8}$$

or adding the Equations (8)

$$\lambda(e^{-\epsilon_0/kT} + e^{-\epsilon_1/kT} + \ldots + e^{-\epsilon_i/kT} + \ldots) = n_0 + n_1 + \ldots + n_i + \ldots \tag{9}$$

$$\lambda = \frac{n_0 + n_1 + \ldots + n_i + \ldots}{e^{-\epsilon_0/kT} + e^{-\epsilon_1/kT} + \ldots + e^{-\epsilon_i/kT} + \ldots}$$

$$\lambda = \frac{\sum_i n_i}{\sum_i e^{-\epsilon_i/kT}} = \frac{N}{\sum_i e^{-\epsilon_i/kT}} = \frac{n_i}{e^{-\epsilon_i/kT}} \tag{10}$$

where N is the total number of molecules and the last equality is given by Equation (7). It is evident that the absolute activity, λ, of molecules in a given energy state is the same for any other molecules in their energy state or for a collection of molecules in their respective energy states when the system is at equilibrium. The last equality in Equation (10) is the Boltzmann equation commonly written

$$\frac{n_i}{N} = \frac{e^{-\epsilon_i/kT}}{\sum_i e^{-\epsilon_i/kT}} \tag{11}$$

Therefore, the fraction of molecules, n_i/N, in an energy state, ϵ_i, is the exponential of minus the energy of that state divided by kT, divided by the same expression summed over all the energy states. This sum-over-states, the denominator on the right-hand side of Equation (11), is called the partition function for a thermodynamic system and when explicitly evaluated can give all the thermodynamic properties of a system. In chemical reactions we are interested in the number of molecules that have sufficient energy to react, that is, the number of molecules that are in a given energy state called the activated state. The Boltzmann expression provides this information.

The use of the perfect gas law, Equation (2), in this derivation restricts its application to perfect gases. However, this limitation is unnecessary, as we shall see by arriving at the same expression from basic considerations without imposing this restriction.

2. *The compounding of systems method.*[2.5] A completely general way of deriving the Boltzmann expression, a way which provides clearer insight as to the quantities and considerations involved, is the compounding of systems method. Basic to this approach is what has been called the zeroth law of thermodynamics. The zeroth law is that if A is in equilibrium with C, and B is in equilibrium with C, then A is in equilibrium with B. This implies that the condition of equilibrium does not specify the nature of A or B which are the two systems in equilibrium. This may be verified experimentally by observing that the spectrum of gaseous benzene, for example, in equilibrium with a container at a given temperature is independent of the nature of the container. In the compounding of systems method one system A in which we are interested will be considered at thermal equilibrium

with another system B. Since the nature of B does not affect A, B may be taken for maximum convenience without prejudicing system A.

Let us take the system B to be a solid container composed of $s/3$ atoms. Since each atom possesses three degrees of freedom, this gives s oscillational degrees of freedom. Consistent with choosing as convenient a B as possible, we consider it made of such soft material that its oscillations act classically even as one approaches the absolute zero of temperature. This choice will not affect system A but will allow us to use kT as the average energy of an oscillator, for the energy of these s degrees of freedom.

For system A we choose any molecular system. In particular, for purposes of illustration, we may take system A to be one benzene molecule. Benzene consists of twelve atoms, each with three degrees of freedom, so that the molecule possesses thirty-six degrees of freedom. We are interested in the number of ways an energy ϵ_i may be distributed among the thirty-six degrees of freedom of a benzene molecule. This is done conveniently by considering the compound system A + B which has a total energy E.

The problem for a compound system may now be stated as one of assigning an amount of energy, ϵ_i, to system A and then determining the number of ways the remaining energy, $E - \epsilon_i$, may be distributed among the s oscillators of system B. This is then done for every possible ϵ_i which can be assigned to system A. The number of quanta, n_i, to be distributed to system B is

$$n_i = (E - \epsilon_i)/h\nu \tag{12}$$

where $h\nu$ is the energy per quantum. The problem is now restated as the number of ways n_i quanta may be distributed among the s oscillators of the container when ϵ_i has been assigned to the benzene molecule in a unique way. Our notation for this is $N(n_i, s, \epsilon_i)$. At this point we must apply an appropriate modification of the ergodic hypothesis due to Gibbs. For this problem, the hypothesis may be stated as follows: any unique, exactly specified way of distributing a constant, total energy, E, to a compound system A + B, is equally likely.

Specifically what we want is the probability, P_i, that the benzene molecule is in a given energy state. This is given by the number of ways n_i quanta may be distributed among s oscillators when an energy ϵ_i has been uniquely given to the benzene molecule, divided by the same quantity summed over the different ways of doing this, each way corresponding to a different ϵ_i, that is

$$P_i = \frac{N(n_i, s, \epsilon_i)}{\sum_i N(n_i, s, \epsilon_i)} \tag{13}$$

The problem is thus reduced to one of evaluating $N(n_i, s, \epsilon_i)$. This quantity may be determined by arranging the quanta and oscillators in a linear fashion with an oscillator on the extreme right and by assigning the quanta as they occur to the oscillator on their immediate right. Denoting the quanta as circles and the oscillators as crosses, for the particular case of $n = 10$ and $s = 6$ we have

$$(oox)(ox)(oox)(ooox)(x)(oox)$$

as a unique distribution. Since the quanta are to be part of the energy, $E - \epsilon_i$, of the system B, they must be assigned to some oscillator. We must therefore start with an oscillator. Then any of the $(n + s - 1)$ remaining quanta and oscillators may be in the second position. For the third position there are $(n + s - 2)$ possibilities, etc., until all the quanta and oscillators have been accounted for. This would give $(n + s - 1)!$ ways of arranging $n + s$ quantities, if these quanta were distinguishable. However, since there are $(s - 1)!$ possible permutations which do not alter the distribution and since the quanta are indistinguishable, we must divide by $n!$ and $(s - 1)!$ giving,

$$N(n_i, s, \epsilon_i) = \frac{(n_i + s - 1)!}{n_i! \, (s - 1)!} \tag{14}$$

Equation (14) when substituted into Equation (13) gives the Boltzmann expression, but to see this a few algebraic manipulations are necessary.

By dividing out the $n_i!$ of Equation (14) one obtains

$$N(n_i, s, \epsilon_i) = \frac{(n + s - 1)(n + s - 2)\ldots(n + 1)}{(s - 1)!} = \frac{1}{(s - 1)!} \prod_{r=1}^{s-1} (n_i + s - r) \tag{15}$$

where $\prod_{r=1}^{s-1} (n_i + s - r)$ is a notation indicating the product of the terms ranging integrally from $(n + s - 1)$ to $[n + s - (s - 1)] = (n + 1)$. By Equation (12), the definition for n_i, Equation (15) may be rewritten

$$N(n_i, s, \epsilon_i) = \frac{1}{(s - 1)!} \prod_{r=1}^{s-1} \left(\frac{E - \epsilon_i + h\nu(s - r)}{h\nu} \right)$$

$$\equiv \frac{1}{(s - 1)!} \prod_{r=1}^{s-1} \left(\frac{E + h\nu(s - r)}{h\nu} \right) \left(1 - \frac{\epsilon_i}{E + h\nu(s - r)} \right) \tag{16}$$

However, the total energy is the average energy of an oscillator, γ, times the number of oscillators, s, plus the energy in the benzene molecule, that is, $E = \gamma s + \epsilon_i$. Therefore

$$E + h\nu(s - r) = \gamma s + g \quad \text{where} \quad g = \epsilon_i + h\nu(s - r)$$

But if the container is very large compared to the benzene molecule and the number of quanta is very much larger than the number of oscillators, as we may assume, then $\epsilon_i \ll E$ and $n_i \gg s$ such that $\gamma s \gg g$. Equation (16) now becomes

$$N(n_i, s, \epsilon_i) = \frac{1}{(s - 1)!} \left(\frac{\gamma s}{h\nu} \right)^{s-1} \left(1 - \frac{\epsilon_i}{\gamma s} \right)^{s-1} \tag{17}$$

The only term in Equation (17) which is a variable is the last, $[1 - (\epsilon_i/\gamma s)]^{s-1}$, and it will now be shown that this term is another way of writing $e^{-\epsilon_i/\gamma}$. By utilizing the binomial theorem one has

$$\left(1 - \frac{\epsilon_i}{\gamma s} \right)^{s-1} = 1 - (s - 1)\left(\frac{\epsilon_i}{\gamma s} \right) + \frac{(s - 1)(s - 2)}{2!} \left(\frac{\epsilon_i}{\gamma s} \right)^2$$

$$- \frac{(s - 1)(s - 2)(s - 3)}{3!} \left(\frac{\epsilon_i}{\gamma s} \right)^3 + \ldots$$

In the limit as s gets very large the above equation becomes

$$\left(1 - \frac{\epsilon_i}{\gamma s} \right)^{s-1} = 1 - \frac{\epsilon_i}{\gamma} + \frac{1}{2!}\left(\frac{\epsilon_i}{\gamma} \right)^2 - \frac{1}{3!}\left(\frac{\epsilon_i}{\gamma} \right)^3 + \ldots = e^{-\epsilon_i/\gamma}$$

The last equality arises since the infinite series is simply the Maclaurin expansion of $e^{-\epsilon_i/\gamma}$. Substitution into Equation (17) results in

$$N(n_i, s, \epsilon_i) = \frac{1}{(s-1)!}\left(\frac{\gamma s}{h\nu}\right)^{s-1} e^{-\epsilon_i/\gamma} = C e^{-\epsilon_i/\gamma} \qquad (18)$$

which upon substitution into Equation (13) gives

$$P_i = \frac{C e^{-\epsilon_i/\gamma}}{\sum_i C e^{-\epsilon_i/\gamma}} = \frac{e^{-\epsilon_i/\gamma}}{\sum_i e^{-\epsilon_i/\gamma}} \qquad (19)$$

At the beginning of this discussion on the compounding of systems method it was emphasized that system B, the container, could be constructed of whatever we choose without affecting system A, the benzene molecule. In particular we choose to make the container of a material, soft without limit, in which case $\gamma = kT$. The value of k is fixed by Dulong and Petit's law that the heat capacity of a mole of solid is six calories in the classical range. Furthermore, realizing that probability is proportional to the number of examples, it follows that

$$P_i = \frac{n_i}{\sum_i n_i} = \frac{n_i}{N}$$

where n_i is the number of benzene molecules with energy ϵ_i when there are a total of N benzene molecules. We may now write Equation (19) as

$$\frac{n_i}{N} = \frac{e^{-\epsilon_i/kT}}{\sum_i e^{-\epsilon_i/kT}} \qquad (20)$$

which is again the Boltzmann expression identical to Equation (11) derived as the barometric formula.

It is now clear that Equation (20) is a general relation independent of the perfect gas law and applicable to any molecular system whether or not it be gaseous, liquid, or solid and therefore also applicable for biological systems. In chemical reactions the velocity is dependent on how many molecules have reached the activated state which has associated with it an energy ϵ_i. The function of enzymes is to lower the required value of ϵ_i so that a larger fraction of the molecules attain it at each instant.

B. Statistical Mechanics and Thermodynamics[2]

In thermodynamics one is interested in changes, changes in internal energy, enthalpy, free energy, entropy, etc., which are quantities defined in such a way as to be particularly useful. These quantities which are called properties of the system are defined with respect to large collections of particles. According to the first law of thermodynamics we know that the change in internal energy, dE, of a system is equal to the heat, dq, *absorbed by* the system less the work, dw, *done by* the system, that is,

$$dE = dq - dw \qquad (21)$$

This is nothing more than keeping track of the internal energy, that is, it is simply a conservation equation. Through considerations arising from the second law of thermodynamics, the property called entropy S is so defined that for reversible processes $dS = dq/T$. This states that the change in entropy is given by the heat absorbed by the system divided by the temperature at which it is absorbed. If we consider the work of Equation (21) to be pressure-volume work, the following statement for the change in internal energy is obtained.

$$dE = T \, dS - p \, dV \tag{22}$$

Another quantity called the Helmholtz free energy, A, is defined as

$$A = E - TS \tag{23}$$

By taking the total differential of Equation (23)

$$dA = dE - T \, dS - S \, dT$$

By using Equation (22) we obtain

$$dA = -S \, dT - p \, dV \tag{24}$$

that is, a relation for the change in Helmholtz free energy as a function of changes in the measurable quantities, temperature, and volume. This relation for the Helmholtz free energy, A, together with the internal energy, E, provides the bridge between statistical mechanics and thermodynamics.

1. *Bridging statistical mechanics and thermodynamics.* The internal energy in thermodynamics is actually the average value of the energy per molecule as used in the preceding section, multiplied by the number of molecules in the large collection which is taken to be a mole. The average value for a property is simply the value of the property times the chance (probability) that it will occur summed over all possible values. Thus the average energy for a molecule is

$$\bar{\epsilon} = \sum_i \epsilon_i P_i \tag{25}$$

which upon substitution of Equation (19) becomes

$$\bar{\epsilon} = \sum_i \epsilon_i \frac{e^{-\epsilon_i/kT}}{\sum_i e^{-\epsilon_i/kT}} \equiv kT^2 \left(\frac{\partial \ln \sum_i e^{-\epsilon_i/kT}}{\partial T} \right) \tag{26}$$

where the identity is easily verified by performing the indicated partial differentiation with respect to temperature, holding all other variables constant. Equation (26) can be used to calculate the average internal energy of a benzene molecule, or of a mole of benzene molecules, depending upon which way the partition function is written.

Since the Helmholtz free energy A is a function of V and T only, for constant composition systems, we can write

$$dA = \left(\frac{\partial A}{\partial T} \right)_V dT + \left(\frac{\partial A}{\partial V} \right)_T dV \tag{27}$$

Comparison of Equation (27) with Equation (24) gives

$$\left(\frac{\partial A}{\partial T} \right)_V = -S; \quad \text{and} \quad \left(\frac{\partial A}{\partial V} \right)_T = -p \tag{28}$$

Thus

$$-T^2 \left(\frac{\partial A/T}{\partial T} \right)_V = A - T \left(\frac{\partial A}{\partial T} \right)_V \equiv E \tag{29}$$

By combining Equations (29) and (26) we get

$$-T^2\left(\frac{\partial(A/T)}{\partial T}\right)_V = -kT^2\,\frac{\partial \ln \sum_i e^{-\epsilon_i/kT}}{\partial T} \tag{30}$$

By dividing out T^2 and integrating we get

$$-\frac{A}{T} = k \ln \sum_i e^{-\epsilon_i/kT} + C \tag{31}$$

If there are w_i states of energy ϵ_i Equation (31) can be rewritten as

$$A = -kT \ln \sum_i w_i\, e^{-\epsilon_i/kT} + CT \tag{32}$$

where the summation is now over the different energies. As T approaches zero all terms in the summation except that for the lowest energy, ϵ_1, are negligible. Thus at very low temperatures

$$A = -kT \ln w_1 + \epsilon_1 + CT = -kT \ln w_1 + \epsilon_1 - kT \ln w_1' = E - TS$$

In the second equality the integration constant, C, has been written as $C = -k \ln w_1'$ for convenience. We must necessarily make the identifications $E = \epsilon_1$ and $S = -k \ln w_1 w_1'$. Here w_1 is the degeneracy of the extra nuclear coordinates while w_1' is the degeneracy of the nuclei. According to the third law the entropy of a pure crystalline substance is zero at $T = 0$ which requires that $w_1 w_1' = 1$. The basis of the third law is the experimental fact that the entropy change, ΔS, for any reactions of crystalline systems at $T = 0$ is zero. This requires only that $w_1 w_1'$ be unchanged by any chemical reaction.* It is accordingly convenient to assume $w_1 w_1' = 1$ and hence $S = 0$ at $T = 0$. Thus we can take $C = 0$ for any system. We then have

$$A = -kT \ln \sum_i w_i\, e^{-\epsilon_i/kT} \tag{33}$$

where the summation is over all energy states.

2. *Explicit expressions for the partition functions.* The energy ϵ_i given to a molecule is distributed among its many degrees of freedom. These degrees of freedom may be grouped as translational, rotational, vibrational, electronic, and nuclear. In general, in chemical reactions there is no change in the nuclear energies so that these may be neglected. When we are interested in free radicals or paramagnetic substances the electronic energies need to be considered, but usually we are interested in molecules that have all their electrons paired. In the common case only translational, rotational, and vibrational degrees of freedom need to be treated, and explicit partition functions can be obtained for these degrees of freedom.

In the benzene molecule, since there are thirty-six degrees of freedom, three associated with each atom, ϵ_i is the sum of thirty-six energies. Classifying these degrees of freedom there are three translational, three rotational, and thirty vibrational. To the approximation

* There are nuclear degeneracies but these do not change in chemical reactions and need not be considered. Also, certain substances such as glasses often have residual entropies.

that these energies are independent,* the partition function for a molecule may be written as the product of partition functions

$$f = \sum_i e^{-\epsilon_i/kT} = \sum_i e^{-(\epsilon_t + \epsilon_r + \epsilon_v)/kT}$$

$$f = f_t f_r f_v \tag{34}$$

Suitable explicit expressions can be derived for f_t, f_r, and f_v, the translational, rotational, and vibrational partition functions.

a. *The translational partition function.* The translational energies may be arrived at by using either the old quantum theory or quantum mechanics. The simplest way is to use the Wilson-Sommerfeld quantization rule from old quantum theory which for a translation in the x direction is

$$\oint mv_x \, dx = nh \tag{35}$$

where the integration is over a complete cycle and m, v_x, n, and h are the mass of, for example, the benzene molecule, the velocity in the x direction, an integer giving the allowed translational energies ($n = 1, 2 \ldots$), and Planck's constant, respectively. Consider a container of volume V and of dimensions a, b, and c in the x, y, and z directions, respectively. Starting at one side of the container and considering motion in the x direction, Equation (35) becomes

$$nh = mv_x a - m(-v_x)a = 2mv_x a$$

but

$$\epsilon_x = \tfrac{1}{2}mv_x^2 = \tfrac{1}{2}m \frac{n^2 h^2}{4m^2 a^2} = \frac{n^2 h^2}{8ma^2} \tag{36}$$

ϵ_x is the energy for translation in the x direction. Substituting this into the partition function gives

$$f_{t(x)} = \sum_{n=1}^{\infty} e^{-n^2 h^2/8ma^2 kT}$$

By replacing the summation sign with an integral sign and integrating over-all values of n one obtains for the partition function, for translation in the x direction,

$$f_{t(x)} = \int_0^{\infty} e^{-n^2 h^2/8ma^2 kT} \, dn = \frac{(2\pi mkT)^{\frac{1}{2}} a}{h} \tag{36a}$$

For the three translations we may write

$$f_t = f_{t(x)} f_{t(y)} f_{t(z)} = \sum_n e^{-(\epsilon_x + \epsilon_y + \epsilon_z)/kT}$$

$$f_t = \frac{(2\pi mkT)^{\frac{3}{2}} abc}{h^3} = \frac{(2\pi mkT)^{\frac{3}{2}} V}{h^3} \tag{37}$$

We now have an expression which can easily be evaluated for a system of known volume, temperature, and mass.

* Though rotational energies do slightly affect vibrational states, the approximation is very good. However, when the approximation is not valid, summation of the individual energies is necessary.

b. *The rotational partition functions.* For nonlinear molecules there are three rotational degrees of freedom. For linear molecules there are two rotational degrees of freedom. The derivation for the three-dimensional rotator is too long to include in this chapter, but starting with the expression for the rotational energies we can easily derive the partition function for a two-dimensional rotator. The rotational energy can be experimentally determined from spectroscopy or theoretically from quantum mechanics. This is one of the areas in which the old quantum theory results were not quite correct. The correct relation for the rotational energy is

$$\epsilon_r = \frac{J(J+1)h^2}{8\pi^2 I} \tag{38}$$

where J represents the variable quantum number, h is Planck's constant, and I is the moment of inertia of the molecule. The two-dimensional rotator has a degeneracy of $w_i = 2J + 1$. If the molecule is symmetric about its center of mass as is the case for O_2 or $O = C = O$, then a particular molecule has the quantum values $J = 1, 3, 5, \ldots$ or $J = 0, 2, 4, \ldots$ i.e., odd or even, but not both. As a result the partition function of the symmetric linear rotator must be divided by a symmetry factor $\sigma = 2$. The partition function for a two-dimensional rotator may now be written as

$$f_{2r} = \frac{1}{\sigma} \sum_J (2J+1) e^{-J(J+1)h^2/8\pi^2 IkT}$$

In most cases the summation sign may be replaced by an integral over J

$$f_{2r} = \frac{1}{\sigma} \int_0^\infty (2J+1) e^{-(J^2+J)h^2/8\pi^2 IkT} \, dJ = \frac{8\pi^2 IkT}{\sigma h^2} \tag{39}$$

Thus if the structure of the molecule is known, the moment of inertia may be calculated $(I = \sum_i m_i x_i^2)$ and the symmetry factor σ is known,* so that the value of the two-dimensional rotational partition function can be calculated for a given temperature. For a three-dimensional rotator the partition function is

$$f_{3r} = \frac{8\pi^2 (8\pi^3 ABC)^{1/2} (kT)^{3/2}}{\sigma h^3} \tag{40}$$

where A, B, and C are the moments of inertia about the three principal axes of the molecule.

c. *The vibrational partition function.* The vibrational partition function is obtained by considering an harmonic oscillator which absorbs its energy in units of $h\nu$. The partition function for vibration is written as

$$f_{1v} = \sum_{n=0}^\infty e^{-nh\nu/kT} = e^{-0/kT} + e^{-h\nu/kT} + e^{-2h\nu/kT} + \cdots$$

this being the sum of the energy states that the oscillator can have when the ground state is taken as the zero of energy. If we rewrite the above equation with the substitution $x = e^{-h\nu/kT}$ we have

$$f_{1v} = 1 + x + x^2 + \ldots = \frac{1}{1-x}$$

---

* The symmetry factor, σ, is the number of orientations a molecule has which, though the atoms have been moved, are indistinguishable from an initial orientation.

The last equality is simply shown by carrying out the division of 1 by $(1 - x)$. Upon resubstitution

$$f_{1v} = \frac{1}{1 - e^{-hv/kT}} = (1 - e^{-hv/kT})^{-1}$$

for many vibrational degrees of freedom one writes the product of the above expression for each of the vibrational frequencies, i.e.,

$$f_v = \prod_i (1 - e^{-hv_i/kT})^{-1} \tag{41}$$

With the explicit expressions for the partition functions the various thermodynamic properties can be calculated. By way of example we indicate the calculation of A and E for a mole of gaseous CO_2. The CO_2 molecule has three atoms and therefore nine degrees of freedom. Since it is a linear molecule it has three translational degrees of freedom, two rotational degrees of freedom, and four vibrational degrees of freedom. By Equation (33) we can write

$$A = -kT \ln (f_t f_r f_v)^N \frac{1}{N!}$$

For N molecules there are N times as many degrees of freedom as for a single molecule which explains the exponent N. Division by the symmetry number $N!$, when the N molecules are identical, depends on the indistinguishability of states arising from permuting identical molecules. By Stirling's approximation, $N! = \left(\dfrac{N}{e}\right)^N$, and using Equations (37), (39), and (41) we have

$$A = -NkT \ln \frac{(2\pi mkT)^{3/2} eV}{h^3 N} \cdot \frac{8\pi^2 IkT}{2h^2} \prod_{i=1}^4 (1 - e^{-hv_i/kT})^{-1}$$

and by Equation (29) for a mole

$$E = -T^2 \left(\frac{\partial A/T}{\partial T}\right) = \tfrac{5}{2}RT + \sum_{i=1}^4 Nhv_i(e^{hv_i/kT} - 1)^{-1}$$

where $I = 18.94 \times 10^{-40}$ gm cm^2

$$v_1 = 3.86 \times 10^{13} \text{ sec}^{-1}, \qquad v_2 = 4.17 \times 10^{13} \text{ sec}^{-1}$$

$$v_3 = v_4 = 7.05 \times 10^{13} \text{ sec}^{-1}$$

and $m = (44.01/6.02 \times 10^{23}$ gm) is the mass of one CO_2 molecule, k ($= 1.38 \times 10^{-16}$ erg deg^{-1}) is Boltzmann's constant, h ($= 6.63 \times 10^{-27}$ erg sec) is Planck's constant, N ($= 6.02 \times 10^{23}$) is Avogadro's number, V is the volume of the container, T is the temperature of the system, R ($= Nk = 8.32 \times 10^7$ erg deg^{-1} mole^{-1}) is the gas constant, $e = 2.72$, and $\pi = 3.14$. If a temperature and volume are assumed, all the necessary information is available. Try it.

C. Statistical Mechanical Derivation of Equilibrium Constants[2,5]

In the compounding of systems method of deriving the Boltzmann expression we were interested in the probability or relative frequency of occurrence of a single energy level, ϵ_i.

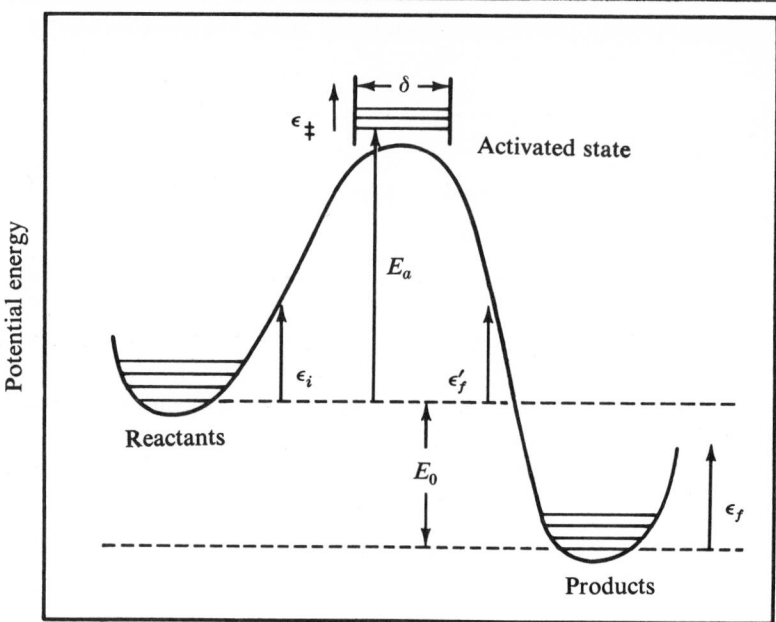

FIGURE 1. Schematic potential energy diagram taken along the reaction coordinate for the reaction $H_2 + I_2 = 2HI$. ϵ_i and ϵ_f' are the energies above the ground state of the reactants for the initial and final states respectively. ϵ_f are the energies of the products above the ground state of the final state. E_0 is the difference in energy at absolute zero of a pair of H_2, I_2 molecules and a pair of HI molecules. E_a is the activation energy at absolute zero. See text under reaction rate constants for discussion of the activated state.

In chemical reactions we are interested in the relative frequency of occurrence of the reactants and of the products. It is useful to consider representative states of a particular reaction. A good example is the reaction

$$H_2 + I_2 = 2HI$$

The potential energy diagram for this reaction is given in Figure 1; the diagram represents the energy changes involved in a chemical reaction as reactants, the (H_2,I_2) pair, collide and cross over a potential energy barrier to form products, the (HI,HI) pair. The abscissa called the reaction coordinate is a function of the interatomic distances and in fact represents the path on the seven-dimensional potential energy surface in configuration space which requires the least activation energy in going from reactants to products and vice versa. In this case our representative initial state is the pair of molecules (H_2,I_2), and the representative final state is the pair of molecules (HI,HI). We are interested in the probability, which is the same as the relative frequency of occurrence, of these states. Whereas earlier we were interested in the probability of a unique energy state, now we are interested in the unique set of energies which comprise the representative states.

We have by simple analogy that the probability of the initial state is the sum of Boltzmann terms for the energy states of the pair of molecules that represent the initial state, divided by the corresponding summation over all possible states which can occur in the reaction vessel, i.e.,

$$P_i = \frac{\sum e^{-\epsilon_i/kT}}{\sum \text{ over all possible states}} \tag{42}$$

where i stands for initial, and the summation in the numerator is over all the energies of the initial state. But the summation over all the energies of the initial state is just the partition function for the molecules involved, i.e.,

$$\sum_i e^{-\epsilon_i/kT} = f_i = f_{H_2}f_{I_2} \tag{42a}$$

Similarly for the final state we have

$$P_f = \frac{\sum_f e^{-\epsilon'_f/kT}}{\sum \text{ over all possible states}} \tag{43}$$

where the subscript f stands for final, and the summation in the numerator is over all the energies of the pair of molecules that are representative of that state. It is necessary to choose a common zero of energy for both initial and final states; the ϵ'_f is to indicate that the reference energy level is the ground state of the initial state and not of the final state (see Figure 1).

In this particular case the representative final state is the pair of identical molecules (HI,HI). However, we have already seen, when discussing the molar partition function for gases, that when there are identical particles we write the partition function for one molecule, raise it to the power of the number of like molecules, and divide by the number of like molecules taken factorially. Therefore we write for this example

$$\sum_f e^{-\epsilon'_f/kT} = \sum_f e^{-(\epsilon_f + E_0)/kT} = e^{-E_0/kT} \sum_f e^{-\epsilon_f/kT}$$

$$= \frac{1}{2!}(f_{HI})^2 e^{-E_0/kT}$$

being careful to correct by the factor $e^{-E_0/kT}$ in order to adjust to the ground state of the products. Since both initial and final states are enclosed in the same reaction vessel the denominators of Equations (42) and (43) must necessarily be the same. The ratio of the probabilities of the states is then

$$\frac{P_f}{P_i} = \frac{\sum_f e^{-\epsilon'_f/kT}}{\sum_i e^{-\epsilon_i/kT}} = \frac{\frac{1}{2}(f_{HI})^2 e^{-E_0/kT}}{f_{H_2}f_{I_2}} \tag{44}$$

Since probability is also relative frequency, we will now consider the number of ways in which the representative states can be attained.

If n_1, n_2, and n_3 are the numbers of molecules of H_2, I_2, and HI, respectively, what is the number of ways in which the pairs (H_2,I_2) and (HI,HI) can be obtained? Clearly one H_2 molecule can pair with n_2 different I_2 molecules, but there are n_1 such H_2 molecules. Therefore there are $n_1 \times n_2$ ways of forming the (H_2,I_2) pair. In terms of relative frequency the probability of the initial state is the product of the number of possible (H_2,I_2) pairs, divided by all the possible combinations that can exist in the reaction vessel, i.e.,

$$P_i = \frac{n_1 n_2}{\text{all possible combinations in the vessel}} \tag{45}$$

The final state is a pair of identical molecules. If we have n_3 molecules of HI, then the first molecule can pair with any of $(n_3 - 1)$ molecules, the second can pair with $(n_3 - 2)$ molecules, etc., until the HI molecules have been used. In such a case we have the sum of possible pairs

$$(n_3 - 1) + (n_3 - 2) + \ldots + 1 = \frac{n_3(n_3 - 1)}{2}$$

When dealing with the molar quantities, 1 is quite negligible when added to 6.02×10^{23}, and we can write for the relative frequency of the final state,

$$P_f = \frac{\frac{1}{2}(n_3)^2}{\text{all possible combinations in the vessel}} \tag{46}$$

Substitution of Equations (45) and (46) into Equation (44) gives

$$\frac{\frac{1}{2}(n_3)^2}{n_1 n_2} = \frac{\frac{1}{2}(f_{HI})^2 e^{-E_0/kT}}{f_{H_2} f_{I_2}}$$

By using Equations (37), (39), and (41), the explicit expressions for the partition functions, we have

$$\frac{(n_3)^2}{n_1 n_2} = \frac{\left[\frac{(2\pi m_3 kT)^{3/2} V}{h^3} \frac{8\pi^2 I_3 kT}{h^2} \frac{1}{1 - e^{-h\nu_3/kT}}\right]^2 e^{-E_0/kT}}{\left[\frac{(2\pi m_1 kT)^{3/2} V}{h^3} \frac{8\pi^2 I_1 kT}{2h^2} \frac{1}{1 - e^{-h\nu_1/kT}}\right]\left[\frac{(2\pi m_2 kT)^{3/2} V}{h^3} \frac{8\pi^2 I_2 kT}{2h^2} \frac{1}{1 - e^{-h\nu_2/kT}}\right]}$$

dividing out the volumes the equilibrium constant is obtained

$$K = \frac{(n_3/V)^2}{\left(\frac{n_1}{V}\right)\left(\frac{n_2}{V}\right)} = \frac{[C_3]^2}{[C_1][C_2]} = \frac{(f_{HI}/V)^2 e^{-E_0/kT}}{(f_{H_2}/V)(f_{I_2}/V)}$$

$$K = \frac{\left[\frac{(2\pi m_3 kT)^{3/2}}{h^3} \frac{8\pi^2 I_3 kT}{h^2} \frac{1}{1 - e^{-h\nu_3/kT}}\right]^2 e^{-E_0/kT}}{\left[\frac{(2\pi m_1 kT)^{3/2}}{h^3} \frac{8\pi^2 I_1 kT}{2h^2} \frac{1}{1 - e^{-h\nu_1/kT}}\right]\left[\frac{(2\pi m_2 kT)^{3/2}}{h^3} \frac{8\pi^2 I_2 kT}{2h^2} \frac{1}{1 - e^{-h\nu_2/kT}}\right]} \tag{47}$$

where the subscripts 1, 2, and 3 refer to the H_2, I_2, and HI molecules, respectively.

As in the calculation of the thermodynamic properties, the equilibrium constant K may be calculated with the knowledge of one more quantity, E_o. This may be obtained most readily from the difference of dissociation energies, D^o, obtained from spectroscopy for the molecules involved

$$D^o_{H_2} + D^o_{I_2} - 2D^o_{HI} = E_o$$

E_o as defined is intrinsically negative. This will give an exponential to a positive power and will weight in favor of the products which are at a lower energy state.

Equilibrium constants can be derived equally well by employing what was learned about absolute activity. And, in fact, the justification for what we have done is rigorously shown by Equation (10), the relation that when a system is at equilibrium the absolute activity is the same for a given state or for a collection of states. We generalized from the probability of a given energy state to the probability of a unique collection of energy states; Equation (10) is the justification for such a generalization.

D. *Statistical Mechanical Derivation of Reaction Rate Constants*[2,4,5]

1. *Formulation of the problem of reaction kinetics.* Once a model is chosen and a statement of reaction kinetics formulated, the statistical mechanical solution is very much the same as that employed in the derivation of equilibrium constants or the Boltzmann expression. We again use the reaction employed in the considerations of equilibrium constants, but now included is a fleeting intermediate, the activated complex

$$H_2 + I_2 \rightleftharpoons \begin{bmatrix} H \\ | \\ H \end{bmatrix} \begin{array}{c} I \\ \\ I \end{array} \rightleftharpoons 2HI$$

The activated complex exists through the distance, δ, at the top of the potential energy barrier as indicated in Figure 1. In order to describe the activated state, six interatomic distances must be specified. Corresponding to each set of six distances between pairs of atoms, that is, to each configuration, there is a potential energy. To graph such a system would require seven-dimensional space. However, there is a continuous set of configurations which describe the lowest energy pass in going from reactants to products. This low energy path is called the reaction coordinate and it is possible to plot this set of configurations against potential energy in a two-dimensional diagram. Such a plot (Figure 1) functions nicely as a description of the reaction. The height of the barrier is the primary factor in controlling the reaction rate, but the width can also affect the rate since a narrow barrier allows for quantum mechanical leakage (tunneling) which results in an increased rate.

Our model may now be stated: as the reactants collide, their kinetic energy is converted into potential energy and the interacting molecules begin to mount the potential energy barrier. If the kinetic energy along the line of centers is great enough and the orientation of the molecules is proper, the activated complex will be attained. This model is true for the above reaction; it is also true for O_2 binding with hemoglobin, or for the amino acid activation process for protein synthesis, or for the many oxidation reduction reactions that occur in biological systems.

With this model in mind we may now formulate the expression for the velocity of a reaction. The problem is one of determining the number of activated complexes which are passing over the barrier per unit time. This problem is clearly a function of the number of activated complexes per unit volume of reaction vessel; it is also a function of the average velocity with which these complexes are traveling through the distance δ, the distance through which the activated state exists. For the above reaction we have

$$v = -\frac{d[H_2]}{dt} = \frac{1}{2}\left(\frac{n^{\ddagger}}{V}\right)\frac{\bar{u}}{\delta}$$

where $n^{\ddagger}$ is the number of activated complexes, and $\bar{u}$ is the average velocity with which the activated complexes are passing through the distance δ. The factor of $\frac{1}{2}$ is introduced because at equilibrium only one half of the molecules are moving in the forward direction.

The above equation appears to be correct in what might be called the ideal case, which is also the usual case. However, for the special cases a factor κ called the transmission coefficient is introduced. In complete generality then we may write

$$v = \kappa \frac{1}{2}\left(\frac{n^{\dagger}}{V}\right)\frac{\bar{u}}{\delta}$$

(48)

However, when κ is not one, it is possible with this model to obtain an explanation for the nonideal behavior and in many cases to calculate a value for κ. There are certain classes of reactions which have characteristic values for κ. Such reactions are ammonia inversion and cis-trans isomerizations in which there are steep and narrow barriers.

In these cases the system may be considered one of high index of refraction, and leakage through the barrier occurs so that κ is greater than one. There are also free radical reactions where there is little or no barrier and the problem is one of dissipating the energy, deactivation, in order to form a stable bond; in this case κ is fractional. κ is also fractional in certain cases where there is reflection from the top of the barrier, that is, when the energy is not properly distributed in the complex. The important thing is that deviations from ideality, that is, $\kappa \neq 1$, can be classed and treated accordingly. For most biological reactions κ may be taken as one.

2. *Statistical mechanical solution of the velocity of a reaction.* As written, Equation (48) cannot be used directly to calculate the velocity of a reaction. However, with the use of statistical mechanics an explicit expression can be obtained. We will employ the same principles of statistical mechanics which were used and arrived at in the derivation of the Boltzmann expression and the derivation of equilibrium constants. Aside from κ there are three quantities, $n^{\dagger}$, $\bar{u}$, and δ which must be evaluated or eliminated.

a. *Explicit expression for* $n^{\dagger}/V$. Considering the forward reaction, we are interested in the (H_2, I_2) pair as representative of the initial state and the activated complex

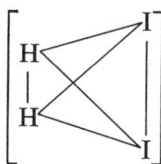

as the representative of the activated state. By proceeding as before, that is, Equation (42), we write

$$P_i = \frac{\sum_i e^{-\epsilon_i/kT}}{\sum \text{ over all states}}$$

and

$$P_{\ddagger} = \frac{\sum_{\ddagger} e^{-\epsilon'_{\ddagger}/kT}}{\sum \text{ over all states}}$$

where $P_{\ddagger}$ stands for the probability of the activated state and $\epsilon'_{\ddagger}$ stands for the energies of the activated state with, as before, the ground state of the initial state as the reference level, that is, $\epsilon'_{\ddagger} = \epsilon_{\ddagger} + E_a$. The subscripts 1, 2, and 3 will be used to indicate hydrogen, iodine, and the activated complex, respectively. And the relative frequency of occurrence is again

$$P_i = \frac{n_1 n_2}{\text{all possible combinations in the vessel}}$$

$$P_{\ddagger} = \frac{n_3}{\text{all possible combinations in the vessel}}$$

where the number of activated complexes is simply n_3. Now we may write

$$\frac{P_{\ddagger}}{P_i} = \frac{n_3}{n_1 n_2} = \frac{\sum_{\ddagger} e^{-\epsilon'_{\ddagger}/kT}}{\sum_i e^{-\epsilon_i/kT}}$$

Since $\epsilon'_{\ddagger} = E_a + \epsilon_{\ddagger}$ we have

$$\frac{n_3}{n_1 n_2} = \frac{\left(\sum_{\ddagger} e^{-\epsilon_{\ddagger}/kT}\right) e^{-E_a/kT}}{\sum_i e^{-\epsilon_i/kT}} \qquad (49)$$

E_a is the activation energy at absolute zero (see Figure 1).

The question at this stage is, what do we write for the partition functions? Obviously, it is the same initial state, so Equation (42a) still applies, but what about the activated state? The activated state certainly has three translational degrees of freedom of its center of gravity. Since it is nonlinear it has three rotational degrees of freedom, so that Equations (37) and (40) in which $\sigma = 2$, apply. The four-atom complex has twelve degrees of freedom. We have already used six. This leaves six degrees of freedom to dispose of, which would normally be vibrational. But there is a uniqueness about an activated complex. There is a motion, which for the normal molecule would be vibrational, that is actually a translation.

The four-atom complex originated from an H_2 and an I_2 molecule and is destined to separate into two HI molecules. Thus we have a translation through the distance δ of the activated state, for which we write the one-dimensional translational partition function $(2\pi m_{\ddagger}kT)^{1/2} \delta/h$. This leaves five vibrational degrees of freedom. Placing the explicit expressions for the partition functions in the preceding equation and dividing out the volume from the translational partition functions yield

$$\frac{\left(\dfrac{n_3}{V}\right)}{\left(\dfrac{n_1}{V}\right)\left(\dfrac{n_2}{V}\right)} = \frac{\left[\dfrac{(2\pi m_3 kT)^{3/2}}{h^3} \dfrac{8\pi^2(8\pi^3 ABC)^{1/2}(kT)^{3/2}}{\sigma h^3} \dfrac{(2\pi m_{\ddagger}kT)^{1/2}\delta}{h} \displaystyle\prod_{i=1}^{5}(1 - e^{-h\nu_i/kT})^{-1}\right] e^{-E_a/kT}}{(f_1/V)(f_2/V)}$$

By factoring out the one-dimensional translational partition function and designating the remainder of the partition function of the activated state as $F^{\ddagger}$ and writing $f_1/V = F_1$ and $f_2/V = F_2$ the expression for (n_3/V) becomes

$$\left(\frac{n_3}{V}\right) = \left(\frac{n_1}{V}\right)\left(\frac{n_2}{V}\right)\frac{(2\pi m_{\ddagger}kT)^{1/2}\delta}{h} \frac{F^{\ddagger} e^{-E_a/kT}}{F_1 F_2} \qquad (50)$$

But

$$\frac{F^{\ddagger} e^{-E_a/kT}}{F_1 F_2}$$

which we will represent by $K^{\ddagger}$ is simply the expression for an equilibrium constant for the case in which δ is chosen so that the partition function along the reaction coordinate is unity, that is, $(2\pi m_{\ddagger}kT)^{1/2} \delta/h = 1$. Upon rewriting Equation (50) with this definition we get

$$\left(\frac{n^{\ddagger}}{V}\right) = \left(\frac{n_1}{V}\right)\left(\frac{n_2}{V}\right)\frac{(2\pi m_{\ddagger}kT)^{1/2} \delta}{h} K^{\ddagger} \tag{51}$$

We see upon substituting Equation (51) into Equation (48) that δ cancels out, leaving only $\bar{u}$ to evaluate.

b. *The evaluation of* $\bar{u}$. In Section B1 we found the statistical mechanical expression for the average energy. The same form is true for any average value. For the average velocity, $\bar{u}$, one has

$$\bar{u} = \sum u_i P_i = \sum u_i \frac{e^{-\epsilon_i/kT}}{\sum e^{-\epsilon_i/kT}} \tag{52}$$

In order to evaluate the above expression it is necessary to find a useful relationship between ϵ_i and u_i. In Section B2a, we used the Wilson-Sommerfeld quantization rule, Equation (35), to obtain an expression for the velocity. The same approach is used here, the only difference being that the translation is now through a distance δ. Upon putting Equation (35) in terms of the variables of interest in this case

$$\oint m_{\ddagger}u_i \, d\delta = nh = m_{\ddagger}u_i\delta - m_{\ddagger}(-u_i)\delta = 2m_{\ddagger}u_i\delta$$

$$u_i = nh/2m_{\ddagger}\delta$$

where $n = 1, 2 \ldots$ and $m_{\ddagger}$ is the mass of the activated complex. For the translational energy we write the well-known formula for the kinetic energy and substitute in the relation for u_i

$$\epsilon_i = \tfrac{1}{2}m_{\ddagger}u_i^2 = \frac{n^2h^2}{8m_{\ddagger}\delta^2}$$

After finding appropriate expressions for u_i and ϵ_i, they are substituted into Equation (52).

$$\bar{u} = \sum_{n=1}^{\infty} \frac{nh}{2m_{\ddagger}\delta} \frac{e^{-n^2h^2/8m_{\ddagger}\delta^2kT}}{\displaystyle\sum_{n=1}^{\infty} e^{-n^2h^2/8m_{\ddagger}\delta^2kT}}$$

Replacement of the summation with an integral between zero and infinity over the new variable, n, gives

$$\bar{u} = \int_0^{\infty} \frac{nh}{2m_{\ddagger}\delta} \frac{e^{-n^2h^2/8m_{\ddagger}\delta^2kT} \, dn}{\displaystyle\int_0^{\infty} e^{-n^2h^2/8m_{\ddagger}\delta^2kT} \, dn} = \frac{\displaystyle\int_0^{\infty} \frac{nh}{2m_{\ddagger}\delta} e^{-n^2h^2/8m_{\ddagger}\delta^2kT} \, dn}{\displaystyle\int_0^{\infty} e^{-n^2h^2/8m_{\ddagger}\delta^2kT} \, dn}$$

Once the integral in the denominator is evaluated, it is clear that it is only a constant and need not be kept within the integral in the numerator. The integral in the numerator is of the form encountered in Section B2b and is readily integrable. The integral in the denominator is the same as Equation (36a). Upon evaluation of the integrals one obtains

$$\bar{u} = \frac{\dfrac{h}{2m_\ddagger\delta}\dfrac{4m_\ddagger\delta^2 kT}{h^2}}{\dfrac{(2\pi m_\ddagger kT)^{1/2}\delta}{h}} = \left(\frac{2kT}{\pi m_\ddagger}\right)^{1/2} \tag{53}$$

The necessary terms have been expressed in calculable form and may be substituted into the equation for the velocity of a reaction. Using Equations (51) and (53), Equation (48) becomes

$$v = \kappa\,\frac{1}{2}\left(\frac{n_1}{V}\right)\left(\frac{n_2}{V}\right)\frac{(2\pi m_\ddagger kT)^{1/2}\delta}{h}\,K^\ddagger\left(\frac{2kT}{\pi m_\ddagger}\right)^{1/2}\frac{1}{\delta}$$

$$v = \left(\frac{n_1}{V}\right)\left(\frac{n_2}{V}\right)\kappa\,\frac{kT}{h}\,K^\ddagger = [H_2][I_2]k' \tag{54}$$

where the number of molecules per unit volume has been replaced by their equivalent concentration expressions and k', the specific rate constant, has been found to be

$$k' = \kappa\,\frac{kT}{h}\,K^\ddagger \tag{55}$$

The specific rate constant is the velocity of the reaction when the reactants are at unit concentration, that is, if the units of k' are taken as liters per mole per second then a one molar concentration each of H_2 and I_2 would constitute unit concentration. It should be stressed that this equation applies to reactions in the gaseous, liquid, or solid states, or in a heterogeneous state when the appropriate partition functions are used in the expression for $K^\ddagger$. In fact, whenever a substance passes over energy barriers this equation can be applied.

    c. *Calculation of the specific rate constant.* Theoretically the velocity of any reaction can be calculated without recourse to experiment, and this would be true in practice if we had bigger and better computers. The limitation is that the quantum mechanical calculations of the potential energy surfaces are too lengthy even for the largest computers except when one is dealing with simple reactions. For the latter, one calculates the potential energies for each given configuration possible in the course of the reaction and makes a table of the dimensions and corresponding energies. One can then determine the lowest energy path in going from reactants to products. With this table the configuration of the activated complex at the top of the barrier is known, allowing the moments of inertia and hence the rotational partition function to be determined. The calculation of the translational partition function for the activated state is as simple as for any molecule, and, of course, the height of the lowest pass has been established giving E_a. This leaves only the vibrational energies to be calculated at the top of the barrier.

    The normal modes of vibration of the activated complex are calculated by applying the theory of small vibrations to the curvature of the potential energy surface at the top of the barrier. The salient point about the theory of small vibrations is that it applies to slight displacements from stationary points, maxima and minima, where the kinetic and potential energies can be expressed as the sum of square terms. Under these circumstances the normal modes of vibration can be determined and hence the vibrational frequencies for the vibrational partition function are obtained. The same considerations apply with less complexity to the reactants. Thus all of the quantities may be calculated entirely theoretically for the simplest reactions.

For more complicated reactions approximate methods are used. Because the activated state has such a fleeting existence there are no spectroscopic data available from which to obtain the moments of inertia and vibrational frequencies as is the case with stable molecules. For certain reactions a stable molecule which is similar to the activated complex is used and values for the activated state are approximated. Two very useful considerations are that 1) the activated complex is linear for three-atom reactions, and 2), barring certain directional effects of orbitals, the activated complex for four-atom reactions is planar. These considerations are of great help in determining the dimensions of the activated complex.

A practical use of reaction rate theory is to take a measured rate and calculate the properties of the activated state and in this way describe the reaction in terms of thermodynamic properties and free-energy diagrams. This will be dealt with later in this chapter when the thermodynamic form of the rate equation is discussed.

III. EQUILIBRIUM AND RATE THEORY IN BIOLOGY

A. *Various Forms of the Rate Equation*[4,5]

The dynamic nature of equilibrium was recognized as early as 1863 by Guldberg and Waage. They described the equilibrium situation as one in which the velocity in the forward direction, v_f, was equal to that of the backward direction, v_b. For the reaction of hydrogen and iodine to form hydrogen iodide, this gives

$$v_f = [H_2][I_2]k_f' = v_b = [HI]^2 k_b' \tag{56}$$

and solving for the ratios of the concentrations, it was observed that

$$\frac{[HI]^2}{[H_2][I_2]} = \frac{k_f'}{k_b'} = K \tag{57}$$

Thus the equilibrium constant is the ratio of two rate constants.

The dependence of the equilibrium constant on temperature was shown by van't Hoff to be

$$\frac{d \ln K}{dT} = \frac{\Delta E}{RT^2} \tag{58}$$

But recognizing that the equilibrium constant is actually the ratio of two rate constants and redefining ΔE, that is,

$$\ln K = \ln \frac{k_f'}{k_b'} = \ln k_f' - \ln k_b'$$

and

$$\Delta E = E_f - E_b$$

we see that Equation (3) becomes

$$\frac{d \ln k_f'}{dT} - \frac{d \ln k_b'}{dT} = \frac{E_f}{RT^2} - \frac{E_b}{RT^2}$$

This suggests that the following equations may be considered

$$\frac{d \ln k_f'}{dT} = \frac{E_f}{RT^2} \; ; \quad \frac{d \ln k_b'}{dT} = \frac{E_b}{RT^2} \tag{59}$$

An interesting phenomenon about the rates of many reactions is that if the temperature is raised by $10°C$, the rate of the reaction approximately doubles, yet the average energy of the system has been increased only fractionally. Arrhenius realized that while the average energy of the system increased but fractionally, the number of molecules of very high energy increased markedly. Aware of the above relations, Arrhenius proposed an equilibrium between "normal" molecules and "active" molecules, and suggested further that only the active molecules, those with a required energy, could react. With the idea of a necessary energy to react, the energies in Equation (59) can be interpreted as activation energies. The integration of Equation (59) gives an equation of the form

$$\ln k' = -\frac{E_{\exp}}{RT} + \ln A \tag{60}$$

$$k' = A e^{-E_{\exp}/RT} \tag{61}$$

The above equation is known as the Arrhenius equation for specific rate constants. A is interpreted as a frequency factor, and the subscript exp on E is to indicate that these energies are experimentally determined. One measures the specific rate constant over a range of temperatures and then plots the $\ln k'$ against the reciprocal of the temperature. The slope $E_{\exp}/R$ is then measured from the graph and $E_{\exp}$ is determined by multiplying the slope by R.

The Arrhenius equation, though useful, proved to have severe limitations, especially in biological systems. Equation (61) predicts an ever-increasing rate with increasing temperatures. This is true in general but in biological systems it is not. Rather than a straight line when plotting $\ln k'$ vs. $1/T$ as predicted by Equation (60), in biological systems a curve with a maximum is obtained. The deviation is due to the nature of the biological catalysts. The increased temperature alters the structure of the protein catalysts, resulting in a decrease in the concentration of the effective enzyme. Also the rate must be measured over a range of temperatures to obtain the experimental activation energy; yet over this range undetermined damage is being done to the protein catalysts. Furthermore, there are recognized entropy effects which are not readily treated with this equation. Entropy can be related to the order of the system. The entropy increases as the system becomes more random. In bimolecular reactions the disoriented molecules form a specifically structured activated state which would be expected to have related entropy effects. Also the basic tenet of Arrhenius, that there is a true equilibrium between the reactants and activated state, is in error. These faults are removed quite adequately by the absolute reaction rate theory derived earlier in this chapter.

1. *Thermodynamic form of the absolute reaction rate equation.* In order to obtain the thermodynamic expression, two additional thermodynamic quantities need to be introduced. These state functions, enthalpy H, and Gibbs free energy F, have the following relations:

$$\Delta H = \Delta E + P \Delta V \quad (P \text{ constant}) \tag{62}$$

$$\Delta F = \Delta H - T \Delta S \quad (T \text{ constant}) \tag{63}$$

Whereas ΔE is the heat change of a reaction at constant volume, ΔH is the heat change of a reaction at constant pressure. ΔH is what one conveniently measures for chemical reactions since the atmosphere provides the condition of constant pressure.

F, the Gibbs' free energy (commonly referred to as "free energy") is a state function that is particularly useful in discussing equilibria under the usual conditions of constant T and P. ΔF is the change in free energy in going from reactants to products. The equation relating ΔF and the equilibrium constant is

$$\Delta F = -RT \ln K \tag{64}$$

This relation and the definition of ΔF will be used to obtain the thermodynamic form of the rate equation. Although $K^{\ddagger}$ is not a true equilibrium constant (it has the translational degree of freedom along the reaction coordinate removed), we can write that

$$\Delta F^{\ddagger} = -RT \ln K^{\ddagger}$$

where $\Delta F^{\ddagger}$ is interpreted as the change in free energy in going from the initial state to the activated state. With this definition, Equation (55) becomes

$$k' = \kappa \frac{kT}{h} e^{-\Delta F^{\ddagger}/RT} \tag{65}$$

But since

$$\Delta F^{\ddagger} = \Delta H^{\ddagger} - T \Delta S^{\ddagger}$$

where $\Delta H^{\ddagger}$ and $\Delta S^{\ddagger}$ are interpreted as the change in the enthalpy (heat content) and entropy, respectively, in going from reactants to the activated state, we have

$$k' = \kappa \frac{kT}{h} e^{-\Delta H^{\ddagger}/RT} e^{\Delta S^{\ddagger}/R} \tag{66}$$

This particular form of the rate equation treats the entropy effects which were not clear in the Arrhenius equation. Also if the concentrations are known and if κ is taken as one, the free energy of activation is calculable with the knowledge of the reaction velocity at a single temperature. One can readily see the value of these equations in describing biological systems. The knowledge of the entropy of activation can be useful in determining the reaction mechanism. A reaction requiring many points of interaction on the enzyme surface would be expected to have a large negative entropy change, that is, the more restricted the activated complex, the greater the negative entropy change.

B. Temperature, Pressure, and Drug Effects on Bioluminescence[5]

1. *Temperature effects on enzyme reactions.* As previously mentioned, characteristic of biological reactions is an optimum temperature for which a maximum rate is obtained. If this optimum temperature is exceeded the rate begins to decrease markedly. The effect is one of enzyme denaturation. The vibrational motions of the protein become so vigorous that the secondary and tertiary structures are changed. If the temperature is not raised too high and if the high temperature is not maintained for too long, the denaturation is reversible. If, however, the temperature is raised sufficiently and held there for a period of time, the primary structure is damaged, that is, the peptide linkages are broken.

It follows from the above discussion that there is an equilibrium between native and reversibly denatured enzymes, that is,

$$E_n \rightleftharpoons E_d, \qquad K_1 = \frac{[E_d]}{[E_n]},$$

or

$$[E_n]K_1 = [E_d]$$

where $[E_n]$ is the concentration of native (active) enzyme and $[E_d]$ is the concentration of denatured (inactive) enzyme. K_1 is the equilibrium constant between the two. If we designate $[E_0]$ as the total enzyme present we can write

$$[E_0] = [E_n] + [E_d] = E_n(1 + K_1)$$
$$[E_n] = \frac{[E_0]}{1 + K_1} \tag{67}$$

With the use of Equations (63) and (64) we have for K_1

$$K_1 = e^{-\Delta H_1/RT} e^{\Delta S_1/R} \tag{68}$$

Thus, to take into consideration the temperature effect on the amount of active enzyme, the total enzyme concentration must be divided by $(1 + K_1)$. In the denaturation process, $T \Delta S_1$ is positive and will increase the value of K_1 though it is a small term relative to ΔH_1.

If the enzyme is particularly stable this means that the enthalpy of activation $\Delta H_1^{\ddagger}$ is large. If ΔH_1 is also large, the equilibrium will lie in the direction of the native enzyme at physiological temperatures, that is, $K_1 \ll 1$. But, if the enzyme is particularly labile with respect to increasing temperature, this means that $\Delta H_1^{\ddagger}$ is small, and if ΔH_1 is also small then K_1 will be significant relative to one and must be considered even at physiological temperatures. In the latter case the Michaelis-Menton equation

$$v = \frac{k_3[E_0][S]}{Km + [S]} \tag{69}$$

becomes

$$v = \frac{k_3[E_0][S]}{(Km + [S])(1 + K_1)} \tag{70}$$

2. *Temperature effects on bioluminescence.* By writing the velocity of the luminescent reaction at low substrate concentration we have

$$v = k'[L][E_n] \tag{71}$$

where $[L]$ is the concentration of luciferin, and $[E_n]$ the concentration of active luciferase. Taking the intensity of light emission proportional to the velocity of the luminescent reaction gives

$$I = bk'[L][E_n] \tag{72}$$

where b is the proportionality constant. Introducing the temperature effect we write upon substitution of k' that

$$I = \frac{bk'[L][E_0]}{1 + K_1} = \frac{b\kappa(kT/h)K^{\ddagger}[L][E_0]}{1 + K_1} \tag{73}$$

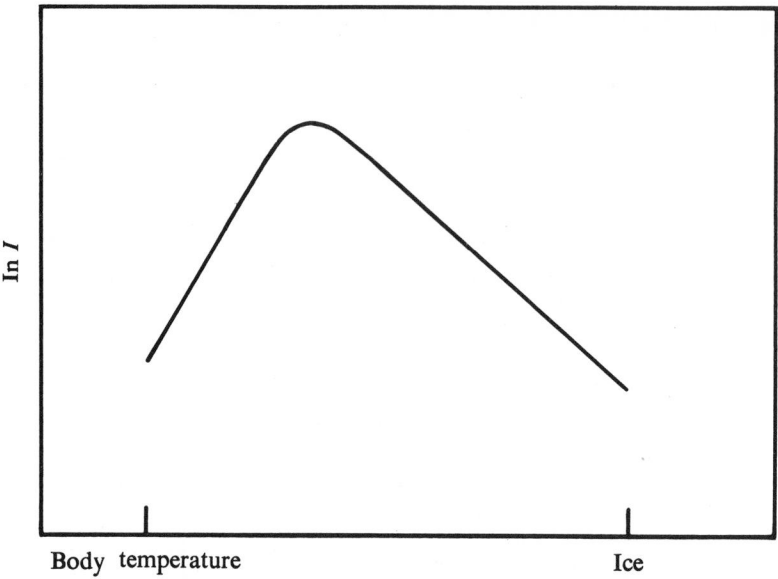

FIGURE 2. A representative plot of the luminescent intensity, I, against the reciprocal of the absolute temperature. A maximum intensity is observed between 0°C and body temperature. The ultimate decline of rate with increasing temperature is due to denaturation of the enzymes involved.

Now replacing $K^{\ddagger}$ and K_1 by their definitions yields

$$I = \frac{b\kappa(kT/h)e^{-\Delta H^{\ddagger}/RT}e^{\Delta S^{\ddagger}/R}[L][E_0]}{1 + e^{-\Delta H_1/RT}e^{\Delta S_1/R}} \tag{74}$$

When considering the temperature effects, Equation (74) may be rewritten as

$$I = \frac{cTe^{-\Delta H^{\ddagger}/RT}}{1 + e^{-\Delta H_1/RT}e^{\Delta S_1/R}} \tag{75}$$

If one plots the intensity of luminescence, I, against the reciprocal of the temperature, a curve with a maximum is obtained. A representative curve is given in Figure 2. One then fits the curve by choosing appropriate values of $\Delta H^{\ddagger}$, ΔH_1, and ΔS_1.

In order to get an idea of the magnitude of the values, the slopes and optimal temperatures are considered. Taking the logarithm of Equation (75) one obtains the equation in the following form

$$\ln I = \ln c + \ln T - \Delta H^{\ddagger}/RT - \ln(1 + e^{-\Delta H_1/RT}e^{\Delta S_1/R})$$

In the low temperature region, the slope is primarily $\Delta H^{\ddagger}/R$. In the high temperature region the slope is approximately $(-\Delta H^{\ddagger} + \Delta H_1)/R$ because the one in the logarithmic term on the right in the above equation becomes negligible, that is,

$$\ln(1 + e^{-\Delta H_1/RT}e^{\Delta S_1/R}) \cong \ln(e^{-\Delta H_1/RT}e^{\Delta S_1/R}) = \frac{-\Delta H_1}{RT} + \frac{\Delta S_1}{R}$$

At the maximum $\dfrac{d \ln I}{dT} = 0$ giving

$$RT_{\text{max}} + \Delta H^{\ddagger} - \frac{K_{T_{\text{max}}} \Delta H_1}{1 + K_{T_{\text{max}}}} = 0$$

or

$$K_{T_{\text{max}}} = \frac{\Delta H^{\ddagger} + RT_{\text{max}}}{\Delta H_1 - \Delta H^{\ddagger} - RT_{\text{max}}}$$
$$= e^{-\Delta H_1/RT_{\text{max}}} e^{\Delta S_1/RT_{\text{max}}}$$

Thus with approximate values of $\Delta H^{\ddagger}$ and ΔH_1, an approximate value of ΔS_1 is obtained. These approximate values are then varied to give the best fit for the experimental curve. In the case of the luminescent bacterium *Achromobacter fischeri* the curve is fit very well by the values

$$\Delta H^{\ddagger} = 34 \text{ kcal/mole}, \qquad \Delta H_1 = 80 \text{ kcal/mole}$$

$$\Delta S_1 = 266 \text{ cal/deg mole}, \qquad c = 0.587 \, e^{56.7}$$

In the above case the concentrations of neither substrate nor enzyme were known since the whole cell was being used. When these quantities are known, $\Delta S^{\ddagger}$ may also be determined and some information relative to mechanism is obtained.

3. *Pressure effects on chemical reactions.* The basic thermodynamic form of the rate equation is Equation (65). When pressure is introduced as a variable it becomes necessary to see how $\Delta F^{\ddagger}$ varies with changes in pressure. By the definition of free energy we have

$$F = H - TS = E + PV - TS$$

By taking the total differential we get

$$dF = dE + p\, dV + V\, dp - T\, dS - S\, dT$$

But the total differential of E is given in Equation (22) in which case the above equation becomes

$$dF = V\, dp - S\, dT \tag{76}$$

By rewriting Equation (76) for the activated state

$$dF^{\ddagger} = V^{\ddagger}\, dp - S^{\ddagger}\, dT$$

and taking the difference results in

$$d\,\Delta F^{\ddagger} = \Delta V^{\ddagger}\, dp - \Delta S^{\ddagger}\, dT$$

where $\Delta F^{\ddagger} = F^{\ddagger} - F$ etc. We can now write the change in $\Delta F^{\ddagger}$ with changes in pressure at constant temperature, that is,

$$\left(\frac{\partial \, \Delta F^{\ddagger}}{\partial p} \right)_T = \Delta V^{\ddagger}$$

So that for a range of pressure the total change in free energy $\Delta F_t^{\ddagger}$ is the change in free energy at a reference pressure plus the change in free energy integrated from the reference pressure p_1 to some higher pressure p_2, or in equation form

$$\Delta F_t^{\ddagger} = \Delta F^{\ddagger} + \int_{p_1}^{p_2} \left(\frac{\partial \, \Delta F}{\partial p} \right)_T dp = \Delta F^{\ddagger} + \int_{p_1}^{p_2} \Delta V^{\ddagger}\, dp$$
$$\Delta F_t^{\ddagger} = \Delta F^{\ddagger} + \overline{\Delta V^{\ddagger}}(p_2 - p_1)$$

where the last equality was obtained by assuming an average value of $\Delta V^{\ddagger}$, that is, $\overline{\Delta V^{\ddagger}}$, and integrating from p_1 up to p_2. We may now write Equation (65) to include the effect of pressure on the rate constant

$$k'_p = \kappa \frac{kT}{h} e^{-\Delta F^{\ddagger}/RT} e^{-\overline{\Delta V^{\ddagger}}(p_2-p_1)/RT} = k'e^{-\overline{\Delta V^{\ddagger}}(p_2-p_1)/RT}$$

where k' is the specific rate constant at the reference pressure which would usually be one atmosphere. Similarly, pressure also affects the equilibrium constants, and we can write by analogy that

$$K_p = K_1 e^{-\overline{\Delta V_1}(p_2-p_1)/RT}$$

Usually the higher pressure is several hundred and often several thousand pounds/in² so that $p_1 = 1$ is negligible when subtracted from p_2 and the above equations simplify to

$$k'_p = k'e^{-p_2\overline{\Delta V^{\ddagger}}/RT} \tag{77}$$

$$K_p = K_1 e^{-p_2\overline{\Delta V_1}/RT} \tag{78}$$

4. *Pressure effects on bioluminescence.* With the preceding considerations, the intensity of the luminescent reaction, Equation (75), (including pressure as a variable) becomes

$$I = \frac{cTe^{-\Delta H^{\ddagger}/RT}e^{-p_2\overline{\Delta V^{\ddagger}}/RT}}{1 + e^{-\Delta H_1/RT}e^{\Delta S_1/RT}e^{-p_2\overline{\Delta V_1}/RT}} \tag{79}$$

It has been experimentally determined that the luminescent intensity decreases with increasing pressure in the low temperature region, but in the high temperature range, pressure increases the luminescent intensity. In the high temperature range (at temperatures higher than the optimal temperature) we have seen that the primary effect is one of denaturation of the enzyme. The fact that pressure increases the output of light in the high temperature range suggests, upon looking at Equation (79), that $\overline{\Delta V_1}$ is positive. In the low temperature region the rate is decreased, suggesting that the activated complex of luciferin-luciferase is more voluminous than its components, that is, $\overline{\Delta V^{\ddagger}}$ is positive. The values which fit the experimental curve for cells of the luminescent bacterium *Photobacterium phosphoreum* are

$$\Delta H^{\ddagger} = 17.2 \text{ kcal/mole} \qquad \overline{\Delta V^{\ddagger}} = (546 + 1.81\ T) \text{ cc/mole}$$

$$\Delta H_1 = 55.3 \text{ kcal/mole} \qquad \overline{\Delta V_1} = (-923 + 3.21\ T) \text{ cc/mole}$$

$$\Delta S_1 = 184 \text{ cal/deg mole}$$

The ΔV's are also a function of the temperature. With this temperature dependence included, the theoretical curves fit the data rather well.

5. *Sulfanilamide inhibition of luminescence.* A very small amount of sulfanilamide will cause bacterial luminescence to cease. We can now readily treat this effect. Proceeding along the same vein as before, we need to enumerate the possible states in which the total amount of enzyme may be found. The resulting equation is called a conservation equation.

$$[E_0] = [E_n] + [E_d] + [E_nS_s] + [E_dS_s] \tag{80}$$

where S stands for sulfanilamide and the subscript s stands for the number of sulfanilamide molecules attached to the enzyme in the native, E_n, and the denatured, E_d, states. There are in this system the following equilibria:

$$E_n \rightleftharpoons E_d \qquad K_1 = [E_d]/[E_n]$$

$$E_n + sS \rightleftharpoons E_nS_s \qquad K_2 = [E_nS_s]/[E_n][S]^s$$

$$E_d + sS \rightleftharpoons E_dS_s \qquad K_2 = [E_dS_s]/[E_d][S]^s$$

That is, the experimental data is explained when assuming the same equilibrium constant for the last two reactions. The total enzyme concentration, Equation (80), may now be re-written in terms of the native enzyme

$$[E_0] = [E_n] + K_1[E_n] + K_2[E_n][S]^s + K_1K_2[E_n][S]^s$$
$$= [E_n](1 + K_1 + K_2[S]^s + K_1K_2[S]^s)$$

Substitution of $[E_n]$ from the above equation into Equation (72) gives

$$I_s = \frac{bk'[L][E_0]}{(1 + K_1 + K_2[S]^s + K_1K_2[S]^s)} = \frac{bk'[L][E_0]}{(1 + K_1)(1 + K_2[S]^s)} \tag{81}$$

where the I_s stands for luminescent intensity in the presence of sulfanilamide. Taking the ratio of I/I_s and using Equation (73) provide us with a very simple relation

$$\frac{I}{I_s} = 1 + K_2[S]^s, \qquad \frac{I}{I_s} - 1 = K_2[S]^s = [S]^s e^{-\Delta H_2/RT} e^{\Delta S_2/R}$$

$$\ln\left(\frac{I}{I_s} - 1\right) \equiv \ln \Gamma_2 = s \ln [S] - \frac{\Delta H_2}{R}\frac{1}{T} + \frac{\Delta S_2}{R}$$

By plotting $\ln \Gamma_2$ against the reciprocal of temperature, ΔH_2 can be determined from the slope ($= \Delta H_2/R$); by plotting $\ln \Gamma_2$ against $\ln [S]$, the number of sulfanilamide molecules can be determined. With the knowledge of s, the intercept of the first plot can be solved to obtain ΔS_2 (Intercept $= \Delta S_2/R + s \ln [S]$). In *Photobacterium phosphoreum*, ΔH_2 was found to be about 12.0 kcal and s was one, that is, one molecule of sulfanilamide combines with and inhibits the enzyme.

6. *Effects of denaturing agents on luminescence.* Many compounds such as alcohol, acetone, ether, and urethane interact with proteins in such a way as to denature them. These lipid soluble substances alter the tertiary structure of enzymes by disrupting their hydrophobic clusters. Alcohol, for example, presents its oily ethyl group to the oily groups of the protein and its OH group to the water, allowing the hydrophobic clusters to disperse. Again our approach is one of writing a conservation equation for the total amount of enzyme present.

$$[E_0] = [E_n] + [E_d] + [E_dX_r] \tag{82}$$

where X represents the alcohol molecule and r is the number of molecules attached to the denatured enzyme. By following the same procedure as with sulfanilamide, we write the equilibria:

$$E_n \rightleftharpoons E_d \qquad K_1 = [E_d]/[E_n]$$

$$rX + E_d \rightleftharpoons E_dX_r \qquad K_3 = [E_dX_r]/[E_d][X]^r$$

A fourth term in Equation (82) was also considered, as was a third equilibrium involving the $E_n X_r$ species, but when included the data were not properly fitted. Equation (82) now becomes

$$[E_0] = [E_n](1 + K_1 + K_1 K_3 [X]^r)$$

Substituting $[E_n]$ into Equation (72) gives

$$I_r = \frac{bk'[L][E_0]}{(1 + K_1 + K_1 K_3 [X]^r)}$$

where I_r stands for the luminescent intensity in the presence of alcohol. Formation of the ratio I/I_r results in

$$\frac{I}{I_r} = \frac{1 + K_1 + K_1 K_3 [X]^r}{1 + K_1} = 1 + \frac{K_1 K_3}{1 + K_1}[X]^r$$

$$\left(\frac{I}{I_r} - 1\right)\left(\frac{1 + K_1}{K_1}\right) \equiv \varphi = K_3 [X]^r = [X]^r e^{-\Delta H_3/RT} e^{\Delta S_3/R}$$

$$\ln \varphi = r \ln [X] - \frac{\Delta H_3}{RT} + \frac{\Delta S_3}{R} \tag{83}$$

The data are plotted exactly as was done with sulfanilamide and the values are determined. Here the number of alcohol molecules r on the enzyme varies with temperature from 2 to 4, and the heats of reaction vary with concentration of the denaturing agent from 50 to 60 kcal. It is also possible to introduce the pressure effect in which case

$$K_{p3} = K_3 e^{-p\overline{\Delta V}/RT}$$

and Equation (83) may be written as

$$\ln \varphi = r \ln [X] - \frac{\Delta F_3}{RT} - \frac{p\overline{\Delta V}}{RT} \tag{84}$$

An increase in pressure favors the native enzyme and can reestablish luminescence in bacteria that have had their light extinguished by alcohol.

Ambystoma larvae when put in 2.5% alcohol go into a drunken stupor, but are rapidly sobered and actively swimming with an increase of pressure to 2000 pounds per square inch. When the pressure is released they rapidly return to the drunken state and the second time the pressure is applied, 3000 psi are required to sober these immature salamanders.

C. Stereochemistry and Kinetics in Protein Synthesis[7]

The current concept of protein synthesis is one of amino acid activation,* transfer to an adaptor which interprets the genetic code, alignment of the adaptors on a template, and condensation into polypeptide linkage. The amino acid is activated by its specific activating enzyme through the formation of a carboxyl phosphate bond. The energy is supplied by adenosine triphosphate (ATP) and the activated amino acid is the aminoacyl adenylate (aminoacyl-AMP). The specific activating enzyme then recognizes a postulated triplet of purines and pyrimidines of soluble ribonucleic acid (sRNA) and transfers the activated amino acid to the terminus of sRNA to form aminoacyl-sRNA. The attachment to the

---

* This is another use of the term "activated" which is consistent with usage by biochemists and the preceding development of reaction rates. An activated amino acid is a stable, though relatively high energy, intermediate in protein synthesis, whereas an activated complex in general is an unstable, transitory intermediate between relatively stable molecular species.

sRNA is by an amino acid ester linkage to the 2'- or 3'-hydroxyl of the terminal adenosine of sRNA, the hydroxyl being part of the ribose of adenosine. The amino acid-charged sRNA then leaves the activating enzyme and diffuses to the ribosomes where it aligns, presumably by base pairing, on a messenger ribonucleic acid (mRNA).

In the process of polymerization an additional energy requirement is noted. Though the mechanism of peptide bond formation is obscure, mRNA is a large, freshly synthesized ribonucleic acid whose sequence of bases appears to have been determined by the genetic material, deoxyribonucleic acid (DNA). With the DNA setting down a specific sequence of bases in mRNA, and with the proposed triplet of bases in sRNA aligning on the mRNA template, specific proteins can be formed.

This entire process is carried out with surprising restriction on the particular optical isomers involved. Only α-amino acids of the L-configuration with an α-hydrogen are incorporated into protein and only β-D-ribofuranose is found in the ribonucleic acids.

1. *Stereochemistry of the amino acid activating process.* A given amino acid activating enzyme is specific for its particular amino acid. That is, there is a special enzyme for activating tyrosines, a second for phenylalanines, etc., one for each amino acid. The same specificity holds for recognizing the particular sRNA to which the activated amino acid is transferred. Both the activation and transfer to sRNA occur on the same enzyme surface.

For this type of specificity it is required that the activating enzyme intimately interact with and identify the R group of the amino acid. Also an argument can be developed to show that the enzyme must be in contact with the $-NH_3^+$ of the amino acid in its zwitterion form. Furthermore, since the enzyme is catalyzing the activation of the carboxyl group and the transfer of the acyl portion to sRNA, it must intimately interact with the carbon of the carboxyl group. In other words, the amino acid must contact the enzyme surface with three of the four substituents of the α-carbon. This is most readily accomplished by having the three corners of the tetrahedron in contact with the enzyme, leaving the fourth, the hydrogen atom, pointing away from the enzyme surface. At the same time the amino acid must be in a position to be transferred to the terminus of sRNA. All this occurs on the same enzyme surface.

If one examines the activation and transfer process with molecular models of aminoacyl adenylate and the terminal adenosine (ribose and adenine) of sRNA, one finds that the transfer to sRNA would have less steric hindrance when the α-hydrogen of the amino acid is directed into the pit on the α side of the terminal ribose of sRNA as the activated acyl group is being transferred to either the 2' or 3' OH of that ribose. The resulting amino acid-charged sRNA has a very interesting interaction between the amino acid and ribose. It can readily be seen that this interaction would demand a substituent no larger than a hydrogen on the α-carbon of the amino acid and also it requires that the sugar be β-D-ribofuranose. The L configuration of ribose cannot interact in this way. Thus this interaction would explain the restriction of optical isomers. In addition, it could explain on the basis of steric strain why the resulting amino acid ester is a bond with as high an energy as the inner phosphate anhydrous bond of ATP. That it is high energy is shown by the fact that the equilibrium constant for the over-all reaction is approximately one, that is, $\Delta F \simeq 0$ for the reaction.

2. *Reaction rates and protein synthesis.* The effect of an enzyme, or any catalyst, is to lower the necessary free energy of activation required for a given reaction. This is accomplished by allowing for lower energy electronic transitions. Figure 3 depicts the effect graphically in terms of free energy and reaction coordinate. The dotted line stands for the

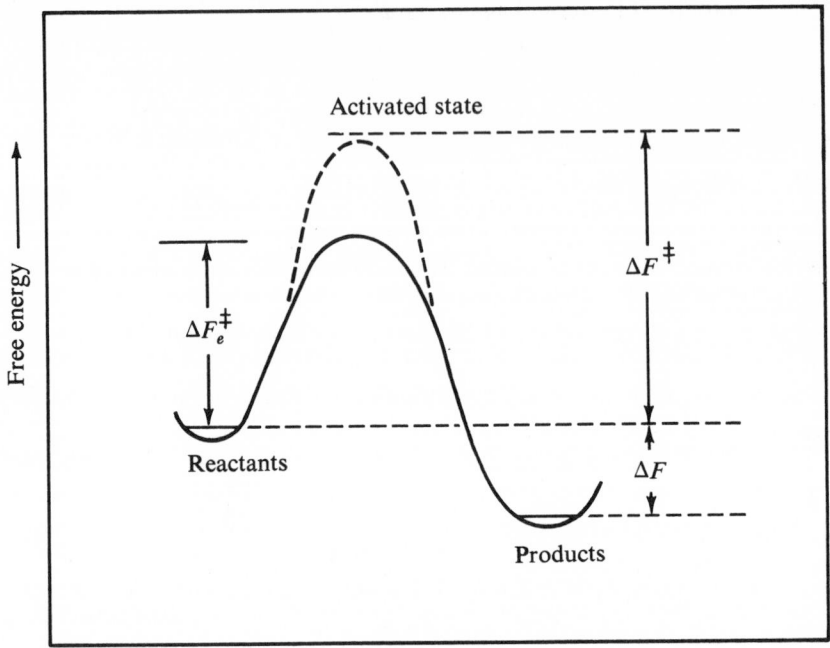

Reaction coordinate

FIGURE 3.   A schematic diagram of the free-energy changes in going from reactants to products. The solid curve represents the enzyme-directed reaction; the dotted curve describes the additional free energy required for the nonenzymatic reaction. ΔF, which controls the equilibrium concentrations, is the same in both cases.

nonenzymatic free energy changes and the solid line describes the enzyme catalyzed reaction. The stereochemistry of the amino acid activating process is quite readily demonstrated by a schematic plot of free energy changes incurred by an amino acid during the course of activation and transfer to sRNA (Figure 4).

The over-all activation reaction may be written as follows:

$$\text{amino acid} + \text{ATP} + \text{sRNA} \rightleftharpoons \text{aminoacyl-sRNA} + \text{AMP} + \text{PP}_i$$

As mentioned above, the equilibrium constant is approximately one; that is,

$$K = e^{-\Delta F/RT} \simeq 1$$

Therefore, $\Delta F \simeq 0$, indicating that the initial and final states are at the same height on the free energy scale. With reference to Figure 4, position 1 is the initial state of free amino acid, ATP, and sRNA; position 9 is the final state of free aminoacyl-sRNA, AMP, and inorganic pyrophosphate (PP_i). Regardless of the amino acid a salt linkage could be formed by passing over a low-energy barrier to a slightly lower free-energy level at position 3. Before the amino acid can be activated the enzyme must interact intimately with the R group of the amino acid, this being the requirement of specificity. At position 5 the amino acid is in contact with the enzyme surface at both its NH_3^+ group and R group.

After having surmounted the first two energy barriers, that is, passed the specificity tests, the amino acid is in position to be activated. The peak at position 6 represents the free energy required to form the activated state which results in the activated amino acid being bound to the enzyme surface as the aminoacyl adenylate at position 7. The aminoacyl moiety is then transferred to sRNA by ascending the barrier indicated by numeral 8 and resulting in products at position 9. The peak at position 10 symbolizes the energy required to distort a wrong amino acid so that it would be in position for activation by the enzyme. Such distortion energy would probably be greater than the nonenzymatic activation energy and would not be expected to occur. Assuming the amino acid-sugar interaction described in the preceding section to be correct, the peak of position 11 would be the energy required to distort an L-ribose sufficiently to allow transfer to it. Again the distortion energy would be prohibitive.

3. *Reaction rates and error in protein synthesis.* It is of interest to consider statistical error in the amino acid activating process. The selectivity for an amino acid appears to reside solely with its corresponding activating enzyme. The question is, how often does an amino acid activating enzyme activate the wrong amino acid? The question in terms of reaction rate theory becomes, how much higher must the peak at position 4 of Figure 4 be so that activation of the wrong amino acid will be minimized? Two amino acids which would be particularly difficult to distinguish are valine and isoleucine. If the valine activating enzyme is so specific that it makes but one error in every 100 activations, the difference in the free energies of activation at 37°C would be 2.8 kcal.

This would be the case if isoleucine could fit on the surface of the enzyme for valine with an additional energy requirement of 2.8 kcal to distort the R group of isoleucine sufficiently to allow its carboxyl group to come into position to be activated. If the selection is such that only one error is made in the synthesis of ten molecules of myoglobin, then the peak at position 4 would need to be 4.4 kcal greater. This situation is helped somewhat since

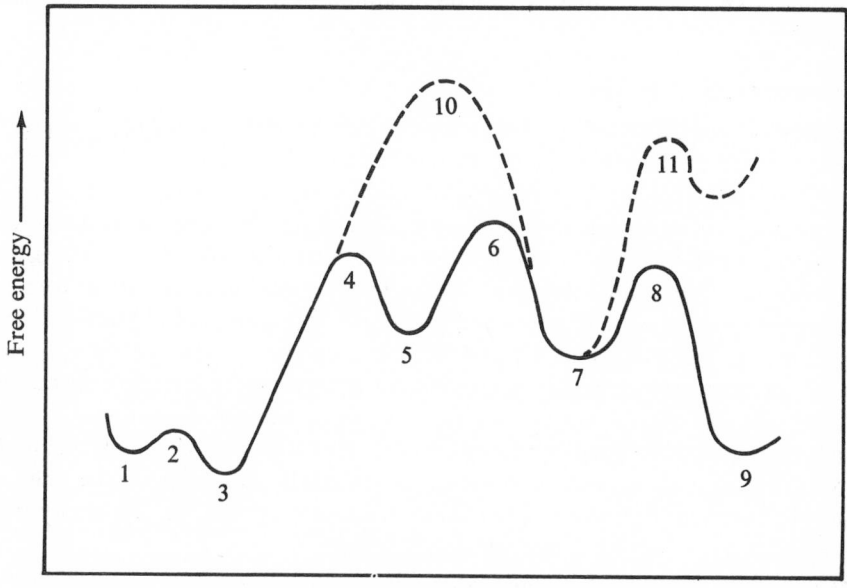

FIGURE 4. A schematic diagram of the free-energy changes expected in the amino acid activating process for protein synthesis. The significance of the maxima and minima 1–11 is discussed in the text.

Berg[1] has shown that during the transfer to sRNA the R group of the amino acid continues to be held, suggesting that peak 8 is also higher for the wrong amino acid. However, the same considerations apply to the transfer process and the highest peak will be the controlling factor. There is additional chance for error in the aligning process. It will be of interest when the polymerization process is better understood to consider the possibility of an error in the base pairing. Both of the above statistical errors could be considered somatic mutations.

4. *Statistical error as a general phenomenon in biological systems.** Whenever one is faced with a selective chemical process, the accuracy of that process depends, of course, on the difference in the energy requirement of the desired result as compared to that of other possible results. One would have to assume that, depending on the method of selection, there is a statistical genetic mutation rate; that is, a nonagent-induced mutation rate which is dependent on the rigorousness of the selective process.† One would also expect that, as the accuracy increased, the over-all rate would decrease because of the intimate nature of the selection. If the R group of the amino acid fits as hand in glove this would require a higher activation energy, and even though it would preclude error it would slow the over-all process.

Similar considerations must hold for the base pairing that is considered part of DNA duplication. In order that greater accuracy be obtained one would be constrained to consider a more selective, higher energy process than the few kilocalories involved in base pairing. The point that is being stressed is that one would expect a statistical mutation rate independent of radiation or mutagens and dependent on the selectivity of the enzyme. These considerations would explain why certain species, with a given set of enzymes directing the genetic duplication, are prone to more or less rapid change. An explanation for the dead-ending of species and for straight-line evolution may also be inherent in such considerations.

D. *Universality of Rate Theory*[2,4]

The validity of the theory of absolute reaction rates can be attested to by its applicability to a great variety of diverse systems. In fact, using rate theory as a basis, many well-established relations can be derived, and in many cases these familiar relationships are limiting situations of a more general rate expression. Rate theory has been the keystone in the development of a theory of overvoltage, a relaxation theory of creep in metals, a theory of non-Newtonian flow, and a theory of viscosity and of self-diffusion. It has been applied in discussing the mass spectra of polyatomic molecules, in treating the physical and chemical properties of high polymers, and in formulating expressions for electrochemical processes. In general, processes which require an activation energy can be treated with rate theory, and if such systems are further complicated by application of shear forces or electrical potentials they can still be handily treated. Simple derivations of Bose-Einstein and Fermi-Dirac statistics as well as formulations of intermediate statistics can be achieved by starting with the theory of absolute reaction rates. As examples we will briefly treat two related applications which have biological significance.

1. *Steady state reaction networks: diffusion through membranes.*[3,6,8] Diffusion like many other physical processes may be described in terms of random walk. In random

---

* Compare with Introduction to Section III and Chapter 12.
† Genetics and natural selection are discussed *in extenso* in Chapter 15.

walk a particle moves in one direction until an obstacle or barrier is encountered. Once the particle has come to a stable state, such as a minimum, it is completely forgetful of its origin. Diffusion through membranes is a random walk process. In this case we have a three-dimensional molecular lattice and we may, in generality, consider this type of diffusion as a network of possible motions in all allowed directions, forward, backward, and sidewise at various angles. As we are interested in the penetration of the membrane we take an x axis perpendicular to the plane of the membrane and measure progress as positive on this axis. If z is the total number of neighboring positions, then on the average $z/2$ positions will advance the particle. The distance traveled due to a single jump is λ_i' and $\lambda_i' \cos \theta_i$ becomes the effective distance of further penetration of the membrane, that is, the distance measured along the x axis where θ_i is measured from the x axis. Upon taking k_i to be the rate constant, the velocity in the forward direction, u_i, becomes

$$u_i = \sum_i \lambda_i' k_i \cos \theta_i = \frac{z}{2} \lambda_i' \langle \cos \theta \rangle k_i \equiv \lambda_i k_i$$

where $\lambda_i = z/2\, \lambda_i' \langle \cos \theta_i \rangle$ is the average distance traveled with each move.

Figure 5 is representative of the free-energy barriers which a particle would encounter in the process of diffusing through the network just described. Using the notation in Figure 5, the net flow of particles from the outside of the membrane is

$$J_0 = C_0 \lambda_0 k_0 - C_1 \lambda_1 k_1'$$

where C_0, the concentration of particles outside the membrane, has been multiplied by $\lambda_0 k_0$, the velocity with which these particles flow into the first position within the membrane, and C_1, the concentration of particles in the first position has been multiplied by $\lambda_1 k_1'$, the velocity with which the particles return to the outside of the membrane. J_0 is, therefore,

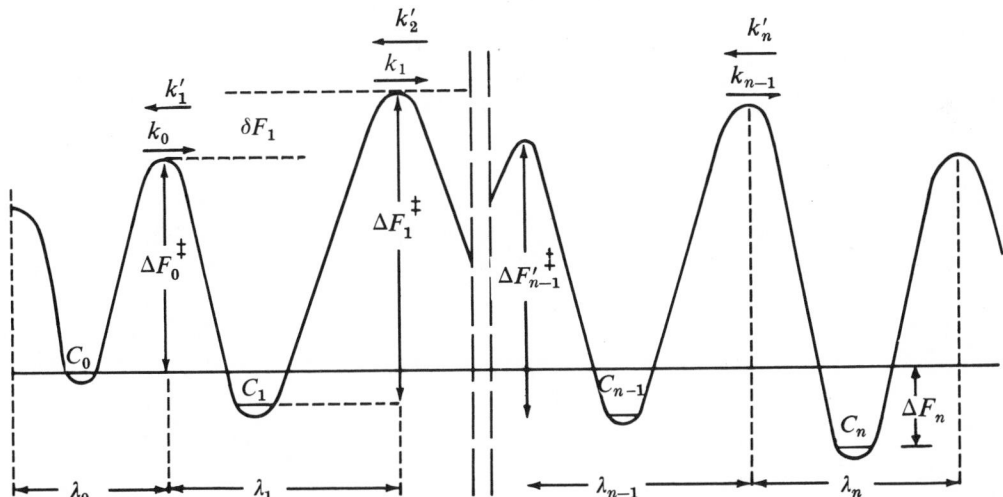

FIGURE 5. A representative plot of a series of free-energy barriers encountered in a process such as diffusion through membranes. The C_i are the concentrations of diffusing material at the respective minima. The k_i are the specific rate constants in the forward directions, the k_i' for the backward motion. The distances between barriers in the membrane are designated by the λ_i. The differences between maxima referred back to the first barrier are the δF_i. The $\Delta F_i^{\ddagger}$ are the free energies of activation, and ΔF_n is the difference in free energy between the outside and inside of the membrane.

the net flow of particles inward over the first barrier. The net inward flow of particles passing the second barrier is

$$J_1 = C_1\lambda_1 k_1 - C_2\lambda_2 k_2'$$

But if we invoke the steady state condition, the flow or flux of particles over each barrier is the same, and we can write the following set of equations (one for each barrier)

$$
\begin{aligned}
J &= C_0\lambda_0 k_0 - C_1\lambda_1 k_1' \\
J &= \qquad\quad C_1\lambda_1 k_1 - C_2\lambda_2 k_2' \\
J &= \qquad\qquad\qquad C_2\lambda_2 k_2 - C_3\lambda_3 k_3' \\
&\ \ \cdot \qquad\qquad\qquad\qquad\quad \cdot \\
&\ \ \cdot \qquad\qquad\qquad\qquad\quad \cdot \\
&\ \ \cdot \qquad\qquad\qquad\qquad\quad \cdot \\
J &= \qquad\qquad\qquad C_{n-1}\lambda_{n-1} k_{n-1} - C_n\lambda_n k_n'
\end{aligned}
\tag{85}
$$

Upon multiplying the second equation by $\dfrac{k_1'}{k_1}$, the third by $\dfrac{k_1'k_2'}{k_1k_2}$, etc., and the last by $\dfrac{k_1'k_2'\ldots k_{n-1}'}{k_1k_2\ldots k_{n-1}}$ and adding, the following result is obtained:

$$
J = \frac{C_0\lambda_0 k_0 - C_n\lambda_n \dfrac{k_1'k_2'\ldots k_{n-1}'k_n'}{k_1k_2\ldots k_{n-1}}}{1 + \dfrac{k_1'}{k_1} + \dfrac{k_1'k_2'}{k_1k_2} + \ldots + \dfrac{k_1'k_2'\ldots k_{n-1}'}{k_1k_2\ldots k_{n-1}}}
\tag{86}
$$

For the case where all of the barriers are the same, i.e., $k_0 = k_1 = k_2\ldots$ and $\lambda_0 = \lambda_n$

$$
J = \frac{\lambda_0 k_0 (C_0 - C_n)}{n}
\tag{87}
$$

where n is the number of barriers encountered in passing through the membrane. If τ is the thickness of the membrane then the diffusion coefficient D and the permeability P are

$$
D = \frac{\lambda_0 k_0 \tau}{n} \quad \text{and} \quad P = \frac{k_0 \lambda_0}{n} = \frac{D}{\tau}
\tag{88}
$$

By taking the thermodynamic form of the specific rate constant (Equation 65) as the expression for the k's and k''s the following identifications are made:

$$
k_0 = \kappa\,\frac{kT}{h}\,e^{-\Delta F_0^{\ddagger}/RT}
$$

$$
\frac{k_1'}{k_1} = \frac{\kappa\,\dfrac{kT}{h}\,e^{-\Delta F_1'^{\ddagger}/RT}}{\kappa\,\dfrac{kT}{h}\,e^{-\Delta F_1^{\ddagger}/RT}} = e^{-(\Delta F_1'^{\ddagger} - \Delta F_1^{\ddagger})/RT} \equiv e^{\delta F_1^{\ddagger}/RT}
$$

$$
\frac{k_1'k_2'}{k_1k_2} = e^{-(\Delta F_1'^{\ddagger} + \Delta F_2'^{\ddagger} - \Delta F_1^{\ddagger} - \Delta F_2^{\ddagger})/RT} \equiv e^{\delta F_2^{\ddagger}/RT}
$$

$$
\frac{k_1'k_2'\ldots k_{n-1}'k_n'}{k_0k_1k_2\ldots k_{n-1}} = e^{\Delta F_n/RT}
$$

where ΔF_n is that defined in Figure 5, the change in free energy between the outside and inside of the membrane. As drawn, ΔF_n would reflect a free energy of dilution with the molecular species at a higher concentration outside of the cell; that is, there is a concentration gradient favoring diffusion into the cell. Using the above relations and definitions, Equation (86) becomes

$$J = \kappa \frac{kT}{h} e^{-\Delta F_0^{\ddagger}/RT} \frac{C_0\lambda_0 - C_n\lambda_n e^{\Delta F_n/RT}}{1 + e^{\delta F_1^{\ddagger}/RT} + e^{\delta F_2^{\ddagger}/RT} + \ldots + e^{\delta F_{n-1}^{\ddagger}/RT}} \tag{89}$$

Equation (89) represents the net flow of particles through a neutral membrane. As biological membranes have a potential across them it is pertinent to consider this effect.

Let us now treat the case of an applied potential imposed on a system which initially had equal and equidistant maxima with no change in free energy in going from outside to inside the membrane. The effect of an applied potential on a single barrier is to change the relative heights of the initial and final states; the free energy of the initial state is changed by a given amount and that of the final state is also changed by the same amount but in the opposite direction; the free energy of activation is increased in one direction and decreased in the other direction and by the same amount.

When a potential E is applied to a series of n barriers with electroneutrality between the initial and final states, and $\Delta F_0^{0\ddagger}$ is the free energy of activation in the absence of a field, then the free energy of activation in the presence of a field, $\Delta F_i^{\ddagger}$, is

$$\Delta F_i^{\ddagger} = \Delta F_0^{0\ddagger} + \frac{(2i + 1)}{2n} z\mathscr{F}E$$

and

$$\Delta F_n = z\mathscr{F}E$$

where z is the valence of the ion, $\mathscr{F}$ is the faraday, and $i = 0, 1, 2, \ldots, n - 1$. By making the substitutions that

$$x = e^{z\mathscr{F}E/nRT}$$

and k_0^0 is the specific rate constant for the first barrier in the absence of a field, Equation (89) becomes

$$J = \frac{\lambda_0 k_0^0 x^{-\frac{1}{2}}(C_0 - C_n x^n)}{1 + x + x^2 + \ldots + x^{n-1}} = \frac{\lambda_0 k_0^0 x^{-\frac{1}{2}}(1 - x)(C_0 - C_n x^n)}{1 - x^n}$$

Multiplication of both numerator and denominator of the above equation by $x^{-n/2}$ gives

$$J = \lambda_0 k_0^0 \frac{(x^{-\frac{1}{2}} - x^{\frac{1}{2}})(C_0 x^{-n/2} - C_n x^{n/2})}{(x^{-n/2} - x^{n/2})} \tag{90}$$

Expanding the exponentials in a Taylor's series and considering the case where $z\mathscr{F}E$ is smaller than RT, we have

$$g/n \equiv \frac{x^{-\frac{1}{2}} - x^{\frac{1}{2}}}{x^{-n/2} - x^{n/2}} \simeq \frac{1}{n} \tag{91}$$

so that

$$\lambda_0 k_0^0 g/n \simeq \frac{\lambda_0 k_0^0}{n} \equiv P,$$

giving the useful relation

$$J = P(C_0 e^{-z\mathscr{F}E/2RT} - C_n e^{z\mathscr{F}E/2RT}), \tag{92}$$

that is, the flow of particles is proportional to the permeability. Consistent with the approximation in Equation (91), the exponentials may be expanded. Keeping the first two terms in the expansion, we have the following result

$$J = P\left[(C_0 - C_n) - \tfrac{1}{2}(C_0 + C_n)\frac{z\mathscr{F}E}{RT}\right] \tag{93}$$

Equation (93) has been applied to membrane phenomena in connection with muscle contraction and nerve impulses.[3]

2. *Irreversible thermodynamics: active transport and the coupling of chemical reactions.*[2] The activated complex is identical in all respects regardless of whether it arose by the forward reaction or by the backward reaction. Those complexes which arise from reactants exist and continue on to products unaware of the presence or absence of complexes that may have arisen from products. Thus one would expect that absolute rate theory is equally applicable to nonequilibrium systems. Absolute rate theory reduces to the familiar expressions of irreversible thermodynamics by giving rise to the Onsager reciprocity relations at the limit of slight displacements from equilibrium.

As an example, we may consider the active transport of an ion, such as sodium, through the cell membrane.* In this case it is convenient to use activities in Equation (93) rather than concentrations. The activity, a, is used in order to retain the simple forms of equations for ideal solutions. The correction factor for nonideality, γ, is called the activity coefficient. It corrects the analytical concentrations to activities or effective concentrations. A standard state is chosen at which concentrations become equal to activities, i.e., $\gamma = 1$, but as the concentrations of electrolytes vary, interactions between the ions vary and effective concentrations change. By rewriting Equation (93) in terms of activities, and referring concentrations both inside and outside the cell membrane to the same standard state, we have

$$J = \frac{P}{\gamma_0}\left[(a_0 - a_n) - \tfrac{1}{2}(a_0 + a_n)\frac{z\mathscr{F}E}{RT}\right]$$

Furthermore, if we define an average activity as

$$\bar{a} = \tfrac{1}{2}(a_0 + a_n)$$

then

$$J = P^0\bar{a}\left(-\frac{\delta a}{\bar{a}} - \frac{z\mathscr{F}E}{RT}\right) \tag{94}$$

where $P^0 = P/\gamma_0$, $-\delta\bar{a} = a_0 - a_n$ and the P^0 used is that defined below Equation (91) but measured at the standard state where $\gamma_0 = 1$.

For open systems, systems in which the number of particles (ions in this case) can vary, it is useful to consider the change in a property, such as free energy, as a function of changes in the number of particles, n. This quantity, μ, is called the chemical potential and may be written in general as

$$\mu = \left(\frac{\partial F}{\partial n}\right)_{T,P}$$

but

$$\Delta\mu = \mu - \mu^0 = \left(\frac{\partial \Delta F}{\partial n}\right)_{T,P} = RT \ln \bar{a}$$

* Ionic conductances and related properties of axonal membranes are discussed extensively in Chapter 6.

where μ^0, a constant, is the chemical potential at some standard state in which $a = 1$. If we take a small variation in the chemical potential, $\delta\mu$, we have

$$\frac{\delta\mu}{RT} = \frac{\delta\bar{a}}{\bar{a}}$$

Substitution into Equation (94) yields

$$J = P^0\bar{a}\left(-\frac{\delta\mu}{RT} - \frac{z\mathscr{F}E}{RT}\right) \tag{95}$$

In the case of sodium extrusion from the cell we may consider that sodium combines with a carrier X giving the equilibrium relation

$$Na^+ + rX \rightleftharpoons Na^+X_r$$

where for complete generality r may be fractional or integral. We will designate Na^+, X, and Na^+X_r as 1, 2, and r, respectively. Then the flow of sodium ions is

$$J_1 = P_1^0\bar{a}_1\left(-\frac{\delta\mu_1}{RT} - \frac{z_1\mathscr{F}E}{RT}\right) + P_r^0\bar{a}_r\left(-\frac{\delta\mu_r}{RT} - \frac{z_r\mathscr{F}E}{RT}\right)$$

and for the carrier the flow is

$$J_2 = P_2^0\,\bar{a}_2\left(-\frac{\delta\mu_2}{RT}\right) + rP_r^0\bar{a}_r\left(-\frac{\delta\mu_r}{RT} - \frac{z_r\mathscr{F}E}{RT}\right)$$

However, for the above reaction the chemical potential at each point is

$$\mu_1 + r\mu_2 = \mu_r$$

so that from one side of the cell membrane to the other

$$\delta\mu_1 + r\,\delta\mu_2 = \delta\mu_r$$

With this relation J_1 and J_2 become

$$J_1 = (P_1^0\bar{a}_1 + P_r^0\bar{a}_r)\left(-\frac{\delta\mu_1}{RT}\right) + rP_r^0\bar{a}_r\left(-\frac{\delta\mu_2}{RT}\right) + (P_1^0\bar{a}_1z_1 + P_r^0\bar{a}_rz_r)\left(-\frac{\mathscr{F}E}{RT}\right) \tag{96}$$

$$J_2 = rP_r^0\bar{a}_r\left(-\frac{\delta\mu_1}{RT}\right) + (P_2^0\bar{a}_2 + r^2P_r^0\bar{a}_r)\left(-\frac{\delta\mu_2}{RT}\right) + (rP_r^0\bar{a}_rz_r)\left(-\frac{\mathscr{F}E}{RT}\right) \tag{97}$$

The flow of charge, J_3, is obtained by multiplying J_1 by $\mathscr{F}$ and the appropriate charge for each flux.

$$J_3 = \mathscr{F}(z_1P_1^0\bar{a}_1 + z_rP_r^0\bar{a}_r)\left(-\frac{\delta\mu_1}{RT}\right) + \mathscr{F}z_rrP_r^0\bar{a}_r\left(-\frac{\delta\mu_2}{RT}\right) + \mathscr{F}(z_1^2P_1^0\bar{a}_1 + z_r^2P_r^0\bar{a}_r)\left(-\frac{\mathscr{F}E}{RT}\right)$$

$$\tag{98}$$

For diffusion through a membrane of thickness τ we have for the change in the chemical potential

$$-\delta\mu_1 = \frac{d\mu_1}{dx}\tau = X_1\tau$$

$$-\delta\mu_2 = \frac{d\mu_2}{dx}\tau = X_2\tau$$

and for the applied potential

$$-E = -\frac{dE}{dx}\tau = X_3\tau$$

The above relations when substituted into the equations for J_1, J_2, and J_3 immediately yield Onsager's reciprocal relations.

$$J_1 = \frac{\tau}{RT}(P_1^0\bar{a}_1 + P_r^0\bar{a}_r)X_1 + \frac{\tau}{RT}rP_r^0\bar{a}_rX_2 + \frac{\tau\mathscr{F}}{RT}(P_1^0\bar{a}_1z_1 + P_r^0\bar{a}_rz_r)X_3$$

$$J_2 = \frac{\tau}{RT}rP_r^0\bar{a}_rX_1 + \frac{\tau}{RT}(P_2^0\bar{a}_2 + r^2P_r^0\bar{a}_r)X_2 + \frac{\tau\mathscr{F}}{RT}rP_r^0\bar{a}_rz_rX_3 \qquad (99)$$

$$J_3 = \frac{\tau\mathscr{F}}{RT}(z_1P_1^0\bar{a}_1 + z_rP_r^0\bar{a}_r)X_1 + \frac{\tau\mathscr{F}}{RT}rz_rP_r^0\bar{a}_rX_2 + \frac{\tau\mathscr{F}^2}{RT}(z_1^2P_1^0\bar{a}_1 + z_r^2P_r^0\bar{a}_r)X_3$$

And we see that in matrix form the coefficients are related, that is,

$$L_{12} = L_{21} = \frac{\tau}{RT}rP_r^0\bar{a}_r$$

$$L_{13} = L_{31} = \frac{\tau\mathscr{F}}{RT}(P_1^0\bar{a}_1z_1 + P_r^0\bar{a}_rz_r) \qquad (100)$$

and

$$L_{23} = L_{32} = \frac{\tau\mathscr{F}}{RT}rP_r^0\bar{a}_rz_r$$

Thus we see that rate theory gives rise to the reciprocity relations in the limit of small displacements from equilibrium. However, when the driving forces are large the approximate exponential expansions do not hold, nor do irreversible thermodynamics and the reciprocal relations. In such cases these should be abandoned in favor of the general reaction rate approach as formulated in Equation (89), which would be expected to apply for large displacements from equilibrium. Here we have another example of the universality of reaction rate theory.

There are many cases in biological systems where these considerations are applicable, any place where there is a coupling of sets of reactions which may or may not occur independently. Examples would be active transport, facilitated diffusion, and the coupling of oxidation and phosphorylation as in the respiratory chain.

IV. CONCLUSION

Thermodynamics and chemical kinetics have been approached from the point of view of statistical mechanics. A bridge between thermodynamics and statistical mechanics was established and expressions for the equilibrium constant and the rate of a reaction were obtained. Having formulated an expression for the rate of a chemical reaction, we saw that it could be cloaked in thermodynamic terms. Thus, it is possible to speak of free energy of activation, of enthalpy of activation, and of entropy of activation. Although free energy of activation controls the reaction rate, knowledge of the entropy of activation can be of particular use in determining the reaction mechanism. As the substrate binds to the enzyme surface it loses degrees of freedom. The more points of interaction on the enzyme surface, the greater this loss is. But these losses are reflected in entropy changes. The more restricted the substrate motion on the enzyme surface, the more negative $\Delta S^{\ddagger}$ will be. The magnitude of the entropy change will depend on the change in the number and type of degrees of freedom in going from solution to the activated state on the enzyme surface. As descriptions of solute in solution become increasingly accurate, this approach will become increasingly useful.

Descriptive information concerning the many metabolic pathways of biological systems is rapidly reaching an advanced stage and much productive effort is now being directed to the elucidation of enzyme mechanisms. It is in the determination of mechanism that thermodynamics and chemical kinetics can have their greatest utility. It is to be anticipated that each step in the manifold pathways can be described in terms of free-energy changes as the substrate and enzyme progress through their various stages of interaction and reaction.

REFERENCES

1. Berg, P., Bergmann, F. H., Ofengand, E. J., and Dieckmann, M. 1962. The enzymatic synthesis of aminoacyl derivatives of ribonucleic acid. I. The mechanism of leucyl-, valyl-, isoleucyl-, and methionyl ribonucleic acid formation. *J. Biol. Chem.* **236:** 1726–1734.
2. Eyring, H., Henderson, D., Stover, B. J., and Eyring, E. M. 1964. "Statistical Mechanics and Dynamics," 508 pp. Wiley, New York.
3. Eyring, H., Lumry, R., and Woodbury, J. W. 1949. Some applications of modern rate theory to physiological systems. *Record Chem. Progr.* (*Kresge-Hooker Sci. Lib.*) **10:** 100–114.
4. Glasstone, S., Laidler, K. J., and Eyring, H. 1941. "The Theory of Rate Processes," 611 pp. McGraw-Hill, New York.
5. Johnson, F. H., Eyring, H., and Polissar, M. J. 1954. "The Kinetic Basis of Molecular Biology," 874 pp. Wiley, New York.
6. Parlin, R. B., and Eyring, H. 1954. Membrane permeability and electrical potential. *In:* "Ion Transport across Membranes," (H. T. Clarke and D. Nachmansohn, eds.), pp. 103–118. Academic, New York.
7. Urry, D. W., and Eyring, H. 1962. Stereochemistry and rate theory in protein synthesis. *Arch. Biochem. Biophys.* Suppl. 1: 52–62.
8. Zwolinski, B. J., Eyring, H., and Reese, C. E. 1949. Diffusion and membrane permeability. I. *J. Phys. Colloid Chem.* **53:** 1426–1453.

[5]

MOLECULAR STRUCTURE, BIOCHEMICAL FUNCTION, AND EVOLUTION

J. D. Bernal

I. INTRODUCTION

Among the problems of biological structure, that of the structure of molecules occupies a central position and ties together the different disciplines, from chemistry to histology, that comprise modern biology. The development of molecular biology is one which I have been fortunate enough to follow from the start with the x-ray structural analyses of fibers, sterols, proteins, and viruses. I am not a biochemist or biophysicist but I have seen these disciplines split off from the older disciplines of organic chemistry, pharmacology, and physiology. Thirty years ago the suggestion of Casperssen[13] that nucleic acid might conceivably have something to do with protein production and even with the reproduction of organisms was derided by biologists and biochemists. At that time the very existence of a virus was in doubt. Some claimed that they had actually seen them as fine points of light in a photograph or on the fluorescent screen of an ultraviolet microscope, but to most competent scientists a virus particle could not exist. It was just a way of describing a filter-passing liquid agent. It was not even clear that enzymes were proteins or that these formed true crystals. From that stage of ignorance to our present stage of ignorance is quite a long way. The purpose of this chapter is to trace the relation of the new knowledge of the structure of these biological molecules to their functions and origins and thus to show in some measure how that gap is being filled.

II. THE NATURE OF BIOLOGY

A. Does Biology Exist?

We may begin by asking a question: does biology exist? I believe there is a radical difference, fundamentally a philosophical difference, between biology and the so-called exact or inorganic sciences, particularly physics. In the latter we postulate elementary particles which are necessary to the structure of the universe and that the laws controlling their movements and transformations are intrinsically necessary and in general hold over the whole universe.

Biology, however, deals with descriptions and ordering of very special parts of the universe which we call life—even more particularly in these days, terrestrial life. It is primarily a descriptive science, more like geography, dealing with the structure and working of a number of peculiarly organized entities, at a particular moment of time on a particular planet. Undoubtedly there should also be a real and general biology but we can only just begin to glimpse it. A true biology in its full sense would be the study of the nature and activity of all organized objects wherever they were to be found—on this planet, on others in the solar system, in other solar systems, in other galaxies—and at all times, future and past.

B. *Dating the Origin of Life*

We do not know how old life is. If life started on this earth, which is no longer to be taken for granted, it is four eons old (4×10^9 years), but not much older, because the earth's surface would have been too hot to hold life at that period, not too hot physically, but radiologically. Radioactive substances that are now either entirely burnt out or in a low state of activity were then so active as to interfere destructively with anything that we would now call life. This places an upper limit to the beginning of life on this earth.

There are various highly mathematical aspects of biology which are general, in the sense mentioned above, that concrete terrestrial biology is not. They should serve equally well for any life discovered anywhere or inferred at any time. There are also intrinsic conditions laid down by the known facts of physics and chemistry which would apply to any kind of life. For instance, it is probable that it is not only on this earth that the properties of any kind of life would be found to depend on those of water, which are in turn deducible from pure quantum mechanical considerations.

C. *A Definition of Life*

At this stage it may be worthwhile to introduce a rather restrictive biochemical definition of life, derived from that of Perrett. Later we will have to consider how far all its conditions are really necessary to a generalized life. It is this:

> "Life is a potentially self-perpetuating open system of
> linked organic reactions, catalysed stepwise and almost
> isothermally by complex and specific organic catalysts
> which are themselves produced by the system."[51]

This may seem long-winded, but careful consideration shows that hardly a word can be left out, and if any more words were put in, they would be restricting it to certain kinds of life. For example, the word "potentially" is meant to include the seeds or the bacteria in which, cooled to 4° absolute, no reactions whatever take place. But alter the conditions appropriately and the seed will germinate and the frozen bacterium will begin to grow again. The phrase "open system" is a thermodynamic term for systems in which matter as well as energy can continuously flow in and out and be changed in the process. By itself it could be taken to include flames which are such open systems and, indeed, have often been likened to life. In the sixteenth century Jean Fernel,[57] the father of physiology, had very percipiently called life "a low flameless fire." Flame, however, is implicitly excluded as a form of life by Perrett's definition which talks of "organic reactions" and "organic catalysts." A restricted definition, as will become evident later, is useful to help us look at terrestrial life, both in the present and in the past, in an intelligible way, to relate its generalized functions to the nature of simple molecules and their reactions.

We need not speculate too much on whether some of these more general definitions of life might not apply at some other time in some other place. I can imagine in the future, for instance, life consisting entirely of connected transistor elements carrying out relations much more complex than any of our present biological ones.

In the first place, somewhere in a living system there must be a constant or periodic source of free energy. No system taken as a whole can remain an open one, unless it is continually or intermittently being fed from some outside source of energy; on earth this outside source is ultimately the sun or, more specifically, the thermonuclear reactions taking place in it. The molecules taking part in the reactions of living systems must have adequate stability coupled with a certain degree of instability. If a molecule were perfectly stable, nothing would ever happen to it; however, it must be stable enough to provide for some kind of what we may call a "material body" for a perceptible time. A new set of elementary particles recently has been discovered which are called "ephemerons" and have a mean half-life of 10^{-26} of a second. Life on the ephemeron time scale would be exciting, but it is difficult to see how it could maintain body or continuity. It would have vanished before we knew it had come into existence.

The methodologically new requirement in biology, foreign to the study of chemistry or other relatively static branches of sciences, is that we are here primarily concerned with the *working* and evolution of systems. Here, also, structure is fully significant only in relation to function and origin. It is in connection with origin that the last part of Perrett's definition is the most characteristic for life as we know it, namely, that the catalysts for the biochemical reactions are produced in the system itself. These catalyst molecules, the biological enzymes, are not produced once and for all, but they are produced over and over again. This applies not only to the life of a particular cell or organism, but to generation after generation of the species. Each single type of enzyme, usually only a slight modification of an enzyme in an ancestral organism, appears first only in the process of evolution. In biology, unlike physics and chemistry, it is not only a matter of saying, for any molecule, organ, or organism, "How does it work?" but also "How did it get to be like that?" This is an extension of the usual practice of biologists. Most biologists have been trained to—and, indeed, they must for the most part—take the biological system they study as given. It is not enough in these days to study, for instance, how a plant uses light to make sugar or how a fish uses that sugar to swim. To complete the biological picture we must strive to understand the chemical evolutionary origin of the chlorophyll which enables the plant to grow in the sun, or of the myosin which enables the fish to swim in the water. All biochemical and biophysical studies lead straight back to the general question of origins. Origin, structure, and function can no longer be separated.

D. *Origin of Pre-Life*

This is a somewhat unpopular view with biologists to whom until very recently mention of origins has been considered rather improper biology. Yet the question of the prelude to modern biochemistry and of the origin of life itself from inorganic precursors can no longer be safely evaded. Indeed, it appears with ever greater insistency as a logical consequence of the acceptance of Darwinian evolution itself. For according to this, organized life was supposed to have evolved from some primitive organism, the eozoon, which provided a more up-to-date but scarcely more logical starting place than the idea of special creation which it replaced, that of deriving all plants and animals from a first week of creation and of humanity from Adam and Eve. In the Darwinian doctrine the question of where this eozoon came from is left unanswered, or, more strictly, unasked. When someone did have the courage to ask Darwin what he thought about the origin of life, he said: "Talk about the origin of life? You might just as well talk about the origin of the elements!"

The attractiveness of such restriction to one simple origin for life is well appreciated today and, in fact, biochemists have now become so excited over the role of nucleic acid in the synthesis of proteins that they use just as illogical a picture. One might paraphrase it as "Once upon a time there existed on the shores of a primitive ocean a small molecule of deoxyribonucleic acid (DNA). This proceeded to duplicate itself more or less correctly and gave rise to a protein which helped the formation of further molecules of DNA which by variation gave rise to organisms." However, what the biochemists in their enthusiasm tend to overlook is that the first DNA molecule is already something very complicated: to ask now how it arose is considered almost as improper as it used to be to ask about the creation of Adam and Eve or of the eozoon; but with the molecule of DNA we are clearly getting nearer a beginning because the components of nucleic acids are rather simple compounds. Its constituent purines and pyrimidines, one particular sugar ribose, and the ever-present inorganic phosphoric acid residues are the kind of elementary molecules that might very well have been formed spontaneously on a primitive earth or other planet. In fact, they have been made synthetically in the laboratory by such simple processes as exposing the gaseous hydrides to any kind of exciting agent, electricity, ultraviolet light, etc., beginning with Miller's classical experiment of 1953.[41]

The next question to be considered is how did these particular kinds of biological molecules, the nucleotides, arise, and why were their three different submolecules joined together rather than any others? Such complexity and specificity imply a long history and one that has to be worked out by the study not just of the organisms as they are now, for they all include the nucleic acids for whose origin we are searching. Rather it will require a reconstruction, very largely in the laboratory, of how by other and simpler means such processes as the functions of enzymes and coenzymes can be carried out.

At the moment we are in the rather paradoxical state in which on the one hand enzymes, which are proteins, are required to synthesize the nucleic acids, and on the other hand nucleic acids are required to synthesize the proteins. It is the old chicken and egg paradox on a molecular level and just as puzzling. To resolve this paradox, an evolution and a history of the nucleic acids and of the proteins must be worked out. We have to presume that before there were the nucleic acids, there was something in the nature of a protonucleic acid, something simpler such as a polymetaphosphate derivative that did some, if not all, of the things the nucleic acid does now in organisms. Similarly, before there were protein enzymes, there were simpler catalysts—we may call them protoenzymes—that were not proteins yet did many of the things that enzymes do now. They did not do them as well or as quickly, but they were effective enough to reach the stage of what might be called reproduction "take-off" which some biochemists consider to be the effective origin of life. If we accept this, what I have been discussing thus far is the origin of pre-life, but this is merely a matter of terminology.

III. CHEMICAL FOUNDATIONS

A. *Biochemical Unity*

The biochemical history of life underlies the organic history of life which is the main field of evolutionary theory. But in that biochemical history the principles of natural selection seem also to hold, but in a modified form, as Horowitz has pointed out.[31] The transition from molecular to organic evolution must have occurred further back than our geological record at present reaches.

One of the most astonishing things in biology is the unity on the biochemical level of everything that is called life on earth. The same molecules, often very complicated molecules such as ribonuclease, are to be found in every cell as are the respiratory proteins such as the cytochromes, while one sophisticated molecule, chlorophyll, is still the basis of nearly all photosynthesis. There is little evidence, indeed, of any radical chemical innovations during the whole course of organic evolution. What improvements have occurred have been in the nature of rather trivial polishing up. The major change for many organisms starting at the microbial level has been in degeneracy, in the abandonment of certain steps in the synthetic chains because the missing molecules, vitamins, or nutrients such as sugar were obtained preformed in food.

The point to be stressed is that life on the earth is one in the biochemical and biological sense. Every molecule is tailored to fit in with the molecules of other organisms.* This is, indeed, an obvious deduction from the commonplace observation that almost every living thing is edible, or at least assimilable, by every other. Through food chains moving usually from plant to animal, they all form part of a common biospheric metabolism. It is this unity on the molecular level of the whole biological system on earth that is the key to the great biochemical-biophysical revolution of our time.

B. Convergence of Chemical and Biological Methods

To understand this revolution we have to see how far it is dependent on the convergence of chemical and biological methods on the one hand and physical methods on the other. Between the two approaches there existed, up to some quarter of a century ago, a gap in which we now know were to be found the most significant and characteristic features of life. The methods of chemistry could then deal with molecules containing up to about 100 atoms, that is, of the size of 20–30 A units (10^{-8} cm) and the smallest thing that could be actually seen, but not resolved, in a light microscope was of the order of 1000 A or a million atoms. Now, with the aid of the electron microscope and x-ray diffraction, that gap has not only been completely closed, but also over a considerable part of it both methods overlap and can be used to study the same structures in different ways.

What has been revealed is a new world of particles beginning with the smallest protein molecules, with an atomic weight of the order of a few thousand, and ranging up to the intimate structure of viruses and small independent organisms[44] such as pleuropneumonia-like organisms which may be as small as 1000 A in diameter. The fine structure of intra-cellular particles has been revealed for the first time and we are beginning to understand mitochondria, ribosomes, centrosomes and other organelles.

C. Analytical Methods

The x-ray analysis of molecules[55b] in a crystalline state has gone so far that even so great an organic chemist as Sir Robert Robinson has said that it may well take the place of traditional analytical chemistry in the structural analysis of organic compounds, leaving to chemistry its proper task of synthesis. For instance, no chemist could have approached the detail that Dorothy Hodgkin and co-workers[29] have revealed in three years' work on

---

* The molecular fitness of the environment was long ago treated ably by L. J. Henderson.[27]

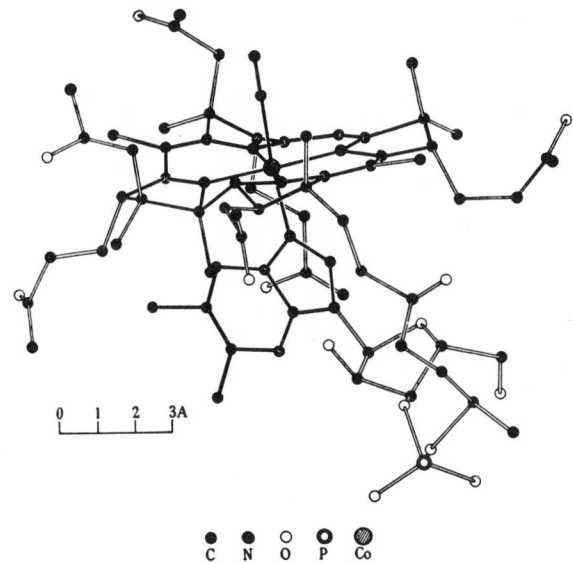

<table>
<tr><td>●</td><td>●</td><td>○</td><td>**O**</td><td>◍</td></tr>
<tr><td>C</td><td>N</td><td>O</td><td>P</td><td>Co</td></tr>
</table>

FIGURE 1. Structure of Vitamin B_{12}. Note the central cobalt atom, its plane porphyrin-like surround, and the nucleotide group attached both directly and through a phosphate ester. (From Hodgkin et al.[29])

vitamin B_{12} (Figure 1). In fact, the x-ray analysis of a crystal with molecules containing anything up to a thousand atoms is now almost routine and computers can further drastically cut down the time required.

A radically different approach is that of the electron microscope which will soon be reaching down to a scale of a few atoms in actual organisms. This instrument is only beginning to be used on an adequate scale and so far suffers from the disadvantage of requiring objects to be seen in high vacuum and therefore not in a live condition.

The exploitation of x-ray analysis and the electron microscope is very new, and although it is true that the gap between chemistry and cytology has been filled in principle, it is very far from being filled in practice over a sufficient number of structures and organisms to make a coherent story. But the story that it does tell is exciting enough and amounts effectively to a new explosion in biology as great, and certainly more complicated and probably as important, as the corresponding explosion in physics earlier in the century which has led us to the present ferment of nuclear and plasma physics.

We now come to our main question, the actual structure of molecules and their biological significance. In working out the structures of these large biomolecules, our ideas of chemistry and biochemistry have become greatly enlarged. The chemical method of analysis, although extraordinarily refined and rational, is essentially an indirect one. Chemistry cannot study a molecule as it is, but only in the process of turning into something else. It acts on the molecule with various reagents, breaks off parts of it, adds other parts to it, and as a result arrives at general deductions as to what the molecule originally was. In favorable circumstances the answer can be checked by synthesis.

There is another method of studying molecules, previously recognized by Pasteur, which is the physical approach, originally by optical rotation but now more through the new methods of spectral analysis, x-ray diffraction, electron spin, nuclear magnetic resonance, and so forth. Here we learn about the nature of the molecule without fundamentally changing it at all. The molecules whose structure can be dealt with by chemical methods are essentially small. For practical purposes we can call them *monomers*. They are a relatively small set of linked atoms usually attached to each other in some rigid form. These links are the valencies of fixed lengths and mutual angles to which we can now attribute their appropriate electron pairs.

D. Macromolecules

For most small molecules the valencies of definite lengths and at definite angles suffice to fix the atoms rigidly, but they do not always do so. For larger molecules this is less and less so because the system generally allows one degree of freedom, the link between two atoms usually allows complete rotation of the rest of the molecule as long as it is a single and not a double bond. Furthermore, the shape of the molecule is not, in such a case, completely specified by the bond lengths and angles. To put it in a different way, such a molecule is like a necklace with rigid links which can be twisted and turned in different ways. Unless there is some system of cross-linking which turns it into a ring or cage, the molecule can exist in a large number of conformations which can neither be distinguished nor adequately described by the usual two-dimensional chemical formula.

The methods of chemistry can do no more than to establish the general sequence of elements along such a molecule. Even at ordinary temperatures the media in which chemists usually work are such that distortion of any flexible molecule is certain. If we wish to know, and this may be biologically important, the particular arrangement in a definite system, another method must be used, and it is here that x-rays have proved the most successful in determining not only the structure but also the conformation of the molecule.

This is particularly true of the biologically and industrially important molecules called *polymers*. Linear polymers, which are the only kind of polymers that have been completely analyzed, consist of sequences of small, relatively rigid monomers, usually with a certain degree of possible rotation of the links between them. The number of conformations, especially in natural polymers like the proteins, built from a number of different monomers from among the 20-odd naturally occurring amino acids, may be very large. Yet in favorable circumstances such conformations can be worked out by x-rays.

IV. PROTEINS

A. Primary, Secondary, and Tertiary Structure

The chemical analysis can establish the order of the different amino acids in a protein. This is what is called the *primary* structure according to the nomenclature of Linderstrøm-Lang.[40] The corresponding and possibly more interesting problem of determining the primary structure of the nucleic acids, that is, the order of the four purine or pyrimidine nucleosides along the chain, has not yet been effectively solved. So the question of using the code of the nucleic acids and correlating them with the code of the protein sequence is one which still has to be attacked by highly indirect and consequently very slow methods.

According to the nature of the amino acids, those belonging to the different parts of the chain may interact and even link together by weaker bonds. The commonest of these is the hydrogen bond which can link together oxygen and nitrogen atoms in different

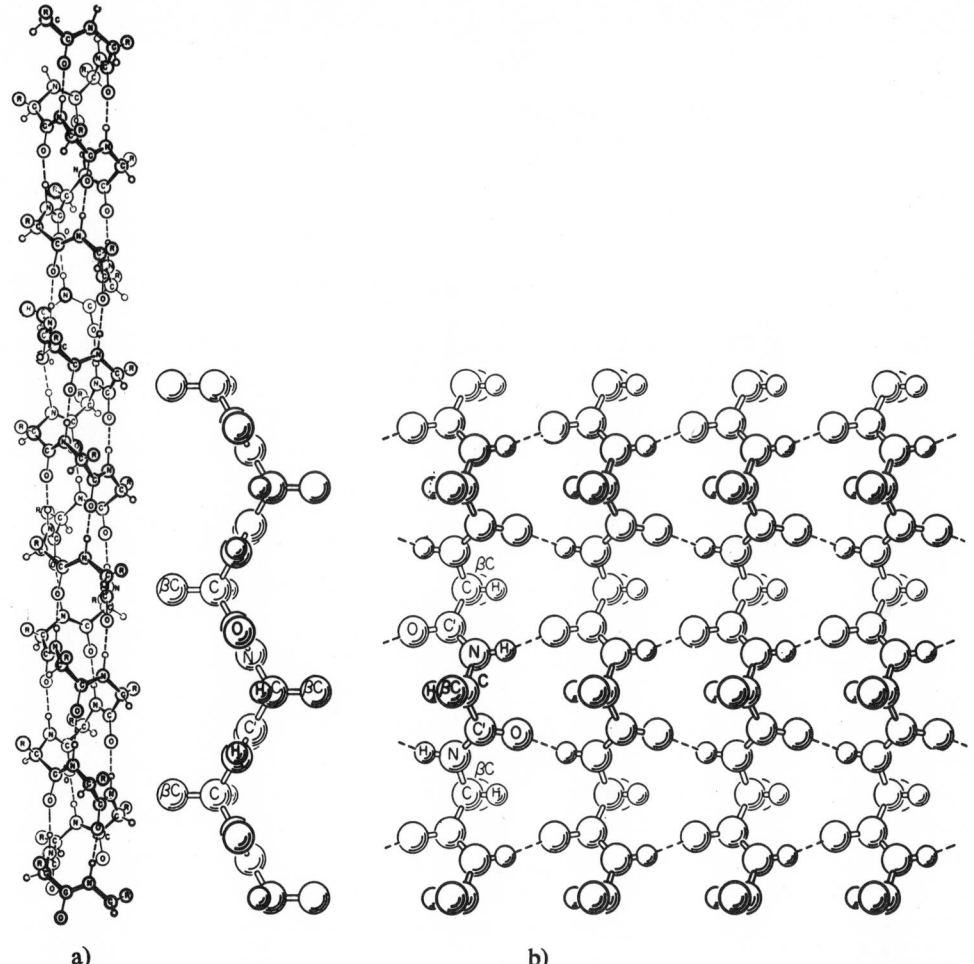

a)   b)

FIGURE 2.   a) The α helix of a polypeptide held together by *internal* hydrogen bonds (dashed lines). (From Pauling, Corey, and Branson.[50]) b) The β form of polypeptide showing two views of pleated sheet held together by *external* hydrogen bonds (dashed lines). (From Pauling and Corey.[49a])

molecules or different parts of the same molecule. In proteins it occurs specially between the positive —NH and the negative O=C— groups in the peptide chain itself. Provided that these links between parts of the chain are sufficient to ensure the rigidity of the macromolecule or any of its parts, they are known as *secondary* structure. In proteins the most important of these structures are those of the α and β chains first described long ago by Astbury and Woods[1] (Figure 2). In the β structure in silk or in stretched wool, the amino acid residues form a fully extended chain linked to other chains by hydrogen bonds. In the α structure, according to Pauling and co-workers,[50] peptide chains form indefinite helices in which each peptide residue is joined by a hydrogen bond to one seven places further along the sequence.

Secondary structure, where it exists, is not the limit to the complexity of a linear polymer. The α helix coils can be further twisted into coiled coils as in wool, twined with each other

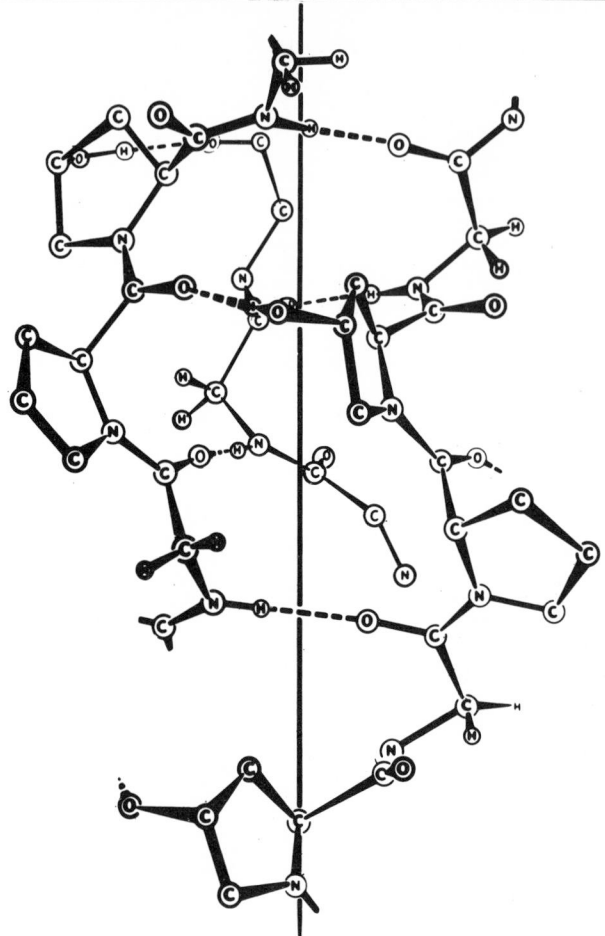

FIGURE 3.   Triple coiled chain of collagen held together by transverse hydrogen bonds.   (From Crick and Rich.[18])

as in fibrous collagen[18] (Figure 3), or linked and folded together as Kendrew has shown in myoglobin[37] (Figure 4) to make an approximately spherical molecule leading to greater solubility.   This is the so-called *tertiary* structure.   The specific functioning of an active protein such as an enzyme seems to depend on this tertiary arrangement, as does the pinning together of protein units to form a particular structure such as the myosin of muscle.

Biologically, it is the tertiary structure that characterizes a particular protein.   Whether in fact the tertiary structure is automatically produced once the sequence of amino acids is laid down is still somewhat of a moot point, but the evidence is rather in favor of its doing so.   With the use of three or more heavy atom substitutions, determinations of tertiary structure of a high degree of accuracy have been worked out in the case of myoglobin by Kendrew and co-workers[37] and hemoglobin with its four chains by Perutz and associates[52] (Figure 5).

In the structure of ribonuclease, studied by Carlisle and others[2] (Figure 6), the chemical sequence of the primary structure can be of help in fixing the tertiary structure as determined by the x-rays. However, it was not possible in this case to proceed entirely by the direct method because so far only one effective substitution of a heavy atom has been made in the ribonuclease crystal.

The biological purpose of the tertiary structure seems to be twofold. First, it enables a long rod-shaped molecule, difficult to maintain in solution, to be replaced by a round one with hydrophilic groups on the outside. Second, it enables amino acids that belong to many different parts of the chain to come close together where they can cooperate to further some specific enzyme action. In ribonuclease, for instance, in the present state of the analyses, a sequence going from amino acid 96 to amino acid 110 appears to be close to that going from amino acid 40 to amino acid 58 (Figure 7). As yet we cannot associate these with any specific enzyme action, although knowledge of enzyme action may become a confirmatory test for the correctness of a tertiary structure.

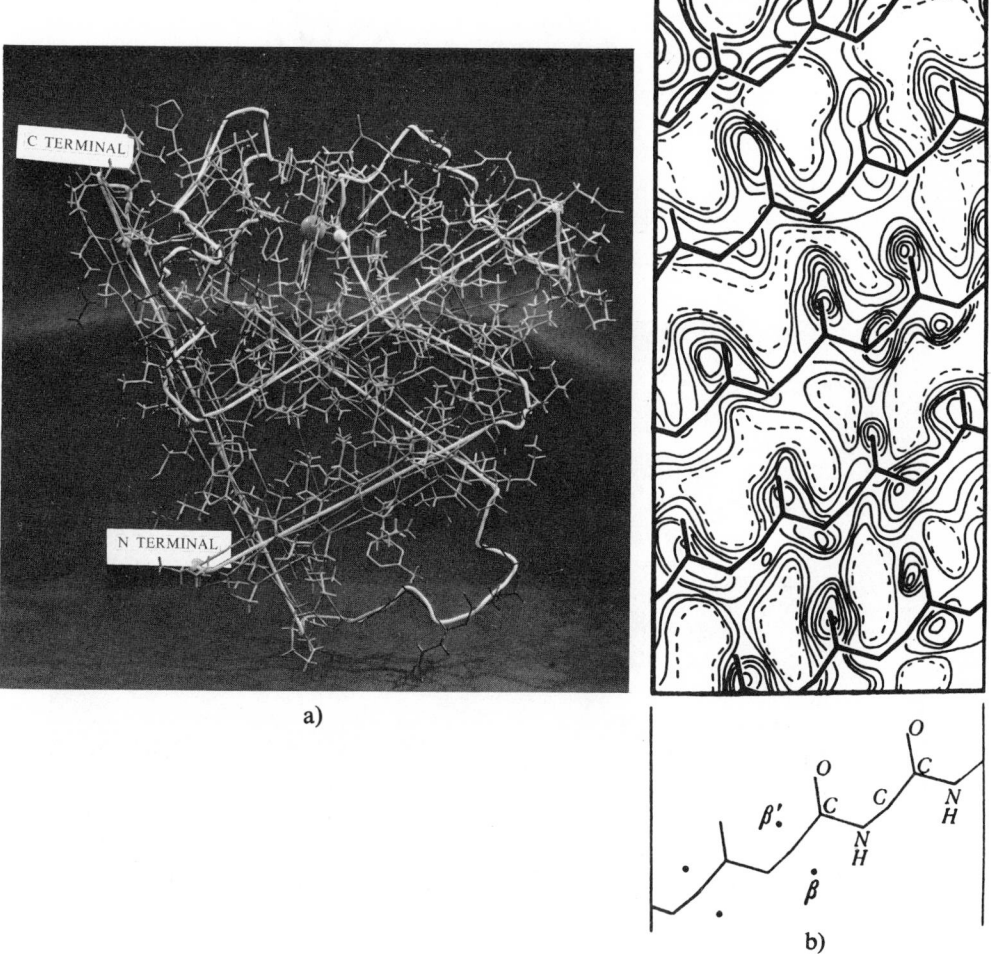

a)

b)

FIGURE 4. a) Structure of myoglobin. (From Kendrew et al.[37]) b) Part of Fourier transform of rod in a myoglobin structure rolled out to show a helix structure. (From Kendrew et al.[36])

FIGURE 5.   Sketch of structure of hemoglobin showing two varieties of submolecules and positions of hemin molecules (shown as disks). (From Perutz et al.[52])

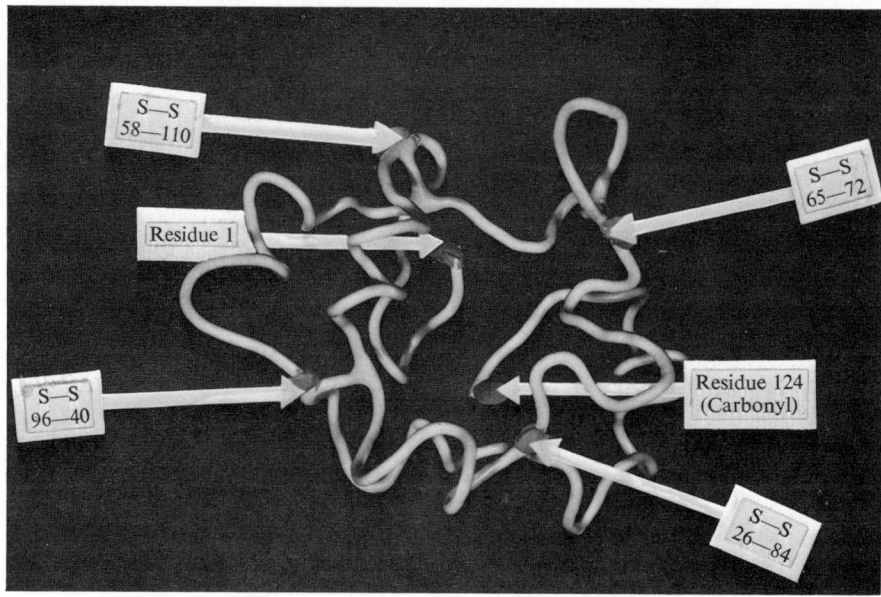

FIGURE 6.   Simplified model of ribonuclease showing the four cystine bridges and the ends of the single peptide chain (residues 1 and 124). (From Avey, Carlisle, and Shukla.[2])

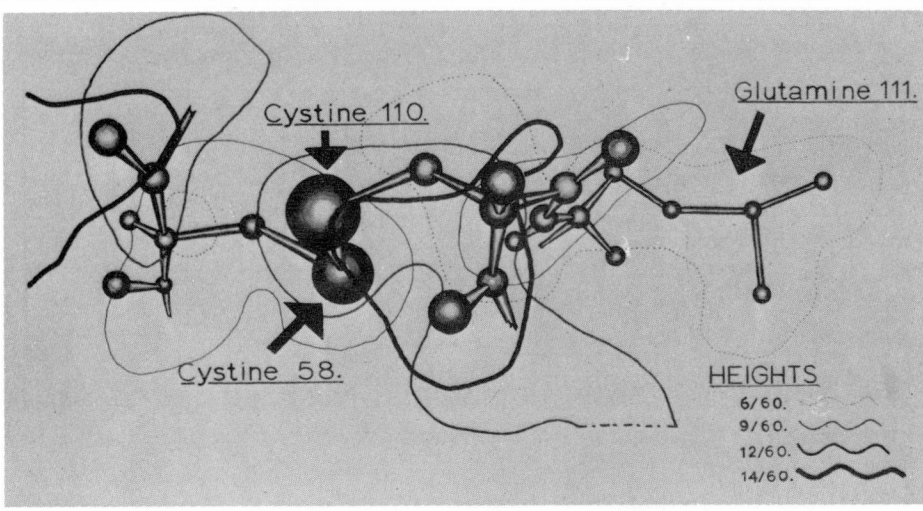

FIGURE 7. Detail of RNAase molecule in the neighborhood of the 110–58 cystine bridge, showing the arrangement of residues by electron density distribution. The large atoms are sulfur. (From Avey, Carlisle, and Shukla.[2])

B. Peptide Interactions

The various complications of a straight single-chain polypeptide molecule are only the first stage of complication of proteins. The larger protein molecules are formed from the joining together of different, more or less folded, chains of proteins. As we have already seen in hemoglobin, there are two pairs of chains, the so-called white and black chains, which are slightly different from each other and are fitted together to make an almost spherical molecule. Such linking of chains seems to be the rule but their patterns are arranged in different ways. For instance, in the comparatively simple protein, insulin, with a molecular weight of 6000, two different chains joined together by cystine bridges[56] are present. Far more complex multiple protein structures are also known, composed of quasi-regular but finite groupings of identical or different protein submolecules. Because these are not arranged in potentially identical three-dimensional lattices, they are free of the restrictions of symmetry that occur in true crystals, but can adapt such "forbidden" symmetries as 5 and 7 or even occur as irrational helices.

A particularly interesting example is hemocyanin which functions as a respiratory pigment in the blood of certain mollusks[20] and crustaceans. Here the molecule has long been known from physicochemical studies to be multiple, and could be broken down and reversibly reassembled from a molecular weight of 45,000 to a molecular weight of 6.3 million.[11a] However, the unit structure has only recently been revealed by the electron microscope.[64] Its shape is that of a barrel, and the molecules are arranged in six rings, each of which is slightly different from the one above it or below it (Figure 8). The structure is not fully crystalline, since there is no lattice; yet it is so complete that a single molecule cannot be added to it or subtracted from it without the whole molecule falling apart. This kind of structure now seems likely to prove of extraordinary biological importance, as mentioned below.

Such aggregates are composed of identical molecules but, unlike crystals, they are not in identical relation to each other. The most significant of these is so-called globular-fibrous

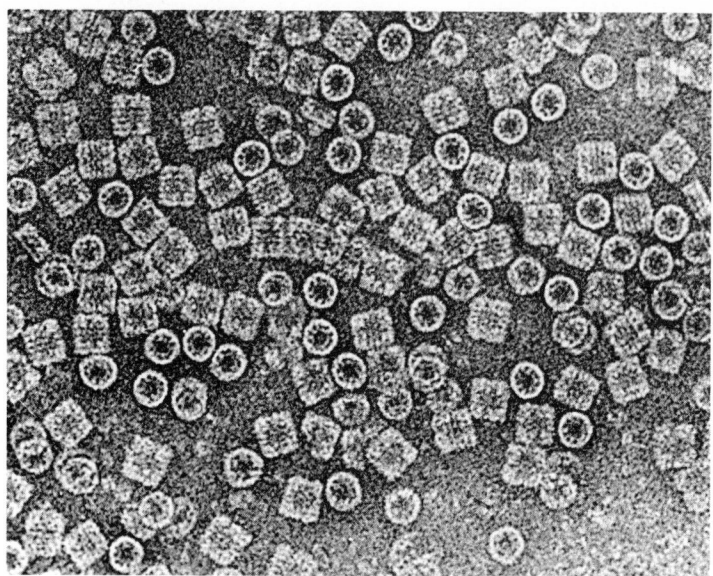

FIGURE 8. *Helix pomatia* hemocyanin molecules showing end and side view of complex molecule and a number of half molecules and smaller fragments. (From van Bruggen, Wiebenga, and Gruber.[61])

FIGURE 9. Diagram of part of tobacco mosaic virus molecule showing ribonucleic acid coil embedded in helically arranged cylinder of virus protein molecules (23 A pitch). (From Klug and Caspar.[38])

transformation, particularly studied by Waugh,[63] in insulin. Normally this hormone is crystalline, but by a reversible acid and heat treatment it can be made into a fibrous form in which the quasi-spherical molecules are arranged, not regularly in three dimensions, but simply in one dimension in a long helical fiber.

C. Virus Protein

Apparently fibers, both natural and artificial, are made by a process of simple and complex twining in a somewhat similar manner. A simple polymer in general will not be straight but coiled because the molecules themselves have no intrinsic symmetry. Intermolecular compounds can be formed in this case by the twining together of three or more of such molecules, as occurs, for instance, in the common supporting protein, collagen. This seems to be a general feature for cylindrical complexes of globular proteins. Evidence for this was found some years ago in the rod-like tobacco mosaic virus. The hypothesis of Watson,[62] verified in detail by Klug and Caspar,[38] is that in the classical tobacco mosaic virus the main part of the cylindrical virus, which is 3000 A long and 152 A in diameter, consisted of a hollow cylinder of identical protein molecules in helical array with a single strand of ribonucleic acid wound through them (Figure 9). However, the ribonucleic acid is not essential, for an identical protein molecule structure can be formed without the ribonucleic acid from a broken-down mixture of virus from which the ribonucleic acid has been decomposed by ribonuclease.

This cylindrical arrangement is not the only one which identical protein molecules can form. Another is that of a hollow sphere or, more correctly, a hollow polyhedron which seems to be the pattern adopted by spherical viruses such as those of poliomyelitis and many others[30a] (Figure 10). These protein molecules, again apparently identical, can find themselves in different configurations. As the diagram shows, in all cases there must be at least some molecules surrounded by five others, whereas the majority are surrounded by six. The most complicated examples of these structures are found in the DNA viruses such as T_2 bacteriophages.[9] Here several different kinds of protein molecules are involved, some forming the head which contains the DNA, others forming the spring which retracts to force a hollow inner tube into the bacterium through which the DNA later passes. Still others form a terminal plate and the six long filaments, which are apparently some kind of detecting devices by which a bacterial surface is recognized. The existence of these different molecules is discoverable genetically because it is possible to produce mutations which alter each of these elements independently.

V. X-RAY ANALYSIS OF IMPERFECT CRYSTALS

A. Basic Concepts

The study of proteins, nucleic acids, and viruses opens up a new field in the structure of matter. Hitherto, x-ray analyses have been limited to true crystals, that is, to repeating patterns which continue without change up a definite face temporarily limiting the size of the crystal. In principle, any crystal could be infinitely large and in some minerals, indeed, they are to be measured in meters. The fact that crystals can grow indefinitely in three dimensions limits the kind of structures they can have. No structure with such *translational*, three-dimensional symmetry can have more than very restricted *rotational* symmetries (twofold, threefold, fourfold, and sixfold, but not five or seven) and these rotational axes

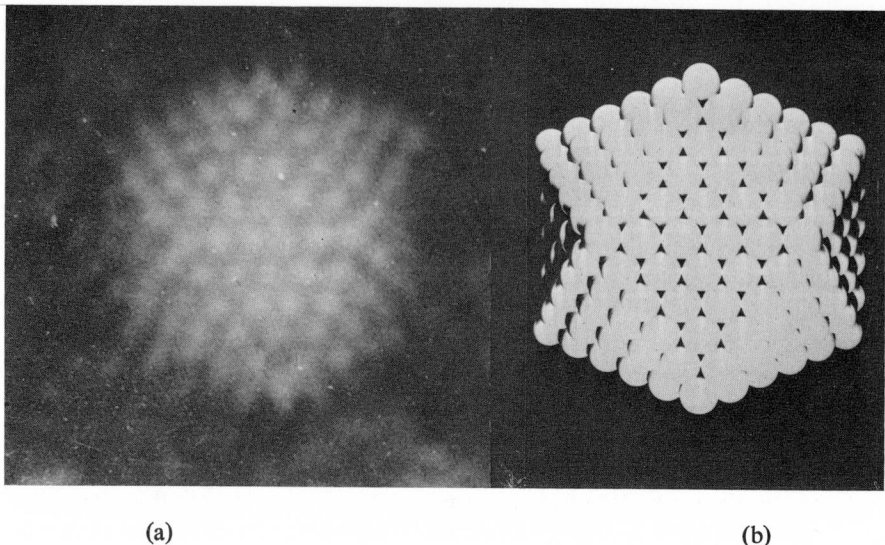

(a)   (b)

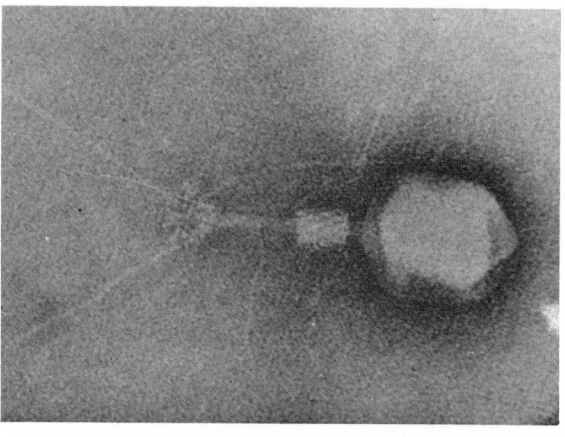

(c)

FIGURE 10.   a) Adeno virus and b) model showing icosahedral form and 5- and 6-fold co-ordination of coat protein molecules. (From Horne et al.[30b]). c) Isolated hydrogen peroxide-treated phage particle, showing the relations of the filled head, contracted sheath, core and tail fibers. (From Brenner et al.[9])

can only be arranged in certain limited ways, forming the thirty-two symmetry classes.

Crystallographers were trained to think in this way and for a long time were apt to dismiss structures which did not fit into this scheme as amorphous and, therefore, without any serious possibility of analysis by x-ray methods. The breakthrough which removed this restriction came with Pauling's study of the nature of the simplest kind of amino acid chain, the polypeptide chain of many fibrous proteins. This kind of chain, the α structure, as first described by Astbury,[1] is found in a great number of proteins such as myosin, keratin, and fibrin. Another kind of chain, the β chain, is straight and is found in silk. Curiously enough, all α chain proteins mechanically stretched under suitable conditions (generally wet and warm) turn into β chains. The β chain was first analyzed and proved to be simply a zig-zag chain of carbon and nitrogen atoms (Figure 2). An α chain with the same number of carbon atoms was definitely shorter.

B. Helical Structures

Thus the α chain appeared to be somehow or other folded or curved. The question was, how was this done? If the α chain were coiled in a helix as Huggins[32] first proposed, and the whole assembly were crystalline, it would have to have a twofold, threefold, fourfold, or sixfold symmetry. Unfortunately, Bragg and co-workers[8] found it impossible to make any of these regular twists give rise to the x-ray patterns that were actually observed.

It was here that Zuckerkandl and Pauling,[64] shaking us crystallographers out of our dogmatic slumbers, broke away from the idea of an integral helix altogether. Corey and Donohue[17] had, by the x-ray analysis of the structure of amino acids, determined very precisely the shape of the peptide link, which is the common element of all polyamino acids. Fitting this into a helical pattern, Pauling found it could be done in only a certain number of limited ways, and none of these led to a coil with any simple number of amino acids per turn. The best fit was one of 3.73 amino acid residues per turn, near enough to 4 but sufficiently different to make a recognizable diffraction pattern which proved similar to what was observed. The helix finally chosen and which remains as *the* α helix, proved to be the key to a large number of protein structures. But its importance was much greater because it gave the general clue as to how to interpret structures based on any kind of helix pattern.

Once the characteristic x-ray diffraction pattern of the helical arrangements was understood, it became easy to recognize the pattern for any substance. Basically it is a characteristic butterfly pattern with empty places above and below and bars at certain heights above the meridian line, representing the repeat unit of the helix. This approach, reduced to a mathematical form by Cochran[16] and others, could be applied to many different substances, including some synthetic products such as the artificial tough polymer polytetrafluoroethylene.

C. The Problem of DNA Structure

The greatest triumph, however, of this method of explanation was reserved for determining the structure of DNA. The analysis of nucleic acid structure which turned out to be such a vital revolution in biology is an example of step-by-step advance. First, attention was drawn by the biologists and biochemists such as Casperssen[14] to DNA's importance in the natural synthesis of proteins. Meanwhile the chemists had shown that there were in fact two nucleic acids differing essentially only in the sugar part of the molecule, ribonucleic acid (RNA), originally yeast nucleic acid found mainly in cytoplasm, and deoxyribonucleic acid (DNA), originally thymus nucleic acid found mainly in the nucleus. Both were found to contain a mixture of two pyrimidines, cytosine and uridine (in RNA), cytosine and thymine (in DNA), and two purines, adenine and guanine (Figure 11), attached to sugar molecules and linked through them by phosphate groups, but there was no chemical way of telling how. The molecule was fairly clearly a high polymer, as shown by its stickiness and its capacity to be drawn out in thin threads.

Astbury, as far back as 1933,[1] examined these with x-rays and with optical methods, noting that nucleic acids showed an unusual feature, a strong negative birefringence. Knowing that the molecule was composed very largely of a series of flat components such as purines and pyrimidines, he guessed that they must be arranged at right angles to the direction of the fiber, and hence probably piled up like a pile of coins. The problem was to

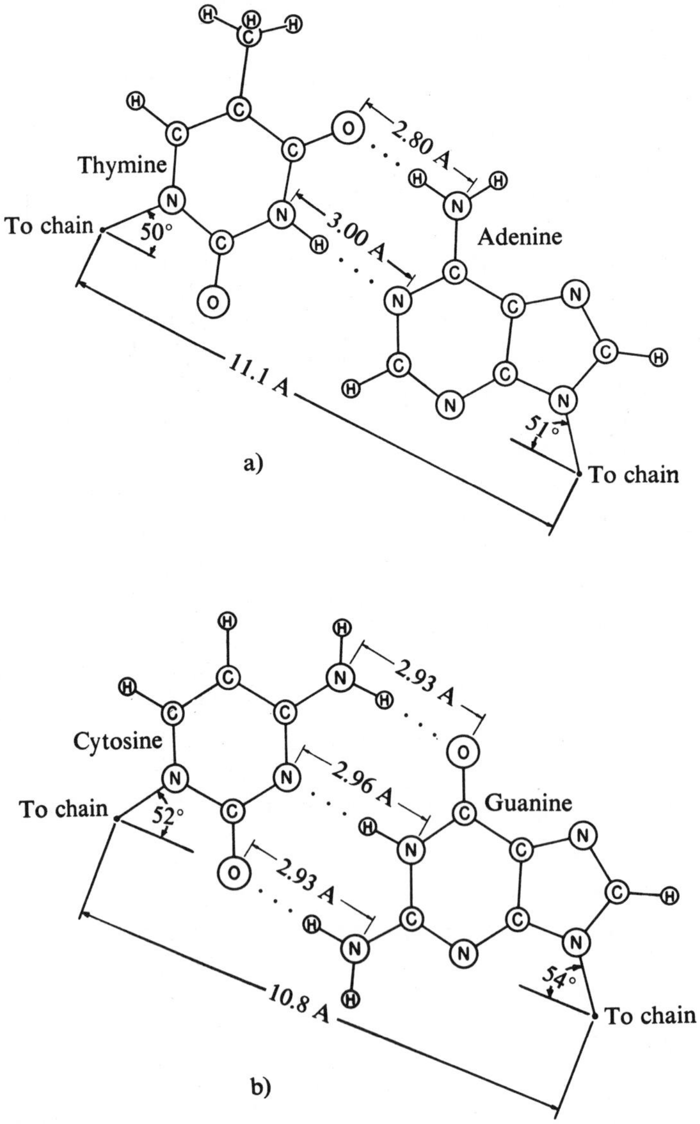

FIGURE 11.   a) Adenine-thymine and b) guanine-cytosine pairing through hydrogen bonds in a double DNA chain. (From Rich.[54])

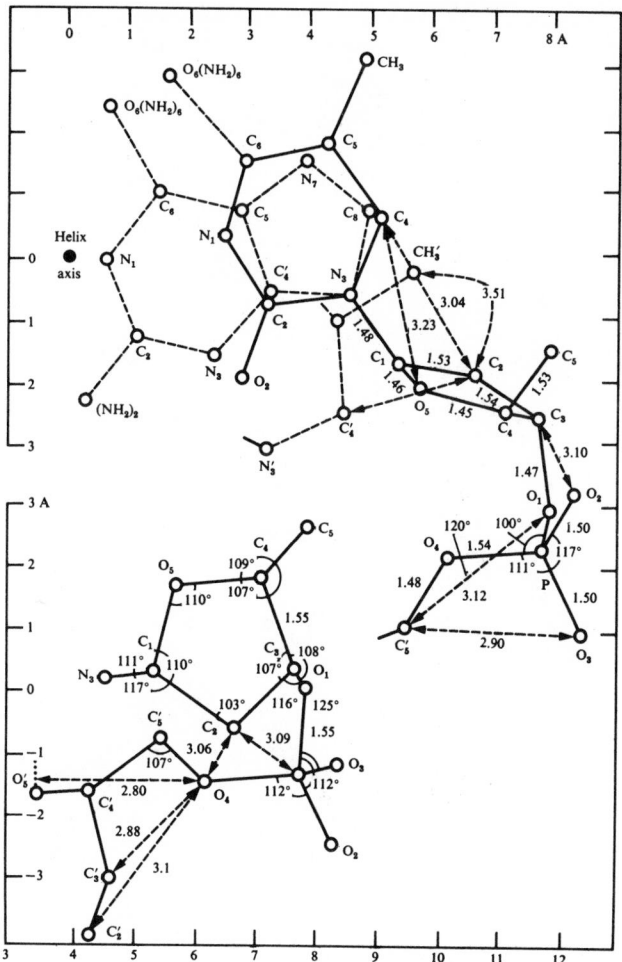

FIGURE 12. Arrangement of purine and pyrimidine nucleotides as part of a single DNA chain. (From Langridge et al.[39a])

find out how the ribose sugar group was arranged and where the phosphates came in. This was done essentially through the work of Furberg,[23] who showed that in a single nucleoside, cytosine, the sugar ring was approximately at right angles to the purine ring. From that he found it easy to make a model of two helical structures embodying these nucleotides. One was favored by Pauling[49b] where the central thread was the sugar-phosphate arrangement, rather like the structure of proteins, with the purine and pyrimidine residues sticking out at the sides. The other was the inverse one favored by Furberg where the purines and pyrimidines were in the middle, while the sugar phosphate formed widescrew helices all the way around them (Figure 12).

D. Double Helices

The single helix model, however, did not fit at all well with the x-ray evidence for the structure of DNA. Only in 1953, after Chargaff and associates[15] had shown that the number of purine and pyrimidine residues were equal, did Crick and Watson have the intuitive idea

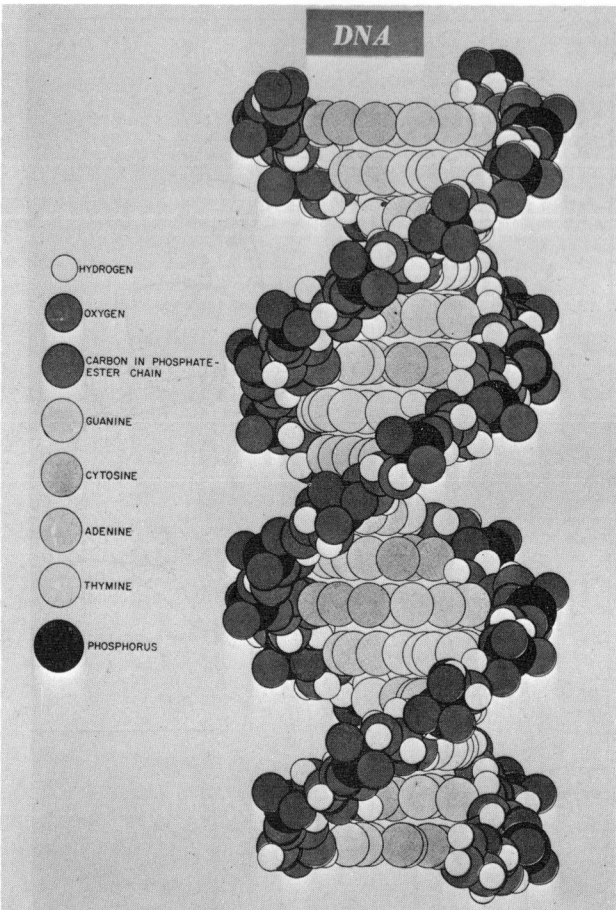

FIGURE 13. Packing model of DNA double helix showing parallel arrangement of bases and uneven mutual spacing of the two sugar phosphate chains, based on the Crick-Watson theory. (From Rich.[54])

that the structure was not a single but rather a double helix, and that the linking of the pairs of purines and pyrimidines in the separate helices was carried out by means of a system of hydrogen bonds (Figure 13).[19] This was, in effect, a most brilliant and fruitful idea. Actually its verification did not involve anything like the amount of work required in working out protein structure, and this was for a fairly elementary reason. The proteins consist of some 20-odd amino acids, all rather different from each other, whereas the nucleic acids consist of purine-pyrimidine pairs which are more or less the same, and consequently give a much more marked repeat unit. For the same reason, namely the close likeness of the purine-pyrimidine pairs, it has proved impossible to make any detailed sequence analysis of any nucleic acid and thus determine the order in which they occur in the chains, the all-important question of genetic codes.

E. *Present State of X-Ray Analysis*

The x-ray picture of crystalline proteins has all the information necessary for working out the atomic positions as, indeed, Kendrew and colleagues have shown.[37] But to work this out requires many, many hours of man and machine time; however, when it is done it can be worked out precisely to the atom. When, nearly thirty years ago,[7] I started the analysis of crystalline proteins by x-rays with Perutz, Crowfoot (Hodgkin), and Fankuchen, we thought it would take only a few years; optimistically we assumed that the structures would be simple. Actually, they were very complex and it required all the skill and patience of Kendrew and Perutz to work out the first complete structures, for which they were most deservedly awarded the Nobel Prizes for 1962.

VI. MOLECULAR REPRODUCTION AND BIOLOGY

A. *Definition*

Although molecular structures are generally on too simple a level to account for complex biological functions, behavior, and natural selection, life as we know it on earth is, nevertheless, absolutely dependent on the physical as well as chemical properties of a number of elements and simple molecules such as CO_2 and especially liquid water.[27] Although there has been much speculation about radically different kinds of life on other planets, no one has worked out a self-consistent alternative. A hydrosphere of some sort seems to be an immediate prerequisite to biochemical evolution so that the isothermal character postulated by Perrett seems to be further limited to temperatures in the range 0–100°C.

The reactions cannot be completely isoenthalpic; when metabolism is actually going on it involves heat production and this must involve some temperature change. The interesting thing is that the thermal gaps are so low. This is another way of saying that life as we know it is remarkably efficient as a thermodynamic engine. This efficiency is in my view at a limit, or approaches a limit, starting from other more primitive systems which were a good deal further from being isoenthalpic and were much less efficient. The biochemical picture of present life is that of an interlinked system of cycles of reactions. This takes into account only as a temporary phase the material content of life. Strictly speaking, the atoms that are involved in life are going through the system constantly; for a short period they hold together to form the organism and then split off and go off somewhere else. This is what is meant by an "open" system; that is, a body, so to speak, is only a temporary being, like the flame itself. We are all familiar with the fact that, apart from various artificial additions of certain parts of the skeleton such as teeth, all the atoms in the body are continually being renewed.

Continual renewal may be considered the essence of life itself. Even among multicellular organisms the chemical aspect of life is dominant. Structure plays very little part, for even in the higher organisms the structural element is only an ancillary that keeps the system in some kind of shape and keeps its various reacting elements in the right mutual positions. The specific vital aspect is the metabolism, the cyclical interplay of the component molecules. In each cycle the reaction takes place in definite steps. In most, these are of the order of somewhere between ten and twenty, each one of which is a very specific chemical step carried out by the appropriate and specific enzymes, which were called catalysts in the definition.

B. *Catalysis*

Now Perrett's definition, as given, really refers to life as we have it now on earth. But it is evident, merely logically, that this cannot be a completely *necessary* definition of life.

It is *sufficient* for present-day life on earth, but some of the points can be waived for life in its most general stages and even on earth for the earlier stages. For instance, the last point, "carried out by specific organic catalysts, themselves produced in the system," refers to life now. It is the essence of the phenomena of reproduction which many biologists consider to be the absolutely essential characteristic of life. However, clearly this cannot always have been the case because we must begin somewhere, and at some stage the catalysts must be provided by what we call the environment and not produced in the system.

One of our great problems is to find out how the catalysts were first produced, for the specific catalysts we now call protein enzymes, though necessary for life now, cannot always have been so. Physical chemists have shown us that a catalyst is not something which carries out a specific reaction which could not be carried out without it. The reactions which the catalysts help to carry out are either exergonic and give off energy, or endergonic and require energy to be given to them. All the catalyst does is to speed up the process. It does not alter the total amount of energy change involved. Catalysts are useful now but life could go on and logically must once have gone on without them.

Now, for instance, recent experiments have shown that many molecules can be made without specific catalysts such as those we refer to as energy-giving molecules or food substances like glucose and other sugars, as well as other simple molecules such as amino acids, purines, and pyrimidines. When we are considering these syntheses we are tacitly dealing either with very simple organisms or with life as a whole because in life as it is arranged at present no organisms, apart from a few autotropic bacteria, will produce all the kinds of molecules they need from inorganic sources. In most cases this work is done by other organisms, beginning with the green plant.

C. Reproduction at a Molecular Level

So far we have followed a purely operational definition of life based on the study of metabolism alone. I must now call attention to a remarkable gap in it, a gap which is implicitly covered in Perrett's definition but actually contains within it the most characteristic feature of life, namely, reproduction. This is most obvious in the reproduction of whole organisms, but deeper research has shown that this notion of reproduction is absolutely fundamental to life as we know it right down to the molecular level.

The action of a specific catalyst is to help produce indefinite numbers of precise replicas of molecules of moderate complexity such as sugars, fats, amino acids, and nitrogen bases which can play their part in the chemical cycles of metabolism and secure an effective exergonic thermodynamic system. More elaborate sets of catalysts are evidently needed for the production of complex polymer molecules, including that of the protein enzymes themselves. The precise reproduction of enzymes is the key to the maintenance of metabolism. Slight variations in enzyme structure, doublings and quadruplings of polypeptide chains, may occur in biochemical evolution, giving rise to modified performance which is preserved if adaptive. Essentially, however, it is exact reproduction that is the constant and common feature of all known life, present and past. The realization of this in recent years has led the once central position of the proteins in biochemistry to be taken over by the nucleic acids which have now been shown to be the only molecules with the property of self-reproduction. To this has now been added their ability to organize the precise reproduction of protein molecules, whether as enzymes or structural proteins. This molecular explanation of reproduction is the great revolution in biochemistry and, indeed, in biology of our day. As we now see it, the relation of enzymes and nucleic acids is one of complete interdependence. Protein enzymes are required to generate nucleic acid and, in turn, an elaborate mechanism of intranuclear DNA, messenger RNA, and a host of soluble RNA's is needed to produce identical protein molecules. As the existence of the whole set of precisely reproduced protein molecules is essential for the normal metabolism of the cell at all times, this mechanism of reproduction of nucleic acid is now seen to be far more important than the former idea of the essential function of nucleic acids in affecting the reproduction of cells and the growth of organisms. Reproduction and hence, in existing terrestrial life, nucleic acid mechanisms are now seen to be an essential function of life as we know it. It might even take a place in the definition of life. However, this is plainly not true for life at all times and in all places. The evolution of the nucleic acid mechanism remains the principal basic problem of the origin of life.

This molecular reproduction is seen to underlie all grosser and more complex forms of reproduction, such as those of whole organisms, because the highly specific action of enzymes requires that all the molecules of a particular protein enzyme be exactly alike. If they are not so, they may promote other chemical reactions, but not those which were part of the original system. The mutation of enzymes brought about by changes in nucleic acids are the driving forces of evolution, but their far more usual precise reproduction ensures the continuity and very existence of biological species. Hardly less important, as we see it now, is the precise reproduction of structural proteins. The intimate structures of tissues, the keratin of skin and hair, the myosin of muscle, the collagen and elastin which account for all the more elaborate structures from cartilage to bone, are functions of the precise reproduction of polymerized, and hence fibrous, proteins, concerning which we know only the grosser structural aspects.

Even more important, although far older, are the intracellular structural proteins found in even the smallest unicellular animal. These proteins build up the flexible but precisely determinate structures of the cell membranes of the elaborately folded endothelial reticulum, and of the cristae of mitochondria that carry out respiratory and energy transfer processes of the cell, and, most important of all, the very ribosomes themselves that are responsible for the synthesis of proteins through the nucleic acid cycle. With the structure of these other proteins we must also consider what may be called transfer proteins that can exist in solution like the ever-present albumins and globulins which play such an essential part in all higher organisms.

As mentioned above, structures of these various kinds of proteins all depend on the assemblage in a precise geometrical way of an almost unlimited number of identical protein molecules, not necessarily all the same kind but of a limited number of kinds. It is now suggested, for instance, that nerve fibrils, the submicroscopic fibers inside neurons, are also made of such aggregates of protein molecules by the globular-fibrous transformation already referred to.

Only less essential than the nucleic acids and probably prior to them because of their greater simplicity, is another vital group of molecules, the coenzymes responsible for energy transfer in particular enzyme reactions. Most important of all is the key energy coenzyme, adenosine triphosphate (ATP), which in its various forms of diphosphate and monophosphate is responsible by itself for most of the over-all energy transfer in all organisms. Most coenzymes, with the exception of the flavones, are themselves either nucleotides or closely related to them. Their continuous transformation provides for the energy transfer required for the whole system. The immediate function of light, for instance, in all photosynthetic plants is not to make glucose, that is the end of an elaborate chain of processes, but rather, in the first place to produce an electron transfer which makes adenosine triphosphate from diphosphate.[11b]

VII. THE BASIC FUNCTIONS OF BIOLOGICAL SYSTEMS

Present-day life exists on a highly sophisticated level which most biologists take for granted as absolutely essential to the living state. But if we are to be logical in considering the evolution of living things, as already hinted above we must look further back and consider the basic functions in their crude state before dealing with the mutually interlocked and precisely reproducing systems now in existence. In such basic evolution there are roughly three processes or stages: 1) that of the rapid performance of chemical reactions requiring specific catalysts, namely, the function at present carried out by enzymes; 2) that of energy transfer carried out by coenzymes; and 3) that of information storage and transfer needed for precise reproduction of molecules provided by the nucleic acids.

The enzymes that carry out the different steps in the metabolic cycle have to be highly specific. The enzyme ribonuclease, whose structure has been described, is the only one concerning which we have any structural information. It is to be found in every cell; it can carry out its functions only if its structure remains the same, within very narrow limits of one or two amino acids. Such differences are found, for instance, between ribonuclease in human beings and in pigs. As Linderstrøm-Lang[40] and others have shown, this limitation does not apply to artificial degradation products of protein enzymes. Quite large segments of the peptide chain can be removed, either without altering the enzyme performance, or altering it only in a limited way, full activity being restored by the addition of the part removed. This, however, does not affect the argument that a particular enzyme as made in the cells of quite different organisms forms a closely related family almost certainly deriving from a single ancestor. Pauling has studied the corresponding changes in hemoglobins and has even deduced something of the geological periods at which the different mammalian hemoglobins split off from each other.[64]

The activity of a particular enzyme, however, is not absolutely specific. Ribonuclease, for instance, will break up not only all ribose-containing nucleic acids but also some simple pyrophosphates; but in order to break up deoxyribonucleic acid a different enzyme is required. Enzymes, accordingly, have only a narrow range of activity but within this narrow range they must possess a determinate structure. Coenzymes, on the other hand, are far less specific. The very fact that a coenzyme like ATP can be so wide in its range of action demonstrates that it does not have such narrow specificity. An enzyme is, so to speak, a jig which holds the substrate molecule until it is altered; a coenzyme is the tool, a quite general one, which operates on the work and supplies the energy needed for the transformation or, in another case, takes it away.

VIII. THE ORIGIN OF LIFE

A. *Foundations*

The structural pattern of life on the molecular level is a highly complicated, self-consistent, and sophisticated one. It is clearly a system to which the modifications given, in the last three thousand million years, let us say, have been relatively small. For that very reason it cannot have been the original system. What were the earlier systems? To cope with this problem is fundamental not only to our philosophical requirements of seeing origins and filling the gap between the energy changes on the surface of a primitive earth and the origin of life on it, but also for the understanding of biochemical functions themselves. The particular kinds of molecules that occur now and are fitting so well into biological systems are, so to speak, the residuum, the living fossils of molecules that have been especially successful in previous aspects of life.

In life as we know it the nucleic acid replicating mechanism, whether it is DNA or RNA, is absolutely necessary to secure precise reproduction of molecules. This is needed on the one hand to secure enzyme action and on the other to enable precise structures such as those of viruses, cilia, and centrosomes to be built out of a small number of identical parts. The precision and the balance of the system is such that we can hardly imagine one part of it without all the others. Yet such complex harmony can hardly have evolved all at once as a complete system. Originally the same basic functions must have been carried out, though less efficiently, in other ways. At some time, molecular, but not necessarily organismal, reproduction must have depended on another kind of template than the nucleic acids because nucleic acids were not yet in existence.

B.   *The Role of Small Molecules*

However, some of the essential components of the nucleic acids were no doubt already present. Purines, pyrimidines, and even some amino acids and sugars, can, as mentioned above, be formed from simple molecules such as methane, ammonia, water, and hydrocyanic acid using a variety of generalized activating agents, essentially photons and ionizing particles.[41] The result of such interactions, in the absence of catalysts, would be an equilibrium mixture of products in which at any moment as many of each kind of molecule were destroyed as were built. In other words, the elementary bricks for building complicated molecules did not always require for their synthesis the reproductive mechanism that exists now, although they are most easily and rapidly made by that means today. The chemistry of life in its evolution is bound to kick away all steps leading to the *first* synthesis of any molecule. Careful study of comparative biogenesis of compounds may, however, throw some light on what they may have been.

The problem of the origin of life has now come to the fore in biochemistry. It is beginning to be considered essential to understand something of how life may have originated in order to understand how it works now. In the first place the very selection of the relatively small number of constituent molecules of life has to be explained. The various types of molecules already discussed are only a few out of the unlimited number, 10^{20}–10^{1000}, of molecules that could be made with the same number of atoms. Why were certain molecules made and not others? Why is the sugar in ribonucleic acid, for instance, ribose and not fructose, and, even more mysterious, why is the peculiar and rare variety of sugar deoxyribose produced? We still do not know quite what its function is. It may be because without the extra oxygen the nucleoside molecules fit close together and are more suitable as a permanent holder of information in DNA than in RNA.

As Horowitz was the first to point out,[31] there has been Darwinian selection of the fittest operating on the molecular level in the early stages of organismic life, and unless we can reconstruct the conditions of those stages, we cannot know why a particular molecule is adaptive. This suggests that possibly the variant of which it is made at any stage, and even now, is not necessarily the most economical one. There may be better arrangements of molecules capable of even more economical, faster, or more intelligent life than anything we know of. However, we cannot more than suspect such possibilities until we can begin to understand the processes that gave rise to them. It would be possible in principle that nucleic acids could be built out of nucleotides other than the four or five that are actually used.

The range of choices of different pathways which exist now in the study of the origin of life has been considerably narrowed. On the one side the experiments, beginning with those of Miller and Urey[41] ten years ago on the synthesis of the simple organic compounds, have brought us up to a point where we can take that for granted without requiring life. On the other hand, the structural studies of nucleic acid and the magnificent analysis by Benzer[5] of the methods of protein synthesis through nucleic acids are teaching us how far upwards we need to look. But an awkward gap remains between the chance assembly of small molecules and the elaborate organized system that we now know as life. Somewhere in the middle of this gap comes the production of enclosed, purely structural entities of organisms, possibly first preceded by that of their constituent organelles.

C. Pre-Organismic Processes

In the definition of life quoted above from Perrett, the existence of organisms was not explicitly stated, nor is it necessarily implied in the sense that molecular reproduction was implicit in the definition. An organism is essentially a limit to the processes of life, that is, a volume inside which all essential vital action takes place. But why should that volume need to be limited? Why should it not be indefinite in extent as, for instance, a cloud? Clouds appear as separate, join together, and then again separate, but through all these changes it is still possible to talk about their physical state. Now, one can at least imagine, and possibly we will be able to reconstruct in the laboratory, indefinite volumes of this sort, in which the linked reactions of early life can take place. Several years ago I postulated that such a situation had occurred in "subvital areas" on the surface of mudbanks in primitive estuaries where there could be actual concentrations of the molecules which could later on give rise to life.[6]

Some evidence for the existence of such molecules of appropriate age has come to us in the most surprising way from the study of the rare carbonaceous meteorites. These have been found to contain complex carbon compounds such as hydrocarbons, purines, pyrimidines, and so on. Some have claimed that these are evidence of life itself. However, whether they are evidence of life itself or of substances from which life originally came still remains an open question. The energetic balance sheet would fit in very well with the latter alternative. To make life work, because it is thermodynamically a downhill process, always diminishing its free energy or increasing its entropy, the presence of free-energy-rich molecules is needed. These may have been provided by a primitive accumulation, such as we now find in the meteorites mentioned above, which in turn were derived from radiations acting on carbon and nitrogen compounds and ice in cosmic dust. This is the view which I now, somewhat tentatively, lean toward.

The more conventional and almost orthodox view is that since the consolidation of this earth the accumulation of energy-rich carbon compounds has been produced from the sea. This now seems unlikely because the particular trapping mechanism, chlorophyll photosynthesis, by which the most energetic solar radiations are utilized, is an extremely sophisticated one and could only have come late into biochemical evolution.

D. Origin of Functions

In analyzing the origin of life we have to find out how the various functional elements found in existing life can have originated. First of all there is the energy transfer mechanism referred to above. Then there are the processes by which chemical reactions can take place, involving specific catalyses; as already indicated, these require *protoenzymes* and *proto-coenzymes*. Then there are the processes for collecting and maintaining information and thus ensuring reproduction, which I have called the *protonucleic-acid* functions.

Now it would seem that we are very near to getting some idea of these precursors. We can imagine a series of molecules of increasing complexity capable of carrying out these functions with increasing efficiency. Take, for instance, a simple enzyme reaction in the breakup of hydrogen peroxide catalyzed by the high-speed enzyme catalase. However, the same reaction can be prompted by a great variety of catalysts starting with such a simple reagent as a hydrogen ion. It works very well with practically all transition element ions and, better still, with various other complexes of transition elements, and with simple nitrogen compounds which with their ions can coordinate themselves; but in all these cases the speed of the reaction is very much lower than with catalase.

Wynne-Jones and colleagues[26] have studied the kinetics of these reactions and have found that the actual quantum-chemical process of breaking the molecule of peroxide is exactly the same in both cases, and that the simple catalyst is just as effective as the enzyme in doing it. The essential difference is that whereas the substrate comes on to the catalyst easily and the catalyst acts on it, the products come off with much greater difficulty; what an enzyme does then is to enable reactants and products to come on and off the activated complex with a minimum exchange of energy.

This points to the way in which enzyme functions may have developed, step by step, from an omnipresent soluble or solid catalyst, perhaps by some iron complex or some clay or iron hydroxide crystal. The operation of the catalyst or enzyme seems usually to be carried out by means of some active center, but the activity of that center can be modified by other parts of the molecule which may be quite some distance away from it and linked to it by some sort of resonance mechanism. The transition from catalyst to a more efficient enzyme could have been brought about by changing the quantum levels so that those levels involved are as close together as possible, facilitating easy separation of substrate molecules.

This leads to a characteristic in the definition of life mentioned at the beginning, namely, that reactions should be carried out quasi-isothermally. In other words, the enzyme-catalyzed system is essentially a series of carefully controlled reactions that involve minimum entropy changes and that operate by lowering potential barriers and hence the necessary activation energy. The evolution of a set of catalysts promoting reactions towards improved efficiency would also probably lead to the production of a large number of identical molecules. In the first place, these protoenzymes would be small molecules not sufficiently complicated at the outset to require enzymes for their formation. Then the protoenzyme reactions must be linked together in definite cycles so that a substrate molecule operated by one can be passed on to the next. Quite possibly in these stages such cycles would be produced entirely accidentally. Thus the whole interacting system would be a large chemical equilibrium containing a number of catalysts which operate as and when their substrates appear in sufficient concentration. It would be an obviously inefficient system which could easily break down under the influence of its own products, either stopping the reaction or turning it in a different direction.

E.   Protovital Chemistry—the Role of Phosphorus

Before the existence of any reproductive system based on polynucleotides instead of a few selected enzymes doing particular jobs particularly well, there would have been a large number of active ions or compounds carrying out the functions of enzyme and coenzyme rather inefficiently and confusedly. The protoenzymes may well have been coordination or clathrate compounds of the transition elements, vanadium, manganese, iron, cobalt, copper, and zinc, together with molybdenum in the next row. The nontransition elements, the alkaline metals, sodium and potassium, and the alkaline earths, magnesium and calcium, seem to have played a different role mostly concerned with ionic equilibrium. The special function of magnesium (replacing iron in porphyrinic chlorophyll) in its all-important role in chlorophyll itself seems to have been a late development.

In contrast, the protocoenzyme function would seem to have been derived from that of the metaphosphates, especially the di- and tri-metaphosphates originating directly from inorganic sources, for these are the active components in the action of coenzymes and nucleic acids of existing life. It is also possible to see, in the light of modern chemistry, why this should be so and thus why phosphorus has such an essential and unique role in biochemistry. Phosphorus lies in a peculiar position among the polyoxygen acids of the nonmetallic elements of the second row of the Periodic Table, namely, those of silicon, phosphorus, and sulfur. The strengths of the links binding these atoms through an intermediate oxygen decrease along the series.

The Si—O—Si bond is a very strong one; it is the basis of the strength of most silicates and of the silicones as well as of silica itself in all its different forms, including quartz. It is, however, too strong to enter easily into reactions at low temperatures. This is probably why silicon, though the second most abundant of terrestrial elements, plays little part in metabolism. The S—O—S bond, on the other hand, is extremely labile; it is very difficult to form and breaks up spontaneously except in strongly acid media. This means that the P—O—P bond is the only one suitable for carrying out the necessary easily operated changes of making and breaking bonds in the ordinary biological range of pH. The reason for this character, usually referred to as the *energy-rich phosphate bond*, is crudely explainable in terms of the repulsion between the oxygen atom attached only to the phosphorus atom and that in a neighboring group—phosphate oxygen in the case of metaphosphates, sugar oxygen in the nucleotides and nucleic acids.

There is another reason, connected with the first, for the invaluable properties of phosphate and metaphosphate changes in organisms; this is their ability to take up or lose protons from different oxygen atoms attached to the same phosphate atom. A phosphate radical may take in a hydrogen atom at one place and simultaneously give another off at another oxygen without any change of total energy and with a relatively small change of activation energy needed to effect the transformation. This allows the movement of protons on what may be called a relay system operated by phosphate. Turkevitch and Smith, by one critical experiment, have demonstrated the great power of this mechanism.[60] In this experiment a phosphate in which the hydrogen was substituted by radioactive tritium was used to catalyze a reaction involving the transfer of hydrogen from one part of a complex molecule to another. Tritium was in fact transferred to the large molecule which showed that the hydrogen atoms on the phosphate could exchange between one part of a molecule and another without ultimately changing the nature of the phosphate radical. Hence, bonds can be shifted or molecules broken or joined together by phosphate which thus can act as the universal changing tool for biochemical reactions.

These properties taken together show that phosphate has a unique role to play and explain why it is so specifically selected for such a role. It is an admirable illustration of Henderson's "fitness of the environment," and an example of what might be called the directive effect of an element's chance properties in determining the structure of atoms or molecules. That phosphates should have all these properties is a somewhat remote consequence of the quantum number arrangements of electrons in the elements of the periodic system, and therefore an intrinsic mathematical necessity. But only at much later and higher stages of evolution do these properties fit conveniently into certain kinds of chemical activities essential for life.

Probably there is a great number of such apparently chance events that must conspire together to make life in any sense possible. Another of these is the lability of the $SH + SH = S_2 + H_2$ reaction. This requires a much smaller energy of activation than the corresponding $OH + OH = O_2 + H_2$ and would point to the priority of sulfur oxidation and reduction, particularly in early photosynthesis. Another important case is the easy and reversible oxidation of divalent to trivalent iron. Such examples taken together would seem to show that the biochemical paths to life are not as interchangeable as it might seem. There are certain, as it were, preselected channels.

Just as the geological structures of the hard rocks being eroded by a river system predetermine the possible water courses, so does the intrinsic nature of atoms and molecules limit, and to some extent channel, the reactions that can occur in living systems. For example, elaborate sets of reactions are known in biochemistry which require just one or two quite special transition elements. For instance, not only is iron required for the blood but copper is also needed to make hemoglobin and cobalt to operate Vitamin B_{12}. Some sea-squirts require vanadium for their blood and others, even more sophisticated, require niobium, one of the rarer elements. Such facts must indicate some kind of effective selection of elements with specific properties occurring in the early beginnings of chemical evolution.

F. Chemical Evolution

The sorting out of potential and actual evolutionary sequences for protoenzymes and protocoenzymes and of the transformation of some of the latter into information-carrying nucleic acids is going to be a difficult, complex, and fascinating task. The process must have been a long and elaborate one and the only doubt is whether there was enough time to do it on earth. Estimates of the earth's age are, however, going up; what was previously considered to be a limit of three and a half thousand million years has now been stretched to between five and six. In the earlier stages of this era, as indicated above, the radio-activity levels must have been rather too high for life as we know it now. Yet the less evolved life was, the more resistant it would have been to the biochemical effects of radiation and the more useful that radiation itself would be in promoting changes.

One important argument that needs to be considered in logical speculation about early life is that before there was reproduction there could have been nothing like evolution in the modern sense, that is, a sequence of almost exact reproduction of organisms broken into from time to time by a gene mutation or inversion. Evolution and metabolism in the earlier stages of imperfect reproduction would be indistinguishable. The extended organized medium or the proto-organisms would be evolving all the time and new organisms would have only a statistical resemblance to their ancestors.

These earlier stages can only be sketched in very roughly but we get on to what is apparently firmer ground when characteristics of existing life are approached more closely. As already indicated above, most of these characteristics depend on the preformation of groups of identical molecules, like proteins or nucleic acids, and there must have appeared at some time a mechanism to ensure that these molecules are precisely reproduced over and over again. There are, therefore, two major difficulties to be overcome, and the order in which these occurred is not at all clear at the present moment. One is reproduction in the molecular sense and the other is a formation of organisms or quasi-permanently separate islands of metabolizing systems.

Most probably the stages occurred in this order, for reproduction is conceivable without organisms, but organisms are not conceivable without reproduction. Molecular reproduction involves the storage of information. According to Crick and Watson,[19] this seems to depend on the various groups of permutations of the four nucleotides in DNA. The reproduction of viruses shows, however, that RNA is quite sufficient to control immediate self-reproduction and protein production, but DNA, with its greater stability, seems to be required for longer period storage and there is evidence that it is a later evolutionary stage.

The mechanism of protein formation from DNA through messenger RNA is the ribosomes, and the collection of individual amino acids by the soluble RNA's demands an elaborate molecular structure which exists in all present-day cells and even in relatively simple non-nucleated bacterial cells. Is all this elaboration really necessary? An intermediate stage may have been a relatively short run of phosphorylated nucleosides forming a protonucleic acid which served to guide polypeptide reactions along definite lines, possibly making relatively simple proteins. A difficulty is that the size for operation of either nucleic acids or proteins has a definite lower limit. Molecules that are too small cannot operate in a medium that allows them to diffuse too rapidly; molecules that are too large are insoluble.

Whatever such stages may have been, they led to the development of a mechanism for producing and maintaining a number of interlinked chemical processes and for passing the essential energy through the system. The origin of that free energy is now in dispute. As has been indicated above, there is current evidence that it may have been in the first place generated by energetic particles on dust before the planets were even formed, and locked in energy-rich molecules which ultimately found their way into the Oparin-Haldane "primitive soup." It must have been in its subsequent running down that life appeared to be stabilized later by the evolution of solar energy traps such as chlorophyll. Before this, the first appearance of life might be likened to the "going bad" of the energy-rich surface layers of a newly formed planet.

G. *Origin of Membranes*

Still another group of molecules which deserve more explicit discussion are the long-chained lipids which seem to be essentially produced by polymerization of acetic acid or one of its derivatives. These fatty substances have one property which marks them off from all others, namely, the capacity to form fairly uniform thin layers of constant thickness. This is due to the presence of a carboxylic or other ionized or water-soluble radical at one end of the molecule while the other end is characteristically fat-soluble. This allows lipids of this sort to form molecular sheets and hence to serve in a general way in separating one part of a reaction from another. Such membranes can either be single and form a layer separating oily and watery media, or they can be double with either a watery layer inside as in a soap bubble or, as is usual in biological systems, with water-soluble external layers and an oily internal one. The outer layer generally contains phospholipids such as the lecithins, the cephalins, and the myelins which form a large part of brain substance and act

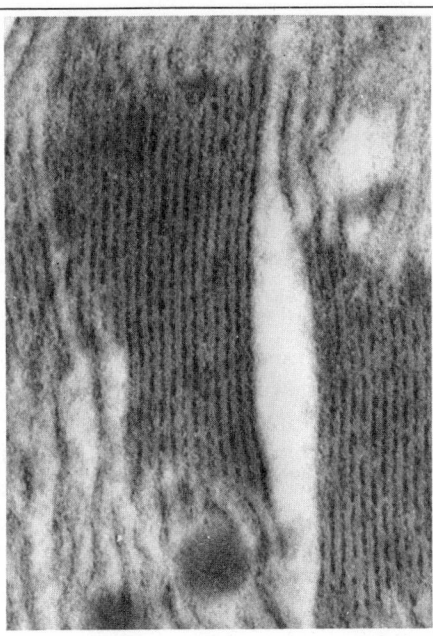

FIGURE 14. Mesophyll chloroplasts in *Zea* showing closely packed lipid lammellae in grana. (From Hodge.[28])

as insulators for the electrical circuits of nerves. Since lipid sheets can be folded into complicated liquid crystals, the double sheets need not be continuous but can form a network full of holes rather like a cane chair seat. The existence of such perforated sheets has been only recently revealed by the electron microscope[3,21,35] in almost all intracellular and cellular membranes, and may be biologically of great importance. It may provide an explanation for the transport of ions and small molecules through membranes, a process fundamental to many cellular processes such as absorption, secretion, and electric impulse propagation, but not yet explained.

It is tempting to regard the membrane formation as the process by which the blocking out of certain regions of what I have called subvital[6] areas took place, leading to the formation of distinct organisms. The size of these original organisms is a moot question. With the electron microscope most cells can be seen to include a large number of bodies which are essentially subcells. The so-called endothelial reticulum, a complex folded sheet, can be pinched off to form active mitochondria and have attached to it the smaller ribosomes. Regularly folded lipid sheets help to form organs reactive to light and include the plastid responsible for photosynthesis and the rhabdoms of insect eyes (Figure 14).

H. Formation of Organisms

Only when a membrane is formed around a whole cell do we have what can properly be called an organism. There must have been a large number of intermediate stages between the undifferentiated but intercommunicating pools of metabolites and the formation of separate free-floating organisms. In fact, the formation of organisms may have been the mechanism by which life managed to become detached from the physical adsorption on clay in the prevital areas. The idea of primary adsorption of organic molecules on clay is one which I put forward many years ago but which has not won general acceptance.[6] It still seems necessary to me in order to account for the earliest pre-organismal evolution because all the small molecules which were first to be produced by prevital processes would, by their very nature, remain in free solution and never reach adequate concentration. As has been pointed out,[33] Miller and Urey's hypothesis,[43] by which concentration of such molecules formed by light in the prevital stages, the so-called primitive soup, could reach about 25%, is difficult to accept. First, there was not that amount of organic material available and, second, if it was in solution it would be destroyed almost as rapidly as it was made by the same radiation that made it. The equilibrium amount present would make it very thin soup indeed. Therefore, some mechanism is really required for removing these molecules and holding them out of the light as soon as they are made. This would be automatically provided by adsorption on clay particles in estuarine conditions.

Such adsorption may also be relevant to the biological requirements of order. Isotactic catalysis which produces not chance linear arrangements of monomers but regular ones could be carried out on exactly such crystals as are formed in these alumino-silicate clays themselves or on free silica or iron hydroxide crystals. The order of life, which is its essential nature and which leads directly to the concept of reproduction, could have been first imposed by the intrinsic crystalline order from which life arose.

Merely physical-chemical limitations would in any case have prevented early life from having detached organisms. These limitations in the first place would require production of polymers sufficiently large to have a limited solubility and to form the coacervate drops which Oparin[47] postulates as an intermediate stage, the "eobionts" of Pirie.[53]

IX. EXTRATERRESTRIAL BIOLOGY

A. *Carbonaceous Meteorites*

These views have become rather more than usually tentative at this stage because the classical picture of the origin of life, in the primitive ocean or on its shores, has now been challenged in a most unexpected way from outer space. The existence of complex carbon and nitrogen molecules in the carbonaceous meteorites cannot be questioned. There is, however, much speculation and controversy about their origin and significance. It appears to some that the evidence puts into doubt accepted theories of the origin of life. We now have to ask whether life originated not only on earth but on other planets and asteroids, as well as whether life on earth actually originated here or was brought from outside. Such extraterrestrial origin is an hypothesis which was elaborated almost eighty years ago by Arrhenius.

In any case the evidence from meteorites must extend our ideas about the time scale of evolution. The age of the meteorites of the order of 4000 million years is beyond dispute, and yet on the so-called carbonaceous meteorites there are found compounds such as purines and pyrimidines, not to mention complex hydrocarbons. These facts lead to one of two possibilities: 1) these chemicals were formed without life, in which case they would have been similarly formed on this earth at such an earlier period; or 2) they are products of life which would push the origin of life back to a far earlier period still, but leave open the question of how they were formed.

One intrinsic difficulty is that the meteorites seem to have been formed from relatively small planets in the asteroidal belt which could not have been large enough to maintain any free water on their surfaces, and up till now we have considered that water with free surfaces, that is, seas or lakes, is essential to the origin of life.

On the other hand, any formation of planets or asteroids from dust would imply the presence, somewhere below their surface, of a layer of damp rock dust which might be a place for the origin of life or at least the basic organic compounds from which it might be formed. If so, the energy needed to form the energy-rich compounds would have to be derived not from sunlight but from radioactive substances themselves responsible for heating the interior of such a body. This is an hypothesis that life originated in outer space but underground. If this is plausible extraterrestrially, why not also on earth?

B. *Recent Evidence*

The weight of evidence,[45] however, now seems to be turning against the view that the particles found in carbonaceous meteorites are actual life forms. In this case all that need be postulated is that the asteroids from which they are derived and, by implication, all planets formed from cosmic dust, possessed the structures necessary for the synthesis, without enzymes, of the complex carbon and nitrogen compounds which are actually found in the meteorites. This material would then appear as a sample of the *primary accumulation* of energy-rich compounds from which life could arise and not as the product of already evolved organisms.

The composition of the carbonaceous material, as far as it can be analyzed, includes nearly all the compounds made artificially from simple molecules by Miller[42] and other workers. In the soluble extracts a number of benzoic acid derivatives,[10] purines and pyrimidines,[12] and long-chain hydrocarbons[46] have been found. The main bulk as yet defies analysis but in many cases resembles a nitrogen containing highly polymerized humic acid. No material found so far in meteorites has shown any optical activity. This argues strongly against its being a product of life. Nevertheless, the controversy about biological formation of the materials of the carbonaceous meteorites and even of the organisms alleged to be found in them still continues and may continue for much longer. This is a controversy which must be settled before we can have a firm basis for *any* theory of the origin of life. But in its present inconclusive state it can still be a stimulus to further investigation of the meteorites and of the elements of synthetic biochemistry.

Given a sufficiently long time scale, the difficulty in understanding the first stages of life is not to form the small molecules which were later essential to terrestrial life processes, but to determine which way these compounds were *actually* formed out of the large number of possible ways of forming them. This now transfers the problem to that of determining the next stages, discussed above, which led to the reproductive processes of molecules with all their biological consequences.

X. PROPERTIES OF LIVING SYSTEMS

The more we study the actual forms of life on a molecular level with the electron microscope on the one hand and microbiochemistry on the other, the more evident it becomes that all of life is at the same time both peculiar and unitary. This has been discussed above from a biochemical point of view but also applies at the microstructural level where the same kind of structures are universally found and may be gradually adapted for different purposes. This can be illustrated by several examples.

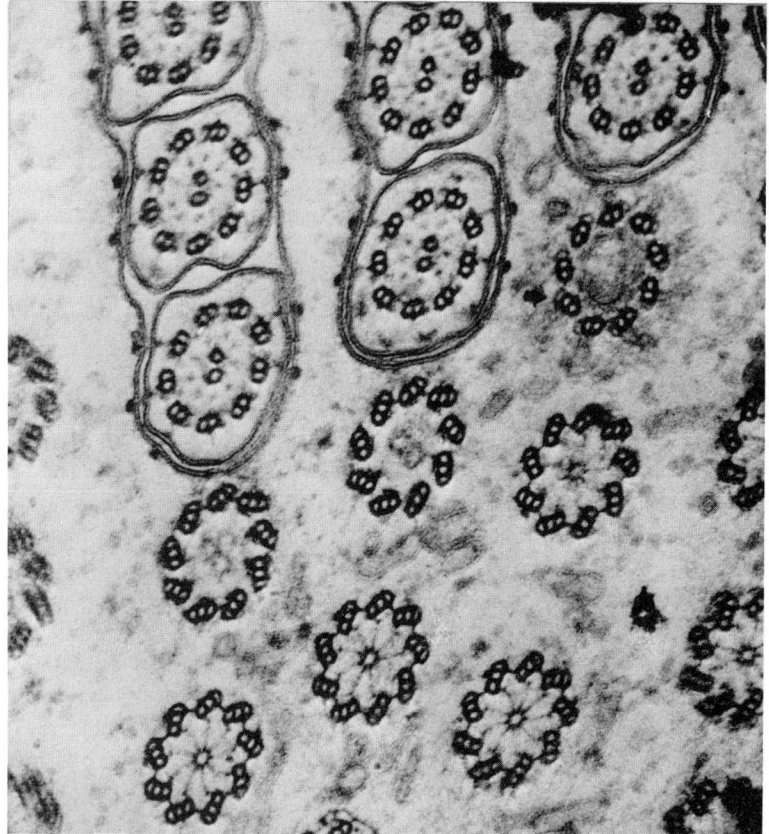

FIGURE 15. Flagella from *Pseudotrichonympha*; sections at different levels showing the 11 double subfilaments passing into treble filaments in basal sections. (From Gibbons and Grimstone.[25])

A. Cilia

It has been known for some time that cilia, including the single cilium that drives a spermatazoon, consist of very peculiarly organized structures of nine fibers in a circle and two slightly different fibers in the middle[58] (Figure 15). This seems to be the universal pattern from the simplest single-celled organisms to the cilia of our own respiratory and reproductive systems. More recently it has been found that the same arrangement of nine plus two fibers is to be found in the structure of hairs[22] composed of a set of agglomerated cilia, just as a rhinoceros horn is formed of an agglomeration of keratin hairs.

B. Centrosomes

What is more surprising is the discovery that centrosomes which are responsible for organizing the mechanism of cell division are themselves the basal elements of cilia with the same nine and two arrangement. The beginning of mitosis is signaled by the apparent division of the centrosome into two, or rather by a process of fresh integration in its neighborhood (Figure 16), which then seems to organize the chromosomes and produces the mitotic spindle. However, detailed study rather unexpectedly shows that the centrosome does not actually divide into two but, rather, that a new centrosome, precisely identical to the first one, is found a few hundred A away in a specific position at right angles to the old one. This is evidently the key to the whole process of cellular division and hence of organic reproduction over and above the continuing process of molecular reproduction that is going on all the time in organisms.

C. Bacteriophage

Another case is that of the complex DNA-bearing T_2 bacteriophage.[9] In a few minutes this arrangement is built within the cell of the host bacterium and from materials provided by the latter's metabolism. In T_2 phage there are at least six types of protein molecules. Mutation and breeding experiments show that the production of each is controlled by a separate gene.

The astonishing and new discovery[9] is that it appears that no gene supervises the building up of the complex structures of the virus coats. They just come together "spontaneously" from specific prefabricated virus protein molecules. The task of the DNA or RNA genes seems simply to direct by coding the correct ordering of amino acids into a one-dimensional protein chain. Such chains, on coming loose, first curl themselves into specific three-dimensional protein molecules. These then, by themselves or associated with others of different kinds, build up structures on an organelle scale. If this view is substantiated, all subcellular structures and, by implication, cellular and multicellular structures as well, derive from the process of mass production of protein chains by nucleic acid-directed reproductive processes.

This points to the extreme antiquity of the process and would suggest that the reproduction of the identical molecules occurred at some stage previous to any of the type of organisms, even the simplest, which we know today. The smallest organism known to us which seems to be able to maintain itself outside a cell providing it with enzymic mechanisms is that of bovine pleuropneumonia.[39b] These bodies seem to be only 1000 A across, that is, smaller than quite a number of viruses; nevertheless, they contain the complete mechanisms of reproduction and of metabolism, including a set of at least 50 protein enzymes, each of

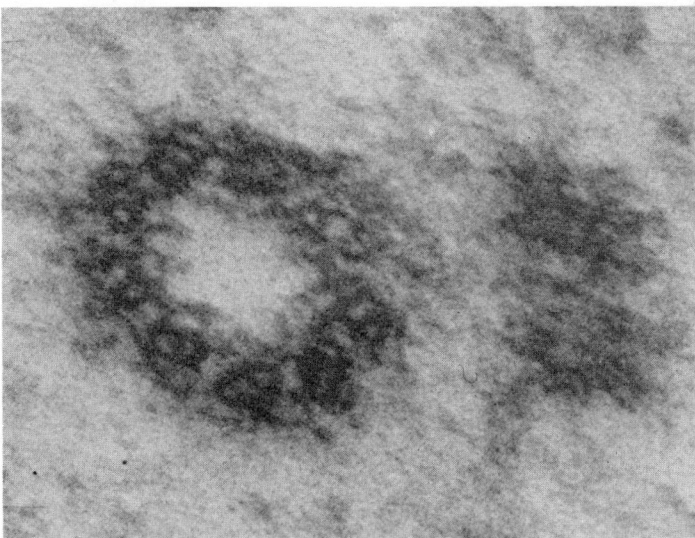

FIGURE 16.   A stage in the duplication of a centriole in a spermatocyte of the snail *Viviparus*. The parent centriole is shown in transverse section, and the short procentriole is seen in longitudinal section growing at right angles to its parent. (From Gall.[24])

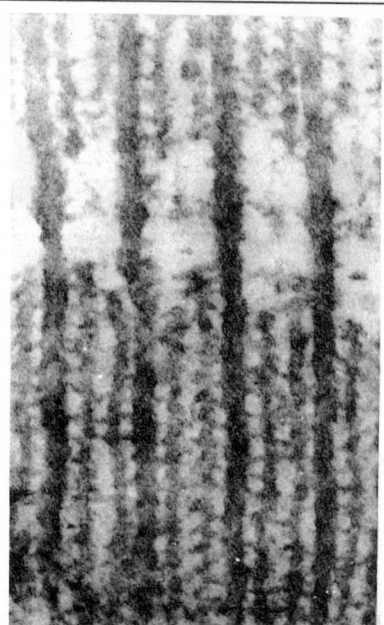

FIGURE 17. High magnification electron micrograph of striated muscle showing the cross-links responsible by their ratchet action for contraction. (From Bennett[4] and Huxley.[34b])

which has to be reproduced, but without many of the particular features such as mitochondria and other organelles found in most cellular structures.

D. Contractile Fibers

Another almost universal structure in multicellular animals is that which is responsible for muscular contraction or for its equivalent in unicellular organisms. The elucidation of muscle structure, one of the triumphs of electron microscopy, shows that muscle, at least striated muscle, which is the only type reasonably well known, contracts by means of a kind of vernier mechanism between fibers of two different kinds, the so-called myosin fibers and the actin fibers.[34a] Actomyosin is shown by x-ray analysis to consist of globular-fiber transformations with slightly different periodicities. Hence the striations are in step for a short distance, then miss a piece and so go out of step, then in step again, which is what is meant by the vernier mechanism (Figure 17).

Now the transference of the in-step region along the fiber leads effectively to contraction by a small number of fiber links. The motion of muscle is essentially like that of the dislocation in a metal, except that it is active and not passive. Thus, almost accidentally, differences in size between characteristic proteins can be made to produce motion.

Motion in itself in an organism would be of very little value if it was not combined with the corresponding mechanism for sensation. There is not much point in moving unless you are moving to a better place. It would appear that sensation, again, is closely related to some preformed molecules arranging themselves, in this case in long lipoprotein molecules forming the basis of neurofilaments.[55a]

E. Ordering of Events

The recent discoveries of the structure and function of intracellular organelles and the appreciation of the roles of the nucleic acid mechanism in forming specific proteins should clarify considerably our notions of the origin and early stages of life. They suggest that the evolution of life should be divided into four periods. First comes the definitely pre-organic formation of simple molecules, amino acids, purines, and so forth, without catalysts or with purely inorganic ones. Second, comes pre-organismal or biochemical evolution leading to the formation of a reproduction of identical molecules such as proteins and nucleic acids. This involves the collection, retention, and transmission of molecular information, but between this and the fourth or Darwinian organismal evolution we have now this new third aspect of what might be called intracellular evolution tracing the elements which have been derived from the complicated structural and functional pattern inside the cell.

XI. CONCLUSIONS

The above review, with its obviously still-provisional hypotheses, should be sufficient to show that biological structural elements are liable to have a larger and larger place both in the explanation of existing living processes and in the parallel explanation of their origin. The picture is anything but complete, but should be sufficient as it emerges in successive discoveries to excite a whole new generation of researchers, larger in number and better armed than their predecessors with all the devices of modern science both in observation and computation. Evidently what we have taken as relatively simple, because familiar, phenomena of life and birth and death, health and disease, are really complicated to a fantastic degree, far greater than any complication found hitherto in the fields of physics or chemistry.

Time was when such considerations would be considered academic. Already, however, the study of microbiochemistry and intracellular organization has led to marvels of medical science, to the conquest of diseases such as that of pernicious anemia through Vitamin B_{12} and the corresponding recognition of the nature of what Pauling calls the *molecular diseases*[64] like sickle-cell anemia. This is caused by a single genetic inversion in a nucleic acid chain which results in just one mistake in amino acid order in building hemoglobin molecules. Though so far a small beginning has been made, more complete understanding of these biological processes, if it could only be reached, should give us far greater control of life forms and processes than any we have imagined. And this control could be exercised not only on existing life but actually on *synthetic life*, if not on the whole of life, at any rate on certain parts of it. Long before we can produce autonomously growing organisms, we can no doubt produce elements which will be able to replace organisms in certain of their functions.

As already discussed in Chapter 1, biology is still largely a naturalistic science; that is, we study nature, find out mechanisms, and then begin to understand the principles on which these mechanisms are constructed. It could become an experimental synthetic science.

The results of a more deductive biology need be applied not only to the remedial or medical side. One of the great practical problems of our time, second only to the removal of the danger of killing ourselves off with nuclear weapons, is that of the so-called population explosion. Biochemically, this is not at all what it seems, but in the author's opinion is essentially a matter of producing adequate amounts of metabolic chemicals assimilable by man or, less efficiently, by the animals on which man lives. Intrinsically, the problem is not very difficult; it is so in practice only because no one has attempted it on a world scale. And here the study of the origin of life is especially relevant, for the basic food chemicals are essentially of a simple kind. No human being can absorb a protein; he has first to break it down into amino acids. We may argue that if life managed to make itself in the first place and to synthesize these simple compounds even before building up the complicated ones, the process cannot be very difficult. Indeed, Oró[48] has taken the step of building the amino acids, as well as purines and pyrimidines, by simple reactions in the cold, using such elementary molecules as those of hydrocyanic acid and ammonia. As a matter of fact, the problem of the production of such metabolites is not a biochemical one but rather one for the social sciences since the barriers to its solution are economic and political. Only 0.1 % of the money now spent in preparing for destruction could support the research and development of the methods of economic chemical production of essential foodstuffs in short supply. This would not be aimed at providing the whole of the food requirement of humanity, which is a matter of running into thousands of millions of tons, but rather in the first place just a few of the amino acids such as are needed to top up vegetable proteins to the extent that they can be equivalent in nutritious capacity to animal protein. On the basis of existing agricultural practice, if fertilizers and machinery were more evenly distributed, the world could provide food for something like ten times the present population.

A factor of ten in increased food production, however, will not do for a population doubling every forty years for as long as 200 years. Either the rate of increase will have to be cut down, for which there would be time enough with increased understanding and education or, if the people of the year 2100 decide to go on, they are more than likely to be able to provide the food and room for a few more centuries on earth, where there are ample supplies of atomic raw materials and energy available in the crust. And if we want to look more into the future, there is sufficient food available in the neighborhood of the earth, in the solar system and probably in the interior of the earth as well, to supply for millenia the needs of any conceivable number of human beings. However, by that time we shall probably have found better ways of creating, maintaining, and employing intelligence than using bodies mostly consisting nowadays of superfluous muscle.

In this chapter we have ranged widely over what may have been and what yet may be, but always within the limits of our knowledge of what is observable. That knowledge is continually expanding and deepening but never at such a rate as now. Consequently, everything said here is of a more than usually provisional character. It is not to be conned over as acquired knowledge but rather considered as a signpost and perhaps as inspiration for the more rapid advances that are to come.

The leading theme is that of the relations between structure, function, and origin of the most basic properties of life. I have aimed to sketch on a molecular plane what D'Arcy Thompson did on that of general macroscopic morphology.[59] The problems on the lower level are much more complicated and are still largely unexplored, but here even a preliminary view may have its uses.

REFERENCES

1. Astbury, W. T., and Woods, H. J. 1933. X-ray studies of the structure of hair, wool, and related fibres. II. The molecular structure and elastic properties of hair keratin. *Phil. Trans. Roy. Soc.* (*London*) **232A:** 333–394.
2. Avey, H. P., Carlisle, C. H., and Shukla, P. D. 1962. A tentative structure for ribonuclease based on X-ray study. *Brookhaven Symp. Biol.* **15:** 199–209.
3. Bangham, A. D., and Horne, R. W. 1962. Action of saponin on biological cell membranes. *Nature* **196:** 952–953.

4. Bennett, H. S. 1959. Structure of muscle cells. *Rev. Mod. Phys.* **31:** 394–401.

5. Benzer, S. 1962. The fine structure of the gene. *Sci. Am.* **206(1):** 70–84.

6. Bernal, J. D. 1959. (a) The problem of stages in biopoesis (pp. 38–53); (b) The scale of structural units in biopoesis (pp. 385–399). *In:* "Proc. 1st Intern. Symp. Origin of Life on Earth, Moscow, 1957," (A. I. Oparin, A. G. Pasynskii, A. E. Braunshtein, and T. E. Pavlovskaya, eds.), Pergamon, London; Macmillan, New York.

7. Bernal, J. D., and Crowfoot, D. 1934. X-ray photographs of crystalline pepsin. *Nature* **133:** 794–795.

8. Bragg, L., Kendrew, J. C., and Perutz, M. F. 1950. Polypeptide chain configurations in crystalline proteins. *Proc. Roy. Soc. (London)* **203A:** 321–357.

9. Brenner, S., Streisinger, G., Horne, R. W., Champe, S. P., Barrett, L., Benzer, S., and Rees, M. W. 1959. Structural components of bacteriophage. *J. Mol. Biol.* **1:** 281–292.

10. Briggs, M. H. 1961. Organic constituents of meteorites. *Nature* **191:** 1137–1140.

11a. Brohult, S. 1940. Investigations of *Helix pomatia* haemocyanin. *Nova Acta Regiae Soc. Sci. Upsaliensis. Ser. IV* **12(4):** 7–69.

11b. Calvin, M., and Androes, G. M. 1962. Primary Quantum Conversion in Photosynthesis. *Science* **138:** 867–873.

12. Calvin, M., and Vaughan, S. K. 1960. "Space Research," pp. vi, 1195. North Holland, Amsterdam.

13. Caspar, D. L. D., and Klug, A. 1962. Physical principles in construction of regular viruses. *Cold Spring Harbor Symp. Quant. Biol.* **27:** 1–23.

14. Caspersson, T., and Schultz, J. 1938. Nucleic acid metabolism of the chromosomes in relation to gene reproduction. *Nature* **142:** 294–295.

15. Chargaff, E., Crampton, C. F., and Lipshitz, R. 1953. Separation of calf thymus deoxyribonucleic acid into fractions of different composition. *Nature* **172:** 289–292.

16. Cochran, W., Crick, F. H. C., and Vand, W. 1952. I. The transforms of atoms on a helix. *Acta Cryst.* **5:** 581–586.

17. Corey, R. B., and Donohue, J. J. 1950. Interatomic distances and bond angles in the polypeptide chain of proteins. *J. Am. Chem. Soc.* **72:** 2899–2900.

18. Crick, F. H. C., and Rich, A. 1958. Structure of collagen. *In:* "Recent Advan. Gelatin Glue Res. Proc. Conf. Univ. Cambridge, 1957," (G. Stainsby, ed.), pp. 20–24.

19. Crick, F. H. C., and Watson, J. D. 1953. Molecular structure of nucleic acids. A structure for deoxyribose nucleic acid. *Nature* **171:** 737–738.

20. Dawson, C. R., and Mallette, M. F. 1945. The copper proteins. *Advan. Protein Chem.* **2:** 179–248.

21. Dourmashkin, R. R., Dougherty, R. M., and Harris, R. J. C. 1962. Electron microscopic observations on *Rous sarcoma* virus and cell membranes. *Nature* **194:** 1116–1119.

22. Fraser, R. D. B., Macrae, T. P., and Rogers, G. E. 1962. Molecular organisation of alpha-keratin. *Nature* **193:** 1052–1055.

23. Furberg, S. 1952. The structure of nucleic acids. *Acta Chem. Scand.* **6:** 634–640.

24. Gall, J. G. 1961. Centriole replication. *J. Biophys. Biochem. Cytol.* **10:** 163–193.

25. Gibbons, I. R., and Grimstone, A. V. 1960. On flagellar structure in certain flagellates. *J. Biophys. Biochem. Cytol.* **7:** 697–716.

26. Haggett, M. L., Jones, P., and Wynne-Jones, W. F. K. 1960. Peroxycomplexes as intermediates in the catalytic decomposition of hydrogen peroxide. *Discussions Faraday Soc.* **29:** 153–162.

27. Henderson, L. J. 1913. "The Fitness of the Environment: An Inquiry into the Biological Significance of the Properties of Matter," 317 pp. Macmillan, New York.

28. Hodge, A. J. 1959. Fine structure of lamellar systems as illustrated by chloroplasts. *Rev. Mod. Phys.* **31:** 331–341.

29. Hodgkin, D. C., Kamper, J., Lindsey, J., MacKay, M., Pickworth, J., Robertson, J. H.,

Shoemaker, C. B., White, J. G., Prosen, R. J., and Trueblood, K. N. 1957. The structure of vitamin B_{12}. I. An outline of the crystallographic investigation of vitamin B_{12}. *Proc. Roy. Soc. (London)* **242A:** 228–263.

30a. Horne, R. W. 1963. The structure of viruses. *Sci. Am.* **208(1):** 48–56.

30b. Horne, R. W., Brenner, S., Waterson, A. P., and Wildy, P. 1959. The icosahedral form of an adenovirus. *J. Mol. Biol.* **1:** 84–86.

31. Horowitz, N. H. 1945. On the evolution of biochemical synthesis. *Proc. Natl. Acad. Sci. U.S.* **31:** 153–157.

32. Huggins, M. L. 1943. The structure of fibrous proteins. *Chem. Rev.* **32:** 195–218.

33. Hull, D. E. 1960. Thermodynamics and kinetics of spontaneous generation. *Nature* **186:** 693–694.

34a. Huxley, A. F. 1957. Muscle structure and theories of contraction. *Progr. Biophys. Biophys. Chem.* **7:** 257–318.

34b. Huxley, H. E. 1957. The double array of filaments in cross-striated muscle. *J. Biophys. Biochem. Cytol.* **3:** 631–648.

35. Kavanau, J. L. 1963. Structure and functions of biological membranes. *Nature* **198:** 525–530.

36. Kendrew, J. C., Dickerson, R. E., Strandberg, B. E., Hart, R. G., Davies, D. R., Phillips, D. C., and Shore, V. C. 1960. Structure of myoglobin. *Nature* **185:** 422–427.

37. Kendrew, J. C., Watson, H. C., Strandberg, B. E., Dickerson, R. E., Phillips, D. C., and Shore, V. C. 1961. A partial determination by x-ray methods, and its correlation with chemical data. *Nature* **190:** 666–670.

38. Klug, A., and Caspar, D. L. D. 1960. The structure of small viruses. *Advan. Virus Res.* **7:** 225–325.

39a. Langridge, R., Marvin, D. A., Seeds, W. E., Wilson, H. R., Hooper, C. W., Wilkins, M. H. F., and Hamilton, L. D. 1960. The molecular configuration of deoxyribonucleic acid. *J. Mol. Biol.* **2:** 38–64.

39b. Lemcke, R. 1963. Introducing the mycoplasmas. *New Scientist* **19:** 498–499.

40. Linderstrøm-Lang, K. 1952. "Proteins and Enzymes," Lane Medical Lectures, Stanford Univ. Publications, University Series, Medical Sciences, Vol. VI, pp. 1–115.

41. Miller, S. L. 1953. The production of amino acids under possible primitive earth conditions. *Science* **117:** 528–529.

42. Miller, S. L. 1959. Formation of organic compounds on the primitive earth. *In:* "Proc. Intern. Symp. Origin of Life on Earth, 1st, Moscow, 1957," (A. I. Oparin, A. E. Braunshstein, A. G. Pasynskii, and T. E. Pavlovskaya, eds.), pp. 123–135. Pergamon, New York.

43. Miller, S. L., and Urey, H. C. 1959. Organic compound synthesis on the primitive earth. *Science* **130:** 245–251.

44. Morowitz, H. J., Tourtellotte, M. E., Guild, W. R., Castro, E., Woese, C., and Cleverdon, R. C. 1962. The chemical composition and morphology of *Mycoplasma gallisepticum*, avian PPLO 5969. *J. Mol. Biol.* **4:** 93–103.

45. Mueller, G. 1962. Interpretation of micro-structures in carbonaceous meteorites. *Nature* **196:** 929–932.

46. Nagy, B., Meinschein, W. G., and Hennessy, D. J. 1961. International control of investigations of rare meteorites. [Discussion of their work in News and Views.] *Nature* **189:** 967–968.

47. Oparin, A. I. 1957. "Origin of Life on the Earth," 495 pp. Oliver and Boyd, Edinburgh.

48. Oró, J. F. 1961. Mechanism of synthesis of adenine from hydrogen cyanide under possible primitive earth conditions. *Nature* **191:** 1193–1194.

49a. Pauling, L., and Corey, R. B. 1951. Configurations of polypeptide chains with favored orientations around single bonds: two new pleated sheets. *Proc. Natl. Acad. Sci. U.S.* **37:** 729–740.

49b. Pauling, L., and Corey, R. B. 1953. A proposed structure for the nucleic acids. *Proc. Natl. Acad. Sci. U.S.* **39:** 84–97.

50. Pauling, L., Corey, R. B., and Branson, H. R. 1951. The structure of proteins: Two hydrogen-bonded helical configurations of the polypeptide chain. *Proc. Natl. Acad. Sci. U.S.* **37:** 205–211.

51. Perrett, J. 1952. Biochemistry and bacteria. *New Biology* **12:** 68–96.

52. Perutz, M. F., Rossmann, M. G., Cullis, A. F., Muirhead, H., Will, G., and North, A. C. T. 1960. Structure of haemoglobin: A three-dimensional Fourier synthesis at 5.5-Å. resolution, obtained by X-ray analysis. *Nature* **185:** 416–422.

53. Pirie, N. W. 1953. Ideas and assumptions about the origin of life. *Discovery* **14:** 238–242.

54. Rich, A. 1959. Molecular structure of the nucleic acids. *Rev. Mod. Phys.* **31:** 191–199.

55a. Robertson, J. D. 1957. New observations on the ultrastructure of the membranes of frog peripheral nerve fibres. *J. Biophys. Biochem. Cytol.* **3:** 1043–1047.

55b. Robinson, R. (Private communication.)

56. Ryle, A. P., Sanger, F., Smith, L. F., and Kital, R. 1955. The disulphide bonds of insulin. *Biochem. J.* **60:** 541–556.

57. Sherrington, C. S. 1946. "The Endeavour of Jean Fernel," 224 pp. Macmillan, Toronto.

58. Sleigh, M. A. 1962. "The Biology of Cilia and Flagella," 242 pp. Pergamon, London.

59. Thompson, D'A. W. 1942. "On Growth and Form," 2nd rev. ed., 1116 pp. Univ. Press, Cambridge.

60. Turkevitch, J., and Smith, R. K. 1946. Unitary theory of hydrocarbon catalytic reactions. *Nature* **157:** 874.

61. van Bruggen, E. F. J., Wiebenga, E., and Gruber, M. 1962. Structures and properties of hemocyanins. I and II. *J. Mol. Biol.* **4:** 1–9.

62. Watson, J. D. 1954. The structure of tobacco mosaic virus. I. X-ray evidence of a helical arrangement of sub-units around the longitudinal axis. *Biochim. Biophys. Acta* **13:** 10–19.

63. Waugh, D. F., Wilhelmson, D. F., Commerford, S. L., and Sackler, M. L. 1953. The nucleation and growth reactions of selected types of insulin fibrils. *J. Am. Chem. Soc.* **75:** 2592–2600.

64. Zuckerkandl, E., and Pauling, L. 1962. Molecular disease, evolution, and genic heterogeneity. *In:* "Horizons in Biochemistry," (M. Kasha and B. Pullman, eds.), pp. 189–255. Academic, New York.

65. The origin of prebiological systems. Report of a conference at Wakulla Springs, Florida, 1963 (in press).

66. The physical and chemical basis of muscular contraction. *Proc. Roy. Soc.* (*London*) **B** (in press).

[6]

THEORY, EXPERIMENT, AND THE NERVE IMPULSE

Kenneth S. Cole

Theory and experiment have much in common, in biology as they have in the physical sciences. A theoretical model is a logical consequence of the assumptions upon which it is constructed. An experimental fact is the necessary consequence of the conditions under which it is observed. To the extent that a model and a fact correspond there is basis to expect that the principal assumptions of the theory represent the principal conditions of the experiment. Some assumptions and models have been so well and so often confirmed as to have achieved an *a priori* strength above that of any single experiment, and some empirical generalizations of numerous experiments may have much of the power of a theory even in ignorance of the appropriate ingredients for an adequate model.

Theory and experiment thus appear in competition with each other, but it is undeniable that neither can make much progress without the other. Theory alone cannot know how far from reality it may have been taken by wrong assumptions. Unguided experiment may create such a wilderness of fact that difficult problems overlie and obscure a simple and a beautiful pattern.

In biology, particularly, with its vast variety of forms and functions, experiment usually could not give firm basis for the development of theory and had to proceed without the help and the challenge of solid organization to guide it. However, the study of the electrical properties of biological systems has been an early, important, and almost unique exception. After a century and a half of confusion and but faltering progress, simple—almost elementary—concepts of classical physics and communication engineering were introduced. With experiment to guide theory and theory to assist experiment, a powerful description of the structure and function of cells and tissues in electrical and ionic terms has been evolved.

I. BIOELECTRIC HISTORY[9]

It was known, long before Franklin, that living things conducted electricity and that static machines and charged Leyden jars produced shocks. And it was in investigating the effects of static electricity on nerves that toward the end of the eighteenth century Galvani touched off electrophysiology as well as the classical study of electricity and electrochemistry.

136

Since then nerve has been a constant problem and a nearly constant controversy. Dr. Eric Ponder has told of a theory that nerve conduction was accomplished by light pulses. But when a curious experimenter saw no light at the cut end of a stimulated nerve he was told, "Well, of course, it disappeared when you looked for it." Then it was argued that, since nerves connected with the brain and must be related with the soul, the speed of the nerve impulse must be immeasurably fast. But von Helmholtz took care of this by showing in 1850 that a frog sciatic nerve conducted at only 100 meters per second. In the same period much else was done, of which DuBois-Reymond's work on animal electricity, 1848, is outstanding.

Rather apart from this was the investigation of the passive electric properties of tissues and organisms that stemmed from the appearance of Ohm's Law in 1827. Human skin received considerable attention, but interest waned as it was found that the measured values of volts per ampere, which should be ohms, depended upon time, the direction and the magnitude of current, and bore no respectable relation to electrode sizes and separations. Kohlrausch, however, surmounted these same difficulties for electrolytes and, along with his contributions to electrochemistry, gave the biologists a method which was one of their early sources of quantitative, reproducible measurements. It is also a method that has had an almost continual development and application up to the present.

Soon after the turn of the century these two lines of studying the electric structure and function of cells were brilliantly, if only momentarily, brought together by the membrane hypothesis of Bernstein.[3] He suggested first that living cells were electrolytes surrounded by a poorly permeable membrane, next that this membrane supported an electrical potential with the inside negative, and then that in activity the membrane became so permeable to ions as to abolish the potential.

From here neurophysiology[54] proceeded by a series of major advances. Lucas,[59] in 1909, and Adrian,[1] in 1914, firmly established the all-or-none law that the impulse transmitted by a single fiber was determined only by its characteristic at each point of distance and time; Lapicque[56] showed that the relation between a stimulating current and its duration was essentially the same, except for scale factors, for many excitable tissues; and finally Rashevsky,[73] Monnier,[63] Hill,[41] and Katz[54] showed that excitation may be opposed by the slower process called accommodation.

$$dU/dt = a_{11}U + a_{12}V + a_{13}I; \quad dV/dt = a_{21}U + a_{22}V + a_{33}I \tag{1}$$

In Equation (1) excitation is given by U, accommodation, V, various coefficients, a_{ij}, and the stimulus, I. These two factors are essentially not defined except in terms of the threshold which is a critical difference between U and V. Even without physical interpretation this two-factor formulation has been very useful.

On the passive side there were rather fewer, but still many, measurements on tissues. Notably among these Höber[42-44] showed by high- and low-frequency measurements in Nernst's laboratory that the red blood cell has a membrane and an interior with the conductivity of biological electrolytes. Osterhout[68] measured the conductance changes in injury, recovery, and death in *Laminaria* at low frequency and attributed them to membrane changes.

All of this, however, was but an essentially untheoretical and unmathematical background and a prelude to certainly one of the first and perhaps the most continuingly successful theoretical and experimental physical analyses of biological structure and function.

II. MEMBRANE CAPACITY

A. Early Measurements

Probably because of Crile's interest in the conductivity of mammalian tissues, Fricke[34] worked on the electrical characteristics of red blood cell suspensions. First, considering the cell as a nonconducting sphere in a uniform field, he took as a first approximation the classical solution in zonal harmonics for the potential at and near it. By calculating the electrostatic energy of the membrane he then determined its capacity from measurements of the capacity of a suspension, the volume concentration of cells and their effective radius. This came to 0.8 $\mu f/cm^2$ and, thinking of the membrane as an oil, he chose a dielectric constant of 3 to obtain the thickness of 33 A, or about the length of a single oil molecule. He further integrated the current flow around and, at high frequencies, through the cell to obtain a measurement of the volume concentration at low frequencies and of the internal conductivity at high frequencies. He then put together the equivalent circuit of the suspension (Figure 1a), and verified it by measurements with Morse[36] from 800 cycles to 4.5 megacycles. Thus good theory and experiment gave in 1925 the first, and probably still the best, evidence for the molecular dimensions of a living cell membrane.

It is worth remembering that shortly before this, Philippson[71,72] had measured the impedance of several tissues over a wide frequency range. He guessed that a parallel capacity and resistance could represent the cell membranes and a series resistance the cytoplasm (Figure 1b). McClendon[60] had also made excellent measurements of packed red cells.

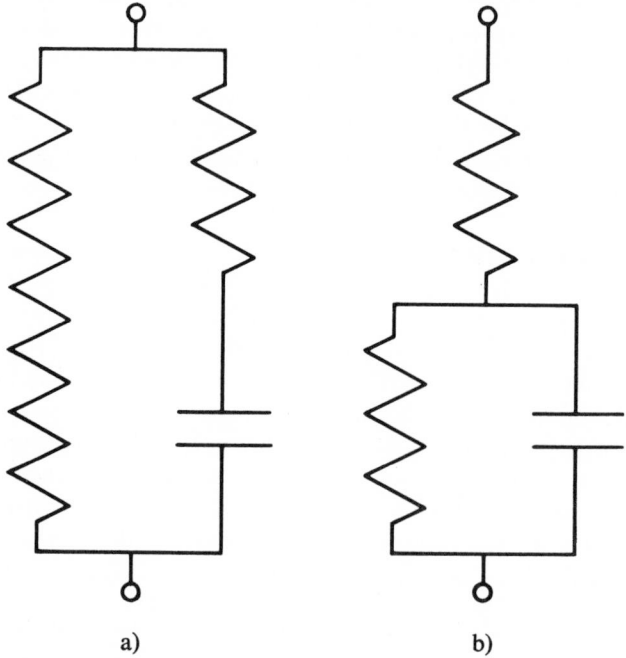

a)   b)

FIGURE 1. Equivalent circuits for suspensions and tissues: a) corresponds to theory; b) is based on intuition. (Redrawn from Cole.[7])

Most ingeniously, he packed his cells so tightly that he was sure no current could flow between them. Then on the basis of the same circuit (Figure 1b) he derived a large value for the membrane capacity and a membrane conductance. In retrospect this has seemed a great misfortune and a grim lesson. Although this is a different circuit from the one Fricke chose on the basis of theory (Figure 1a), it is easily shown that measurements alone cannot tell these two circuits apart. Had McClendon but picked the other circuit he too would have obtained the answer that Fricke got by analysis and which seems increasingly certain to be the better one.

B. Impedance of Suspensions and Tissues[22]

The theory of suspensions has been considerably improved and the measurements have been extended to many forms and tissues. Fricke[34-36] turned immediately, and again recently, to ellipsoidal harmonics for the resistance and capacity of suspensions of spheroids as a better representation of red cells. By using the complex admittance concept I found that the Clausius-Mossotti local field theory of dielectrics and Maxwell's two-phase sphere gave[7] a better and a general expression up to higher volume concentrations. An analogous development for parallel cylinders was belatedly found to be a similar extension of Rayleigh's work.

$$Z = r_1 \frac{(1 - \rho)r_1 + (\gamma + \rho)(r_2 + Z_m/a)}{(1 - \gamma\rho)r_1 + \gamma(1 - \rho)(r_2 + Z_m/a)} \qquad (2)$$

Equation (2) is the impedance, Z, of a suspension that is random but uniform, and it involves among other things a volume concentration, ρ, the shape factor, γ, and characteristics of the membrane surface of the cells, Z_m. This gave a red cell capacity of about 1 $\mu f/cm^2$. If the membrane is in fact the pure capacity to be expected of a thin nonconducting layer, this is a bilinear equation. When we express the impedance in terms of a dissipative part R, which gives rise to heat, and a conservative part iX, where the energy is later returned, complex variable theory predicts that this equation should be a semicircle. The original data of Fricke on red blood cells is nearly a semicircle (Figure 2). Fricke found, as had Philippson, that the membrane capacity varied somewhat with frequency, as had long been known for electrode polarization. Then on the complex impedance plane the semicircle became a circular arc with a depressed center.

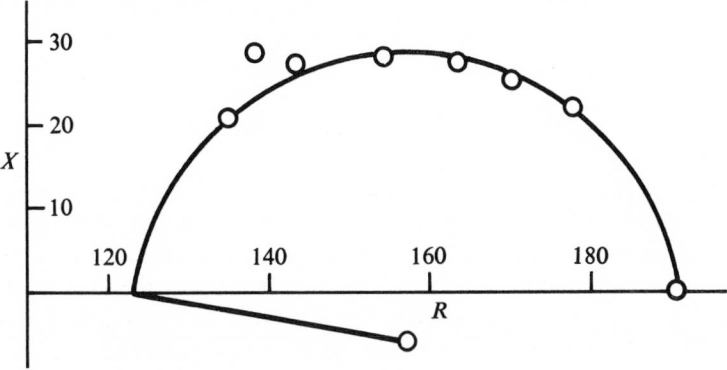

FIGURE 2. Complex impedance locus for red blood cell suspension: R is series resistance; X, series reactance. (Data from Fricke and Morse;[36] redrawn from Cole.[8])

On the experimental side there has been an impressive array of work that cannot be covered in detail. Fricke and Curtis worked on both red and white blood cells,[34,36] *Chlorella*, a bacterium, and yeast[35] and uncovered a new component at low frequencies. Our group at Columbia[19,20,25] worked on several echinoderm eggs, muscle, whole nerve, and, among other unpublished results, *Laminaria*. The Frankfurt group published the characteristics of a variety of mammalian tissues, not always reducible to cell membrane properties. Since World War II, Schwan and his collaborators[70,75–78] have considerably extended the frequency range at both ends, and have progressed downward in size from muscle, to bacteria, to mitochondria, and to pleuropneumonia-like organisms. They have also obtained data on tissues *in situ* and interpreted low- and high-frequency phenomena.

The general conclusions drawn from experiments on suspensions are that all cells, from the largest to the smallest, have membranes with capacities of about 1 $\mu f/cm^2$, that some of these membrane capacities have a loss component with the characteristics often found in solid dielectrics, and that the cell interiors have conductances in the range of those of biological electrolytes, of the order of 100 ohm cm. These are indeed amazing generalizations.

The first correlates somewhat with the electron microscope results. The railroad tracks seen running hither and yon in sections of fixed tissue, stained with a heavy metal and imbedded in plastic, thus seem to be at least a reasonable facsimile of the membrane of a living cell. The dielectric-like loss mechanism has received much attention. For a while it seemed possible that a distribution of cell sizes and capacities might account for it. But more work has shown that it is indeed the property of a single membrane, and without going into detail we can only say that the answers seem to lie in solid state theory yet to come.

Beyond these generalizations there were increasingly apparent difficulties. There is still no analysis of current flow around and through cells in high volume concentrations such as are found in most tissues. The almost insidious anomalies at frequencies below one kilocycle have become increasingly important as will be shown later. The indications at the high megacycle frequencies were that the cell interior is not the simple electrolyte assumed.

But the most worrisome difficulty was the nearly complete absence of any hint that ions might pass through a living cell membrane. Obviously metabolites had to cross the membrane to keep the cell alive. But it was not so compellingly obvious that ions too had to cross because the electrical potential across the membrane was not yet known to change as Bernstein[3] had so shrewdly guessed. However, there seemed to be some hope after Blinks obtained first a value of 5000 ohm cm^2 for the *Valonia* membranes[4] and then 100,000 ohm cm^2 for *Nitella*.[5] Much more has followed the pioneering work with cell suspensions, and still more needs to be done.

III. SQUID GIANT AXON

All of the above progress was only a prelude to John Z. Young's rediscovery of the giant nerve system of the squid in 1936[84] and his introduction of the use of the hindmost stellar nerve that has led so many of us so unsuspectingly into our present fabulous era.[16,45]

Long before, a friendly biologist had told me that nerve was the kind of thing I ought to be interested in; it was built somewhat like a cable and a physicist was supposed to know about cables. I asked about the resistance of the core, but he had no idea. What about the insulation? The leakage and the capacity are important parameters. "Nobody knows any of these things." This was both discouraging and intriguing. Although we did

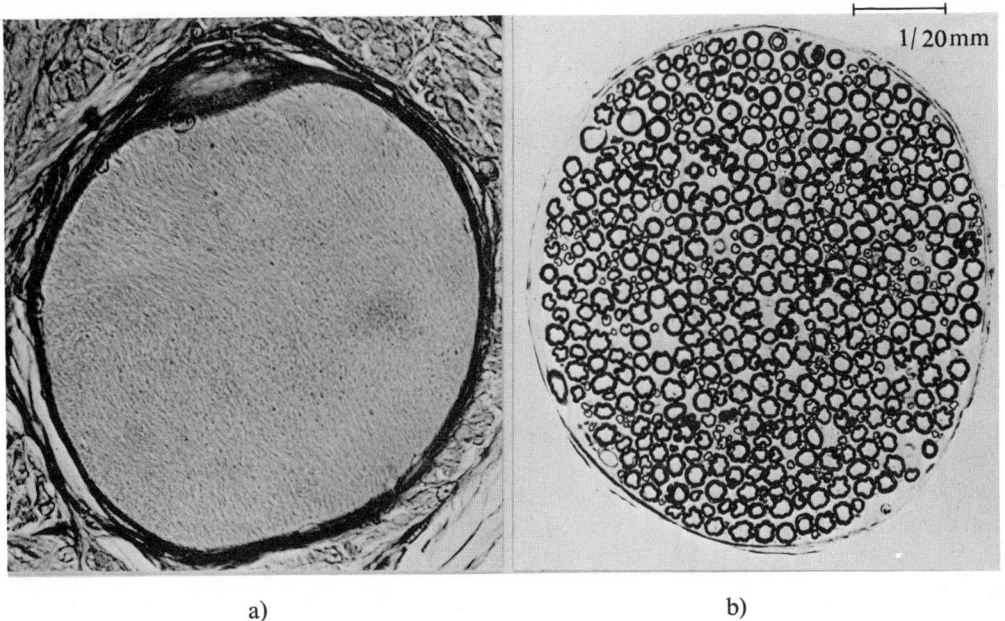

FIGURE 3. Micrographs of a) squid giant axon, and b) rabbit leg nerve. (From Young.[85])

work initially with several nerves we did not get anywhere until the squid giant axon appeared.

The reason for the importance of this neuron is shown in Figure 3 in which the vast cross-section of one of these axons, with an average diameter of 0.5 mm or 500 μ, is compared with the more usual axons in a rabbit leg nerve. We measured the axon by the familiar cell suspension technique, and it was no great surprise that the value for the membrane capacity also came out 1 μf/cm^2, with an internal conductivity of about 30 ohm cm. But we could detect no leakage or conductance for the membrane and we had to use a different approach. Hodgkin and I[23] used the arrangement of Figure 4 with a squid axon about 5 cm long, and sea-water electrodes. The resistance, R, between these was measured as the electrodes were moved to give the points along the curve. Once again potential theory was invoked, this time in the form introduced by Lord Kelvin in his work on the first Atlantic cable, to give the equation

$$R = \frac{r_1 r_2}{r_1 + r_2} s + \frac{2r_1^2 \lambda}{(r_1 + r_2)(\kappa + \coth s/2\lambda)} \tag{3}$$

The separation between the electrodes, s, is the independent variable and the equation is represented by the solid line, for a membrane resistance of 1000 ohm cm^2. Most surprisingly this value for the squid axon is of the same order of magnitude as for many other animal cell membranes at rest.

A. Impulse Propagation

Now that all the cable characteristics of the axon were known, its behavior at different distances from the point at which a very short stimulus was applied could be predicted from Kelvin's treatment, as in Figure 5a. The pulse decreases very rapidly, and moves more slowly,

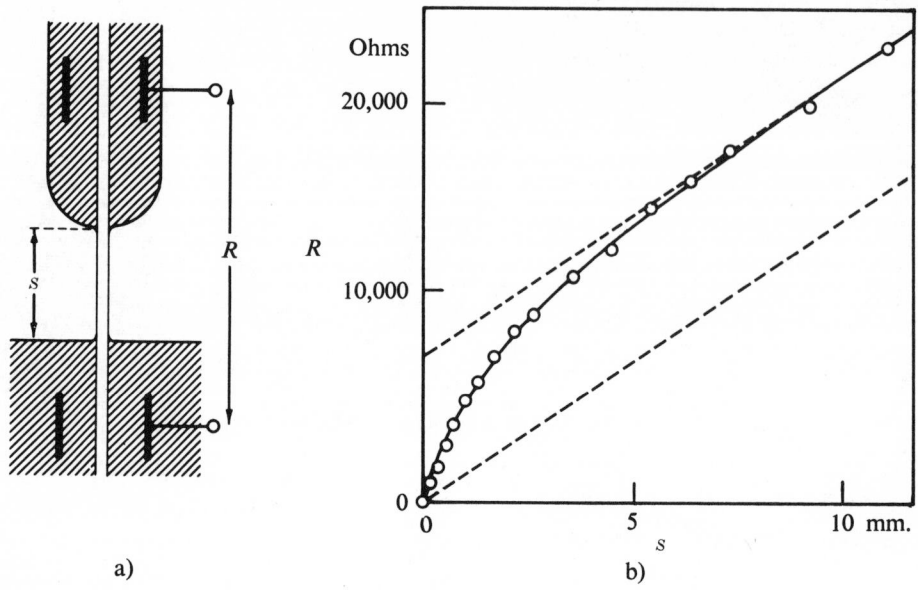

a)   b)

FIGURE 4. Membrane resistance of squid giant axon. a) Experimental arrangement for measuring resistance R against length s; b) experimental points and cable theory curve. (From Cole and Hodgkin.[23])

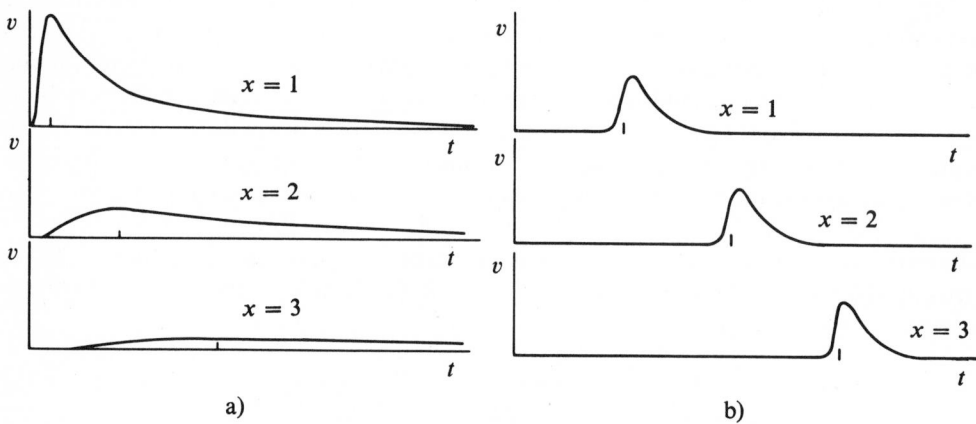

a)   b)

FIGURE 5. Potential, v, against time, t, after a short pulse applied at $x = 0$, $t = 0$ for the three distances, $x = 1, 2$, and 3, with all variables given in arbitrary units. a) is calculated for the spread of potential in a passive cable. The index on the time axis marks the maximum of potential at each distance, to show that the potential at the successive distances is not only drastically altered but also progresses with a continually decreasing speed. b) is an approximate representation of the behavior of uniform single nerve fibers as a result of initial impulse stimulation somewhat above threshold. The index on the time axis marks the point of inflection of the potential which may be taken as the time of arrival of the active process at each distance. This shows, in contrast to the passive cable, that disturbance in the axon moves at a constant speed as well as with a constant wave form of a constant amplitude.

the farther it travels along the axon. This is completely useless for biological communication; it would take some kilovolts at the spinal cord to produce millivolts at the finger tip, and that would only come some seconds later. Nature had to do considerably better than that. In fact, it is well known that at the same intervals of distance the impulse maintains the same height and the same wave form and is traveling with a uniform velocity (Figure 5b). This is indeed a beautiful performance by the cell, but it led us from simple, straight-forward physics into a deluge of confusion.

First we used *Nitella*, a plant cell of about the same size as the squid axon, that carries an apparently useless impulse with an almost unbelievably slow conduction rate of centimeters instead of tens of meters per second. The impedance of the membrane was measured (Figure 6a) at several different frequencies and was found to decrease, and then to recover as the impulse went past.[19] In Equation (2) the membrane may be represented by a capacity

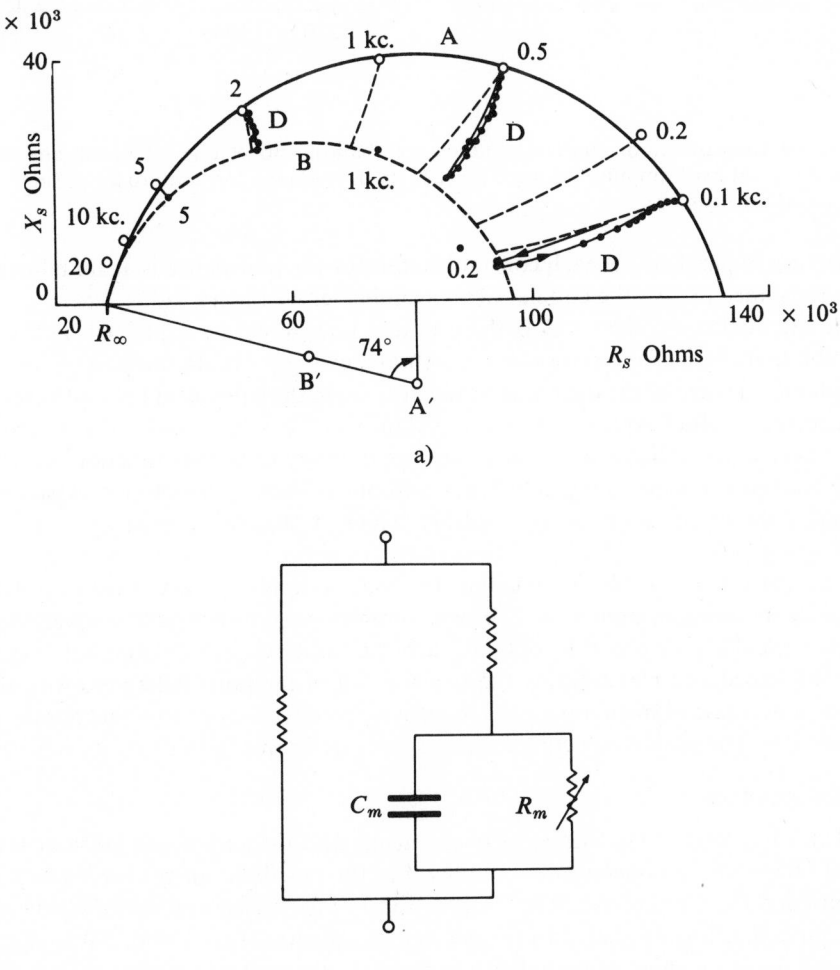

FIGURE 6. a) Complex impedance loci for *Nitella* during the passage of impulses at the indicated frequencies. b) Equivalent circuit with varying membrane conductance. (Redrawn from Cole and Curtis,[19] and Cole.[16])

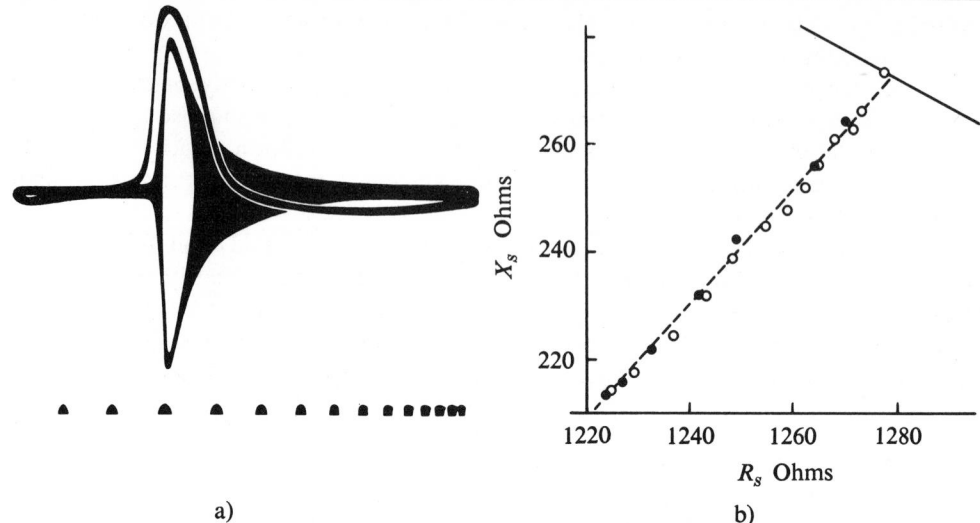

FIGURE 7. a) Increase of membrane conductance (band), and change of membrane potential (line) during squid axon impulse. 1 msec marks. b) Impedance locus at 10 kc during impulse. (From Cole and Curtis.[20])

and resistance in parallel. At each constant frequency the impedance is again bilinear for a variable resistance to give the circular arcs, as indicated in Figure 6a.

To the extent that the data follow these dotted lines, they are explained by the simple assumption that the leakage across this membrane changes during the passage of the impulse without a change of the membrane capacity. So in the equivalent circuit the resistance of the membrane, often expressed as a conductance, is the only variable (Figure 6b). Here again we have a generalization, found to be true in many cells, that function is correlated with the change of membrane conductance without change of membrane capacity. One exception is the fertilization of egg cells in which a change in capacity is sometimes found.[25]

After having found on *Nitella* that Bernstein was certainly correct in his postulate that permeability increases in excitation, the next summer we returned to the squid axon and were not particularly surprised to obtain much the same results[20] (Figure 7a). Again the path on the impedance plane during the rise and fall of the potential agrees with that expected for a decrease of membrane conductance without a change of the membrane capacity (Figure 7b). The peak conductance increase averaged some forty times its value at rest.

B. *Inside An Axon*

All of this had been done with electrodes outside and we were doing more or less conventional things with an unconventional fiber, but the possibility of getting inside the fiber really intrigued Dr. Curtis. When he proposed inserting an electrode down inside to measure the potential, I remember, to my considerable chagrin, that I said, "Well, so what? All you will see is an action potential upside down." But we[26] went ahead at Woods Hole, at the same time as Hodgkin and Huxley[47] did in Plymouth. Both at Plymouth and Woods Hole a considerable overshoot was found in the directly measured action potential (Figure 8a). Whereas Bernstein's hypothesis would have the potential only approaching zero, the observed rise was much more than this, and overshot zero by some tens of millivolts. This

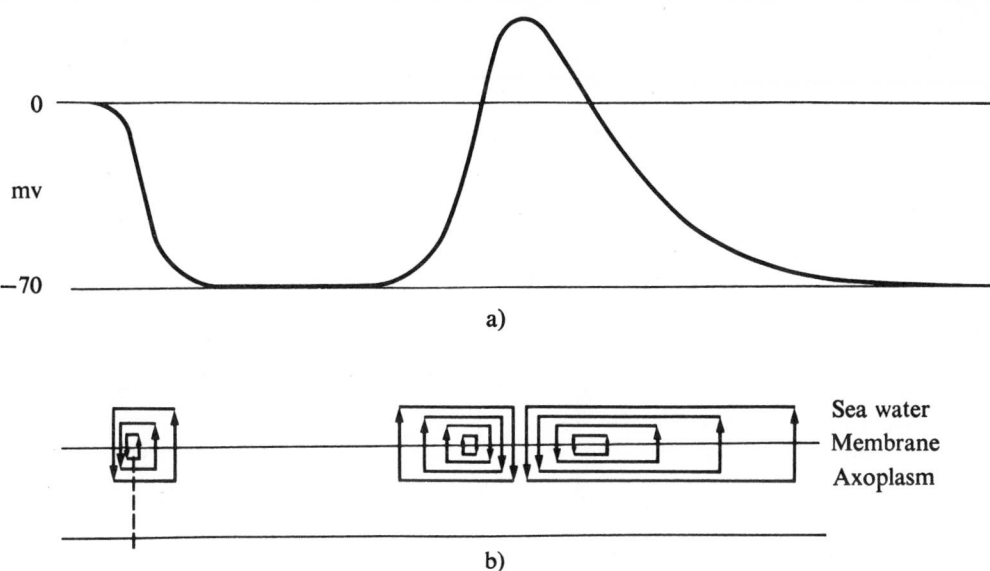

FIGURE 8. a) Membrane potential along a squid axon for an impulse moving toward the killed (depolarized) end at the left. b) Local circuit paths of current flow for the action potential and the end. (Redrawn from Curtis and Cole,[26] and Cole.[16])

too has become rather the trademark of an excitable tissue where the action potential usually exceeds the resting potential. And once again new explanations were in order.

C. Nonlinear Membranes

If only we could have realized it, we were deeply involved in the broad, difficult, and then relatively primitive field of nonlinearity. Something was changing the membrane conductance and from the cable theory, or the local circuit theory as it was then called, we could calculate current flow through a membrane as shown in Figure 8b, so it seemed that this conductance might depend upon current flow to be nonlinear. Conductance measurements made 1) at very high frequencies, and 2) with a very nice assist from cable theory, at long times, both show (Figures 9a, b) that current flow did indeed produce radical changes of conductance consistent with a high degree of nonlinearity. Then there was a most bewildering observation that Hodgkin and I had first made but set aside for a number of years. This required that, in addition to the capacity characteristic to be expected from the cell membrane, this structure behaved, quite unreasonably, as an inductance (Figure 10). In fact such behavior would ordinarily be obtained in a physical laboratory by an inductance of 0.1 henry, which requires that a mile of small wire wound on a pound of iron must match a square cm of membrane that is probably only 100 A thick!

All these results can be put together rather simply as a consequence of the nature of nonlinear systems.[10,12] Quite generally the mechanism responsible for a nonlinear characteristic appears to operate at a finite rate. An example is the so-called rectification curve of current, i, versus potential, e, for a squid axon membrane as in Figure 11a. Small slow changes can be represented by the conductance g_∞ because the nonlinear mechanism is in its steady state for each point along the curve. But for sufficiently short durations or high frequencies the mechanism will be unable to respond and a different conductance g_0 will

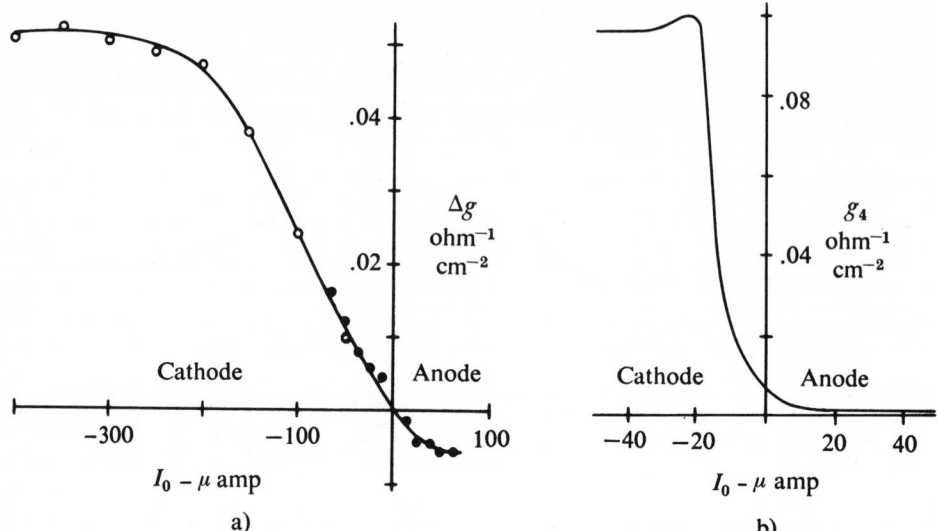

FIGURE 9. Squid axon membrane conductances as functions of current: a) at high frequencies (redrawn from Cole and Baker[17]); b) at long times (redrawn from Cole and Curtis.[21])

be measured. When it is then assumed that the nonlinear process proceeds in proportion to its time constant τ and to the difference from the steady state characteristic, the response may be described formally[10,12] by

$$\frac{di}{dt} = g_0 \frac{de}{dt} + (i - g_\infty e)/\tau \qquad (4)$$

Both the transient and the steady state sinusoidal behaviors at intermediate times and frequencies are then either capacitative or inductive according to the sign of $g_0 - g_\infty$ and

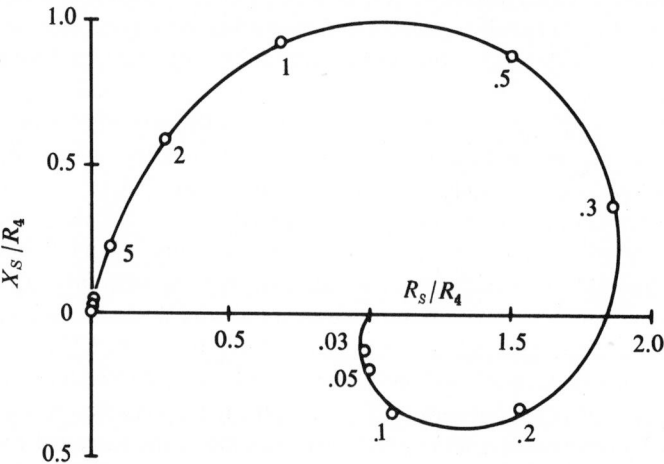

FIGURE 10. Complex plane impedance for squid axon membrane showing an anomalous inductive reactance. Components are in relative units, and frequencies in kc. (Redrawn from Cole and Baker.[18])

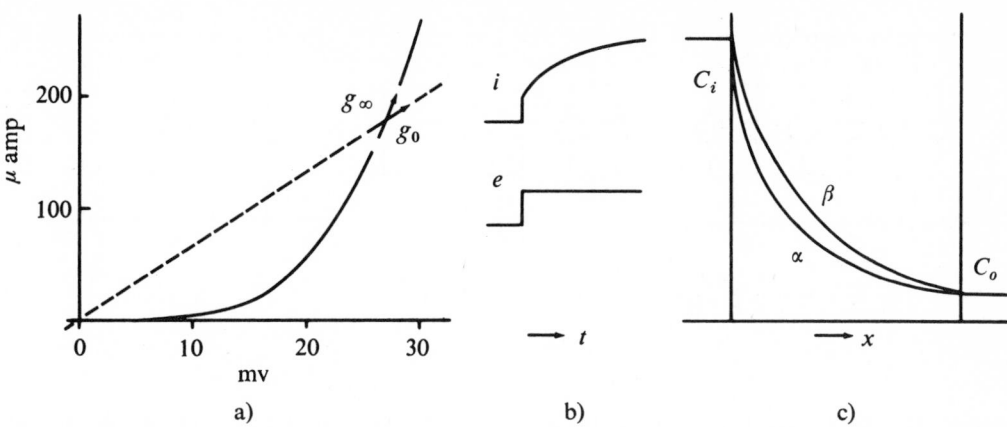

FIGURE 11. a) A nonlinear characteristic for squid axon membrane with a steady state conductance, g_∞, and an instantaneous conductance, g_0. (Redrawn from Cole.[16]) b) Transient change of current, i, for a sudden change of potential, e. c) Ion concentration change within a membrane for a sudden change of potential from the initial profile, α, to the final steady state distribution, β.

the observed and predicted reactance is anomalous in that it is produced by other than the usual mechanism.

The details for such a mechanism might be as shown in Figure 11c for an ion-permeable membrane separating electrolytes of two different concentrations. At the operating point the steady state concentration profile across the membrane is represented by curve α. At the time of a small sudden increase of the potential there will be a sudden increase of the current through the conductance of the membrane, g_0. As the current continues to flow, ions will accumulate within the membrane until the new steady state profile, represented by β, is reached. During this process, the ion concentration at each point increases and the over-all conductance increases to the steady state value, g_∞. The current then also increases to its steady state value as it would in a linear circuit including an inductance (Figure 11b). Although this is a useful qualitative example it has not yet been possible to derive a theoretical value of the time constant, τ, for it. This can, however, be estimated from another approach to be mentioned later.

IV. TAMING THE AXON

Although considerable progress had been made towards an understanding of the phenomena and mechanisms of nonlinearity in the membrane, there was no certain indication as to what made the nerve impulse go. We did a considerable amount of theorizing and experimentation on the initiation of excitation and its propagation. These were much too complicated to be helpful except to demonstrate the complexity of the problem.

Although the Kelvin cable equation in its general form (Figure 12a) was clearly quite adequate, it was also much too difficult for us to handle. Even in a physical cable or an axon near its rest potential, where the leakage current flow is proportional to a change of membrane potential, the analytical solutions require a moderate amount of mathematical sophistication. The examples given in Figure 5 were expressed as a probability integral in

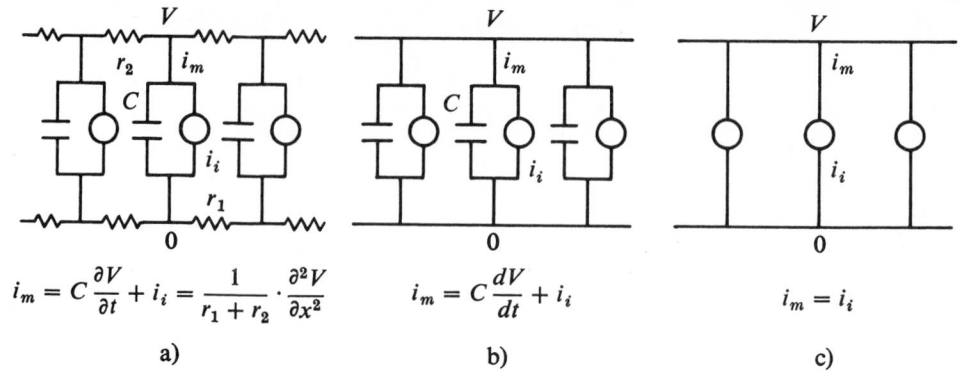

$$i_m = C\frac{\partial V}{\partial t} + i_i = \frac{1}{r_1 + r_2} \cdot \frac{\partial^2 V}{\partial x^2}$$

a)

$$i_m = C\frac{dV}{dt} + i_i$$

b)

$$i_m = i_i$$

c)

FIGURE 12. Equivalent cable circuits for an axon: a) normal axon and partial differential equation representation; b) axon with internal and external electrodes to eliminate spatial variations and to give the ordinary differential equation; c) after a change of potential between these electrodes only an ionic current flows across the membrane. V, inside potential of membrane relative to outside, O; C, membrane capacity; r_1, r_2, outside and inside longitudinal resistances; i_m, i_i, membrane and ionic currents; x, t, distance and time. (Redrawn from Cole and Moore.[24])

the variable $x/\sqrt{t}$. But for a known nonlinear relationship, such solutions are in general not possible and numerical solutions may tax the power of modern computers. Consequently, it seemed entirely hopeless to extract an unknown relationship between potential, v, and current, i, from phenomena which were solutions of this parabolic partial differential equation.

The first simplification of the problem came soon after World War II, when Marmont[61] proposed replacing the internal potential electrode with a current-carrying electrode along the axis of the axon and flanking an external electrode by guards at each end of it. Thus both the current and potential would be uniform over the central measuring region and the partial differential equation in time and distance would be replaced by an ordinary differential equation in time alone, as in Figure 12b. Del Castillo and Moore[27] have recently shown how effective this "space clamp," as it is now called, can be. They first fired an impulse along an axon and measured the action potential at two points 15 mm apart (Figure 13a) to give a normal velocity of about 20 m/sec. They then inserted a platinized

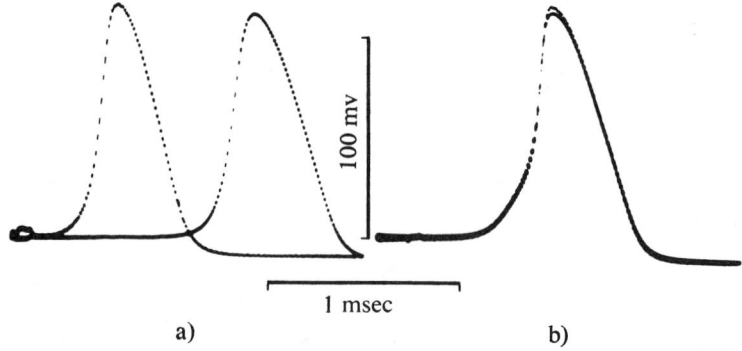

100 mv

1 msec

a)   b)

FIGURE 13. a) Normal impulse propagation past two microelectrodes in squid axon; b) simultaneous responses at these electrodes after the insertion of an axial electrode in axon. (Modified from del Castillo and Moore.[27])

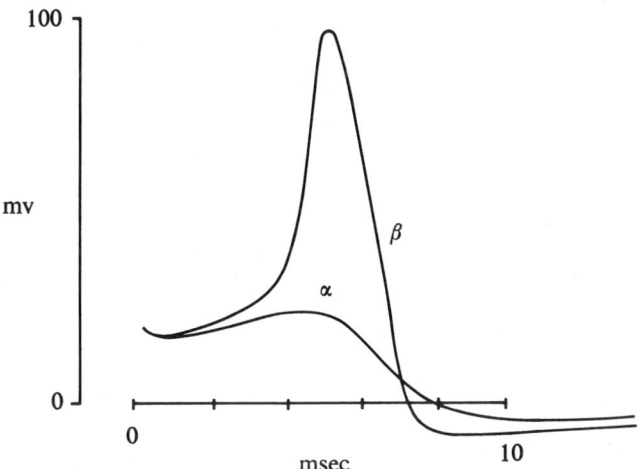

FIGURE 14. Near-threshold responses of "space-current clamped" squid axon. Curve α is result of just subthreshold current pulse; curve β, result of threshold current pulse. The membrane current was zero except for a short initial pulse. (Cole and Marmont, unpublished.)

platinum wire along the axis and repeated the experiment. In this case the potential change is practically synchronous over the whole of the axon (Figure 13b), giving an almost infinite velocity for the impulse, far exceeding anything nature has done without a wire!

With this arrangement, the membrane capacity and, for small currents, the membrane resistance were both shown directly to be about the same as previously found. If a short pulse of just subthreshold outward current flow suddenly raised the potential of the inside of the membrane, then after the current was returned to zero, the potential across the membrane rose slightly but then turned to come back to its initial value (Figure 14, α). For a current pulse only a few per cent larger, the potential rose with increasing rapidity to give a full-blown all-or-none spike (Figure 14, β). It was closely similar to the spike of a propagating impulse although this one was standing still, with all parts of the membrane doing the same thing at the same time and with no net current flow, i_m, across the membrane. Thus the ionic current, i_i, could be computed from the rate of change of membrane potential. This showed, quite directly, as had been computed without any great confidence from propagating impulses, that the ionic current was flowing inward as the inside of the membrane was becoming more positive and even exceeding the resting potential. The membrane capacity was thus providing current for the ionic path that had the characteristic of a negative resistance from which unstable behavior might be expected.

A. *Negative Resistance Analogs*

A negative resistance is not an easy concept to deal with. It is found in many physical systems that might be used for illustration. But since none of the mechanisms seemed reasonably possible in an axon membrane, it was useful to consider other analogies.

As the ordinary spring of Figure 15a is compressed, the force required increases. But the linkage and spring arrangement of Figure 15b is quite different.* Here the force

* The history of this ingenious device is unknown to the author.

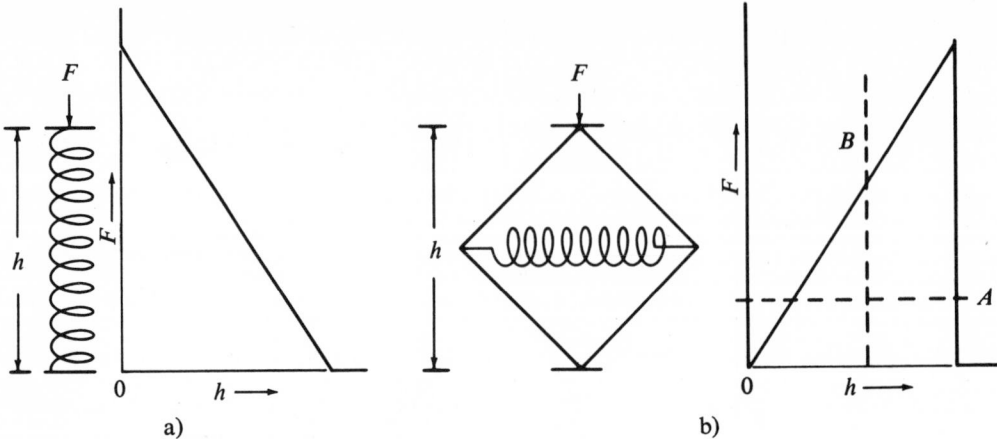

FIGURE 15. a) Force-length characteristics for an ordinary spring; b) for a "negative spring" linkage. The negative region is unstable under the "force clamp" *A*, and stable for the "length clamp" *B*.

decreases steadily from the large initial value to become zero as it is compressed and then rises rapidly again when stopped at the bottom. Since the ordinary spring is characterized by the ratio of force to shortening, this arrangement may be called a "negative spring."

The performance of this spring depends upon what it is to do. If it is opposed by a very weak spring, such as a weight on top which provides a "force clamp," there are the three equilibrium positions, given by line *A*. The upper and lower positions are stable but the center one is unstable because the weight will continue to rise or fall after it is moved above or below this position. This is somewhat analogous to nerve excitation. As we increase the potential above the resting potential at the bottom, we come to the unstable, threshold position after which the weight is carried to the top or spike. In the face of such instability it would be almost as difficult to determine the characteristics of this "spring" by the use of weights alone as it is to investigate an axon membrane with constant currents, now known as a "current clamp."

On the other hand, if this negative spring is opposed by the much stronger, positive spring which provides a "length clamp," given by line *B*, there is but a single equilibrium position and it is stable. Thus we might expect to avoid the threshold and the other usual unstable characteristics of nerve by applying a constant potential, or "voltage clamp," to the membrane. It then seems that there should be a transition between the unstable and the stable situations (Figure 15b, *A* and *B*, respectively). We can expect, as is correct, that this occurs when force is applied through a positive spring which just balances the negative spring. Then the strength of the critical positive spring, such as given by the slope of Figure 15a, will be numerically equal to the slope in the negative spring region of Figure 15b.

Another useful and more usual analogy is the ordinary gunpowder fuse. This can be "space clamped" by applying heat uniformly over a length of the powder. After a small amount of heat the temperature rise will be too small to burn an appreciable amount of powder before even the small heat losses return it to the initial temperature. A larger supply of heat can raise the temperature to a point where the heat of combustion exceeds the losses and the ensuing, near adiabatic, flash is analogous to the membrane "current clamp." Similarly, by removing the heat as it is produced, a steady burning under isothermal conditions is the counterpart of the "voltage clamp."

Another, and the most complete, analogy is the passive iron wire model of an axon of Ostwald[69] and Lillie.[57,58] In fact, it was for this model that the possible power of a voltage clamp was first recognized. This approach has been used extensively by Bartlett[2] and Franck[32] but the mechanisms are not yet fully understood.

B. Squid Axon Voltage Clamp

The next stage for the control of the squid axon membrane was to restrict the membrane potential (Figure 12c). As the membrane potential was changed rapidly from the resting potential to a more positive potential, the capacitive membrane current was held at zero after an initial transient. The current flow then was restricted to the ionic path, i_i, and the constant potential might not allow this pathway, with its negative resistance characteristic, to indulge in its normal, unstable, threshold and excitation performance. The potential was controlled electronically as shown in Figure 16a. The potential between the axial and external electrodes was compared with a command signal, E, and the control amplifier, δ, provided the current, I, necessary to make the potential follow the command.

One of the first families of records for the membrane current after the potential had been increased by different amounts is shown in Figure 17. These currents were found to be entirely continuous functions of time and potential without any indications of instability. The inward current appearing for a potential increase between 18 and 27.5 mv was in the direction to increase the membrane potential of an uncontrolled membrane and was thus adequate to account for a threshold.

The maximum of inward current between 38 and 64 mv leads one to expect a maximum rate of increase for the potential in this range. The disappearance of the inward current between 64 and 128 mv will then limit the change of potential, or the height of the action

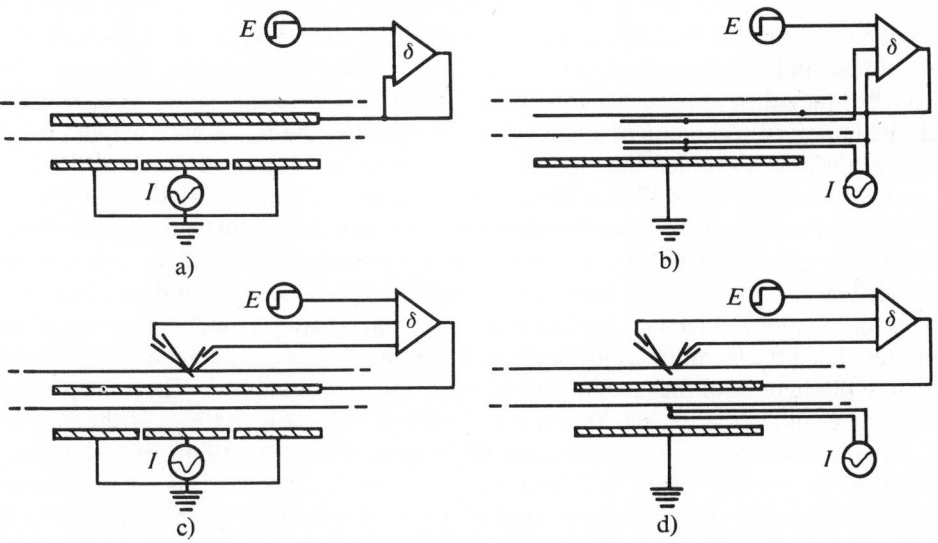

FIGURE 16.   Development of squid axon voltage clamp techniques to measure membrane current *I* as membrane potential is forced to follow command *E* by control amplifier δ: a) with a single axial current and potential electrode; b) with added internal and external electrodes for potential and current measurements; c) with an internal micropipette and external reversible electrodes to measure local potential; and d) with added external differential electrodes to measure local current density. (Redrawn from Cole.[15])

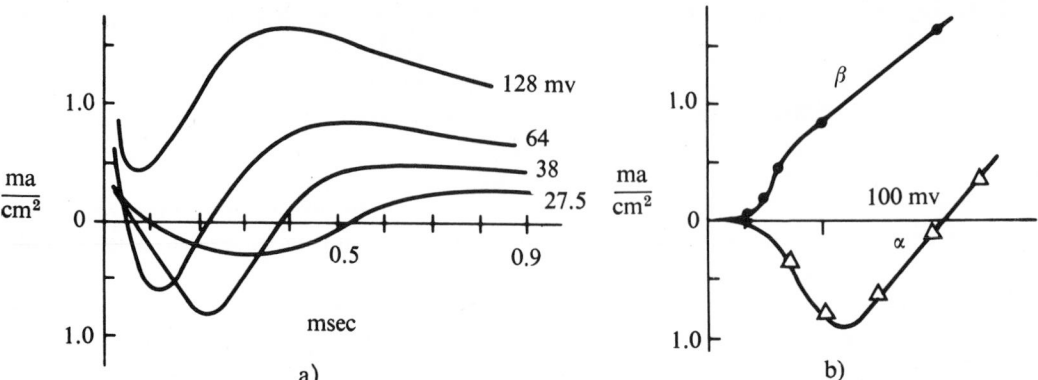

FIGURE 17. Early voltage clamp results. a) Membrane current density after increase of potential from rest by amounts given for each curve. (Redrawn from Cole.[11]) b) Peak values of early, α, and late, β, membrane currents against membrane potential increase.

potential, to some intermediate value, while the later outward currents at all potentials are in the direction to return the potential to the resting level during recovery. By this excitation process a propagated nerve impulse may be maintained. The maximum early and late currents from this experiment show at least a transient negative resistance characteristic for the early current at potential increases between 20 mv and 50 mv (Figure 17b).

V. THE HODGKIN-HUXLEY AXON

At about the time of the first voltage clamp results at Woods Hole, Hodgkin and Katz[50] had evolved and tested their sodium theory of the action potential at Plymouth. With Huxley[48,49] they then applied the concept, to which they gave the name "voltage clamp," with the improved technique of Figure 16b. Except that the added internal and external potential electrodes avoided the electrode polarization which caused much of the decline in the late currents (Figure 17a) in the earlier arrangement (Figure 16a), they confirmed the earlier results. Hodgkin and Huxley[47] then used this technique to extend and elaborate the sodium theory into a detailed and highly specific formulation of squid axon membrane behavior that has proved to be both provocative and spectacularly useful.

This formulation, which may be called the "Hodgkin-Huxley axon," is a group of equations describing the membrane currents in terms of the membrane potential, V. It is shown in Figure 18 where six of the functions are presented in graphical form. The principal energy sources here, and in Figure 20a, are the electromotive forces, E_K and E_{Na}, of the potassium and sodium concentration cells across the membrane. The current flow of each ion is the product of the driving force, $V-E$, and the permeability, expressed as an instantaneous conductance, g_0. These conductances are highly nonlinear and are given as functions of the membrane potential. Their steady state values show an increase with temperature of about 3% per degree but their rates of change, as expressed by τ, increase at about 12% per degree.

The relationship between an instantaneous or "chord" conductance and the steady state potential-current characteristic is illustrated in Figure 19. For a component e.m.f., E_1, more negative than the range in which g_0 is changing, the assumed linear variation of g_0 with potential V will give rise to a "rectification" curve E_1, I_1 (Figure 19b, α), as also in

$$I_i = g_K\, n^4(V - E_K) + g_{Na} m^3 h(V - E_{Na}) + g_L(V - E_L)$$

$$dn/dt = (\underline{n} - n)/\tau_n \qquad dm/dt = (\underline{m} - m)/\tau_m \qquad dh/dt = (\underline{h} - h)/\tau_h$$

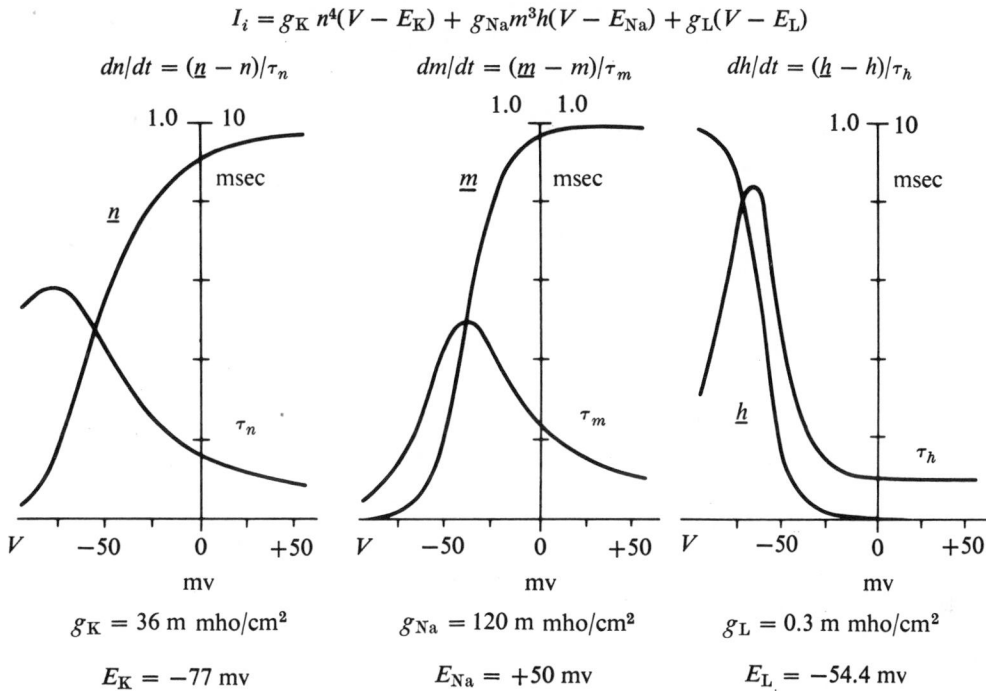

$$g_K = 36 \text{ m mho/cm}^2 \qquad g_{Na} = 120 \text{ m mho/cm}^2 \qquad g_L = 0.3 \text{ m mho/cm}^2$$

$$E_K = -77 \text{ mv} \qquad E_{Na} = +50 \text{ mv} \qquad E_L = -54.4 \text{ mv}$$

FIGURE 18.   Hodgkin-Huxley Axon. Analytical and graphical expressions for the ionic current as a function of the membrane potential. m, n, and h are the parameters describing the potassium "on" and the sodium "on" and "off" processes respectively. (Modified from Cole.[16])

Figures 11 and 17. Here the steady state, or "slope," conductances, $g_\infty = dI/dV$, are everywhere positive throughout the transition region. However, for the more positive component e.m.f., E_2, the E_2, I_2 characteristic may show a negative steady state conductance, or resistance, in this region (Figure 19b, β). These two schematic curves correspond roughly to the late and early voltage clamp current characteristics such as in Figures 17 and 22.

The instantaneous conductances may be thought of as controlled by two small boys, Kal and Nat, acting under orders of the membrane potential as shown in Figure 20.* At rest g_K is small but still much larger than g_{Na}. After a sudden 50 mv increase of V, Nat increases g_{Na} rapidly and then allows it to return more slowly toward zero while Kal increases g_K to a steady value. The analogy of the unknown control systems to small boys is particularly apt in that both react more promptly and more completely to a shouted command of 100 mv than to a 25 mv whisper.

The process of excitation can now be described qualitatively in these terms. A small short pulse of current may not increase V and raise g_{Na} enough to give a net inward ionic current before g_K increases and brings V back to rest. The increase of V by a larger pulse can soon increase g_{Na} enough to produce an inward current. This current, coming from the condenser charge, further increases the potential, so each response by Nat brings him an order for a larger and faster increase of g_{Na}. This runaway process slows down as V

* The small and unidentified leakage current with its e.m.f., E_L, and linear conductance, g_L, will be ignored here.

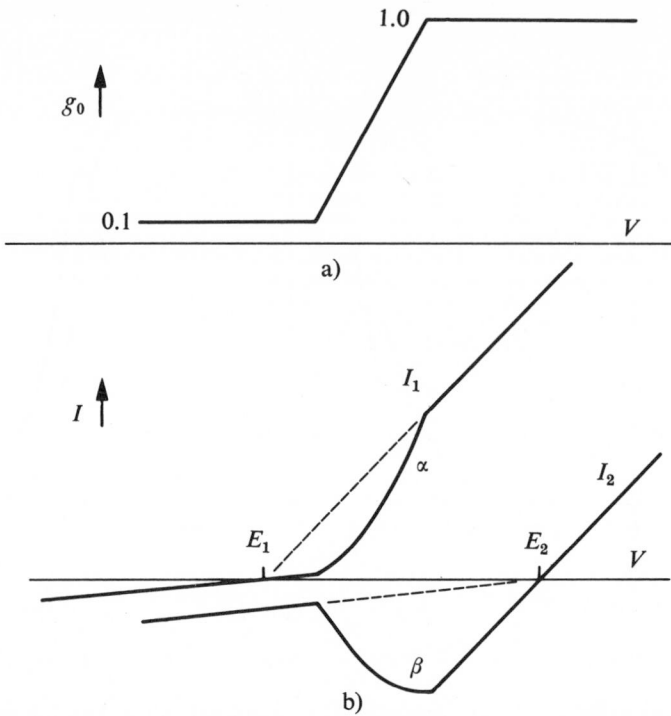

FIGURE 19. a) An illustrative variation of the instantaneous conductance g_0, with potential V; b) the corresponding steady state characteristics, V, I, for two different component e.m.f.'s, E_1 and E_2.

approaches E_{Na}, and as g_{Na} starts to turn off, and g_K to turn on. After V reaches a maximum, where the Na and K currents are equal and opposite, the outward K current more slowly returns the potential to its resting value.

The value of the threshold current pulse may be calculated from the equations represented in Figure 18 with a desk calculator or, far more efficiently, by analog or digital automatic computers and with an accuracy far beyond anything experimentally possible. But the calculations and experiment are in reasonable agreement for this and practically all of the many other well-known nerve phenomena. These include 1) passive properties such as resting resistance and rectification, the anomalous inductive and capacitive reactances shown in impedance and transient measurements and ionic fluxes; 2) the strength-duration relationship for threshold stimuli, the form and amplitude of subthreshold and action potentials, and the accommodation phenomena of utilization time and liminal gradient; and 3) the refractory and recovery phases and, to some extent, repetitive responses for continuing currents. The form and the velocity of a propagating action potential are more difficult to calculate, but close agreements with experiments have been obtained (Figure 21).

These results and others clearly indicate that the Hodgkin-Huxley axon is at least a broad and accurate representation of a real axon. To the extent that their formulation is merely an expression of the voltage clamp data, these data provide a far more complete and powerful description of the axon than is yet available from any other kinds of experiments. Furthermore, the success of the Hodgkin-Huxley axon in presenting these data as functions of membrane potential alone suggests both that a successful theory of

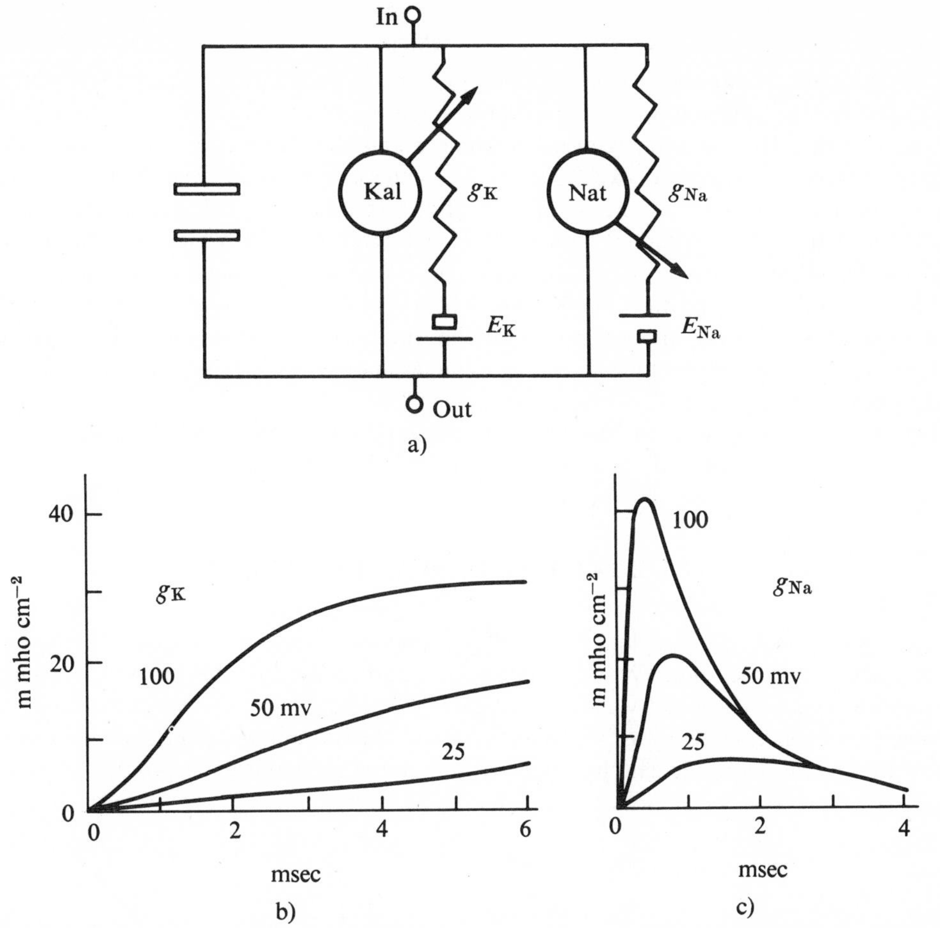

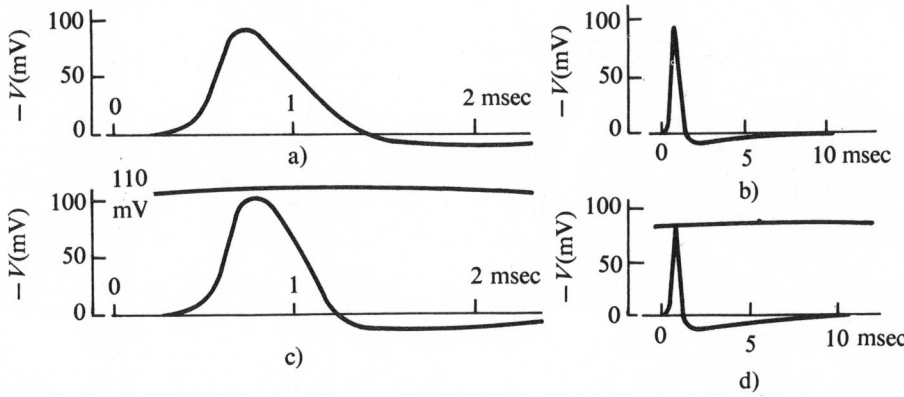

FIGURE 20.   Representation of the Hodgkin-Huxley axon. a) In the membrane circuit the ionic conductances g_K and g_{Na} are controlled through Kal and Nat by the membrane potential. b) and c) The curves show the time courses of the conductances of K and Na after sudden increases of potential. (Redrawn from Cole.[13])

FIGURE 21.   Comparison of calculated, a) and b), with observed, c) and d), squid axon propagated action potentials. The calculated propagation velocity was 18.8 msec, and that observed was 21.2 msec at 18.5°C. (Redrawn from Hodgkin and Huxley.[47])

155

membrane conductance can be based upon this potential, and that this may be the fundamental reason for the amazing usefulness of the voltage clamp concept.

The Hodgkin-Huxley axon is also a complete and detailed exposition of the sodium theory of nerve function. It expresses the key experiment, which was the overshoot of the action potential beyond the amplitude of the resting potential, and it includes the variation of the action potential with external Na concentration, which was the first test and confirmation of the theory. The calculations of the propagated action potential predict the Na inflow and the later K loss to be about 4 pica mol/cm² during an impulse. It is a highly significant and most important confirmation of the theory that the completely independent isotope measurements of this ion exchange agree with the calculations to within experimental errors.

The Hodgkin-Huxley axon has been an outstanding development presenting a new axonal physiology completely expressed in terms of Na and K permeabilities.

VI. SUBSEQUENT DEVELOPMENTS

The achievements of Hodgkin and Huxley presented several challenges. The first was to test and confirm or modify their experimental and analytical work as well as some of its implications. The second was to investigate and restate more of neurophysiology and as much neuropharmacology as possible in terms of the sodium and potassium parameters. The third and most spectacular challenge was to find the mechanisms or processes by which

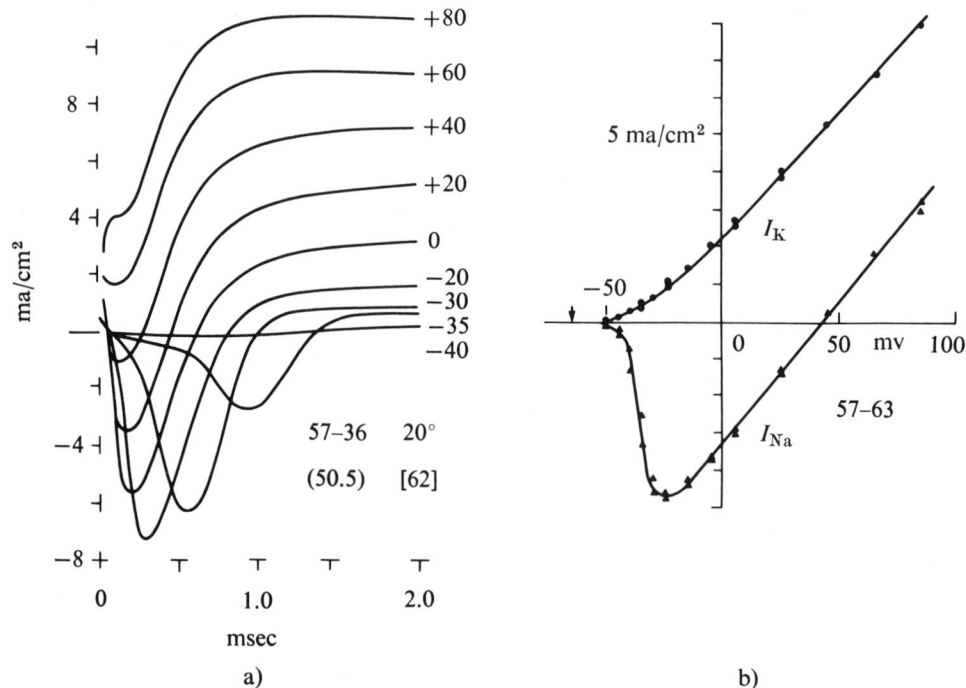

FIGURE 22. Recent voltage clamp results. a) Membrane current densities after change of membrane potential from -62 mv to value given for each curve. b) Peak early currents, I_{Na}, and steady state currents, I_K, after changes of membrane potential. (Redrawn from Cole and Moore.[24])

membrane ion permeabilities were controlled, perhaps quite directly by the membrane potential.

For these many reasons, we soon resumed voltage clamp experiments at Woods Hole and initiated an automatic computer program at the National Bureau of Standards.

A. Squid Axon

The voltage clamp technique was again improved (Figure 16c); microtip and external reference electrodes were used for a better measure of the membrane potential. This and other requirements led to some invention and considerable development in the control electronics. Better experiments on better axons usually gave larger membrane current densities, but in general the results were similar to those obtained earlier (Figure 22). However, occasionally the new pattern of Figure 23 appeared. This, along with similar observations by Frankenhaeuser and Hodgkin[33] and more bizarre aberrations produced by Tasaki and collaborators,[80] raised several questions which were, however, formulated only during the investigation.[14,24,81] Were these better axons under adequate experimental control? If so, the simpler earlier data, and in particular the Hodgkin-Huxley axon, could only be considered and used as the characteristics of weak and comparatively ineffective axons. What additional factors or new approaches would be needed to describe more nearly normal axons? If the experiments were not adequate, what were the shortcomings? Could sufficiently good experiments be done on the best and the strongest axons?

After the early observation that the "notch" of Figure 23 was correlated with both a fresh, strong axon and an axial electrode of considerable surface impedance, such experiments were shown to be much more complicated than had been assumed. At the same time a simple physical explanation was developed and this in turn led to an even simpler improvement of the technique which has so far been found entirely adequate.

B. Membrane Potential Control

It has been pointed out that the peak inward sodium currents of Figures 17 and 22 at least resemble a negative resistance characteristic when expressed as a function of the clamp potential. If this is assumed to be a steady state characteristic of the membrane, then the current and potential (Figure 24) will be stable or unstable as the effective resistance

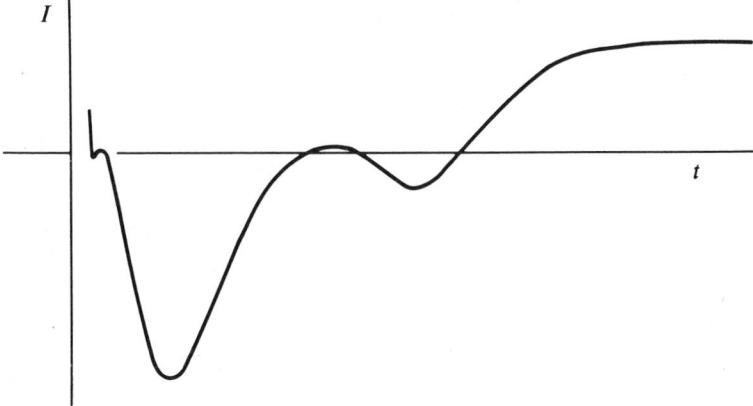

FIGURE 23. Current pattern for membrane under inadequate voltage clamp. (Redrawn from Cole.[15])

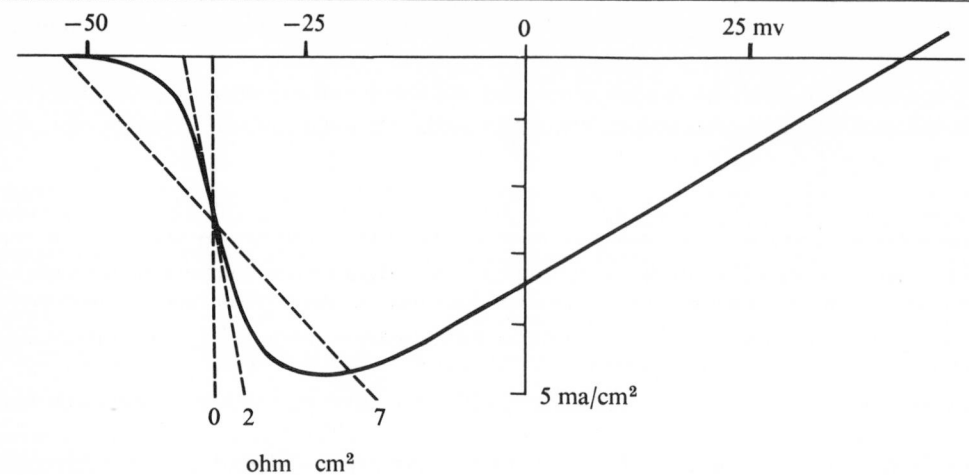

FIGURE 24. Quasi-steady state characteristic for squid membrane. Relation between membrane voltage and early peak membrane current. The equilibrium in the negative resistance region is stable, neutral, or unstable depending on whether the potential is controlled through a resistance of 0, 2, or 7 ohms for a cm² of membrane.

in series with the membrane is less or more than 2 ohm cm² as was stated for the analog (p. 150) and proved for this case by Cole and Moore.[24] The external and axial current electrodes as well as the axoplasm and sea water between them and the membrane may have the combined resistance of 7 ohm cm², shown in Figure 24. With a constant potential applied to these electrodes, the membrane current and potential will fluctuate and start to move from the unstable center point towards a stable point on one side or the other. As the membrane potential at the control point between the potential electrodes of Figure 16c starts to change in either direction, the electronic control will vary the potential between the current electrodes to return the membrane potential at this point to the command value. The effective series resistance is then practically zero and the membrane potential control is nearly perfect.[24]

At other points along the axon the spontaneous fluctuations of the membrane potential will be different and the corrections needed and applied at the control point will not be appropriate. Thus all of the rest of the axon tends to move away from the potential and current at the control point. This tendency is somewhat curbed near the control point by local longitudinal current flow in the axoplasm and sea water but more distant regions are forced close to one or the other stable point. The membrane current density is then everywhere different from that at the control point and the average over a length of axon cannot be expected to correspond to the control potential. Again by means of the cable equation,[14] with suitable modifications and experimental conditions as stated, the error of the average current is calculated to be less than 10% only when it is measured over a length of axon less than 0.3 mm on either side of the control electrode.

The analyses outlined above are simple in concept and far simpler than any experiment. A reasonably complete theoretical treatment in space and time seems virtually impossible and the corresponding numerical solutions appear to be impractical at present. Some of the obvious approximations have been investigated, some models have been tested, and many experiments have been performed without exposing any serious discrepancies.[81] For example, the use of the locus of the peak inward currents vs. potential for a steady state characteristic as in Figure 24 is an obviously questionable assumption. It has been tested by detailed calculations of the maximum series resistance allowable for stability of the Hodgkin-Huxley axon at various times after the application of clamp potentials in the critical region.[6] These show that the maximum allowable resistance comes about 20% earlier and is about 10% less than the value obtained from the inward peak locus. Interestingly, another experimental curve, the isochronal locus, with an equally uncertain theoretical basis, gives somewhat better agreement with the calculations.

Quite apart from any theory, the measured membrane currents obviously have meaning only to the extent that they are the result of a known and constant membrane potential. For an unstable axon-electrode combination as considered above, the current may be measured only close to the potential electrodes. This has been done with external differential electrodes, which had an equivalent length of about 0.3 mm, as indicated in Figure 16d.

Improved cell design and external current electrodes and, particularly, improved axial electrodes have more recently shown sufficiently uniform potential as well as current distributions to permit current measurements over several mm lengths of the strongest axons. Under such conditions of adequate membrane potential control neither the "notch" of Figure 23 nor any other obvious aberration of the earlier current patterns has made its appearance. Consequently, it has been concluded that the properties of the best and strongest axons so far available are not essentially different from the early results, and the Hodgkin-Huxley axon, based on them.

C. Other Preparations

The voltage clamp concept has been successfully applied to single nodes of medullated frog and toad axons by Frankenhaeuser[33] and Dodge and Frankenhaeuser.[28] The membrane potential at one node was measured at the adjacent node on one side and controlled by current supplied through the adjacent node on the other side, as leakage along the outside of the myelin internodes was prevented electronically. Under adequate control, the voltage clamp current patterns found by Dodge and Frankenhaeuser[28] are qualitatively similar to those of the squid. The current densities and maximum conductances reported are an order of magnitude or more larger than for the squid. The Hodgkin-Huxley formulation has been somewhat modified and all of its parameters redetermined to give a comparable description of the nodal membranes. A similar approach has been made[51] to lobster axons with sucrose gaps acting as artificial myelin. Similar current patterns are again obtained under adequately controlled conditions and their properties are close to those of the squid axon.

The voltage clamp concept has been applied to several more nearly spherical central cells by Hagiwara and others.[39,40] They used one intracellular micropipette electrode for potential and a second one for the control current. Although the characteristics for an excitable cell were similar to those for squid, they were quite different for other, inexcitable, cells. This same technique has been applied to *Nitella* by Findlay[30] and, with improvements, by Kishimoto;[55] again results are similar to those for squid except that the current patterns were far smaller and much slower.

The absence of voltage clamp data for skeletal and cardiac muscle fibers is both notable and important. Although there is good basis to believe that the sodium theory is a satisfactory explanation for the excitation in both cases, there is considerable evidence that their potassium characteristics are quite different from those of the Hodgkin-Huxley axon.

The appearance of similar voltage clamp current patterns for several membranes was rather to be expected. Much of normal cell membrane behavior was demonstrated to be implicit in these data and electrophysiologists have long been impressed by the many similarities of these characteristics in numerous excitable tissues.

Probably the most noticeable variation among the voltage clamp results for these various preparations is the degree of approximation with which the late outward currents are indeed steady state phenomena. These currents are strikingly constant for the lobster axon and perhaps somewhat less so for the node of a myelinated fiber. They may vary considerably, particularly with temperature in the squid axon, whereas in at least one preparation Hagiwara[40] found a striking decrease with a rate not more than a few times that of the rise of the late current.

On the other hand, the direct evidence of an early negative resistance characteristic for the inward current in each of these excitable preparations is particularly important.

D. Negative Resistances

It seems highly probable that the existence of the potentially unstable negative resistance characteristic is both a necessary and a sufficient condition for the usual performance of excitable tissues.

The normal negative resistance is reasonably attributed to the Na ion, except for *Nitella*. However, this need not be the case. Lithium and ammonium ions produce practically the same negative resistance characteristics as Na, and other known Na substituents can be expected to do the same. In *Nitella* the ion responsible may be chloride, although calcium has been suggested. And the excitability of a crustacean muscle in barium and strontium makes a negative resistance seem highly probable for these ion-membrane combinations.

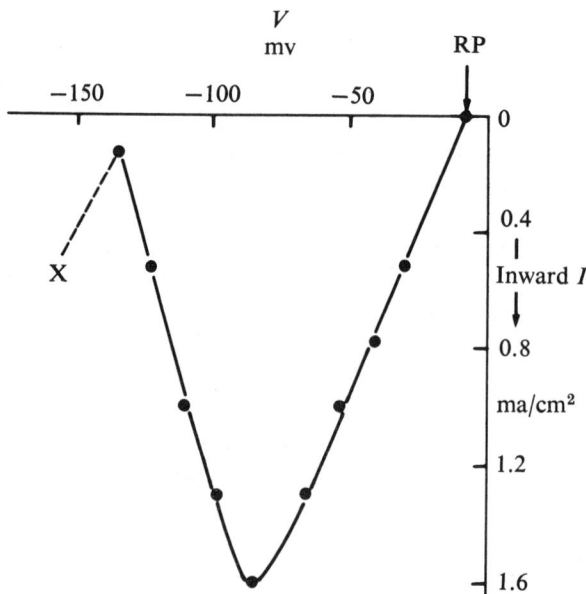

FIGURE 25. Steady state membrane currents for lobster axon in isosmotic KCl. (Redrawn from Julian, Moore, and Goldman.[51])

The normal role of the K ion has been much less interesting. It is restricted entirely to the recovery of the membrane potential after excitation, and it needs nothing but a conventional rectification characteristic to perform this slow, but important, operation. However, experiments[65] on the frog myelinated fiber node and on the squid axon in isosmotic KCl produced excitation phenomena which strongly suggested a negative resistance for the K ion. This could have been predicted as a steady state characteristic of the Hodgkin-Huxley axon, as suggested in Figure 19, but the direct experimental demonstration of it by voltage clamp measurements on the squid axon by Moore[64] was far more impressive even though the currents did decrease slightly with time. Entirely similar negative resistance characteristics with more or less time decay have been found for central cell bodies,[39,40] toad myelinated axon nodes (Frankenhaeuser, personal communication), and lobster axons.[51] The lobster axon characteristic, shown in Figure 25, is so stable for 100 m sec that it should be considered as a steady state.

These various observations are another striking demonstration of the power of the voltage clamp technique and the effectiveness of the Hodgkin-Huxley axon as an expression of the results. They show a remarkable similarity between the properties of several different membranes. They also show that the membrane properties which may find expression as a negative resistance characteristic are not limited to a particular ion or a particular membrane, but have already appeared in such diverse ion-membrane combinations as to predict an even more widespread occurrence. Most encouragingly, however, some of these observations show that the negative resistance membrane characteristics are not necessarily transient phenomena and that a steady state theory may have an immediate as well as an intermediate usefulness

E. *Calculations*

In addition to, and including some of the calculations already mentioned, the Hodgkin-Huxley axon has inspired considerable calculation both in its original form and with considerable modifications. The correction of an early mistake showed that although the Hodgkin-Huxley axon membrane did not respond in a truly all-or-none manner, the effect of the correction was not experimentally detectible in this and other phenomena. The calculated effect of temperature on the form and velocity of squid action potential agreed well with experiments except for an interesting detail at high temperature that has not been observed. The calculated repetitive response with low external Ca ion showed that the experimental modification of the clamp data was again adequate to predict the classical performance under these conditions.

Some features of the initiation and propagation of excitation from node to node have been calculated satisfactorily for some assumed properties of an entire medullated axon, but the necessary computer resources have not been available to investigate threshold phenomena in this model or to start similar work on the Hodgkin-Huxley axon.

In the absence of voltage clamp data several investigators have made extensive computations of the consequences of skillful alterations of the Hodgkin-Huxley axon parameters in order to correlate many of the decidedly different cardiac and abnormal axon phenomena.

A rather different approach has been a formal consideration of unstable systems,[31] of which the Hodgkin-Huxley axon is but one example. This has led to a functional simplification and a reduction of the number of variables and has produced a model that is more general, more easily computed, and more closely correlated with conventional electrophysiology than is the Hodgkin-Huxley axon.

VII. MEMBRANE PROBLEMS

A. *Experimental Procedures and Analyses*

There are several unsolved technical problems in the application of the voltage clamp concept. There are three apparently successful geometries. 1) The original with an axial internal current electrode, and now a micro-potential electrode, requiring a giant axon. 2) The node and pseudo-node with electronic or sucrose insulation and the current supplied from one end while the potential is measured at the other, as applied to medullated and lobster axons. 3) The use of two microelectrodes, one for current and the other for potential, on central bodies and *Nitella*.

In each case the requirements for stability and accuracy are still a problem and really reliable answers are not imminent. The adequacy of the new techniques to be expected before the present considerable need for voltage clamp measurements abates should be carefully examined.

The question of the accuracy of the squid axon membrane potential measurements is considerable and important. There has been ample evidence of a resistance of a few ohm cm² in series with the membrane capacity. This cannot be accounted for by the resistances of normal axoplasm and sea water and might be a characteristic of the Schwann cell sheath around the axon. If, as seems probable, this resistance is also in series with the ion conductances, a perfect clamp at the potential electrodes may allow significant errors.

Much has been done to improve the accuracy, speed, and stability of the measuring and control electronics but there are still problems that require further improvements.

The reproducibility and survival of the various preparations are often not adequate. The use of sucrose on squid and for an artificial lobster node avoids internal and surface injury but produces a puzzling hyperpolarization. Just as the direct measurement of the membrane potential inside the squid axon sparked our present era, so we may expect much when indirect and fragmentary information about the axoplasm is replaced by the certain knowledge to be had with the internal perfusion now achieved at the marine laboratories of Plymouth, Woods Hole, and Misaki. The essential assumptions about the passive permeability characteristics seem well supported. The current activity in this field is producing much data and many questions.

The separation of Na and K currents by choline substitution for Na was an effective tool for the original analysis. It is, however, so arduous as almost to preclude its use as a routine experimental procedure. There are a number of alternatives. The time dependences of the "potassium on," the "sodium on," and the "sodium off" effects are so similar that a brute force curve-fitting of voltage clamp currents is not yet completely out of the question. If this is successful, experimental indices should produce at least approximate values for the ion conductance parameters. This procedure might be not only in error but even blatantly wrong.

Next a previous hyperpolarization seems to delay specifically the K current. Regardless of mechanism this gives a procedure which, although tricky in detail, may yet be the most powerful for current separation. Again, simultaneous measurements of current and high-frequency conductance lead to the separate components if only the ion potentials are known. This has not been particularly successful in years past, but improved instrumentation and more experience may develop it into the method of choice.

At present there is considerable reason to expect quantitative but not qualitative modifications of the original formulations for the Na and K current of squid. An attempt to isolate the K current showed the original description to be of restricted application, and the possibility of similar difficulties for the Na current must be expected. For the peak Na current of the node, an ionic conductance has been replaced by a Goldman permeability[37] which makes the node seem an even more complicated problem; but the small and linear leakage current of the squid is also becoming more involved. It rectifies considerably in the outward direction in less than $100 \, \mu$ sec and more so in 1 m sec. The failure so far to identify the leakage current as ionic is yet another problem and may require another conduction process.

The identifications of the early and late squid clamp currents respectively as primarily Na and K seem so certain as practically to preclude mistake. The choline experiments and other changes of the Na potential are quite clear and self-consistent whereas the K has received less attention. The calculation of the net fluxes during a propagating impulse is an amazing chemical analysis on a millisecond time scale and is supported by the agreement of the integrated net fluxes with the tracer data. But it has been suggested that there is no independent evidence for the time courses ascribed to the Na and K currents in either the propagating impulse or a voltage clamp. A tracer answer to this problem seems difficult for the impulse but possible for the clamp current. The tracer outflow of Na into choline sea water agrees with the integrated early clamp current to within 20%. The difference for K is considerably more, as it is for Na at normal and other external Na concentrations. However, it is not at all certain whether this problem is one which depends on failure to understand the electrical current or the tracer kinetics.

B. Interpretation of the Membrane Capacity

The considerable uniformity of the membrane capacities for many cells, in the neighborhood of 1 μf/cm^2, has made it easy to assume a uniformity of structure. The comparative constancy of this capacity even when accompanied by many-fold changes of membrane conductances during function urges us to think of this structure as virtually independent of function. These views are confirmed to the extent that the "unit membrane" generalization from electron microscopy is valid for intact cells. The variations in chemical analyses, as of red cell ghosts from different species, are then to be discounted as of minor electrical significance.

The possible approaches need to be examined carefully, presumably by solid state theory, but a qualitative consideration starting with dipole theory is of interest. On the complex plane the dielectric constant of a dilute assembly of polar molecules rotating against kinetic agitation and viscosity is a circle with a rather small time constant (Figure 26, α). As barriers of intermolecular forces appear at lower temperatures and phase transitions, the time constant increases, the rate of change with frequency becomes less, and the low frequency extrapolation, ϵ_0, may increase as in curve β until for some common solid insulators only the remnant γ is found in the most usual frequency range.

Beyond this some of the best polymer insulations appear as hardly more than a point barely above the ϵ' axis. Some aspects of relevant membrane behavior are indicated for comparison in Figure 26b, but on a complex capacity plane in order to avoid choosing an effective thickness. Here too there is no indication of a finite ϵ_0 or of a finite time constant. Hence we may by analogy think of these membranes as highly condensed and strongly cross-linked structures, such as one expects at temperatures far below any phase transitions

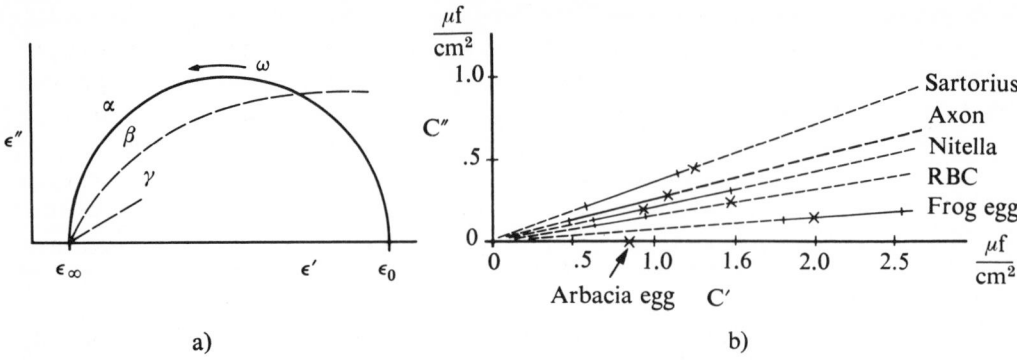

FIGURE 26. Dielectric characteristics represented on complex planes. a) Curves show the dielectric behavior of: α, dilute solutions of dipoles; β, some concentrated dipole solutions; and γ, many solid insulators. ϵ' and ϵ'' are the real and imaginary components. b) The capacitive behavior of some living membranes as measured over ranges indicated by solid lines. C' and C'' are the real and imaginary components. (Redrawn from Cole.[10,12])

and where polarization barriers are considerable. Unfortunately there are but few and not entirely consistent data on the temperature coefficients of any membranes. At the high-frequency end the data extrapolate to the origin, and it does not seem probable that this can be in error by much more than 10% of the values in the measured ranges. Since a value of $\epsilon_\infty < 1$ is not to be expected, the dielectric constant in the measured range should not be less than 10. This value then gave the effective thickness of 100 A.

The conclusions from the electrical evidence that the living membrane is a firm, solid structure with an approximate thickness of 100 A seems to be reasonably well confirmed by electron microscopy and chemical analyses. Yet the electrical measurements clearly are not yet relatable to the "bimolecular leaflet" membrane structure that these other approaches are developing with increasing power and detail.

C. Some Models for Membrane Ion Permeability

Membrane permeabilities have long been a problem of major interest. The two most important developments have been those relying upon the lipid solubility and upon the ion sieve behavior of membranes. Neither is adequate and it seems predictable that some aspects of both will correspond to reality. The relative independence of membrane capacity argues that but a small part of the membrane structure is detectibly involved in function. This does not, however, preclude a major effect of membrane composition and structure upon the characteristics of ion flow.

An ionic conductance, the ion flow under a unit driving force, is a measure of an ion permeability. The ionic conductances are so intimately correlated with the life and death of cells, and are so satisfactory a description of nerve function in particular, that an acceptable explanation of them is likely to be of fundamental importance. Certainly a most challenging and obviously significant problem for all of biology is the nature of the ionic conductances and their control by the membrane potential.

It has now been fifteen years since the first application of the voltage clamp concept measured ionic currents in clear and obviously important detail, and ten years since Hodgkin and others[45-50] confirmed the data, analyzed them into K and Na components, and expressed them as functions of membrane potential alone. There is yet no outstanding candidate to explain them. The amazing ability of the Hodgkin-Huxley equations, and so far only these equations, to contain so much of the classical facts about nerve makes it hard to see how any theory that cannot predict the essential findings can be seriously considered. The similarity of several other membranes strongly suggests common features of irritable cells. These equations are, however, so complicated that only automatic computers can do much with them and we may have to focus attention first on the most characteristic and crucial behavior.

As mentioned above, a negative resistance characteristic has been found to be sufficient for the basic phenomena of excitation and propagation. The characteristics which can give rise to it have now appeared in enough ion-membrane combinations to suggest that among all other possible origins of nerve behavior a negative resistance is by far the most probable. I suggest that the first, the necessary, and the most promising goal of any membrane theory is to be able to produce a region of steady state or quasi-steady state negative resistance.

Although many physical systems show this characteristic, only a few are of the right kind. A passive iron wire is probably the oldest, but it is only now yielding to theory and is not a promising candidate for a membrane mechanism. The dynatron characteristic from secondary emission in vacuum tubes also seems an unlikely model. An inverse thermistor, one with a positive temperature coefficient, is known and has the right characteristics, but temperature seems an unlikely intermediate variable.

The appearance a few years ago of the Esaki[29] semi-conductor diode was of great interest since it had characteristics analogous to those which have been possessed by the squid giant axon for millions of years. In this diode an extra current is contributed by quantum mechanical electron tunnelling and this seems so improbable for ions as to be impossible. Mauro[62] is studying the ion counterpart of this diode with calculations and experiments on the junction between positive and negative ion exchangers. He has found one $\mu f/cm^2$ for the capacity of such an arrangement, but we must wait to see if a negative conductance can make an appearance.

If, as seems probable, there is no source of extra current, we are faced with the need to find out what cuts off the current at the high potentials farther out on the characteristic curve (Figure 25). The values of the average and the breakdown field strengths in the membrane are of the order of 10^5 v/cm. This average value for the normal operations of the membrane is strikingly high and it may be particularly significant as more becomes known of the behavior of nonliving systems under such conditions.

The Wien effect should perhaps be considered. At the high field strength all ions may be free to move, but considerably below a 10^5 v/cm some of these ions may be able to combine with fixed ions. Then with fewer ions free to move under the small fields the membrane would have a smaller conductance. This would, however, require a biasing potential of about 50 mv and a symmetry that are neither known nor expected.

If there are pores, there seems to be little evidence for deciding whether every molecular interface may become such a channel under thermal jostling or if each has a definite structure fixed in position. Then, too, either kind might be uniformly distributed over the whole area of the membrane or perhaps restricted to patches.

The Hodgkin-Huxley equations were set up to follow enzyme kinetics in the hope that perhaps a catalytic process was able to activate stepping stones by which an ion could be passed from one active point to another and so on all the way through the membrane. Four such points would then account for a fourth power in the equation that they have used. Mullins[66,67] has suggested K and Na and some other ions may move in an 8 A channel with a single hydration layer, and that electrostatic forces may change this pore size. Solomon[79] finds pores of about this size in several membranes and following him Villegas[83] finds the same for the squid axon. Mullins as well as Goldman[38] and Karreman[52,53] invokes a blocking effect of calcium on ion movement, particularly that of Na. There is no compelling evidence that each kind of ion has its own pores, and the close correspondence between the decay of the sodium current and the rise of the potassium current rather suggests that they may both use the same transportation facilities across the membrane.

Much theory and many models for living membranes have been based on the Planck liquid junction theory for electrolytes, either directly or with the constant field approximation of Goldman[37] or the fixed charge elaboration of Teorell[82] or finally the ion species generalization of Schlögl.[74] In none of these does a negative conductance make its appearance. However, Teorell has been able to achieve this by adding the phenomena of electroosmotic and hydraulic flow through the fixed charge membrane, although much important detail is still needed. Some discussion of thermodynamic models of membrane permeability and active transport is given in Chapter 4.

A large part of the work in the past has been based upon the kinetic theory of a perfect gas in which all motion is completely random. A membrane may be so well structured and so crowded and the ions may be so few and move with such difficulty that a reliance on this theory is quite unrealistic. So it may be worthwhile to go to the other extreme, that of perfect order such as in a crystal. The motions of ions and the vacancies in ionic crystals have been studied for many years and they are known to create barriers to oppose further movement. The rapid development of this part of the theory of solids may give a more useful approach to the behavior of membranes.

D. Partial Interpretation of Voltage Clamp Data

Considerable effort has been devoted to the expression of membrane parameters in terms of centimeters and seconds but we are rapidly reaching the stage at which molecular units may be more immediately significant. It is interesting and perhaps provocative to consider some of the membrane phenomena on other scales.

Membrane conductances range from very small values below the resting potential to much larger maximum values at positive potentials. The nominal value of 1000 ohm cm² at rest corresponds to a column of sea water 50 cm long. A maximum conductance equivalent to 5 ohm cm² is approached in a number of membranes under positive voltage clamp and 0.1 ohm cm² has been found for a node. Then the nominal value of 1 ohm cm² is equivalent to 0.5 mm of sea water.

Next, assume that the membrane is 100 A thick (it is probably more than 50 A and less than 200 A); then take the hexagonal faces 150 A across (which seem a convenient and even possible unit of structure) as shown in Figure 27, and use the m sec as an appropriate unit of time.

For a resting potential of -60 mv and a capacity of 1 $\mu f/cm^2$ there will be an average excess of one negative univalent ion over the inside and one positive ion over the outside of the hexagonal element with face areas of $2 \cdot 10^4 A^2$ each. When these charges are removed the potential falls to zero and, to the extent that the conventional resting membrane resistance of 1000 ohm cm² is linear, this would result in an ion flow through the element of one ion per m sec. At the peak of a 120 mv action potential the membrane ion pair is reversed. The ion exchange during the passage of an impulse is interpolated to be 5.6 pica mol/cm² at 15°C. This becomes the entrance of a mere 7 Na ions and the later exit of the same number of K ions through our membrane element. And, further, the loss of Na

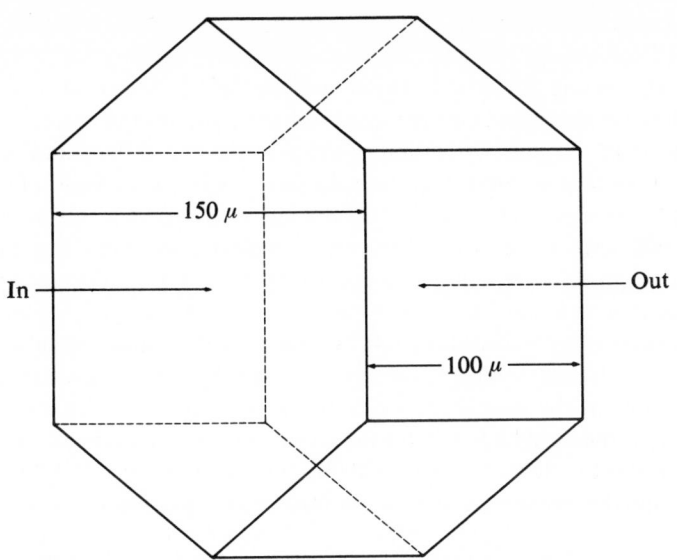

FIGURE 27.   A suggested elementary unit for a cell membrane.

from the outside during the impulse corresponds to the average Na content of a layer of sea water about 1 A thick and the K of axoplasm is similarly depleted.

However, it seems highly desirable, as well as possible, that a membrane be able to function normally by the use of only a small fraction of its ultimate resources. The voltage clamp does produce membrane performance considerably in excess of normal and may in this way give a much better measure of the membrane's potentialities. For example, if we generously assume a maximum Na inflow of 10 ma/cm² for 1 m sec under voltage clamp, about 100 of these ions would have moved through the element. It is a fact that the maximum current densities measured under voltage clamp may be 10 ma/cm² for squid and 50 ma/cm² for a myelinated fiber node. For a figure of 20 ma/cm² about 200 monovalent ions will be moving through our hexagonal element in 1 m sec. This may seem to be rather dense traffic until we calculate by ordinary kinetic theory that the membrane element is being bombarded inside and out by $2 \cdot 10^9$ ions/m sec. Thus only one ion out of 10^7 goes through and the membrane still appears as a very formidable barrier even at such a high current density.

It is more difficult to look into the interior of the membrane and we will lessen the strength of our facts by adding some assumptions. Consider the membrane as an electrolyte in which the current is the product of a field strength and a conductance. Now the conductance of an ion, say K, may be taken as the product of a concentration, the charge, and a mobility. From kinetic theory I estimated a mobility

$$u = kT/X^2 e^2 \tau$$

where X is the field strength and τ a transition time.[10,12] Using $\tau = 0.5$ m sec from the Hodgkin-Huxley axon we find a mobility of $2 \cdot 10^{-8}$ cm/sec per v/cm at 15°C. Some data suggest that the membrane may be rather well emptied of K during hyperpolarization. Experiments show that the current then rises to half maximum in 0.5 m sec after the clamp potential is changed to the Na potential. This may be interpreted as a transit time and gives about the same mobility.

This figure is about 10^{-5} times as fast as the mobility in aqueous solution, $8 \cdot 10^{-4}$ cm/sec per v/cm. The "sodium on" effect is everywhere faster than this and the other processes are slower near the resting potential but all mobilities seem to be extremely small. However, such small values are somewhat compensated in their effect on the current by the high field strength acting upon the ions. A mobility ratio of the order of magnitude of only 10^{-5} should be a warning that we are extrapolating our concepts into a region far removed from that in which they have so long been useful. But since this figure seems to be the only value of its kind, it will have to serve until it can be replaced by something more significant.

The estimate of an ionic mobility and the knowledge of a conductance in a membrane allows us to proceed to a concentration of mobile ions. A 1.0 ohm cm² membrane would require the amazing ion concentration of 1.0 molar. For a squid membrane it would be about 0.1 M which is not a high value for ion exchange materials. This concentration puts about 120 ions in the membrane element we have chosen. The average face area of 170 A² for an ion is then only a few times the cross-section of a lipid complex. On the other hand, the generous estimate that a voltage clamp pulse can produce 100 Na ions encourages us to think about the possibility that these ions may all come from the interior of the membrane.

When the resting membrane resistance of 1000 ohm cm² is considered, the decrease of mobility is relatively unimportant, and the average ion concentration falls to about 0.002 M. It may well be that the concentration of an ion exchanger could be reduced so much throughout a membrane in 1 m sec. But it seems much more interesting to ignore this possibility and look for barriers to appear at one or both surfaces of the membrane, leaving the interior unchanged. This attractive prejudice might even be true no matter how false this basis for it may be!

VIII. WITHIN A FEW DECADES

Only thirty years ago it was not yet certain that ions could cross living cell membranes, and twenty years before that there was not even direct evidence for the existence of a membrane. The steady application of simple but powerful theoretical, mathematical, and experimental concepts has given increasingly broad and detailed descriptions of many membranes and their ionic permeabilities. But the quest for an understanding of the passage of an ion through a membrane continues. The membranes of both stable and excitable cells are now so well known in electrical and ionic terms that there is good basis to expect that these data may suggest and support, or perhaps even dictate, the successful molecular plan and operations of a living membrane. As we correlate the rapidly accumulating evidence for membrane structure and composition, a reasonably satisfactory model of the membrane seems not only inevitable but highly probable in the quite near future.

REFERENCES

1. Adrian, E. D. 1914. The all-or-none principle in nerve. *J. Physiol. (London)* **47**: 460–474.
2. Bartlett, J. H. 1945. Transient anode phenomena. *Trans. Electrochem. Soc.* **87**: 521–545.
3. Bernstein, J. 1912. "Elektrobiologie, die Lehre von den Elektrischen Vorgängen im Organismus auf Moderner Grundlagedargestellt," 215 pp. Vieweg, Braunschweig.
4. Blinks, L. R. 1930a. The direct current resistance of *Valonia*. *J. Gen. Physiol.* **13**: 361–378.
5. Blinks, L. R. 1930b. The direct current resistance of *Nitella*. *J. Gen. Physiol.* **13**: 495–508.

6. Chandler, W. K., FitzHugh, R., and Cole, K. S. 1962. Theoretical stability properties of a space-clamped axon. *Biophys. J.* **2**: 105–127.

7. Cole, K. S. 1928. Electric impedance of suspensions of spheres. *J. Gen. Physiol.* **12**: 29–36.

8. Cole, K. S. 1932. Electric phase angle of cell membranes. *J. Gen. Physiol.* **15**: 641–649.

9. Cole, K. S. 1933. Electric conductance of biological systems. *Cold Spring Harbor Symp. Quant. Biol.* **1**: 107–117.

10. Cole, K. S. 1947. "Four Lectures on Biophysics," 75 pp. Inst. of Biophysics, Univ. of Brazil.

11. Cole, K. S. 1949a. Dynamic electrical characteristics of the squid axon membrane. *Arch. Sci. Physiol.* **3**: 253–258.

12. Cole, K. S. 1949b. Some physical aspects of bioelectric phenomena. *Proc. Natl. Acad. Sci. U.S.* **35**: 558–566.

13. Cole, K. S. 1957. Beyond membrane potentials. *Ann. N.Y. Acad. Sci.* **65**: 658–662.

14. Cole, K. S. 1961a. An analysis of the membrane potential along a clamped squid axon. *Biophys. J.* **1**: 401–418.

15. Cole, K. S. 1961b. Caractéristiques électriques dynamiques de l'axone géant de la seiche. *Actualités Neurophysiol.* **3**: 251–263.

16. Cole, K. S. 1962. The advance of electrical models for cells and axons. *In:* "Proc. Symp. Intern. Biophys. Congr., Stockholm, 1961," *Biophys. J.* **2(2,2)**: 101–119.

17. Cole, K. S., and Baker, R. F. 1941a. Transverse impedance of the squid giant axon during current flow. *J. Gen. Physiol.* **24**: 535–549.

18. Cole, K. S., and Baker, R. F. 1941b. Longitudinal impedance of the squid giant axon. *J. Gen. Physiol.* **24**: 771–788.

19. Cole, K. S., and Curtis, H. J. 1938. Electric impedance of the *Nitella* during activity. *J. Gen. Physiol.* **22**: 37–64.

20. Cole, K. S., and Curtis, H. J. 1939. Electric impedance of the squid giant axon during activity. *J. Gen. Physiol.* **22**: 649–670.

21. Cole, K. S., and Curtis, H. J. 1941. Membrane potential of the squid giant axon during current flow. *J. Gen. Physiol.* **24**: 551–563.

22. Cole, K. S., and Curtis, H. J. 1950. Bioelectricity: Electric physiology. *In:* "Medical Physics," (O. Glasser, ed.), Vol. II, pp. 82–90. Year Book, Chicago.

23. Cole, K. S., and Hodgkin, A. L. 1939. Membrane and protoplasm resistance in the squid giant axon. *J. Gen. Physiol.* **22**: 671–687.

24. Cole, K. S., and Moore, J. W. 1960. Ionic current measurements in the squid giant axon. *J. Gen. Physiol.* **44**: 123–167.

25. Cole, K. S., and Spencer, J. M. 1938. Electrical impedance of fertilized *Arbacia* egg suspensions. *J. Gen. Physiol.* **21**: 583–590.

26. Curtis, H. J., and Cole, K. S. 1950. Nervous system: Excitation and propagation of nerve. *In:* "Medical Physics," (O. Glasser, ed.), Vol. II, pp. 584–595. Year Book, Chicago.

27. del Castillo, J., and Moore, J. W. 1959. On increasing the velocity of a nerve impulse. *J. Physiol. (London)* **148**: 665–670.

28. Dodge, F., and Frankenhaeuser, B. 1959. Sodium currents in the myelinated nerve fibre of *Xenopus laevis* investigated with the voltage clamp technique. *J. Physiol. (London)* **148**: 188–200.

29. Esaki, L. 1958. New phenomenon in narrow germanium *p-n* junctions. *Phys. Rev.* **109**: 603–604.

30. Findlay, G. P. 1962. Calcium ions and the action potential in *Nitella*. *Australian J. Biol. Sci.* **15**: 69–82.

31. FitzHugh, R. 1962. Computation of impulse initiation and saltatory conduction in a myelinated nerve fiber. *Biophys. J.* **2**: 11–21.

32. Franck, U. F. 1956. Models for biological excitation processes. *Progr. Biophys. Biophys. Chem.* **6**: 171–206.

33. Frankenhaeuser, B., and Hodgkin, A. L. 1957. The action of calcium on the electrical properties of squid axons. *J. Physiol. (London)* **137:** 218–244.

34. Fricke, H. 1925. The electric capacity of suspensions with special reference to blood. *J. Gen. Physiol.* **9:** 137–152.

35. Fricke, H., and Curtis, H. J. 1934. Electric impedance of suspensions of yeast cells. *Nature* **134:** 102–103.

36. Fricke, H., and Morse, S. 1925. The electrical resistance and capacity of blood for frequencies between 800 and 4-$\frac{1}{2}$ million cycles. *J. Gen. Physiol.* **9:** 153–167.

37. Goldman, D. E. 1943. Potential, impedance and rectification in membranes. *J. Gen. Physiol.* **27:** 37–60.

38. Goldman, D. E. 1962. Membrane structure and the effects of calcium on ion permeability. *Proc. Intern. Congr. Phys. Sci.*, 22nd, *Leiden* **1:** 583–585.

39. Hagiwara, S., and Saito, N. 1959. Membrane potential change and membrane current in supramedullary nerve cell of puffer. *J. Neurophysiol.* **22:** 204–211.

40. Hagiwara, S., Watanabe, A., and Saito, N. 1959. Potential changes in syncytial neurons of lobster cardiac ganglion. *J. Neurophysiol.* **22:** 554–572.

41. Hill, A. V. 1936. Excitation and accommodation in the nerve. *Proc. Roy. Soc. (London)* **B119:** 305–355.

42. Höber, R. 1910. Eine Methode die elektrische Leitfähigkeit im Innern von Zellen zu messen. *Arch. Ges. Physiol.* **133:** 237–253.

43. Höber, R. 1912. Ein zweites Verfahren die Leitfähigkeit im Innern von Zellen zu messen. *Arch. Ges. Physiol.* **148:** 189–221.

44. Höber, R. 1913. Messingen der inneren Leitfähigkeit von Zellen. *Arch. Ges. Physiol.* **150:** 15–45.

45. Hodgkin, A. L. 1958. Ionic movements and electrical activity in giant nerve fibers. *Proc. Roy. Soc. (London)* **B148:** 1–37.

46. Hodgkin, A. L., and Huxley, A. F. 1939. Action potentials recorded from inside a nerve fibre. *Nature* **144:** 710–711.

47. Hodgkin, A. L., and Huxley, A. F. 1952. A quantitative description of membrane current and its application to conduction and excitation in nerve. *J. Physiol. (London)* **117:** 500–544.

48. Hodgkin, A. L., Huxley, A. F., and Katz, B. 1949. Ionic currents underlying activity in the giant axon of the squid. *Arch. Sci. Physiol.* **3:** 129–163.

49. Hodgkin, A. L., Huxley, A. F., and Katz, B. 1952. Measurement of current-voltage relations in the membrane of the giant axon of *Loligo*. *J. Physiol. (London)* **116:** 424–472.

50. Hodgkin, A. L., and Katz, B. 1949. The effect of sodium ions on the electrical activity of the giant axon of the squid. *J. Physiol. (London)* **108:** 37–77.

51. Julian, F. J., Moore, J. W., and Goldman, D. E. 1962. Current-voltage relations in the lobster giant axon membrane under voltage clamp conditions. *J. Gen. Physiol.* **45:** 1217–1238.

52. Karreman, G. 1951. Contributions to the mathematical biology of excitation with particular emphasis on changes in membrane permeability and on threshold phenomena. *Bull. Math. Biophys.* **13:** 189–243.

53. Karreman, G., and Landahl, H. D. 1953. On spontaneous discharges obtained from a physicochemical model of excitation. *Bull. Math. Biophys.* **15:** 83–91.

54. Katz, B. 1939. "Electric Excitation of Nerve," 151 pp. Oxford Univ. Press, London.

55. Kishimoto, U., and Akabori, H. 1959. Protoplasmic streaming of an internodal cell of *Nitella flexis*. *J. Gen. Physiol.* **42:** 1167–1183.

56. Lapicque, L. 1926. "L'Excitabilité en Fonction du Temps; La Chronaxie, sa Signification et sa Mesure," 371 pp. Presses Universitaires, Paris.

57. Lillie, R. S. 1920. The recovery of transmissivity in passive iron wires as a model of recovery processes in irritable living systems. *J. Gen. Physiol.* **3:** 107–143.

58. Lillie, R. S. 1929. Resemblances between the electromotor variations of rhythmically reacting living and nonliving systems. *J. Gen. Physiol.* **13:** 1–11.

59. Lucas, K. 1909. The "all or none" contraction of the amphibian skeletal muscle fibre. *J. Physiol. (London)* **38:** 113–133.

60. McClendon, J. F. 1926. Colloidal properties of the surface of the living cell. *J. Biol. Chem.* **69:** 733–754.

61. Marmont, G. 1949. Studies on the axon membrane. *J. Cellular Comp. Physiol.* **34:** 351–382.

62. Mauro, A. 1962. Space charge regions in fixed charge membranes and the associated property of capacitance. *Biophys. J.* **2:** 179–198.

63. Monnier, A. -M. 1934. "L'Excitation Electrique des Tissus," 322 pp. Hermann, Paris.

64. Moore, J. W. 1959. Excitation of the squid axon membrane in isosmotic potassium chloride. *Nature* **183:** 265–266.

65. Mueller, P. 1958. Prolonged action potentials from single nodes of Ranvier. *J. Gen. Physiol.* **42:** 137–162.

66. Mullins, L. J. 1959a. The penetration of some cations into muscle. *J. Gen. Physiol.* **42:** 817–829.

67. Mullins, L. J. 1959b. An analysis of conductance change in squid axon. *J. Gen. Physiol.* **42:** 1013–1035.

68. Osterhout, W. J. V. 1922. "Injury, Recovery and Death in Relation to Conductivity and Permeability," 259 pp. Lippincott, Philadelphia.

69. Ostwald, W. 1900. Periodische Erscheinungen bei der Auflösing des Chroms in Säuren (Parts I and II). *Z. Physik. Chem. (Leipzig)* **35:** 33–76; 204–256.

70. Pauly, H., Packer, L., and Schwan, H. P. 1960. Electrical properties of mitochondrial membranes. *J. Biophys. Biochem. Cytol.* **7:** 589–601.

71. Philippson, M. 1920. Sur la résistance électrique des cellules et des tissus. *Compt. Rend. Soc. Biol.* **83:** 1399–1402.

72. Philippson, M. 1921. Les lois de la résistance électriques des tissus vivants. *Bull. Acad. Roy. Belgique* **7:** 387–405.

73. Rashevsky, N. 1933. Outline of a physico-mathematical theory of excitation and inhibition. *Protoplasma* **20:** 42–56.

74. Schlögl, R. 1954. Elektrodiffusion in freier Lösung und geladenen Membranen. *Z. Physik. Chem. [N.S.]* **1:** 305–339.

75. Schwan, H. P. 1957. Electrical properties of tissue and cell suspensions. *Advan. Biol. Med. Phys.* **5:** 147–209.

76. Schwan, H. P., and Cole, K. S. 1960. Bioelectricity: Alternating current admittance of cells and tissues. *In:* "Medical Physics," (O. Glasser, ed.), Vol. III, pp. 52–56. Year Book, Chicago.

77. Schwan, H. P., and Maczuk, J. 1959. Electrical relaxation phenomena of biological cells and colloidal particles at low frequencies. *In:* "Proc. Natl. Biophys. Conf., 1st, Columbus, Ohio, 1957," (H. Quastler and H. J. Morowitz, eds.), pp. 348–355, Yale Univ. Press, New Haven.

78. Schwan, H. P., and Morowitz, H. J. 1962. Electrical properties of the membranes of the pleuropneumonia-like organism A5969. *Biophys. J.* **2:** 395–407.

79. Solomon, A. K. 1960. Red cell membrane structure and ion transport. *J. Gen. Physiol.* **43 (5, Suppl.):** 1–15.

80. Tasaki, I., and Spyropoulos, C. S. 1958. Nonuniform response in the squid axon membrane under "voltage clamp." *Am. J. Physiol.* **193:** 309–317.

81. Taylor, R. E., Moore, J. W., and Cole, K. S. 1960. Analysis of certain errors in squid axon voltage clamp measurements. *Biophys. J.* **1:** 161–202.

82. Teorell, T. 1953. Transport process and electrical phenomena in ionic membranes. *Progr. Biophys. Biophys. Chem.* **3:** 305–369.

83. Villegas, R., and Barnola, F. V. 1961. Characterization of the resting axolemma in the giant axon of the squid. *J. Gen. Physiol.* **44:** 963–977.

84. Young, J. Z. 1936. Structure of nerve fibres and synapses in some invertebrates. *Cold Spring Harbor Symp. Quant. Biol.* **4:** 1–6.

85. Young, J. Z. 1951. "Doubt and Certainty in Science," 168 pp. Clarendon, Oxford.

[7]

COCHLEAR MECHANICS

Georg von Békésy

I. INTRODUCTION

A. The Problem

At the present time our understanding of the mechanism of hearing is in an unsettled state. We have come to recognize that the mechanical properties of the inner ear depend both on the physics of vibration and on hydrodynamics. Yet it is very difficult to understand how the system works and almost impossible to predict its behavior. Most likely some new mathematical functions must be developed before further headway can be made. The present essay is intended to demonstrate the main principles involved in inner ear mechanics and to indicate some of the difficulties which may force the invention of a fresh mathematical approach.*

The interest of physicists, like myself, in hearing has a long history. Pythagoras and his school (6th century B.C.) had already made one of the most important discoveries in the field; namely, if the vibrating length of a plucked string is reduced to one half by stopping it in the middle, the pitch of the tone which is heard is one octave higher. Pythagoras further showed that this sensation of the octave is a very general one whenever the length of a vibrating string is halved, regardless of the thickness of the string or the tension on it.

Now, this was perhaps the first psychophysical law relating a physical stimulus and a sensation. Even so, with all our knowledge of the anatomy, physiology, and biophysics of the ear we would be hard put to state another law as simple and clear as this one of the ancient Greeks.

Another basic discovery in hearing was also made by a physicist in a clear and simple way. This was Savart's demonstration (1830) that two short clicks produced by nails on the rim of a wheel turning against a piece of cardboard were enough to give rise to a sensation of pitch dependent on the period separating the two sound peaks. Such a discovery was quite contrary to all the physical and engineering knowledge of vibrations. In particular, it was contrary to Helmholtz' later experiments and theories of resonance since at least three or four cycles are required for that.

B. Functional Organization of the Ear

If we review the structural organization of the human middle ear we can see that it acts essentially like a mechanical transformer in which the low-stiffness vibrations of the air,

* The need for further development of mathematical and other modeling or analytical techniques has already been mentioned in other connections (Chapters 1, 2, and 3).

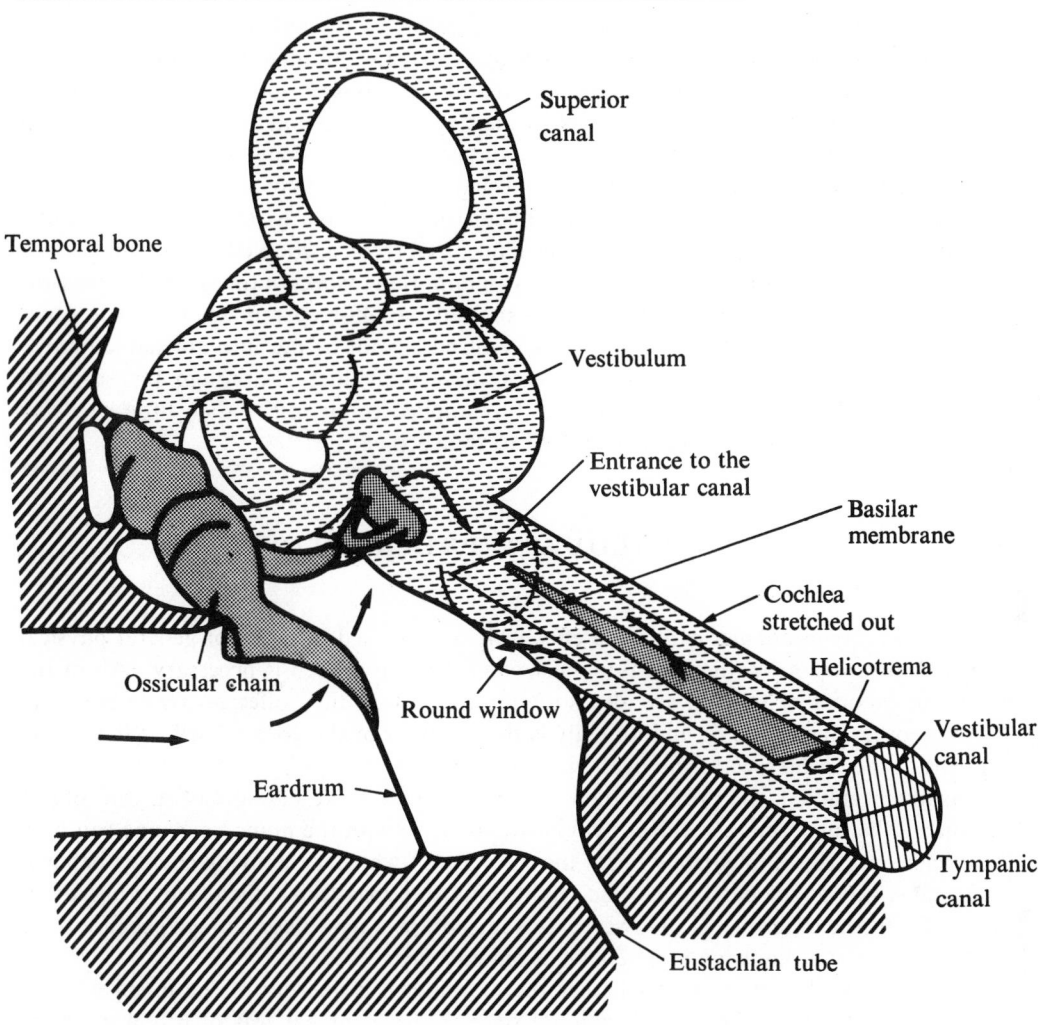

FIGURE 1. Diagram of the inner ear showing cochlea and basilar membrane uncoiled.

picked up by the eardrum, are transformed via the ear ossicles and the oval window to the much stiffer vibrations of the cochlear fluid. Because of the difference in areas between the eardrum and the oval window the over-all structure acts as a hydraulic press with a gain in force of about 22×.

The transmission of vibrational energy by this system is perfect for certain frequencies around 1000 cps, which is near the region of maximum sensitivity. All the energy at such frequencies is transmitted without loss into the inner ear. At higher and lower frequencies part of the energy is reflected and hence is not available for hearing.

In the inner ear (Figure 1), the oval window's vibration in turn oscillates the cochlear fluid whose displacement is accommodated by movements of the round window at the far end of the transmission system. Lying between the two columns of vibrating cochlear fluid is the basilar membrane which is the site of all the auditory nerve endings. Hence, from the point of view of cochlear mechanics, the basilar membrane must play a crucial role.

Unfortunately for understanding the principles involved, the basilar membrane is not a simple structure like the membrane in a telephone ear-piece. In man the basilar membrane is about 35 mm long and changes markedly in stiffness (about 1:100) and in width (about 1:2) between its lower and upper ends. Near the stapes it is stiff and thick; in the direction of the cochlear apex it becomes progressively thinner and more compliant.

A physicist will recognize at once that the mechanical properties of a system like this with continuously varying coefficients will be difficult or impossible to treat mathematically. Furthermore the fact that this complex mechanical vibrator is coupled to the fluid which fills the inner ear means that hydrodynamics is an important aspect of the system's behavior. This is unfortunate since hydrodynamics at present has more paradoxes than any other field of science. The fact that the problems involved cannot be put into amenable mathematical form is undoubtedly at the heart of these difficulties. Although the so-called Grenzeschicht Theorie can be quite successfully applied to air foils today, little headway can be made with the same methods applied to the cochlea.

II. AN ADEQUATE PREPARATION

A. *Work with Cadavers*

Since cochlear mechanics cannot be effectively approached in terms of general physical principles or tractable mathematical models, some other approach is necessary. All of the numerous theories of hearing are also so complicated that they offer no ready solution. The only other one available undoubtedly is the behavior of the system itself. What really happens in the cochlea when the oval window vibrates?

This much granted, the problem then becomes how to make measurements and observations on the functioning cochlea. Obviously to do so with the human ear, one can only use a cadaver. This immediately raises the question of whether the living cochlea behaves in the same way as the dead one. One might think to bypass this difficulty by using other mammals for the experiments. However, this introduces a new disadvantage because there is no simple way of knowing precisely what animals hear.

Consequently, the question of whether the mechanical properties of the inner ear of a cadaver can be kept in the same functional state as the living ear was of primary importance. Perhaps the best way to determine this is to follow the lead of the musician who plucks a string to find out if the pitch, damping, and so on, of his instrument are all right. In exactly the same way the physical properties of a telephone membrane can be tested in a few seconds, and so can the properties of the human ear, by plucking the eardrum. This can be done as readily in a living man as in a cadaver.

When such measurements are made, the eardrum is found to have more than one degree of freedom in its vibration. The main movement is an in-and-out oscillation, but there is some rotation too. If a little cotton wool is put in the external meatus, the high frequencies of the sharp click are damped out and a smooth simple response curve is readily obtained (Figure 2). With appropriate filters this can be analyzed into the contribution of each of the two motions involved. Then with a micrometer the resonant frequency and the damping may be measured very precisely.

With this simple and sensitive method measurements proved that the mechanical properties of a cadaver's inner ear could be maintained under certain circumstances for some days in normal mechanical condition. An important condition for this was adequate

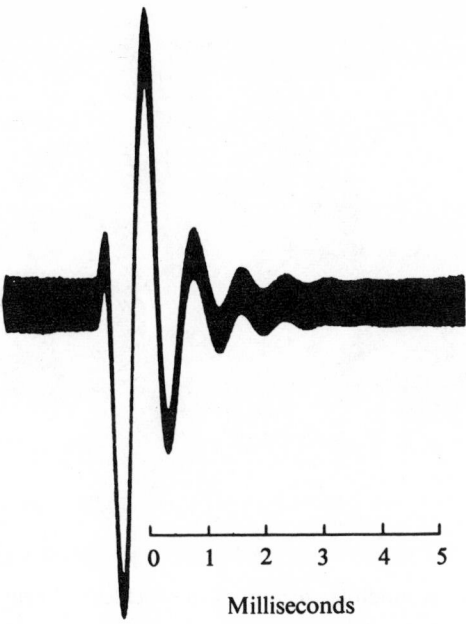

0 1 2 3 4 5

Milliseconds

FIGURE 2. Damped vibrations of human eardrum. (From von Békésy.[9])

humidity since the three very thin layers of the eardrum are highly sensitive to loss of moisture. In this way the first important problem, that of obtaining an adequate experimental system, was solved.

B. The Reduced Cochlea

However, another important difficulty remained. This related to determining which element in the cochlea vibrates and in what manner. Potentially the system is complicated by the anatomy of the cochlea (Figure 3). Although this tubular structure is essentially circular in cross-section, it is divided into upper and lower halves by the spiral lamina. The inner part of this is the bony osseous lamina, but stretched between the outer edge of this shelf and the distal wall of the cochlea is the basilar membrane which is the site of the mechanosensory organ of hearing. A second membrane, Reissner's membrane, running obliquely upward from the base of the osseous lamina to the outer wall of the cochlea, cuts off a wedge-shaped cochlear duct (scala media) filled with endolymphatic fluid of high viscosity.

Thus there are two membranes and a gelatinous wedge which may vibrate when the oval window oscillates. Of the four or five possible kinds of oscillation in such a system, which is the one important in hearing? To begin with, one might ask which is the largest vibration and what are its characteristics. Fortunately for answering such questions, the complex wedge of the intact cochlea may be replaced just by the basilar membrane which has only one degree of freedom.

Evidence that such a reduced system is justified can be found by measuring the effect of vibrating Reissner's membrane. A 1000 cps oscillation of this structure immediately sets both it and the basilar membrane vibrating together in exactly the same phase. This justifies the replacement of the whole wedge-shaped structure by a single membrane. In

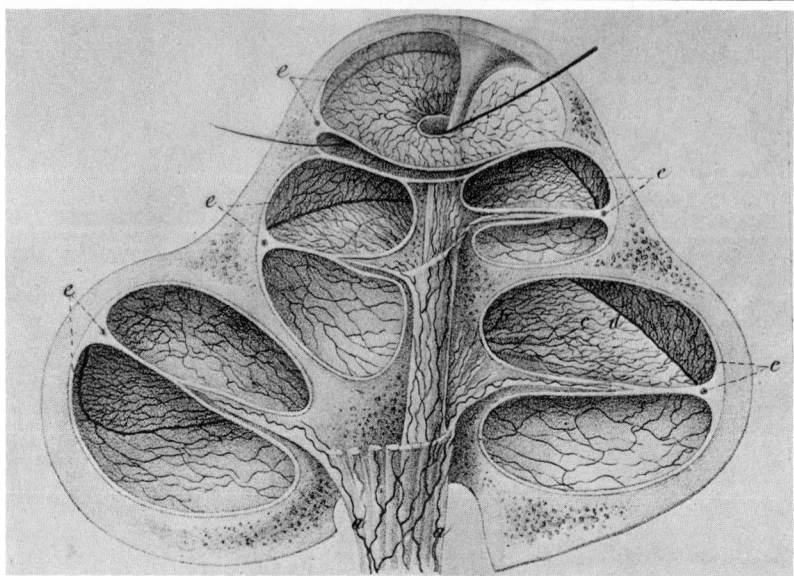

FIGURE 3. A modiolar section of the cochlea. (From Lincke.[1])

practice this important simplification may be achieved by brushing off the single-cell-thick Reissner's membrane and the whole organ of Corti, which is a soft fragile structure, thus isolating the basilar membrane without affecting the vibration pattern.

III. BASILAR MEMBRANE PROPERTIES

Now the basic question is how does the basilar membrane vibrate? The answer to this has been a matter of controversy for about 100 years. One reason for such a protracted argument is that the cochlea is very small in the guinea pig ear; it is only about as large as a drop of water. Within that scale the cochlea and its basilar membrane undergo four helical turns. Obviously the problems of trying to determine how this structure moves and what aspects of its movement are crucial for hearing are so difficult that it is scarcely surprising that they remained in the discussion stage for a long time.

A. Four Theories

From all this discussion essentially four different kinds of theories for cochlear mechanics emerged. These are neatly separated in the textbooks: 1) the telephone theory, 2) the resonance theory, 3) the traveling wave theory, and 4) the standing wave theory. Although such compartmentalization is obviously fine for a textbook, it probably was not the right research approach. In fact, when noting the similarities between the various theories, it turns out that the differences between them are quite small and mathematically they all belong to the same family of vibrations; only the numerical values are different.

The best way to approach this crucial question is to examine the implications of the various hearing theories for the mechanical properties of the basilar membrane. For example, Helmholtz' resonance theory requires that the basilar membrane be laterally stressed between its origin on the osseous lamina and its insertion on the spiral ligament at the opposite side of the cochlea. This lateral stress would in effect produce transverse fibers which resonated at different frequencies like the strings of a harp. In this connection it is interesting that the first human basilar membrane I studied had transverse stripes that looked almost like piano wires. However, this preparation had been in formaldehyde for some time. In fresh cochleas the basilar membrane is completely transparent so that special tricks are required to see it at all.

B. Responses to Deformation

But more to the point is the behavior of the membrane when it is deformed. In such a structure, under the stress postulated by Helmholtz, pressing it with a needle should produce an elliptical deformation. Yet in the basilar membrane such point pressure never leads to elliptical deformation. Hence no lateral stress is present on this membrane.

The next points of interest here are the stiffness of the membrane and the question of whether it actually consists of a thick gelatinous plate or a thin elastic membrane. The deformation of membranes of different thicknesses and mechanical properties can be studied in models (Figure 4) and compared with the actual deformation observed in the cochlea. Thus, if a model membrane is prestressed as required by the resonance theory, its vibration pattern to a given pressure frequency is just as predicted (Figure 5). Furthermore, if this system is examined stroboscopically, neighboring areas around the resonance point are seen to be moving in opposite directions which is quite characteristic of any array of tuned resonators.

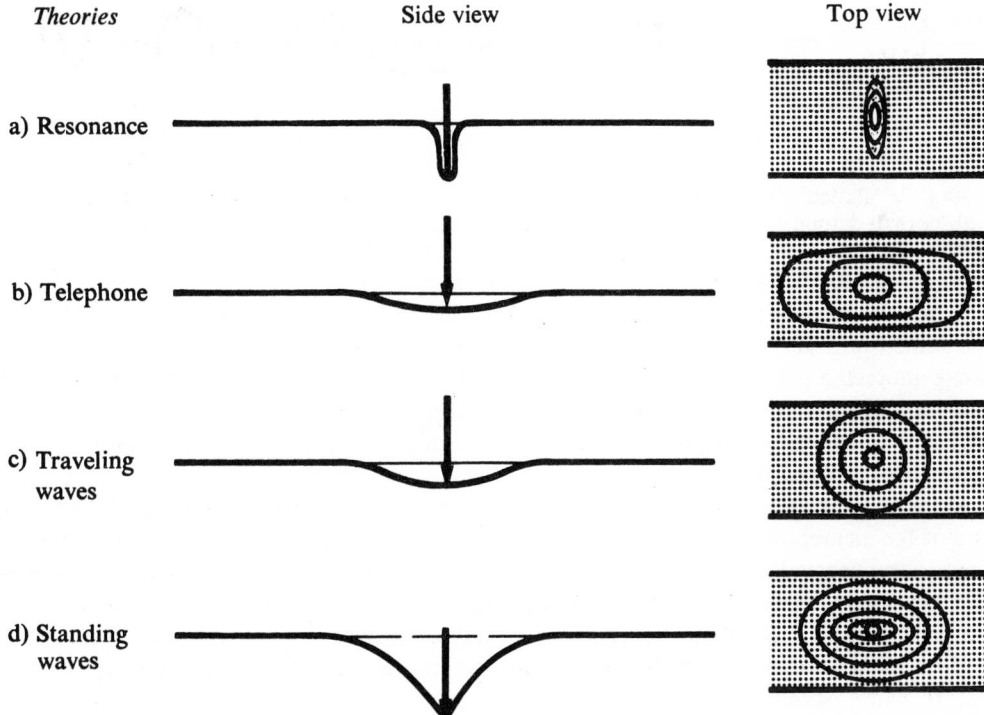

FIGURE 4. Patterns of deformation produced in different kinds of membranes by applying force at one point. The membranes would behave differently according to the four theories, as indicated. (From von Békésy.[3],[9])

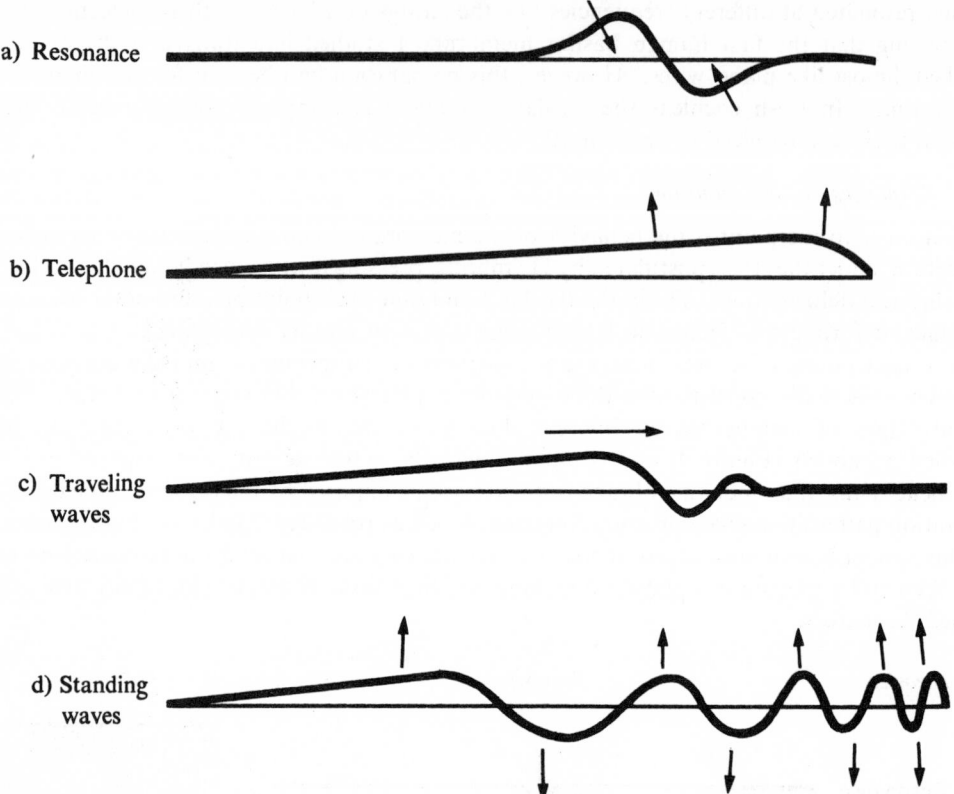

FIGURE 5. Patterns of vibration produced by a continuous tone in different kinds of membranes with normal damping. The arrows indicate the direction of motion at a given instant. (From von Békésy.[9])

When the model membrane is quite stiff, then its whole length will move up and down at the same time. If it is stiffer on one side than on the other, the more compliant side will move more than the stiff one. A curious thing happens as such a membrane is made thinner and thinner. From oscillating all in phase, as the telephone membrane does, at higher frequencies a traveling wave will appear. Such behavior is required by the traveling wave theory of hearing.

If the membrane is made even thinner still, traveling waves are reflected back from the end of the membrane to form a pattern of standing waves. According to the standing wave theory, frequency differences in the sound affect the pattern of the wave nodes whose position obviously depends on the wavelength; the brain is informed of this via the auditory nerve. Note also that with standing waves, neighboring parts of the membrane at nodes and anti-nodes are moving in opposite directions which is a characteristic of an array of resonators, as we have seen.

According to the traveling wave theory, there will be a maximum displacement of the membrane in positions which will be determined by the frequency of the stimulus. Thus a low frequency will produce maximum vibration at one point along the basilar membrane and this point will move along the cochlea to another position for a higher frequency.

From the point of view of cochlear mechanics the telephone theory is of little interest since for all frequencies there would be just vibrations of the membrane linearly following the pressure on the stapes and leaving all frequency discrimination entirely to higher centers in the central nervous system.

Actually the simple experiments on the effect of local pressure on basilar membrane deformation can distinguish clearly between the four theoretical possibilities of cochlear mechanism. As mentioned above, if the deformation is elliptical, the resonance theory is correct; if it is very flat like that of a sheet of gelatin, the telephone theory is correct; and if it is something in between, like a thin rubber membrane, then the traveling wave theory is correct.

In effect, then, observations on the deformation of a few cochleas to local pressure from a needle should quite simply settle the whole problem. The only significant difference between the theories is the numerical value for membrane stiffness. Hence all four theories could even be described with the same equations. The actual observations (Figure 6) show clearly that the kind of vibrations sustained by the human cochlear membrane must be traveling waves. Despite their common occurrence in many everyday situations, traveling waves still have not been studied adequately. Furthermore, in cases with continually changing coefficients of stiffness, as in the basilar membrane, the system is difficult to deal with mathematically.

C. Direct Observations

Although these determinations of basilar membrane displacement patterns are quite conclusive proof of the mechanism involved in the membrane's auditory function, a second proof of the validity of the traveling wave theory has been obtained by direct observation of cochlear membrane vibration. To do this the organ is dissected under flowing water to

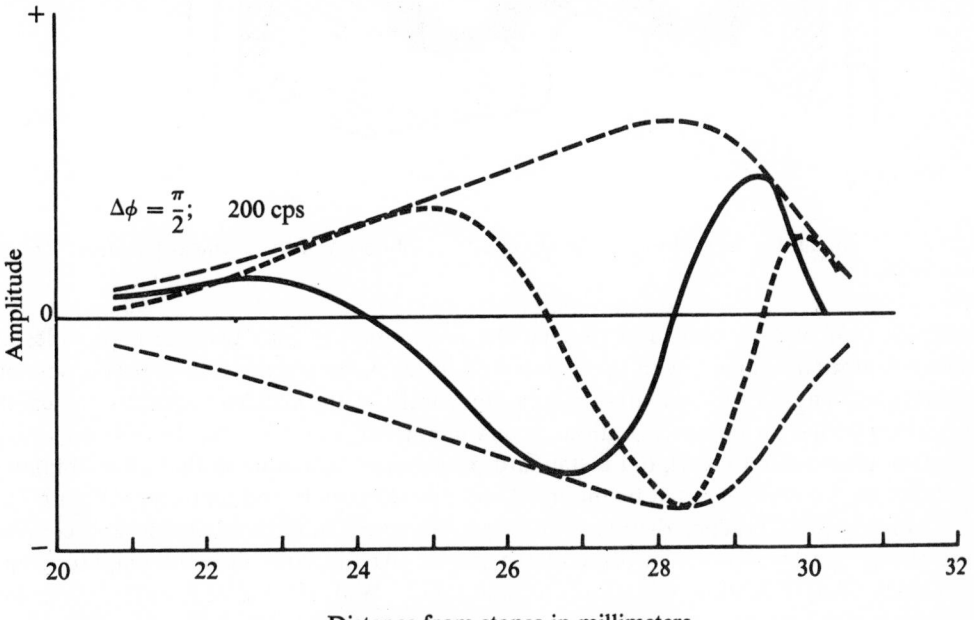

$$\Delta\phi = \frac{\pi}{2}; \quad 200 \text{ cps}$$

Distance from stapes in millimeters

FIGURE 6. Detail of the form of the cochlear partition vibration for 200 cps at two instants within a cycle. (From von Békésy.[2])

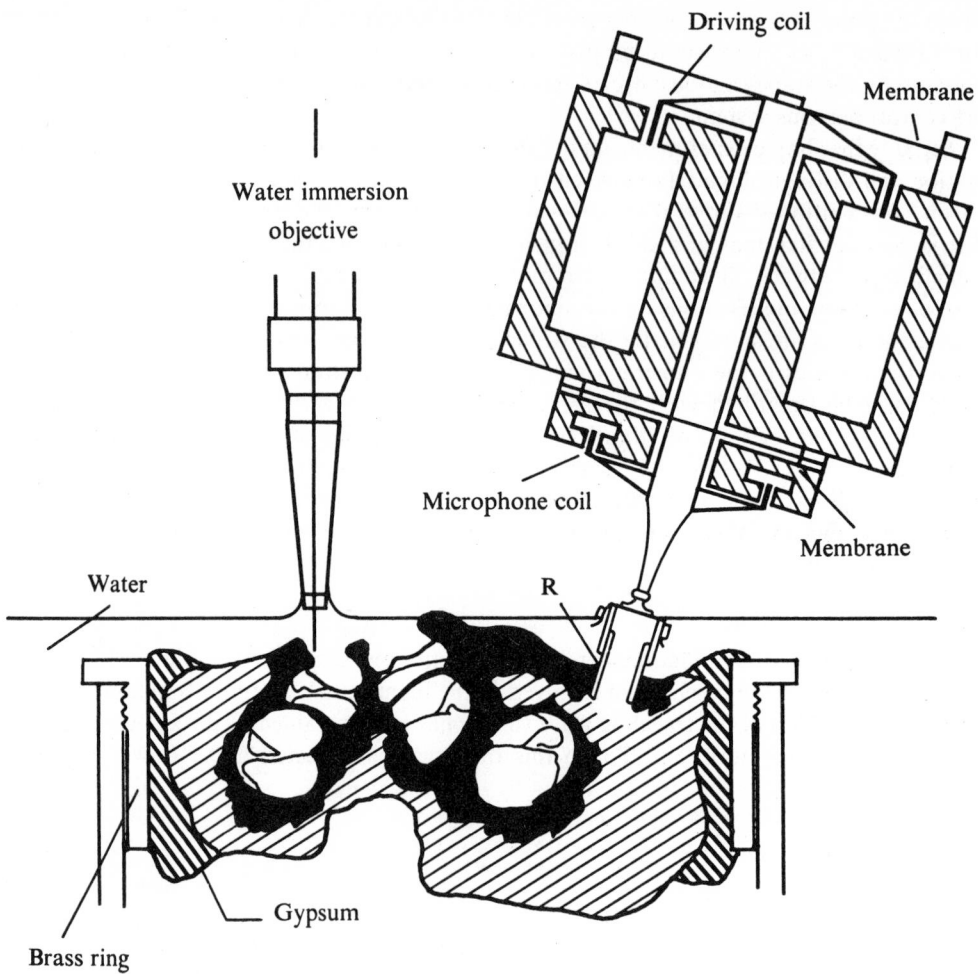

FIGURE 7. Apparatus for measuring the amplitude of vibration of the cochlear partition. (From von Békésy.[9])

keep the field of view clear and to keep the preparation moist. Because it provides an effective impedance match with the endolymph inside, submergence also makes it possible to make openings in the bony and membranous walls of the cochlea without significantly disturbing basilar membrane vibrations, a very important consideration. In this connection it was of great value to work out a standard preparation technique so that after obtaining an inner ear for study it could be mounted and opened rapidly and uniformly (Figure 7).

1. *Methods.* In practice the oval window is driven by an electrodynamic unit coupled into the system by a piston in place of the stapes. At the same time the amplitude and frequency of oval window vibration are monitored. With the aid of a water immersion microscope, the movements of the basilar membrane are observed through a window cut through the cochlear wall. But because of the transparency of the membrane special techniques have to be employed to make any useful observations. One good method is to sprinkle minute silver crystals on Reissner's membrane or the basilar membrane. Since

these are thin flat crystals with mirror-like surfaces, they lie flat on the membrane and reflect back brilliant points of light.

A second method of observation requires the use of a slit lamp which provides a narrow, high-intensity light beam 0.01 mm in diameter. When this strikes the organ of Corti it is reflected by curved cell walls so that single cells such as Hansen cells appear as glittering points of light. The slit lamp has a second good feature since deterioration in the state of the preparation increases turbidity which shows up strongly as Tyndall scattering. The lamp actually used was a stroboscopic quartz lamp driven at 10,000 volts.

The next problem to be solved was that of precisely measuring the phase of the basilar membrane vibration. This is essential to understanding how a wave may travel along the membrane. For this purpose both the amplitude and phase of the displacement must be accurately determined in different sections of the membrane. Stroboscopic illumination provides a solution to this. If a single flash per cycle is given, slow stroboscopic movements of the usual kind appear when the flashes and the cyclic activity have nearly the same period.

If, instead, two flashes a cycle are given, a simple and informative method of determining the local phase angle is provided. In those regions of the membrane where the phase of the flash unit and that of the oscillating membrane are not the same, two points of reflected light from the silver crystals will appear. The nearer their phases match, the closer together will the points appear until only a single point is seen when the flash sequence and the membrane at that point are exactly in phase (Figure 8) and the section of the membrane is illuminated when going through the zero point. Thus with the aid of a phase shifter and a suitable frequency range of vibration, the dynamic properties of the membrane can be accurately measured. An accuracy of 1° can be achieved by this method if alternate stroboscopic flashes are red and green. In that case the in-phase regions appear as sharp white lines separated by areas of red and green points of light.

2. *Measurements.* Measurements of this kind proved conclusively that the oscillations of the basilar membrane are made up of traveling waves. They reach their maximum amplitude at one point, the position of which depends on the vibration frequency. High

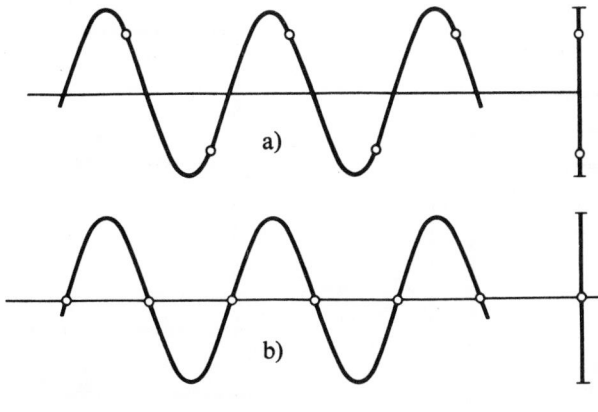

Time →

FIGURE 8. Principle of the phase stroboscope. The small circles show the positions of the moving object at which it is illuminated by the flashes of light. What is seen is indicated on the right. In a), two spots of light are seen; in b), the phase of the flashes has been adjusted so that only one spot is seen. (From von Békésy.[2])

frequencies have their wave maxima near the oval window; low frequencies have theirs near the helicotrema at the cochlear apex. At 1600 cps the maximum is about in the middle of the membrane's length in man. Thus the membrane acts like a filter system whose maximum response moves up and down its length as a function of frequency.

D. Oscillator Stability

One of the most challenging problems remaining in cochlear mechanics relates to the remarkable stability of the oscillating system despite apparently drastic changes imposed on it. This constitutes a mathematically exciting problem too. For example, cuts may be made in the basilar membrane, or it may be loaded with a bit of gelatin, without altering the pattern of the traveling waves. Even a model of an uncoiled cochlea (Figure 9) shows some rather astonishing properties of this sort.

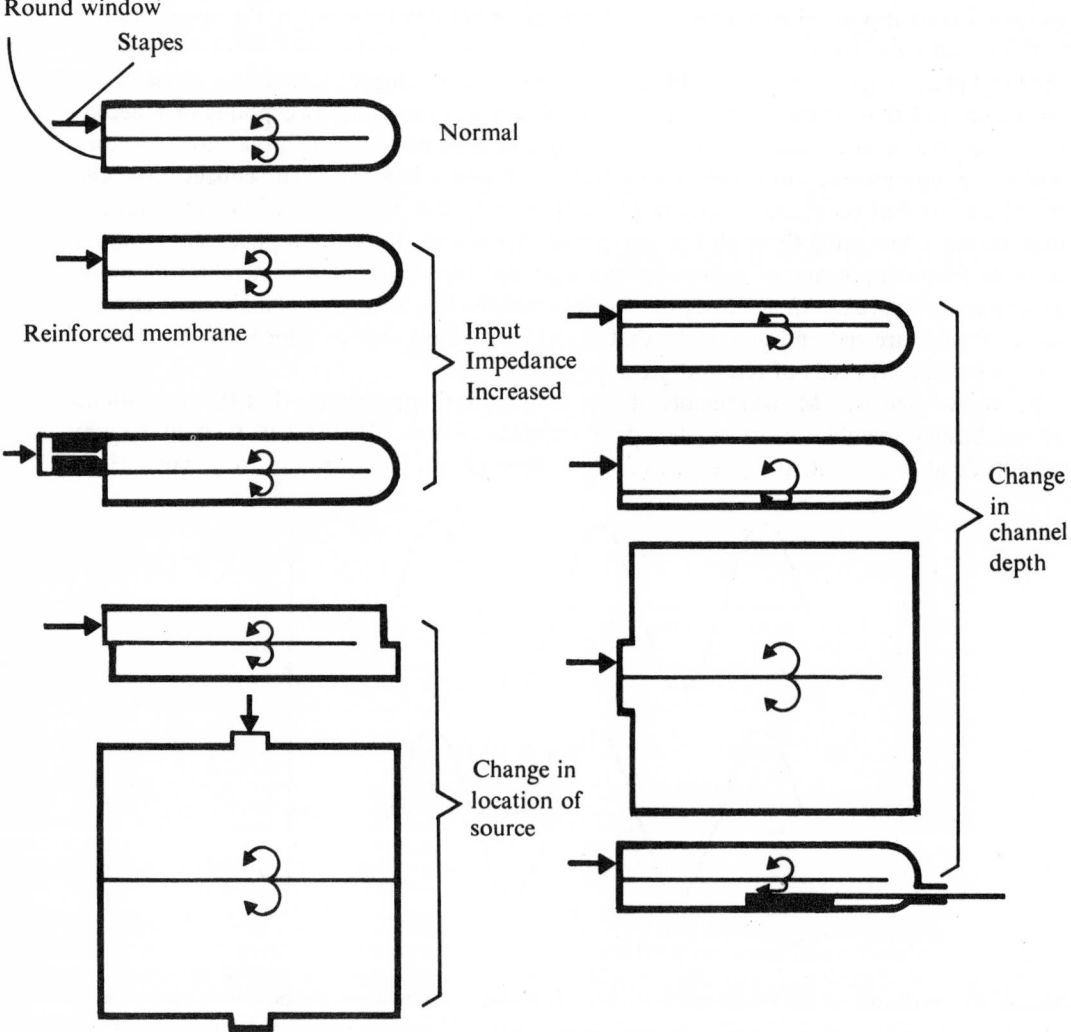

FIGURE 9. Models of uncoiled cochleas. (From von Békésy.[4])

In such a model constructed to reproduce the elastic and dimensional properties of the cochlea, eddy currents in the fluid within the model are made visible by a suspension of minute silver crystals. When the oval window of the model is vibrated, a characteristic local current flow occurs at the region of maximal vibration amplitude of the rubber membrane modeling the basilar membrane. Now this eddy current can be used to show what effect various parameters of the cochlea have on this position of maximum displacement in the traveling waves.

Considerable changes in the relative dimensions of the channels modeling the upper and lower parts of the cochlear canal, changes in input impedance for the vibration, obstructions in the channels, and even drastic changes in the location of the structures modeling the oval and round windows do not affect this position of maximum membrane displacement for a given vibration frequency. About the only alteration which did change the oscillation pattern was to decrease the channel depth of the upper cochlear canal to one-third of its normal dimensions. Hence one must conclude that the human cochlea is so constructed that despite marked disturbance in its normal structure, this organ will nevertheless continue to give its normal frequency response.

Obviously this situation is mathematically a challenging and frustrating one. In fact it is a point of departure for a new kind of hydrodynamics. The real difficulty here is that usually in mathematics when important factors change, the whole system changes its properties drastically. Yet we have seen that a biological system such as the cochlea maintains stable behavior despite strong alterations.

For example, suppose one makes a mathematical deduction which proposes that some component is logarithmically related to the rest of a system. A set of measurements is made and it fits very nicely on a logarithmic curve. However, further measurements of the system show that the data may be fitted as well by a power function. But if a power function is introduced, the mathematical treatment must be completely changed. Hence more than one mathematical model, perhaps each quite different, can account for certain properties of the system. The question then arises which is the better model in the sense that it more nearly deals with meaningful parameters and relations in the natural system. In the present case then we must ask, what is the best mathematical model for cochlear mechanics?

IV. COMPARATIVE DATA

Since the cochlear mechanics dealt with so far have been completely restricted to the human ear, we may well ask about the cochlear mechanics of other animals. Does the traveling wave mechanism which underlies human hearing operate in other species, or are different principles involved? As far as has been determined, the ears of other mammals ranging, say, from a mouse to an elephant all have exactly the same kind of traveling waves as the human cochlea.

In the mouse the whole basilar membrane is only about 7 mm long, but the ratio of the elasticity at the stapes to that at the apex is about $1:100$, as it is in man and in all the other vertebrates measured. With a 200 cps oscillation on the stapes the traveling wave maximum in the mouse ear is at the apical end of the membrane and no displacement of the maximum occurs with increasing frequency until about 400 cps. Then with higher frequencies the maximum moves toward the stapes, near which the highest frequencies are maximal. Although measurements were made only to 5000 cps, extrapolation indicates that about

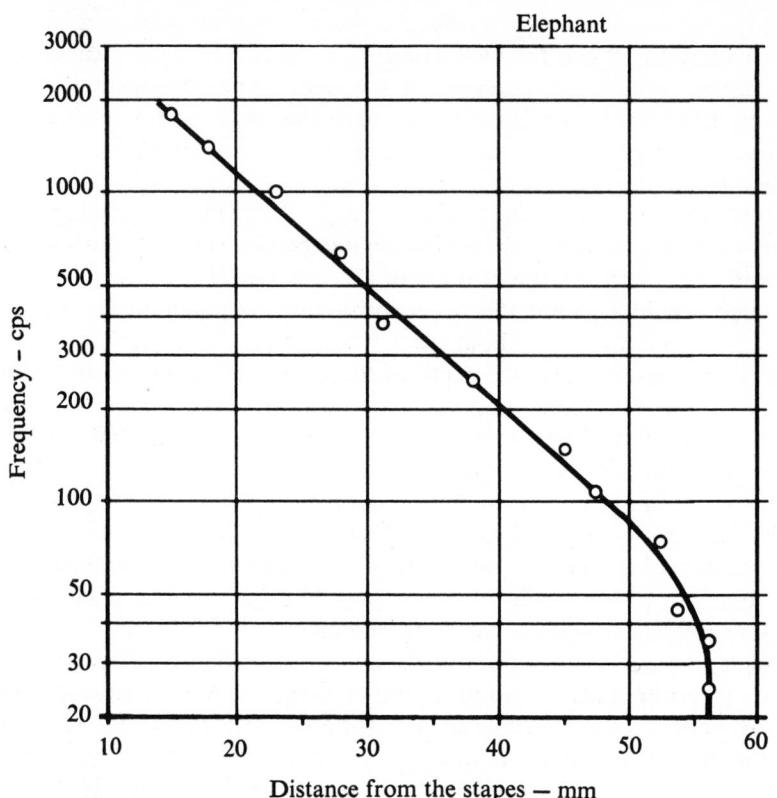

FIGURE 10. Positions of maximum stimulation along the cochlear partition of the elephant. (From von Békésy.[9])

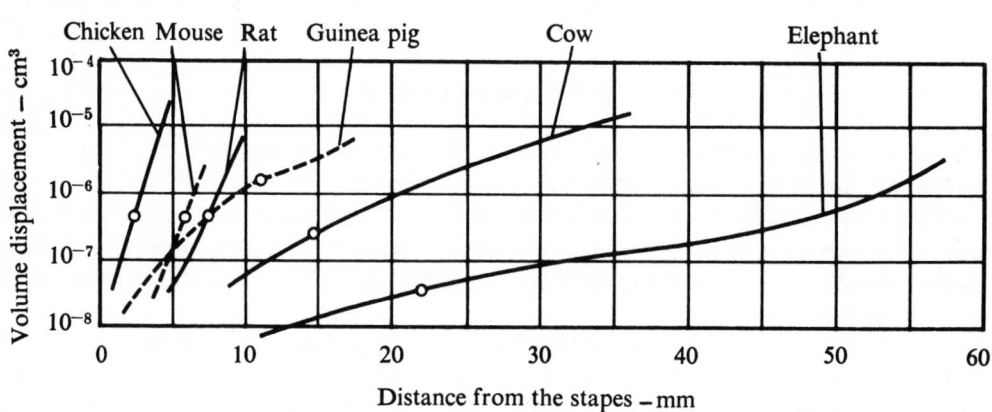

FIGURE 11. Comparison of the elasticity of the cochlear partition of different animals, measured as the volume displacement produced in a 1 mm segment by a pressure of 1 cm of water. (From von Békésy.[9])

20,000 cps is peaked at the lower end of the basilar membrane in the mouse. Hence the whole range of its effective frequency distribution is from 400–20,000 cps.

In the case of the elephant, of which I was very lucky to get a fresh cochlea, the basilar membrane is about 60 mm long, and the cochlea instead of being helical is coiled flat in one plane. The traveling wave maximum is at the inner end of the coil at about 20 cps, and above 30 cps it begins to move outward along the basilar membrane toward the stapes (Figure 10). By 2000 cps the wave peak is already within 15 mm of the stapes; for 3000 cps the distance is about 10 mm and extrapolation indicates that the maximum frequency at which the elephant has good pitch discrimination is around 8000 cps.

From what we have seen so far, the difference limen for pitch discrimination should be limited, among other things, by the length of the basilar membrane. Consequently, when the lengths of these structures are compared in various animals (Figure 11), some estimate may be made of this.

V. NONAIRBORNE STIMULATION

For ordinary airborne sounds the traveling wave theory seems to account quite well for the mechanical function of the cochlea. But there are two other kinds of hearing whose mechanisms might be different from that already discussed. These are 1) direct electrical stimulation of the cochlea which also gives rise to sensations of sound, and 2) bone conduction in which the sound of a vibrating object, say touched to the head, may be heard. So there are really three kinds of hearing and there could be three absolutely different phenomena involved.

A. *Electrical Stimulation*

The simplest assumption to make for the case of electrical stimulation is that the current simply activates the auditory nerve fibers to conduct periodic bursts of spikes which are then conducted to the brain. If this were so, all questions of cochlear mechanics would be irrelevant. A critical question here is whether or not electrical stimulation gives rise to sensations of pure tones.

From an electrophysiological point of view, one would not expect to hear pure tones when the auditory nerve is electrically stimulated, say by a 1000 cps alternating current. One would instead expect that lack of strict synchrony of the resulting action potentials, as well as failure of individual fibers to follow the stimulus at frequencies greater than a few hundred cycles, would produce some noise in the system.

The first good relevant observations were made by Gershuni on soldiers with head injuries. Direct stimulation of the auditory nerve never gave rise to a pure tone for, say, a 1000 cps stimulus. Instead there was a broad frequency band of white noise which conveyed some impression of high or low frequency, but never that of a clear pure tone.

Recently this question was reopened by an engineer who wished to apply modern methods with a view toward developing a new kind of hearing aid which would involve putting an electrode on the auditory nerve. However, the results were the same as in the earlier tests. An alternating current on the auditory nerve produces a white noise with a particular band width corresponding to the stimulus frequency. With speech, the loudness of the white noise is modulated by the envelope of speech sounds.

Consequently, with experience it is possible to learn to recognize what someone is saying, but it really is impossible to understand normal speech. The effect of this system can be readily imitated by taking a source of white noise and modulating its output amplitude with the envelope of speech sounds. In addition to these functional restrictions of this method of direct auditory nerve stimulation, it was found that the problem of chronically implanted electrodes was a severe one too.

From what has been said, the perception of pure tones as a result of electrical stimulation cannot be initiated by direct nerve stimulation, and must, therefore, arise in some other way. This other way seems quite probably to be by means of electrostatic effects initiated at the eardrum. An electrode in the middle ear will induce electrostatic charges which in turn will generate forces which move these structures, just as pressure displacement of the eardrum does. Similar middle ear effects would be induced by electrostatic charges on the eardrum when a stimulating AC current flows in the external ear canal.

B. Bone Conduction

The problem of hearing by means of bone conduction is an even more difficult one to solve. Again the direct solution would seem to be that compression of bone, caused by sound waves, would in turn squeeze the auditory nerve which could stimulate the latter and produce the sensation of a tone in that fashion. This matter was first approached by experiments on mechanoreceptors in the skin.

1. *Mechanoreceptor analog.* It was already well known from Meissner's observation that when one's finger is dipped into a pool of mercury, no pressure is felt under the liquid. A pressure sensation is felt only at the surface edge. If this experiment with constant pressure is extended to include sinusoidally alternating pressures, still no sensation at all is felt by the finger dipped in the liquid except at the edge again. These observations suggest that compression of the auditory nerve should not be expected to evoke a tone.

If this is so, then compression as a stimulus must be supposed to act somewhere else. One likely possibility is that it compresses the middle ear in such a way that the stapes is moved relative to the surrounding bone. This would, of course, displace the oval window and induce cochlear responses such as those resulting from airborne sound stimulation, namely, basilar membrane vibration.

2. *Dual stimulation.* Another line of evidence can be obtained by an experiment in which the interaction of bone-conducted and airborne sounds is studied. If bone conduction is acting by displacing the stapes as suggested above, then an airborne pure tone, of the same frequency and effective amplitude but having a phase difference of 180° in comparison with the bone-conducted sound, should be able to compensate completely for the latter, with the net result that complete silence results. If the bone-conducted sound were stimulating auditory nerve endings directly, it would be most unlikely that complete compensation could be obtained since the airborne sound, as we have seen above, gives rise to highly complicated phase variations along the basilar membrane. Exact matching of such a complex pattern would be quite improbable.

In execution this experiment is difficult to carry out, but when properly set up and the subject adequately trained, no difficulty is experienced in getting complete compensation of a bone-conducted tone by an airborne one, or vice versa, over a frequency range from 100 to 10,000 cps.

This method is extremely precise and so sensitive that full compensation cannot be maintained for long. For example, swallowing which displaces the middle ear ossicles, and changes in the circulation which change blood pressure, will immediately affect the balance. Even different phases of the heartbeat will influence this.

If such experiments are extended to include electrically induced sound, the previous conclusion that pure tones are heard through a mechanism involving normal vibration of the basilar membrane is fully confirmed. Electrically induced tones can be fully compensated with airborne or bone-conducted ones of the same frequency.

VI. MODELS OF BASILAR MEMBRANE ACTIVITY

At this point some problems relating to the unique behavior of the basilar membrane will be considered. The main point is that its ability to produce a traveling wave is not observed in daily life and differs considerably from our usual concepts of waves. Such phenomena are largely a consequence of the peculiar wave propagation in media which are not homogeneous. For example, under this condition waves do not propagate in straight lines. An instance of this is that in an auditorium or concert hall (Figure 12) the presence of the audience deflects the sound waves and damps them in ways quite inexplicable on the basis of direct propagation. Sometimes one can notice a 15 db increase in sound intensity merely by standing up at the back of a theater.

A comparable effect had already been noted out of doors by Rayleigh. If one is in a meadow listening to the ringing of a far-away bell, there is a striking increase in intensity of the sound when one raises his head from a level close to the grass to one, two, or three feet above it, even though there is no obstacle between bell and ear in either case.

A. Tuned Reeds

A rather similar situation occurs in the ear. Perhaps the best way to demonstrate this is to deal first with a model consisting of a tuned-reed frequency analyzer (Figure 13). Here one has a series of differently loaded springs which can be set into oscillation so that resulting wave patterns can be observed under different conditions. As already mentioned, with an array of resonators of this kind the components near the resonant point will be oscillating in antiphase. But if coupling between the resonators is introduced, say by connecting them with a rubber band, then a traveling wave pattern of vibration is introduced. If all the resonators are tuned to the same frequency and have the same coupling, they will all vibrate in the same phase, and no waves at all will be produced. But waves will be formed if a change or discontinuity is made in the degree of the coupling.

Sound wave

Audience in the pit of a theater

FIGURE 12.   Deflection of sound waves near an absorbent layer. (From von Békésy.[9])

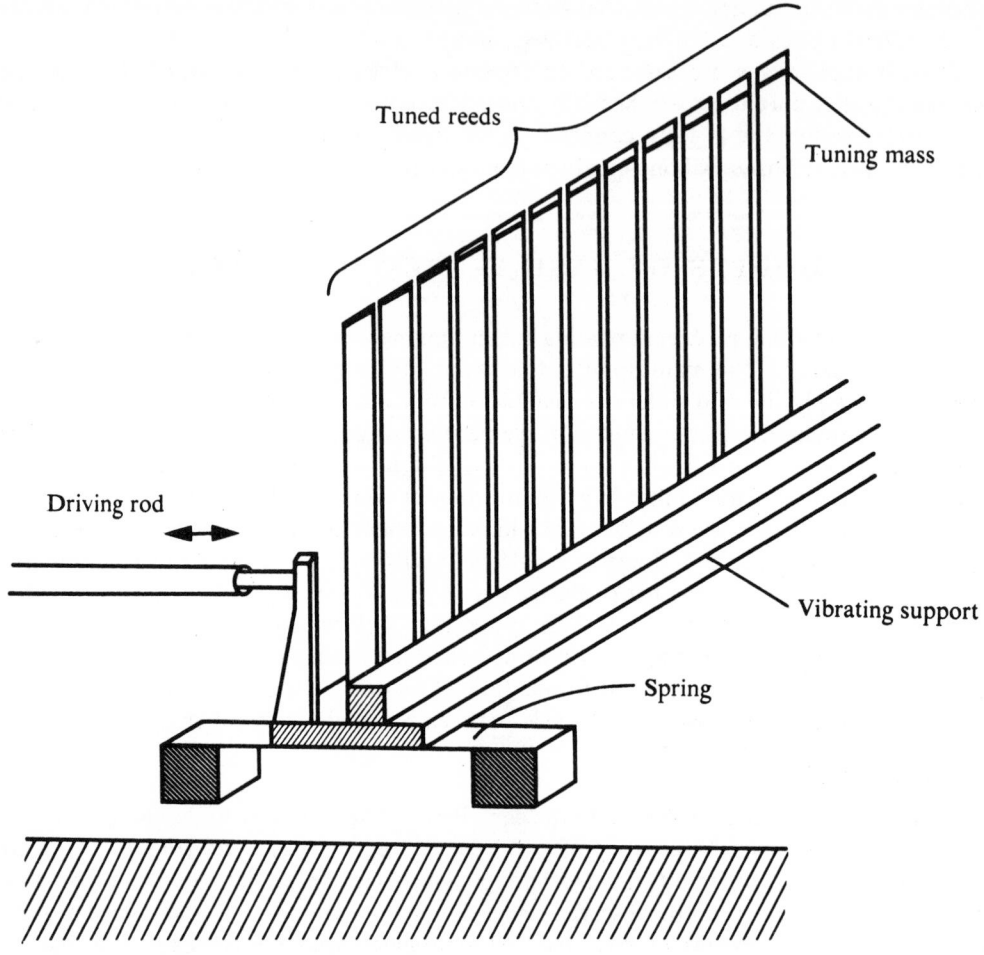

FIGURE 13.   A tuned-reed frequency analyzer. A series of reeds are fixed on a vibrating support and tuned with an added mass so adjusted that the natural frequency of each reed is about 0.5 cps lower than its neighbor to the left. A continuous sinusoidal force applied to the driving rod sets one or two reeds into maximum vibration and thereby directly indicates the frequency of the driving force. (From von Békésy.[8])

This experiment shows that discontinuity in some property of the system starts a wave. Hence in the mathematical treatment of a complicated model of this kind, each discontinuity should be treated as a wave generator and the system's response found by adding the calculated contributions for all components.

B.   Coupled Pendulums

A better model of such systems can be built by using an array of pendulums, each made of a ball bearing suspended by a thread (Figure 14). The length of the pendulums is changed progressively from one end of the system to the other so that one of its properties changes continuously. Coupling can be introduced between pendulums by connecting them together in series with threads weighted with small ball bearings. To drive the system all these pendulums are suspended from a rotatable rod which in turn is oscillated by a heavy pendulum fixed to it.

In studying the performance of such a system, a point of particular interest is the flow of energy through it. At the start the driving axis has all the energy. This may flow either directly from the rod to each pendulum, or it may flow from one pendulum to another through the coupling. The question is which of these routes is more important. The answer to this question clearly will depend on the coupling and also on several other factors.

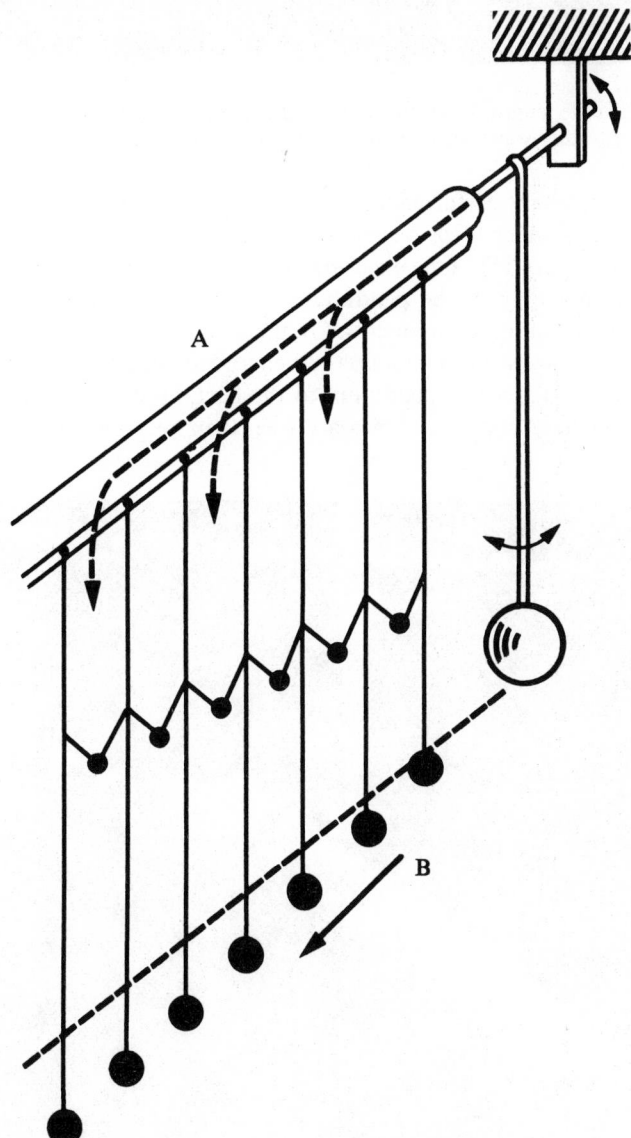

FIGURE 14. Pendulum resonator model. A is a solid cylinder which drives the pendulums. B indicates the direction of the resultant traveling wave. (From von Békésy.[9])

$\Delta t = 1/6$ sec

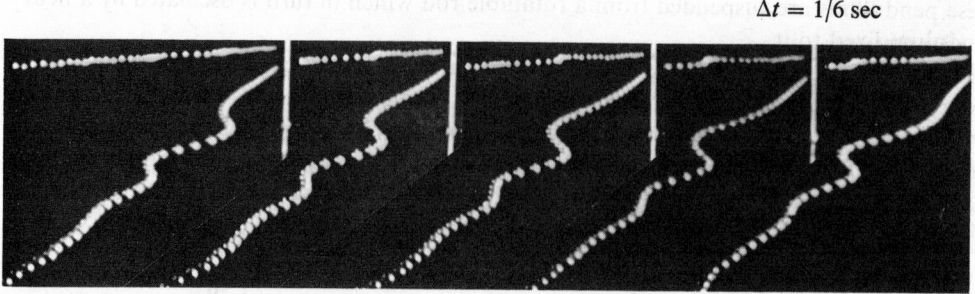

FIGURE 15.   When the length of the pendulums changes progressively, the effects of these changes summate and a traveling wave forms with a maximum in one place. (From von Békésy.[9])

Examination of system performance shows that these pendulums, like the tuned reeds, show traveling waves which always move from the stiffer to the more compliant region, just as in the cochlea (Figure 15).   One experiment to test the path of energy flow in the pendulum system is to fix some of the pendulums so that energy from the rod can only flow directly into the remaining components.   If the long compliant pendulums are the ones fixed, the stiffer ones are seen to pick up their energy directly from the rod (Figure 16), and energy does not flow from one pendulum to the next.   But, if the short stiff elements are blocked and the longer compliant ones are free, their response has a considerably lower

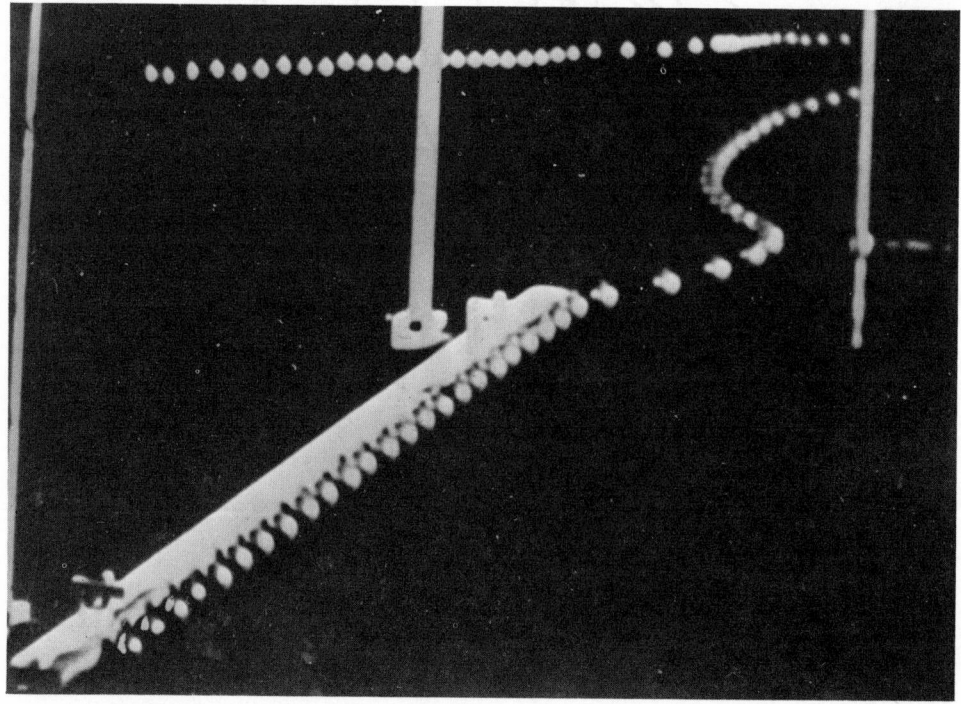

FIGURE 16.   Bar covered with foam rubber used to stop the vibrations of the longer pendulums. (From von Békésy.[9])

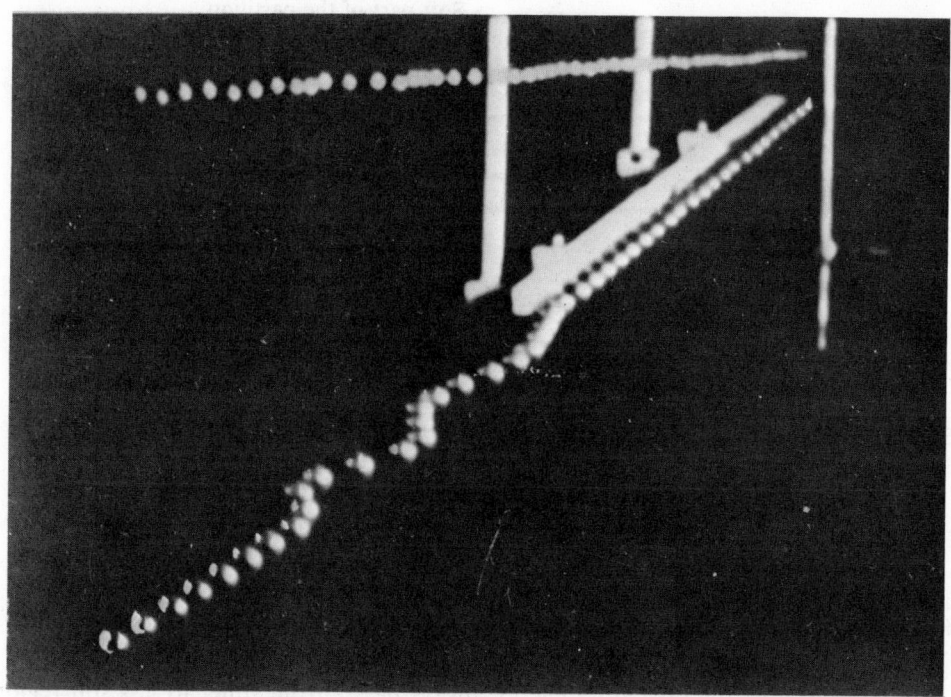

FIGURE 17. Bar used to stop the vibrations of the shorter pendulums. (From von Békésy.[9])

amplitude (Figure 17). This proves that the less stiff pendulums derive their energy in large part from the stiffer ones and not from the rod. If the whole system is vibrating and the stiffer end is stopped, the other end will be seen at once to begin losing amplitude. Thus energy flow occurs in one direction from the stiffer to the less stiff resonators.

This can be further demonstrated in another test in which all the pendulums are first quiet, then the less stiff ones are all swung out to a given angle and released at once. The potential energy of their starting position is then transferred into kinetic energy of movement when they are released. Some noise but no wave passes into the stiffer section; instead more and more energy is passed down into more compliant units whose vibration amplitude grows. Finally all the energy flows into the last pendulum which develops the largest amplitude of all (Figure 18).

| 0 | 10 | 20 | 30 sec |

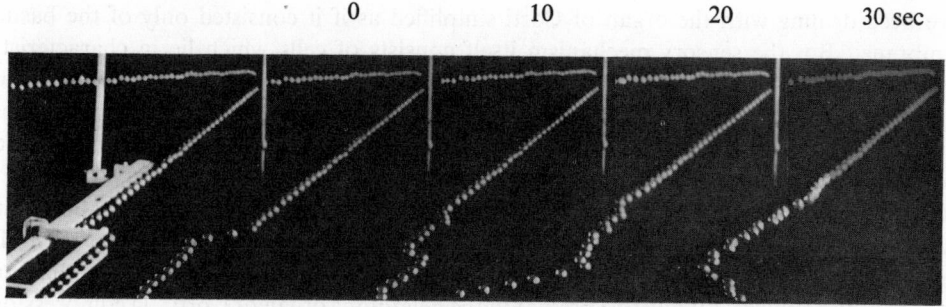

FIGURE 18. Growth of vibration amplitude in a series of large pendulums. (From von Békésy.[9])

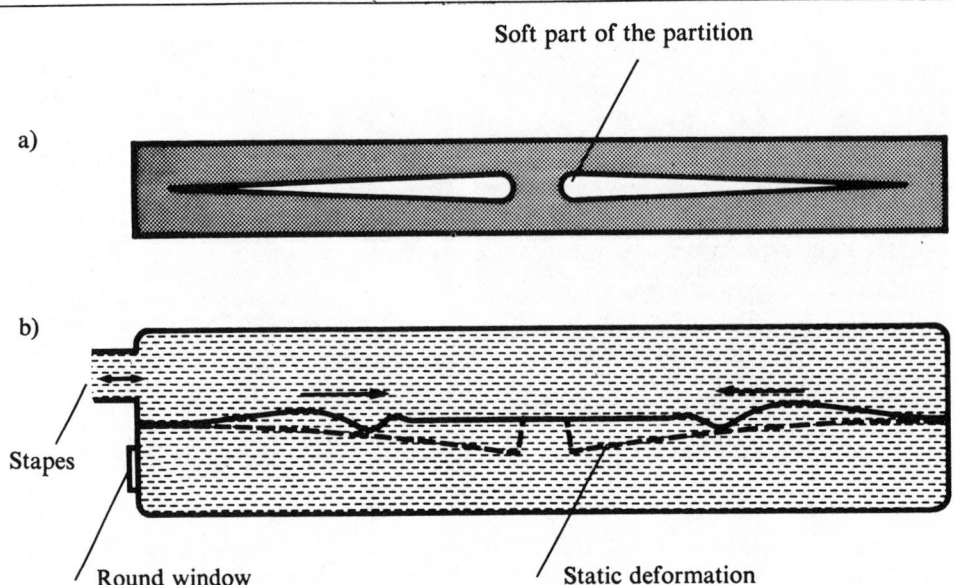

FIGURE 19. Mechanical model of the cochlea with two partitions in which progressive changes in stiffness are oriented in opposite directions. (From von Békésy.[7])

Now, the fact that the oscillatory energy always passes from stiffer to less stiff regions can give rise to paradoxical effects. For example, if a cochlear model is made with two analogs of the basilar membrane in which the change in stiffness is oriented in opposite directions (Figure 19), waves will travel also in opposite directions, even though the driving force comes from the same direction. In both cases, the wave, which is a phase wave, travels from the stiff end to the loose end of the membrane, but in one case it moves away from the energy source and in the other toward it.

Systems such as this are not only important in the cochlea but undoubtedly will have many technical applications. Little work has been done on energy transmission in systems with changing coefficients and a new kind of mathematics will be needed to deal with it completely.

VII. HAIR CELL STIMULATION

At this point we should once more turn our attention back to the cochlea. So far we have been dealing with the organ of Corti simplified as if it consisted only of the basilar membrane. But the sensory mechanism itself consists of cells which lie in characteristic pattern on the upper surface of the basilar membrane. These are a single row of inner hair cells and outer hair cells, of which there are three to five rows at different levels. Every hair cell has a basketwork of sensory innervation made up of ten or more terminals from one or two auditory neurons.

Clearly the relation of the vibrations in the basilar membrane to the vibrations and ultimate stimulation of the receptor cells and neurons is a matter for primary concern. To begin with, the vibrations of the hair cells must be extremely complicated. Five different types of waves (Figure 20) must be present in the gelatinous organ of Corti: 1) compression, 2) shear, 3) dilatation, 4) Rayleigh, and 5) bending. The question of which of these five

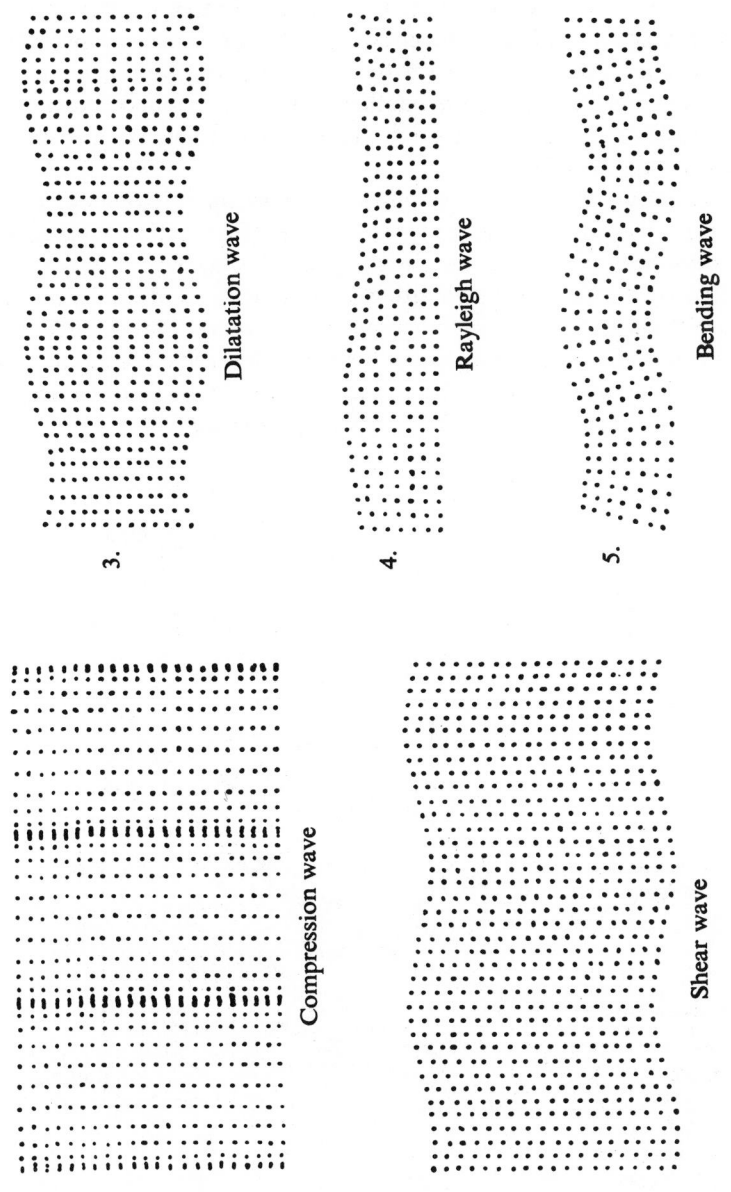

FIGURE 20. Possible forms of traveling waves. (From von Békésy.[6])

kinds of waves is important for hair cell stimulation is naturally a difficult but crucial one to answer.

One difficulty in dealing with such a system is that instead of one degree of freedom, as there is in the oscillation of the basilar membrane, there can be three in the organ of Corti, all of which can carry waves at once. In addition, each of the several waves as it travels along the membrane may be damped in a different way, and those waves which are damped earlier may take over some energy from wave types which still have some energy. So energy is transferred from one wave pattern to another. Although this makes mathematical treatment almost impossible, recognition of this situation makes many questions much clearer than they would otherwise be.

If the vibrations of the organ of Corti are observed under the microscope, a peculiar interaction can be seen between the different types of waves (Figure 21). Thus at a given frequency the hair cells near the stapes are vibrating radially, next a group of cells are vibrating vertically, then an area of cells vibrating longitudinally, and finally an inactive region. Apparently in the region of maximum vibration amplitude all the different types of vibration occur together and tend to sharpen the focus for the active area at a given frequency. The subject of my present research is exactly this matter of how sharply these active regions are delimited, and over what frequency range a given hair cell will be stimulated.

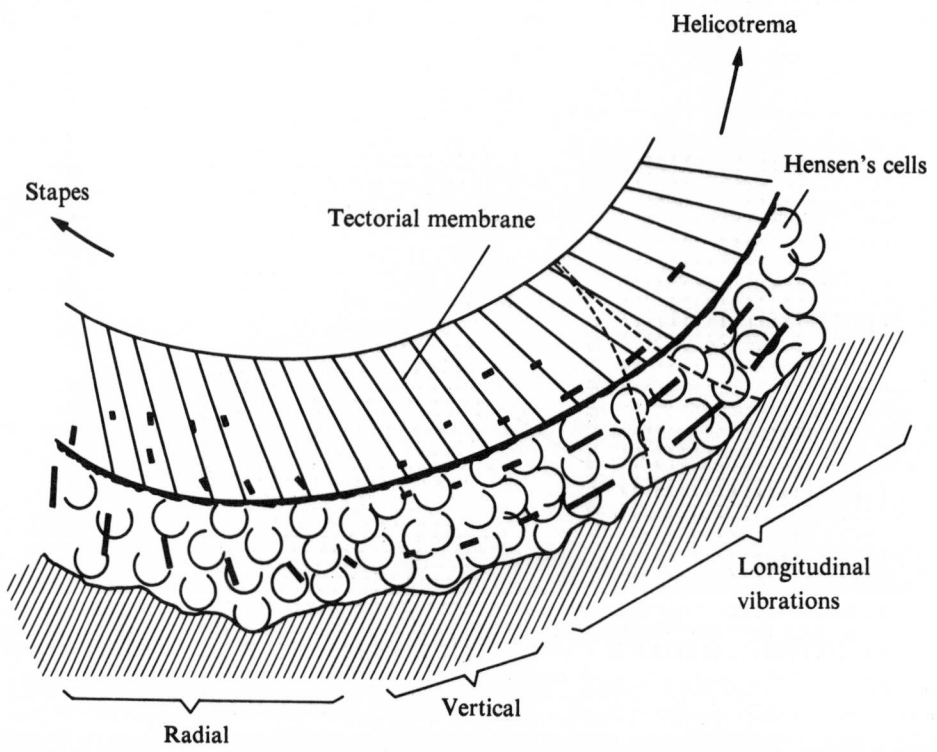

FIGURE 21. Distribution of radial and longitudinal vibrations along the organ of Corti during tonal stimulation. Viewed through Reissner's membrane. (From von Békésy.[6])

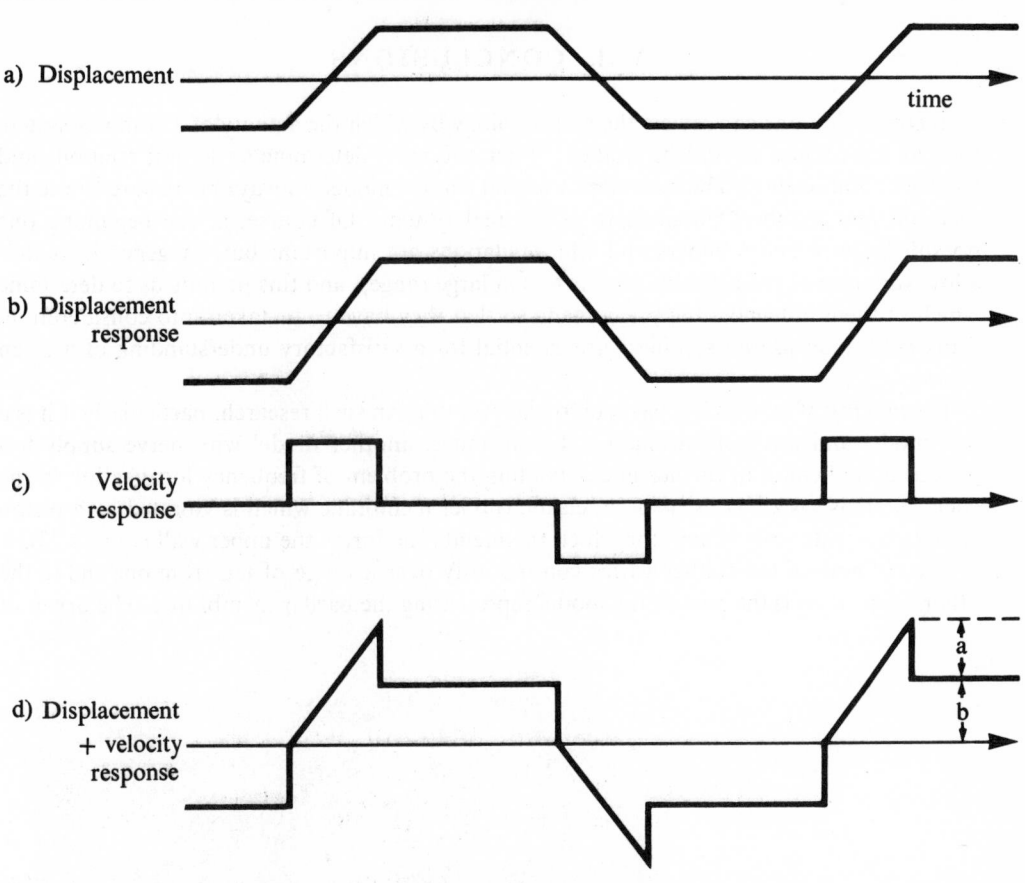

FIGURE 22. a) Wave forms of the stimulus to a hair cell; b), c), and d), possible forms of microphonic response. (From von Békésy.[5])

To deal with this, the effective stimulus for a hair cell must be considered. Its velocity of movement or the pressure acting on it are two likely alternatives. These can be discriminated by observing the cochlear microphonics. If the effective stimulus produced by local displacement in the form of a clipped sinusoidal vibration (Figure 22) is pressure due to displacement, then the wave form will appear trapezoidal; if the microphonics are the differential of the trapezoidal curve, then the effective stimulus must be velocity. When this is tested, the wave form is trapezoidal; hence we know that the effective stimulus of the hair cells must be their displacement.

This type of discrimination is highly sensitive and is useful in testing whether the organ of Corti is intact or damaged. If the membrane is loose, for instance, part of the stimulation will come from friction which is proportional to velocity, so the resulting record will show effects of both kinds of stimulation. This is an important check on the normality of the organ of Corti and is also a sensitive detector of damage which may be the end point of a particular experiment, say, on the maximum wave amplitude which the system can sustain.

VIII. CONCLUSIONS

In conclusion one can review the methodology by which the activity of a complex system such as the cochlea should be studied. First one must determine structural relations and measure components. The next step is to make a few models, always being sure to use the relations and numbers obtained from the real system. Of course, at the beginning one doesn't know which numbers and which relations are important but, in general, models allow variation of the different parameters in large ranges, and this permits us to determine which of them influences the phenomena so that they have to be taken into consideration. Thus both analysis and synthesis are essential for a satisfactory understanding of a given system.

The making of models is a particularly helpful thing in such research, particularly if it is a real model and not just an analog. For instance, another model with nerve supply has proved quite helpful in further understanding the problem of frequency localization in the cochlea. This system consists of an elastic rubber membrane which is vibrated by a piston acting on a water-filled canal for which the membrane forms the upper wall (Figure 23).

The stiffness of the rubber varies continuously over a range of ten from one end to the other. This then is the part of the model representing the basilar membrane. The organ of

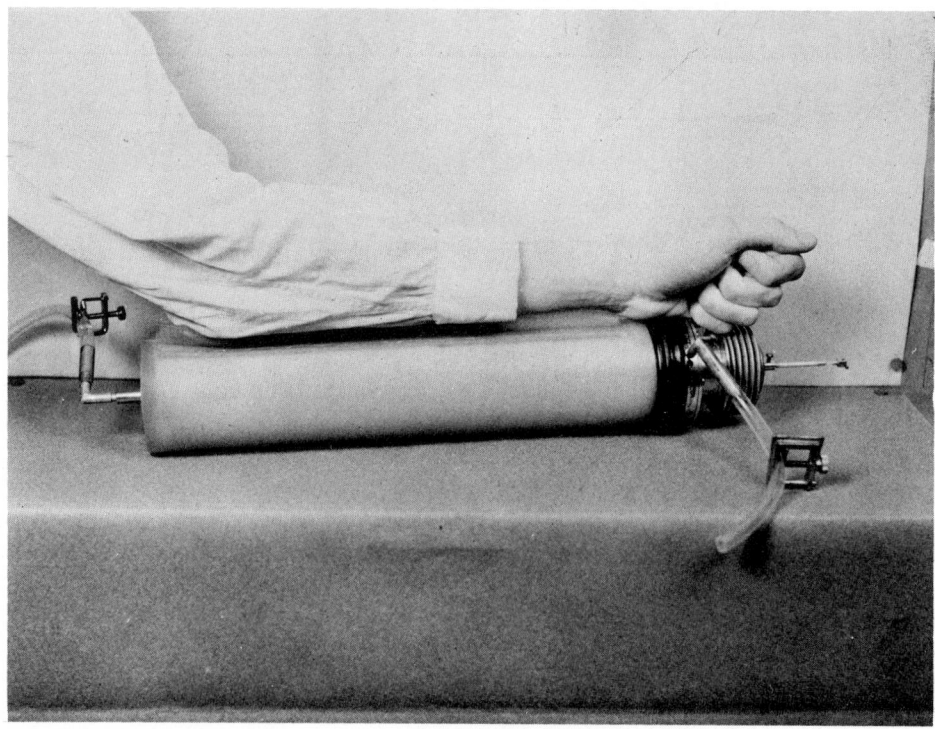

FIGURE 23. Mechanical model for a traveling-wave theory applied to the skin of the arm. (From von Békésy.[8])

Corti, auditory nerve, and relevant brain centers are modeled by a human forearm laid on the rubber membrane whose vibratory behavior was not significantly altered by this contact. The most interesting thing to do with this model is to compare the physical response of the rubber membrane with the vibratory sensations evoked in the human detector.

When the rubber membrane is vibrated, the sensation evoked is restricted to a small area of skin in contact with the oscillating system. The position of this localized responding area moves from one place to another along the forearm but is not extensive. In contrast, when the movement of the membrane is monitored with a small condenser microphone, traveling waves are found to be present. These show some time delay, but rather quickly build up to a steady amplitude which has a maximum in a characteristic longitudinal position for each frequency. Actually the amplitude distribution of the oscillations is quite flat and differs remarkably from the sensation picked up by the arm in a narrowly restricted zone.

This localization phenomenon is a curious and interesting one, but since it has little to do with cochlear mechanics directly, not much more about it will be considered here. However, in the basilar membrane the sharp localization of the frequency response to a small band results from the combined effects of neural lateral inhibition and the mechanical time delay in membrane displacement. Such phenomena are apparently widespread both in sensory systems and in the operation of the sensory nervous system.

REFERENCES

1. Lincke, C. G. 1837. "Handbuch der Theoretischen und Praktischen Ohrenheilkunde," Vol. I. Leipzig.
2. von Békésy, G. 1947. The variation of phase along the basilar membrane with sinusoidal vibrations. *J. Acoust. Soc. Amer.* **19:** 452–460.
3. von Békésy, G. 1948. On the elasticity of the cochlear partition. *J. Acoust. Soc. Amer.* **20:** 227–241.
4. von Békésy, G. 1949. The vibration of the cochlear partition in anatomical preparations and in models of the inner ear. *J. Acoust. Soc. Amer.* **21:** 233–245.
5. von Békésy, G. 1951. Microphonics produced by touching the cochlear partition with a vibrating electrode. *J. Acoust. Soc. Amer.* **23:** 29–35.
6. von Békésy, G. 1953. Description of some mechanical properties of the organ of Corti. *J. Acoust. Soc. Amer.* **25:** 770–785.
7. von Békésy, G. 1955a. Paradoxical direction of wave travel along the cochlear partition. *J. Acoust. Soc. Amer.* **27:** 137–145.
8. von Békésy, G. 1955b. Human skin perception of traveling waves similar to those on the cochlea. *J. Acoust. Soc. Amer.* **27:** 830–841.
9. von Békésy, G. 1960. "Experiments in Hearing," 745 pp. McGraw-Hill, New York.

Statistical Analysis and Computer Applications

The methodology of theoretical and mathematical biology is, of course, a major theme of all sections of this book, whether it relates to formal theory established with a set of differential equations, physical theory derived from quantum mechanical aspects of metabolic reactions, or systems theory analyzing the encoding mechanism and channel capacity of a sense organ with conditional probability methods. However, in the next four chapters methodology of very broad importance is given primary emphasis; two of these deal with statistics (Chapters 8 and 9) and two with computer applications to biological problems (Chapters 10 and 11).

The relevance of statistical methods to biology is probably no different than it is to any observational experimental field where enumeration and measurement provide the basic data. Similarly the proper design of experiments and the planned collection of observations are fundamental requisites for progress in any part of science. Nevertheless a significant part of the development of statistics has in fact come from attempts by R. A. Fisher, Karl Pearson, and others, to increase the effectiveness of this branch of applied mathematics in dealing with biological problems. Questions of sampling, distribution, error, variation, significance, and the indeterminacy that arises at the statistical mechanical level (Chapter 4) are all acutely important in biology and sometimes form the central theme of particular experimental problems as, for example, the absolute threshold of vision.

Biology does, however, differ from the physical sciences in the complexity and multiplicity of the components that have usually to be treated. In addition, and partly as a result of this, variability assumes a much more important role in biological systems than in many purely physical or chemical ones. Consequently, the planning of elaborate experiments, as well as the statistical reduction of the inevitable mass of complex data to a comprehensible set of generalizations becomes a common part of the biologist's task.

Since multivariate systems cannot be understood or even efficiently analyzed by methods adequate for one- or two-variable problems, the emergence in recent years of multivariate statistical methods is an advance of great potential importance. Discrimination between complex entities (discriminant functions, canonical variates), estimation of "distances" separating them (generalized distance functions), analysis of variance extended to the multivariate case (MANOVA), determination of the minimum number of significant independent parameters in a given complex (principal component or factor analysis), and analysis of the nature of multivariate correlation between two systems (canonical correlation) are some of the kinds of problem for which statistical techniques have been developed.

Obviously these are directly applicable to all biological problems involving comparisons, whether they relate to comparative physiology, comparative biochemistry, or processes of development and evolution. In other words the objectives of many-variable classification in its broadest sense (including the specific case of taxonomy) can be approached quantitatively by one or more of the available techniques. Nevertheless it seems clear that further advances in statistics itself are needed to provide better solutions of certain problems or to provide solutions where none now exist.

Since there is enormous computational work involved, many of these multivariate methods would be quite impractical to apply without their execution by high-speed automatic computers. Consequently, it is convenient here to introduce the two chapters on computers following the two dealing with aspects of multivariate analysis and some of its applications to problems of numerical taxonomy. However, in these chapters on computers, as well as in other parts of the book where their use is described, it is clearly shown that computers can do much more than just quickly carry out complex and lengthy calculations. Their versatile attributes allow them not only to produce a direct reduction or summary of the data, but also to derive the general law to which specific observations are subject or in some explicit way to model the mechanism by which a particular system acts.

Although the distinctions between description, explanation, and simulation may not always be clear-cut (Chapter 1), there seems little doubt that the further development and application of computers, especially in the biological use of systems analysis considered in the following section of this book, will have far-reaching and as yet unpredictable, stimulating effects on the progress of the field. For example, small computers have now been designed to program actual experiments, concurrently analyze and store the results, and modify the procedure on the basis of the cumulative outcome.

[8]

MULTIVARIATE STATISTICS

M. S. Bartlett

I. INTRODUCTION

A. Statistics and Quantitative Biology

There should be no need to argue a case for the essential role of statistics in quantitative biology. If there is still any argument between biologists who accept the importance of statistics and those who do not, it might sometimes be the prejudice that we all are apt to feel against some technically rather difficult subject which we do not altogether understand, and sometimes perhaps a valid criticism of the over-use of statistics in particular problems that do not need them in any sophisticated way. What does seem relevant to emphasize is that such difference of opinion is largely a question of degree. All biologists must use the statistical approach in some sense, even if they do it intuitively rather than explicitly.

For example, if we consider the question of discrimination, we all think we know how to distinguish a human being from a chimpanzee; but if one has to decide whether a given pair of twins is monozygotic or dizygotic, then we are involved in a more delicate decision, especially if this is to be attempted on the basis of physical characteristics alone. Therefore, an acceptance of statistics seems quite justifiable to start with. However, it is of course impossible to give here any complete exposition of the whole field and a certain amount of familiarity with statistical methods and terminology must be assumed.* Otherwise little headway can be made with an explanation of our more specific topic, multivariate statistical analysis; that is, the study of several variables at once, either as a means of greater efficiency of analysis, or greater power of interpretation.

B. Multivariate Analysis and Biology

Strictly speaking, multivariate analysis as above defined would comprise a large part of statistical analysis, for it is not uncommon to be studying several variables, especially in biology, in order to understand as far as possible some whole interacting complex system. But any analysis should be undertaken for a specific and logical purpose, and various systematic techniques can be distinguished. When speaking of multivariate analysis it is usual to have in mind the use of several "dependent" variables whose simultaneous correlation among themselves, or possible dependence on other variables or classifications, is under discussion.

---

* Those not familiar at all with statistical methods should consult one of the textbooks written especially for biologists, for example Bailey's.[2]

This is in contrast with the more classical concept of regression of *one* dependent variable on another so-called independent variable, first studied by Francis Galton, and extended to multiple regression on several variables by G. Udny Yule and others. Modern multivariate analysis (apart from "factor analysis" which is concerned with the internal relations between several variables without any necessary consideration of their further dependence on external variables) has owed its development to three main schools initiated by R. A. Fisher in England, P. C. Mahalanobis in India, and H. Hotelling in the United States. Some of their specific contributions will emerge from the detailed discussion below.

C. *Level of Approach*

Biologists who wish to understand the technical discussion that follows should try to distinguish between the logical ideas that should be clear even to those with no technical knowledge, and the mathematical details. The latter are conveniently symbolized in terms of matrices, a form of mathematical shorthand that is well worth being familiar with.* Psychologists using factor analysis have been for a long time expert in handling matrices; and even in classical multiple regression analysis the formulae and theory are much simplified. Multivariate analysis itself is now standard enough to be described in statistical textbooks (for example, Rao[22]), though the discussion here will be partly based on the author's own contributions and general approach to the subject. The reader is reminded of Chapter 9 which deals *in extenso* with applications of multivariate analysis to various biological fields. Further useful illustrative or review papers not explicitly referred to in the text are references.[3,7,10,15,18,21,26]

II. DISCRIMINATION

A. *Fundamental Importance and Definition*

The discrimination problem referred to above is obviously a fundamental one, not only for biologists discriminating between two populations or species, but also for doctors diagnosing between two or more diseases, or even for university professors attempting to select candidates for the university. On the basis of their performance at school, or by examination, or interview, we have to try to discriminate the students who will do well from those who will not.

This problem as such is not necessarily a multivariate one, and the ideal solution can be formulated quite simply in terms of probability, though we shall see that multivariate techniques naturally arise when all the available data are assembled. If all our data about some individual are denoted by d, and if the probability of d, on the hypothesis that this individual belongs to some group or population denoted by suffix i, is $P_i(d)$, then a comparison of the $P_i(d)$ for different i is an inevitable step in the individual's classification.

B. *Comparison Between Two Groups*

1. *The best criterion.* In particular, if there are only two groups being compared, discrimination should be based on the "likelihood ratio," λ, where

$$\lambda = \frac{P_1(d)}{P_2(d)} \tag{1}$$

* One concise mathematical account of this field is given in the little book by A. C. Aitken.[1]

or equivalently on its (natural) logarithm

$$\log_e \lambda = \log_e P_1(d) - \log_e P_2(d) \tag{2}$$

How this ratio is used can of course depend on the situation. In a simple case, one might say: if λ is greater than one, assign the individual to the first group, but if it is less than one, assign the individual to the second. In some cases further complications will affect the choice of dividing line. One species may be more abundant than another, and hence there will be a greater prior probability of an individual belonging to it even before λ is known.

Also the use of probability stresses uncertainty and hence the possibility of error which can be of two kinds. An individual of type or group 1 may be wrongly assigned to group 2, or an individual of type 2 may be wrongly assigned to 1. The "cost" of such misclassifications might be more relevant to consider in some problems than others. When classifying into species, each kind of error might be equally bad; but if a particular applicant were being accepted or not for a university place, and accommodation and finance were not limiting factors, then it would perhaps be more serious to deny a suitable individual a place than to accept an unsuitable individual. Hence, the boundary line adopted may be affected by such prior probabilities and costs, but it should still be formulated in terms of the likelihood ratio, λ.

In general, comparative data may be either qualitative or quantitative. Usually the former may be reduced to "0 or 1" categories representing the presence or absence of a particular character, for example, webbed feet.

2. *Application of the likelihood ratio.* Although historically the use of such "0 or 1" categories has been studied only comparatively recently (for example, reference[9]), the ideal solution in this case is simple enough to be given first. In principle the use of several categories of this nature would define various "multiple states" to be used in distinguishing various species or populations. For example, if there were five 0, 1 categories *a*, *b*, *c*, *d*, and *e*, the scores for some individuals, taken in the order *a*, *b*, *c*, *d*, *e*, might read 0, 0, 1, 0, 1. Theoretically, one could assume that the probability of each such multiple state is known for each of the two or more categories involved, and that for an individual with *given* multiple state, the species with maximum probability might be chosen. In the case of only two species, this means a direct use of λ.

There are, however, two difficulties about this. One is that if many such 0, 1 categories are used it becomes extremely laborious to classify the results by the complete multiple state, and the use of some simpler combination of the scores becomes tempting. The other difficulty is that even if the complete multiple state is retained, it cannot be used unless the relevant probabilities are known. These are usually based on a special sampling investigation with individuals of known group membership. For example, in the case of university student selection, the criterion "suitable applicant" might be defined in terms of results in the final degree examination, which would be ascertained for the individuals in the sample. Notice that no logical basis for discrimination exists without the relevant probabilities, and that no observational basis for these probabilities exists without such a sample.

Now with some highly complicated multiple state symbolized by *d*, only one or two individuals from each group may occur, or possibly none at all. Hence the required *relative* probability, or likelihood ratio $\lambda = P_1(d)/P_2(d)$, may at worst be quite unknown. So although this type of qualitative data theoretically provides an ideal criterion for discrimination, there are, even for 0, 1 data, considerations that often make it reasonable to go over to a quantitative criterion based on some combination of the observations. For variables already quantitative, we shall see below that under appropriate conditions a combination of the observations is the ideal criterion.

A further point has already, in effect, been noted. Although it is usually reasonable to seek the most efficient criterion, sometimes we may compromise for reasons of expediency or convenience. This depends partly on the importance of the classification being carried out, but also partly on the extent to which discrimination is possible. Sometimes even the best available criterion is of little use, and there is not much to be said for trying to find it; at other times a very crude criterion is quite adequate. Only in more critical cases does a refined analysis become important.

3. *Vector variables and the multivariate case—the concept of generalized distance.* Before coming to the standard quantitative case of, say, p variables with constant dispersion matrix (defined below), let us consider the discrimination between two groups based on a single measurement, x. Then the likelihood ratio $P_1(x)/P_2(x)$ is of course a function of x. If we assume that the probability functions $P_1(x)$ and $P_2(x)$ are *normal* with the same variance σ^2, but different means μ_1 and μ_2, then the mathematical expression for $\log_e \lambda$ may be written

$$(\mu_1 - \mu_2)[x - \tfrac{1}{2}(\mu_1 + \mu_2)]/\sigma^2 \tag{3}$$

For the p variable case, let us denote the variables by $x^{(1)}, x^{(2)}, \ldots x^{(p)}$, or for short, by the vector x which has these variables as components. (A *vector* is simply a special case of a matrix or rectangular array of quantities with only one column or row. It is denoted in bold type, but, unlike a more general matrix, A say, is written in small type. The *transpose* A' of A has rows and columns transposed, and for definiteness x is a single *column*. The corresponding row is thus x'. Further matrix notation and algebraic manipulation are standard.)

Let the population mean of x for group or population 1 be denoted by μ_1 and for population 2 by μ_2. Then the dispersion or variance-covariance matrix of x for population 1 is defined as the mean of $(x - \mu_1)(x' - \mu_1')$ over this population, and similarly for population 2. These matrices are denoted by V_1 and V_2 respectively, or simply by V if they are the same. Then the extension of (3) to p normal variables with dispersion matrix V reads

$$(\mu_1' - \mu_2')V^{-1}x - \tfrac{1}{2}(\mu_1'V^{-1}\mu_1 - \mu_2'V^{-1}\mu_2) \tag{4}$$

The important feature of expression (4) is that it depends on the *linear* combination of the variables in x given by the new variable

$$y = (\mu_1' - \mu_2')V^{-1}x = \delta'V^{-1}x \tag{5}$$

where $\delta = \mu_1 - \mu_2$. Thus under appropriate conditions a linear combination of variables is not just convenient, but in fact specifies the ideal criterion.

The sampling properties of y are important and not difficult to deduce. Thus the difference in the means of y for the two populations is

$$\delta'V^{-1}\delta = D^2 \tag{6}$$

and the variance of y (for either population) is also D^2. Hence the ratio of the difference in the means of y to its standard deviation is $D^2/D = D$, known as Mahalanobis' *generalized distance** between the two populations or species.[16] In the special case when all the variables

---

* Strictly speaking, this was defined by D^2, but it seems better to refer to D as the "distance."

are independent with the same unit variance ($V = I$, the so-called unit matrix),

$$D^2 = \boldsymbol{\delta}'\boldsymbol{\delta} = \sum_{i=1}^{p} (\mu_1^{(i)} - \mu_2^{(i)})^2 \tag{7}$$

where $\mu_1^{(i)}$ is the mean of variable $x^{(i)}$ for population 1, etc. In particular, if $p = 2$ and*
$\delta_i = \mu_1^{(i)} - \mu_2^{(i)}$

$$D^2 = \delta_1^2 + \delta_2^2 = \delta_1^2(1 + f^2) \tag{8}$$

where $f = |\delta_2/\delta_1|$. The reason for expressing the function in terms of f is to emphasize that as the situation gets more complicated it is no longer easy to see whether the "distance" D increases with the inclusion of more variables. Thus Cochran[8] has recently mentioned that if $x^{(1)}$ and $x^{(2)}$ are correlated to an extent ρ, the expression for D^2 in place of Equation (8) is (for positive δ_2, δ_1)

$$D^2 = \delta_1^2 + \frac{\delta_1^2(f - \rho)^2}{1 - \rho^2} \tag{9}$$

which is greater than the expression in Equation (8) if

$$(f - \rho)^2 > f^2(1 - \rho^2)$$

So negative correlation is always helpful, but positive correlation will be harmful unless

$$\rho > 2f/(1 + f^2) \tag{10}$$

4. Multivariate discrimination techniques

a. The multiple regression approach. So far the approach to discrimination has been via probability, but in the case of multivariate normal variables we have seen that a linear function, $\mathbf{c}'\mathbf{x}$ say, of the variables provides the best discriminator. In regression analysis, however, linear functions are used in a somewhat wider context, as "good" functions even when not strictly the best. Thus a regression approach to discrimination problems is not only possible, but also has the advantage that all the sampling theory known in regression can be taken over to the discrimination case.

An actual example will be useful at this stage; the one to be given here is of historic interest because it is the one originally used by R. A. Fisher[11] in presenting the discrimination technique. The review of some of these early examples is instructive in order to see how far our better understanding of these techniques enables us now to improve on the original analyses.

Four measurements were taken on each of fifty specimens of *Iris versicolor* and of *I. setosa*: sepal length and width, and petal length and width.

Fisher in effect first calculated an estimate of the coefficients of the discriminant function defined by Equation (5), using the observed mean differences to obtain $\boldsymbol{\delta}$, and estimating the dispersion matrix V by dividing the total sums of squares and products within species by the appropriate number of degrees of freedom, 98. Fisher also mentioned the equivalent "regression approach," but was not able at that time to carry it through as far as we shall do here.

Without attempting to provide a complete justification, let us first try to grasp the rationale of this second approach. To do this, reconsider the problem of trying to select university

---

* Note that for convenience the suffix i now replaces a superscript distinguishing each variable and does not refer to the population or species.

students on the basis of their school record, interview, et cetera. In England, university students are classified from their final university examination as first class, second class, and so on; those who were first class could be considered one species while those who were not belonged to the other species. The discrimination problem was to sort out such students on data available prior to university entry. Now if predicting the actual mark in their final examination was required, this would have been a standard regression problem. But it may be transformed into a discrimination problem by assigning a "pseudo-variable" which can have values of 0 or 1 (like our earlier 0, 1 categories for quantitative observations), depending on whether the individual is first class or not.

TABLE 1

Discriminant function coefficients with standard errors

Sepal length	Sepal width	Petal length	Petal width
−0.0285	−0.1681	+0.2030	+0.2876
±0.0337	±0.0332	±0.0410	±0.0880

TABLE 2[11]

Analysis of variance of pseudo-variable

	Degrees of freedom	Sums of squares	Mean square
Between species	4	24.0854	
Within species	95	0.9146	0.009627
Total	99	25.0000	

($R^2 = 24.0854/25 = 0.96342$ estimates the square of the multiple correlation of the pseudo-variable with the four measurements.)

Since the values 0, 1 are arbitrary, values may be conveniently chosen with mean zero over the whole sample, say $-\frac{1}{2}$ for species 1 and $\frac{1}{2}$ for species 2. These values of the pseudo-variable in our sample of 100 specimens are then used to calculate the multiple regression on the four variables: sepal length and width, petal length and width. The full details of the calculation because it is standard are not given here, but relevant tables are given in Appendix Tables A 1 and A 2. The final discriminant function coefficients are also listed (Table 1). Note that this technique provides standard errors for the coefficients which permit the assessment of coefficient significance. Fisher's original analysis of variance of the pseudo-variable (Table 2) makes clear the overwhelming significance of the discriminant function as a whole, but for this particular example such an outcome is not particularly surprising in view of the large mean differences. Before the analysis, however, it is not obvious that the coefficient for the first variable is not significant, so that little purpose has been served by considering sepal length.

b. *Size and shape factors.* The multiple regression technique, though standard, can become complicated when many measurements are made. The calculations involve finding the inverse of a matrix, and for many variables an electronic computer is advisable. However, as noted above, the complete analysis may not be necessary in some cases, but a simpler, useful approach, as suggested some years ago by Penrose,[20] is based on the fact that often the correlations among the measurements are much about the same, so that if the variables are scaled to have unit standard deviations, their dispersion matrix could be approximated by

$$V = \begin{pmatrix} 1 & \rho & \rho & \cdots & \rho \\ \rho & 1 & \rho & \cdots & \rho \\ \cdot & \cdot & \cdot & & \cdot \\ \cdot & \cdot & \cdot & & \cdot \\ \cdot & \cdot & \cdot & & \cdot \\ \rho & \rho & \rho & \cdots & 1 \end{pmatrix}$$

For this matrix, which can be written

$$V = (1 - \rho)\mathbf{I} + \rho l l' \tag{11}$$

where l denotes a vector with all components unity, it is not difficult to prove that

$$V^{-1} = \frac{1}{1 - \rho}\mathbf{I} - \frac{\rho}{1 - \rho}\frac{1}{1 + (p - 1)\rho}l l' \tag{12}$$

Hence the coefficients $\delta' V^{-1}$ are proportional to

$$\left[1 - \frac{p\rho}{1 + (p - 1)\rho}\right]l' + \left[\frac{p\delta'}{\sum\limits_{i=1}^{p} \delta_i} - l'\right] \tag{13}$$

where the coefficients in (13) have deliberately been separated into two parts which represent two uncorrelated new variables, y_1 and y_2. The first variable, which may be defined by

$$y_1 = l'x \tag{14}$$

is naturally called the *size* variable, and is often the variable calculated by investigators for discrimination purposes (for example, the total mark in an examination). The second variable was called by Penrose the *shape* variable, and is defined by

$$y_2 = \left[\frac{p\delta'}{\sum\limits_{i=1}^{p} \delta_i} - l'\right]x \tag{15}$$

If V is in fact given by relation (11) and y_1 and y_2 are therefore uncorrelated, the ideal discriminant function is

$$\frac{\Delta_1}{v_1} y_1 + \frac{\Delta_2}{v_2} y_2 \tag{16}$$

where Δ_1, Δ_2 are the mean differences between the two populations or groups for y_1, y_2 respectively, and v_1, v_2 the corresponding variances.

The relevant numerical calculations for Fisher's example, first made by Penrose to illustrate the value of his proposal, are indicated in Appendix Tables A 3, A 4, and A 5. The final

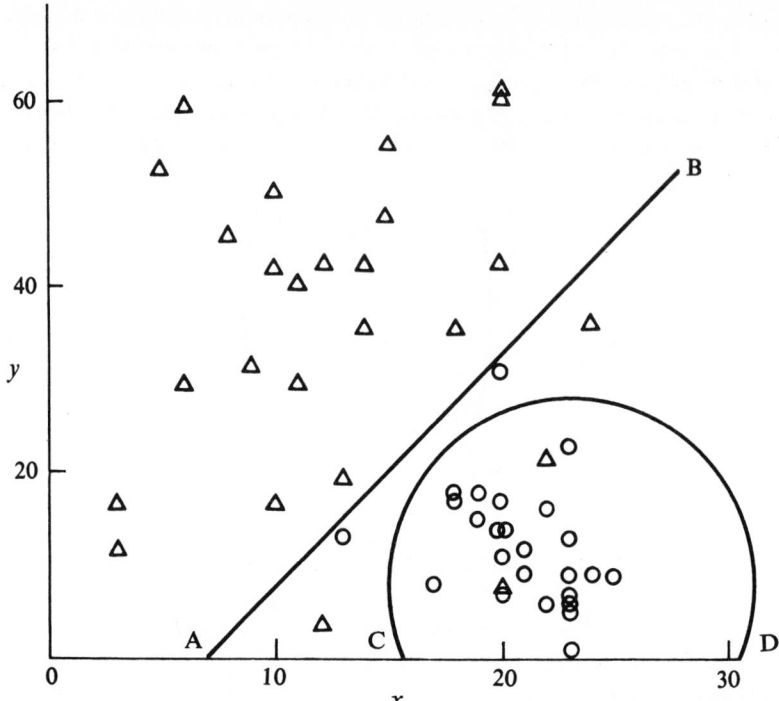

FIGURE 1. Discrimination on the basis of two variables, x and y, between normal individuals, ○, and psychotics, △. (From Smith.[25])

coefficients for the single discriminant function are (proportionately) not very dissimilar from the coefficients in Table 1; and if an analysis of variance of the final discriminant function is made for comparison with Table 2, it is found that $R^2 = 0.96329$, almost as good as its maximum value 0.96342.

5. *Further complications*

   a. *Different population variances.* Finally, to end this discussion of the discrimination problem for two groups, let us see what further complications and approximations are possible. One assumption, important whether the probability or regression approach is made, is that the two groups or populations have equal dispersion matrices. In particular, if there are just two uncorrelated variables, y_1 and y_2 (like Penrose's size and shape variables), what happens when the variances differ for the two populations? In this case, discussed by C. A. B. Smith,[25] the log likelihood criterion gives rise to an elliptical boundary in place of a straight line if a normal distribution is assumed. This can be transformed into a circle by appropriate scaling of the variables. The illustration used by Smith was an attempt at discrimination between normal* and psychotic individuals on the basis of certain tests in which the psychotic population was obviously more variable than the normal.

   In Figure 1 there is a small but detectable gain over the use of a linear boundary. Of the various misclassified individuals, one or two errors would have been eliminated, but the

* Normal in the psychological sense, not the statistical one of belonging to a "normal" (that is, Gaussian) population.

rest would remain. This underlines the point that biological variation often prevents infallibility.

b. *Case of zero mean differences.* The possible occurrence of different variances allows consideration of one further case, when the mean differences are zero. This is an unpromising situation because the linear discriminant function depends essentially on these mean differences. However, there is still some discriminating power in the different variances. This case is, of course, included as a special illustration of Smith's problem.[25] If the mean differences are zero, the circular boundary in the case of two variables will be centered at the means of both groups, and observations inside the circle ascribed to the population with the smaller variance.

This case arose quite naturally in a problem of finding a discriminant function from physical measurements on pairs of twins, to distinguish dizygotic and monozygotic pairs. A more powerful discriminatory procedure involves an investigation of blood groups, et cetera,[19] but the problem, as posed once to students in a practical examination, was to work with simple physical measurements, taken from data by Stocks.[29]

In this example the mean differences are zero because discrimination is to be based on the similarity or dissimilarity of the two individuals comprising each pair of twins. Hence differences within twin pairs constitute the basic measurements, and such measurements, when either twin in a pair might be taken first, already automatically have zero means.

With many variables the further difficulty of handling different dispersion matrices for the two groups suggested the use of an approximating assumption similar to that made by Penrose in the case of size and shape variables. The exact expression for the log likelihood ratio when the means are all zero becomes

$$-\tfrac{1}{2} \log_e |V_1|/|V_2| - \tfrac{1}{2}(x'V_1^{-1}x - x'V_2^{-1}x) \tag{17}$$

where $|V|$ stands for the determinant of the matrix V. Suppose we assume that

$$\begin{aligned} V_1 &= (1 - \rho_1)I + \rho_1 ll', \\ V_2 &= \sigma^2[(1 - \rho_2)I + \rho_2 ll'] \end{aligned} \tag{18}$$

that is, the variances of all the variables in the second group are the same multiple (σ^2) of the corresponding variances of the standardized variables (that is, scaled to unit variance) for the first group. For both groups the correlations between the variables are constant (ρ_1 for the first groups, ρ_2 for the second). As a further assumption, we might put $\rho_1 = \rho_2$, though this is not essential. Using relation (12) we find

$$\begin{aligned} V_1^{-1} - V_2^{-1} &= \left[\frac{1}{1 - \rho_1} - \frac{1}{\sigma^2}\frac{1}{1 - \rho_2}\right]I \\ &\quad - \left[\frac{\rho_1}{1 - \rho_1}\frac{1}{1 + \rho_1(p - 1)} - \frac{\rho_2}{\sigma^2(1 - \rho_2)}\frac{1}{1 + \rho_2(p - 1)}\right]ll' \end{aligned} \tag{19}$$

This implies that the quadratic expression in (17) acquires the form

$$aZ_1 + bZ_2 + c \tag{20}$$

where Z_1 is the sum of squares of all the measurements, and Z_2 is the square of the shape variable (that is, the square of the sum of all the measurements). Using Z_1 and Z_2 as new variables enables us to plot the discriminating boundary as a straight line (Figure 2). The numerical details of the analysis for this example will be found in Bartlett and Please.[6]

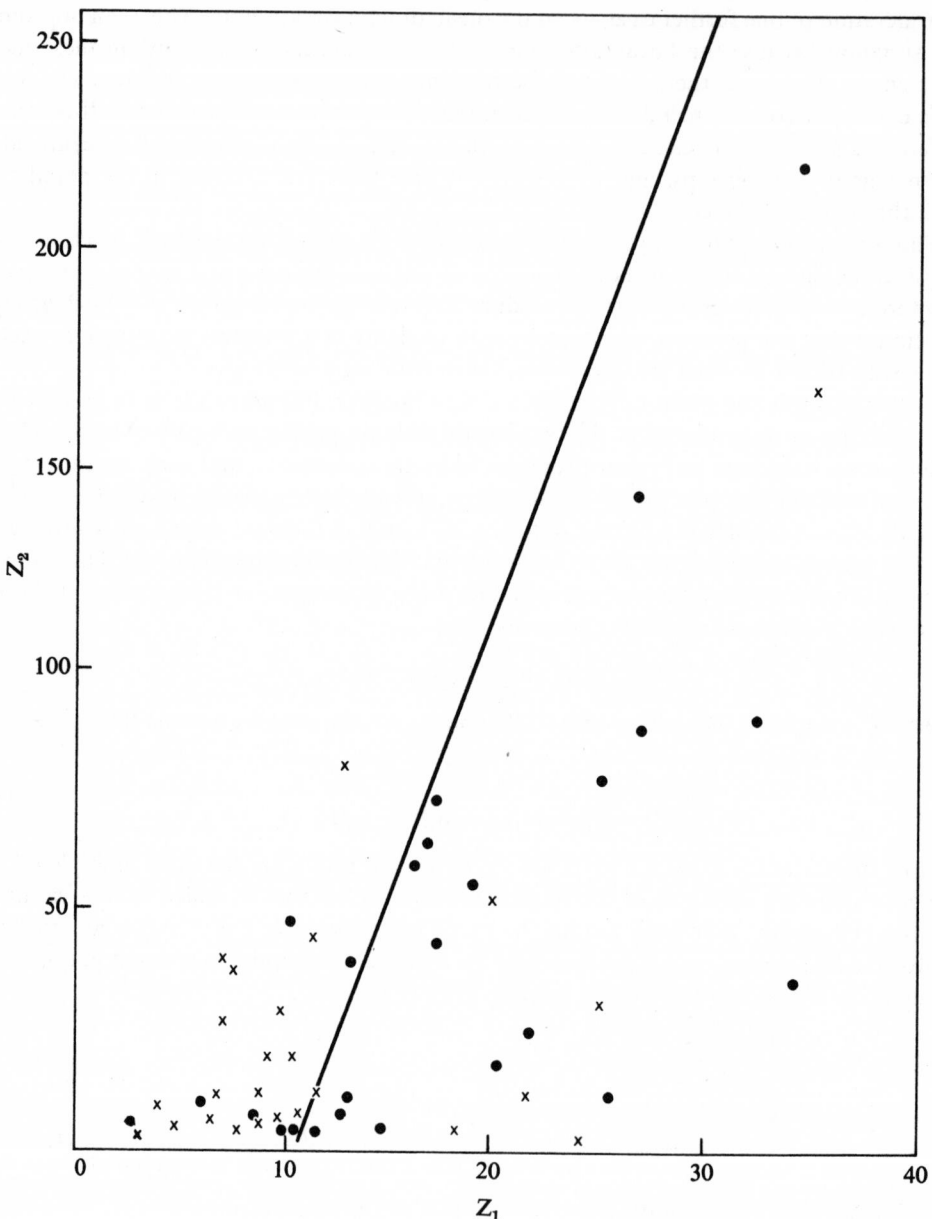

FIGURE 2.   Discrimination between monozygotic, ×, and dizygotic, ●, twin pairs on the basis of certain physical measurements.   Three observations for dizygotic pairs to the right of the boundary occur beyond the range of the graph.   (Modified from Bartlett and Please.[6])

C. Comparisons Among More Than Two Groups

1. *The basic problem.* So far emphasis has been put on discrimination between two groups or species, and in particular we have seen how standard regression analysis may be adapted to handle this problem. Cases involving several groups or species are also important, and we have noted that in principle they can also be dealt with by a direct probability approach. Such an approach reminds us that they constitute a problem in "decision theory," but even with the omission of assessments of misclassification errors and prior probabilities the use of likelihood ratios is complicated by the sampling problem, and it is often reasonable or adequate to use the regression type of analysis when suitably extended to this more general case. This is particularly valid for normal populations with a common dispersion matrix, but provides an appropriate linear technique in other cases, though the stability of dispersion is an advisable requirement. Cases may occur in which the dispersion is heterogeneous (see, for example, Reyment[23]), but for simplicity we shall not discuss this complication further here,* except to remark that it can sometimes be avoided by a suitable choice of variables.

Before the technique (which is called "canonical analysis" and was first introduced by Hotelling[13]) is outlined *in extenso*, it may be helpful to see in geometric terms what is involved. If sample observations are plotted in a coordinate system with one axis for each variable, we hope to see the points for two different populations more or less separated, and the separation of the two populations will, at least for standardized dispersions ($V = I$), be given by the distance along the line separating the two vector means. The linear discriminant function is represented by a plane boundary perpendicular to this line dividing the two populations as well as possible.

If a third group is added, there is one distance between the first and second groups, one between the first and third, and one between the second and third. It is thus possible to try to analyze the several-groups case in terms of the two-groups case, and sometimes this is done, but this procedure becomes unnecessarily complicated as the number of groups increases. Thus, for three groups their means must lie in a plane (see Figure 3), and any boundaries separating the means can be constructed out of *two* new variables at the most.

The well-known fact that a comparison among three means represents only two "degrees of freedom," should be emphasized here. Notice that even two variables may not be needed in the discrimination problem; if the three-group means lie on a straight line, the same discriminant function (with, of course, a different constant term to shift its position) could be used for identification as far as possible among all three groups. This tells us that when discussing the relationship among three or more groups, the "dimensionality" of the relations is important.

There is another limitation which should be mentioned. If instead of a multivariate problem only one variable is available, all the differences among the groups will be spread along the axis representing that variable. Similarly with only two variables, all differences must lie in a plane. So, in general, the effective number of dimensions cannot be more than the minimum number of variables and one less than the number of groups.

This reciprocity between the variables and the groups' degrees of freedom can affect the way the analysis is carried out. With only two groups, and thus one degree of freedom representing the contrast between the groups, it was convenient to introduce a pseudo-variable to represent this contrast, and carry out the analysis on such a variable. With

---

* For appropriate statistical tests in this case, see James.[14]

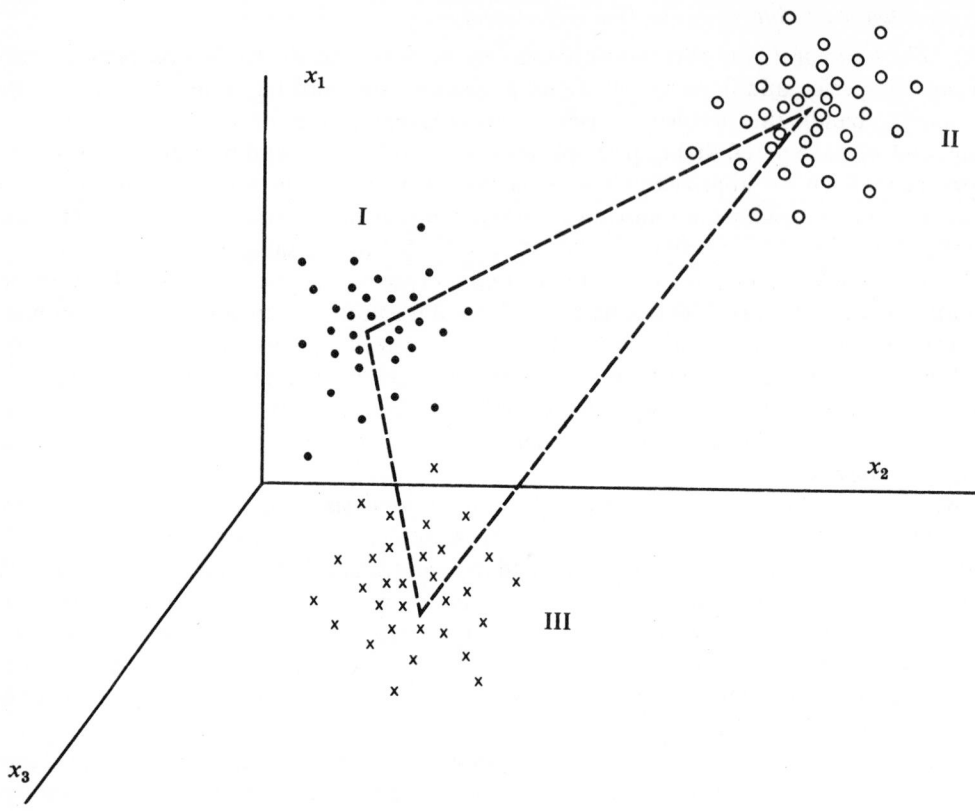

FIGURE 3. Schematic diagram of measurements (x_1, x_2, and x_3) on individuals from three different groups I, II, and III.

several groups, this method, though possible, would not be so convenient, especially if the number of variables is smaller than the number of group contrasts. Usually the standard analysis of variance and covariance technique is preferable to separate the degrees of freedom for the group contrasts. (This switch in the way we carry out the analysis is perhaps rather puzzling, and is only fully clarified by noting that analysis of variance technique can be regarded as a special case of regression technique with pseudo-variables; the general statistical problem is one of correlating one set of p variables with another set of q variables, and we can do this starting from either set.)

2. *Canonical analysis.*   To illustrate this technique the example chosen is one with only two variables, so that a check on the statistical analysis would not be too difficult. The results are taken from a standard replicated agricultural experiment, with eight different manurial treatments tested on a cereal crop, with the yields of grain and straw recorded as the two variables. In this example the treatments represent the different "populations." Notice with the randomized blocks layout used in the experimental design that the degrees of freedom for blocks are irrelevant and are removed, just as the degree of freedom for the general mean is removed in the case of simple random samples.

The calculations for this Example are recorded in the Appendix. However, before discussing any of the results, the technique should be explained in general algebraic terms so that its general nature and scope will become clear. Let us denote the relevant part of the analysis of variance and covariance table as follows ($x_1, x_2, \ldots x_p$ denoting the p variables):

	Degrees of freedom	*Sums of squares and products*			
		x_1^2	$x_1 x_2$	x_2^2	$\ldots$
Among groups	q	a_{11}	a_{12}	a_{22}	$\ldots$
Within groups	$n-q$	b_{11}	b_{12}	b_{22}	$\ldots$
Total	n	c_{11}	c_{12}	c_{22}	$\ldots$

In this tabulation the various sums of squares and products have been set out in rows as they would appear in the numerical analysis, but they define three symmetric ($a_{ij} = a_{ji}$) matrices A, B, and $C = A + B$. For example,

$$A = \begin{pmatrix} a_{11} & a_{12} & \ldots \\ a_{12} & a_{22} & \ldots \\ \vdots & \vdots & \end{pmatrix}$$

Suppose our discriminant function is

$$y = \alpha' x$$

where the coefficients represented by the vector α have to be determined. Then the analysis of variance of y is:

Among groups	$\alpha' A \alpha$
Within groups	$\alpha' B \alpha$
Total	$\alpha' C \alpha$

To make the variable y as effective as possible in sorting out the groups, the ratio

$$R^2 = \alpha' A \alpha / \alpha' C \alpha \tag{21}$$

should be as large as possible; the known solution of this problem is to solve the set of linear equations represented by

$$(A - R^2 C)\alpha = 0 \tag{22}$$

for which a nonzero solution is possible provided R^2 is a root of the equation

$$|A - R^2 C| = 0 \tag{23}$$

where the vertical strokes denote finding the determinant of the enclosed matrix, $A - R^2 C$. From Equation (21) we obviously require the largest root; but the other roots are also of interest if further variables are needed to separate the groups.

Let us define the p roots of Equation (23) by $R_1^2, R_2^2, \ldots R_p^2$ (assuming $p \leq q$), and the corresponding solutions of Equation (22) by $\alpha_1, \alpha_2, \ldots \alpha_p$. It may be shown that the set of "canonical variables," $y_1 = \alpha_1' x, y_2 = \alpha_2' x, \ldots$ are mutually uncorrelated, and that a measure of separation of the groups, by generalizing R^2, is $1 - \Lambda$, where

$$\Lambda = (1 - R_1^2)(1 - R_2^2) \ldots (1 - R_p^2) \tag{24}$$

$$= |B|/|C| \tag{25}$$

In the example, Λ is 0.4920, and to determine whether or not this is significant we may use the χ^2 test by calculating

$$-(n - \tfrac{1}{2}[p + q + 1]) \log_e \Lambda$$

with pq degrees of freedom. If this is significant, the largest root may be separated by subtracting from the total χ^2 the expression

$$-(n - \tfrac{1}{2}[p + q + 1]) \log_e (1 - R_1^2)$$

leaving a χ^2 with $(p - 1)(q - 1)$ degrees of freedom. (This is an approximation adequate under certain conditions.[5]) From Table A 11, we see that this remainder term is insignificant,[4,5] so that only *one* canonical variable or discriminant function appears to be needed, namely,

$$y_1 = x_2 - 0.535x_1 \qquad (26)$$

where x_1 denotes straw, x_2 is grain.

It might be asked how we can test the adequacy not of the empirical canonical variable obtained from the sample, but of some hypothetical new variable we had in mind. This is simple enough in the two-groups case, as we only have to take this new variable as one of our variables, and see if the corresponding coefficient is significant when compared with its standard error. The procedure is rather more complicated in the case of several groups, so it is outlined in a separate section. For completeness, however, it has been included as it is rather important in showing how the accuracy of the coefficients can be assessed in the more general case.

3. A priori *canonical variables and coefficient significance.* Suppose the canonical variable z given *a priori* is defined in terms of the original variables by

$$z = \beta'x$$

The new variable z will have its own measure of separation φ, and we factorize Λ by writing

$$\Lambda = (1 - \varphi)\Lambda' \qquad (27)$$

where

$$\varphi = \beta'A\beta/\beta'C\beta \quad \text{[compare (21)].}$$

The χ^2 test for φ is

$$\chi_1^2 = -[n - \tfrac{1}{2}(q + 2)] \log_e (1 - \varphi) \qquad (28)$$

with q degrees of freedom, whereas that for the *remaining* significant variation is

$$\chi_2^2 = -(n - 1 - \tfrac{1}{2}[p + q]) \log_e \Lambda' \qquad (29)$$

with $q(p - 1)$ degrees of freedom.

Thus in the numerical example suppose for z we wish to consider the total yield of grain and straw

$$z = x_1 + x_2$$

Then $\varphi = 0.08926$, $\Lambda' = 0.5402$, and $\chi_2^2 = 31.10$ with 7 degrees of freedom. This is significant, showing that the variable z does not remove all the significant variation; but notice that this χ^2 contains in effect all the degrees of freedom representing the further canonical variable already seen to be insignificant. A more sensitive test of the adequacy of z as the first canonical variable results from eliminating this residual χ^2, leaving*

$$-(n - \tfrac{1}{2}[p + q + 2]) \log_e [(1 - R_1^2)/(1 - \varphi)] \qquad (30)$$

with $p - 1$ degrees of freedom. In the present example, this is 28.01, with one degree of freedom, which is very highly significant.

To show how this technique may be used for constructing "confidence regions" for the coefficients, let φ_0 be the critical value of φ for significance, corresponding to a critical value of the expression (30); it is obtained by noting the critical $[P = 0.05]$ value of χ^2 with $p - 1$ degrees of freedom, that is, 3.841 for one degree of freedom. We find in our example $\varphi_0 = 0.43565$. The equation for φ_0 in terms of z is

$$\beta'B\beta = (1 - \varphi_0)\beta'C\beta$$

and inserting the values for B, C, and φ_0 we have in general a confidence region for the ratios (which are alone meaningful) of the coefficients β. In the present example with only two variables, there is only one ratio β_1/β_2 with a confidence interval

$$-0.827 \leq \beta_1/\beta_2 \leq -0.288$$

This result is of course consistent both with our optimum estimate of -0.535 for β_1/β_2, and our rejection of the *a priori* value 1.

4. *An example on blood tests.* As a further example some discussion is given in G. L. Taylor's data, cited in Fisher,[12] on qualitative reactions noted with twelve sera on twelve samples of human blood. This section may be skipped by those not wanting to go into all the finer details of the technique, but it has seemed worth including as an illustration of the flexibility and power of the method. (Appendix: Example III.)

The basic data, which were first discussed by Fisher,[12] are shown also in the Appendix (Table A 13) so that an idea is obtained of their nature. The symbols $-$, ?, W, (+), +, were intended to represent increasing degrees of reaction. There was no *a priori* claim that they were in arithmetic proportion, though some scale such as $0, \tfrac{1}{4}, \tfrac{1}{2}, \tfrac{3}{4}, 1$, would be worth checking. To avoid any *a priori* assumptions, we assign pseudo-variables y_1, y_2, y_3, and y_4 to each contrast, by the following scheme:

	$-$	?	W	(+)	+
y_1	0	1	0	0	0
y_2	0	0	1	0	0
y_3	0	0	0	1	0
y_4	0	0	0	0	1

Since sorting out both the sera and the blood samples is of interest, group comparison will be taken to include comparisons among sera (11 degrees of freedom) and among blood samples (11 degrees of freedom), making 22 degrees of freedom in all. Each of these two sets could be discussed separately, but for simplicity they have been pooled (following Fisher). The analysis is carried through exactly as with the last example (for some further details see Appendix), but here there are four instead of two variables. Hence there are

---

* The best multiplying factor is slightly arbitrary but has been taken to agree with that for χ_2^2. The multiplying factor for the residual χ^2 was taken to be $n - \tfrac{1}{2}(p + q + 1)$, so that the χ^2's are not precisely additive.

four roots, R_1^2, R_2^2, R_3^2, and R_4^2. Note that because in this example we are in effect working with dummy or pseudo-variables for both sets of variables, we can hardly claim to have normal distributions for them. In spite of this, it is believed that they are broadly correct provided the tests of significance are not taken too precisely.

The first interesting feature of the analysis is the emergence of only one significant root R_1^2, implying that the symbols can be equated on a *one-dimensional* scale. The second is that the values

$$- \qquad ? \qquad W \qquad (+) \qquad +$$
$$0 \quad 0.193 \quad 0.585 \quad 0.958 \quad 1$$

do come out in the order expected. The third is that the hypothetical values, 0, $\frac{1}{4}$, $\frac{1}{2}$, $\frac{3}{4}$, 1, are *not* compatible with the data.* To examine this last conclusion in more detail requires the assessment of the accuracy of the coefficients, as explained in the previous section. With four variables three coefficient ratios are involved simultaneously, and to simplify this situation the estimates of all but one of the coefficients are inserted in the equation for the critical values (with an obvious adjustment of the degrees of freedom from $p - 1$ to 1). Doing this in turn for the symbols ?, W, and (+) (with − at zero and + at 1) gives the approximate confidence intervals

$$? \qquad 0.036\text{---}0.320$$
$$W \qquad 0.507\text{---}0.654$$
$$(+) \qquad 0.863\text{---}1.089$$

This shows that W can hardly be placed at $\frac{1}{2}$; but, more significantly, (+) cannot be put at $\frac{3}{4}$, and is hardly worth separating from +.

5. *A psychiatric example with* 0, 1 *categories.* The final illustration, due to Maxwell,[17] is another example of data with 0, 1 categories, this time of the kind referred to above with reference to the likelihood ratio. The data analyzed (Table A 17) consist of the presence (1) or absence (0) of four symptoms: a, "anxious"; b, "suspicious"; c, "schizophrenic type of thought disorder"; d, "delusions of guilt." These are recorded for three groups of patients: I, Schizophrenic (224 in sample); II, Manic Depressive (279); and III, Anxiety State (117). Maxwell used these data to illustrate how canonical variables could be calculated for such 0, 1 scores. These constituted four recorded variables, but as there are only three groups, there are at most two canonical variables. These were in fact both significant, yielding the results

$$y_1 = -0.49a + 0.46b + 0.70c - 0.06d \quad (R_1^2 = 0.9533)$$
$$y_2 = 0.29a + 0.03b + 0.06c - 0.34d \quad (R_2^2 = 0.2009)$$

The scale of the coefficients for each new variable is, as we have seen, arbitrary, but Maxwell adopts the practice of arranging that the sum of squares of the coefficients is equal to the corresponding root R^2, so that the new variables reflect the relative sizes of these roots. A somewhat better, though slightly more complicated, procedure would be to scale so that the variances of the y's correspond to the appropriate R^2's.

To see how far this quantitative analysis, which is clearly useful in depicting the separation of the three groups conveniently, has been able to cope with the original qualitative variables, let us at once note two important points. The first is that we could attempt to discriminate directly from the relative frequencies of the different multiple states, and it is of interest to

---

* Compare reference[5]; this conclusion differs from Fisher's original analysis.

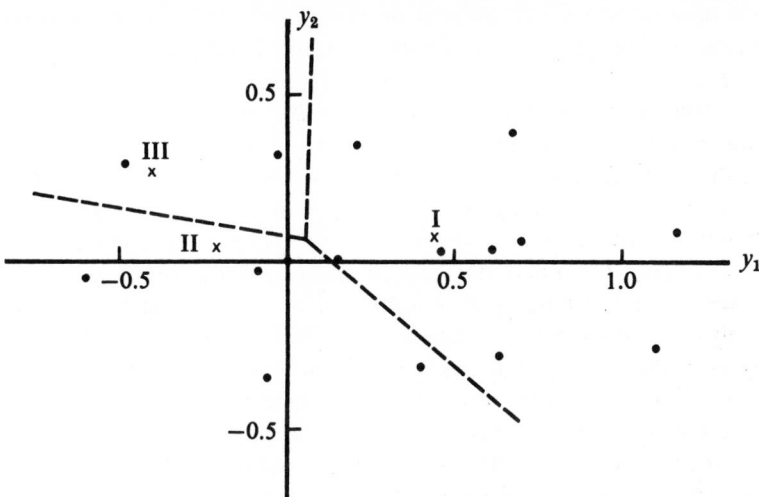

FIGURE 4. Possible values, ●, of the two canonical variables (y_1, y_2) obtained from 0, 1 scores for psychiatric tests. Group means are marked by crosses; Group I, schizophrenics; Group II, manic depressives; Group III, anxiety states. Suggested classification boundaries shown by dashed lines. (Modified from Maxwell.[17])

see how far linear boundaries based on y_1 and y_2 are consistent with such an approach. The second is that if these scores (which were primarily used by Maxwell for illustrative purposes) were intended to be efficient for discriminating purposes, they would need extension, especially for discriminating groups II and III. As they stand, the multiple state 1, 0, 0, 0 has 80 II's out of 279, and 92 III's out of 117, so whatever we do with the data we cannot avoid having most III's in this state. As the chance of this state is by no means negligible for group II, misclassification errors are bound to be fairly serious, at least for discriminating II and III.

If the tests are increased in number, better discrimination may be possible, but the sampling difficulties mentioned earlier with complicated multiple states suggest that the quantitative approach may often be useful. The converse technique of turning quantitative variables into qualitative ones has been suggested in the literature, but it would seem to have rather doubtful value, especially if the quantitative variables define a definite ordered scale which is thrown away in such a procedure.

With these comments said, let us see how far the regression approach seems successful in Maxwell's example. Figure 4 depicts not only the average values of the three groups for our canonical variables, but also each possible pair of values for the various multiple states. It will be seen that no assessment based on these variables need conflict with any assessment that might have been made on the original scores by a direct probability approach.

III. CONCLUSION

A. *Scope of Techniques Described*

At this stage it will be helpful to review the techniques described above and their purpose. They deal broadly with the discrimination problem approached by the analysis of multivariate data, whether qualitative or quantitative. The optimum probability procedure was cited first, but then attention was focused on the quantitative regression approach. The latter is particularly appropriate for normally distributed variables (with stable dispersion matrix), but is often useful in other cases, even for qualitative variables. The assumption of normality is strictly needed for tests of significance, but even without it these are often at least asymptotically correct, as in other statistical problems; compare the χ^2 test of independence in a contingency table.

In all cases it is important to emphasize that discrimination between groups or species is made with reference to the statistical variability within groups; therefore information about the latter is first needed. This point may be made clearer by comparing some recent relevant techniques based on classifying groups in terms of internal patterns or clusterings.

"Factor analysis" and even the precise technique of "principal components analysis," although they are multivariate techniques, were not included in the above detailed discussion because they were irrelevant to the discrimination problem as here defined. Such analyses do occur in the literature, for example in the form of a principal components analysis of individual variability within a single species, and may be useful as a preliminary aid in specifying the main components of variation. But this still has no necessary relevance to the problem of discrimination between species. To give a rather crude illustration, the main physical attributes of twins as human beings may or may not be of any discriminatory power between the two types of twin pairs.

In psychology the more usual factor analysis of test scores on a sample of persons has in suitable circumstances (and sometimes in unsuitable ones!) been inverted into a factor analysis of persons on a sample of test scores. This has some analogy with the choice of which set of variables to work with in canonical analysis, and in discrimination problems inverted factor analysis has been advocated by Sokal and Michener[28] for classifying groups or species. Such analysis falls logically in the same broad category as the methods of Sneath[27] and Rogers and Tanimoto.[24]

Although the last workers assemble data of the 0, 1 multiple state type with an eye towards the use of computers, their analyses appear to resemble factor analysis in relying on the clustering that emerges to classify their species without reference to any other yardstick. Of course, higher hierarchies of species structure may be studied, just as much as species segregation by comparison with variability within species; but the essential "relativity" of this method should be recognized. Certain species differences that appeared small at first might be made to look much larger by assembling more measurements on close varieties.

There seem to be other arbitrary aspects of some of these techniques, though it would be unfair to be too critical without more extensive study of them. For example, Sneath[27] advocates ignoring the communal absence of some characteristic, but not its communal presence, on the grounds that, say, no information is lost in classifying races of man by ignoring the fact that none of them has wings. Statistically, this is an unsymmetric viewpoint which is dangerous because it could so easily be logically inverted; on the same basis one could argue that the fact that humans all have arms could be ignored. There is an arbitrariness in the species we examine and the measurements we make on them, but some biological relevance could perhaps be taken for granted.

B. *Future Prospects*

Undoubtedly multivariate techniques in biology have been slow to develop both because they are technically rather complicated to learn and understand, and because the statistical computation is correspondingly lengthy. Recent developments in the use of computers are helping greatly to reduce the second difficulty at least so that a greater use of multivariate methods may be expected. Although this is basically most desirable, it should not lead us to indulge in mammoth analyses without proper regard to logical relevance.

On the narrower front of discrimination by comparison of variability within species, more study seems needed of the direct probability approach, especially in the case of 0, 1 scores. Bearing in mind the sampling problem, further experience is needed not only when the quantitative regression approach promises to be useful, but also in examining methods of combining the scores (for example, by a neglect of higher-order interactions between the different 0, 1 categories) which might be simpler and more direct.

On a broader front, further study is needed of the relation between the methods described here and other statistical classification techniques, such as those briefly mentioned above. Ultimately a synthesis of available methods should be provided for the biologists including an analysis of relevant scope, efficiency, and simplicity. These matters are discussed further in the next chapter.

APPENDIX

Example I. Regression calculations on pseudo-variable (Fisher,[11] Penrose.[20])

TABLE A 1

Mean values (in cm) from 50 specimens for each species

	Iris versicolor	*Iris setosa*	Difference
Sepal length (x_1)	5.936	5.006	0.930
Sepal width (x_2)	2.770	3.428	−0.658
Petal length (x_3)	4.260	1.462	2.798
Petal width (x_4)	1.326	0.246	1.080

(From Fisher.[11])

TABLE A 2

Inverse of matrix of total sums of squares and products

+0.1178286	−0.0721063	−0.0752879	+0.0486021
−0.0721063	+0.1143400	+0.0707685	−0.0578136
−0.0752879	+0.0707685	+0.1742439	−0.3359552
+0.0486021	−0.0578136	−0.3359552	+0.8039509

TABLE A 3

Mean measurements in terms of common standard deviation and reduced to common zero mean

	Iris versicolor	*Iris setosa*	Difference	Shape coefficient
x_1	+1.0628	−1.0628	+2.1256	−0.4362
x_2	−0.9551	+0.9551	−1.9102	−1.5067
x_3	+3.9894	−3.9894	+7.9788	+1.1165
x_4	+3.4426	−3.4426	+6.8852	+0.8264
Total	+7.5397	−7.5397	+15.0794	0.0000
Variance	10.5076	10.5076		

(From Penrose.[20])

TABLE A 4

Mean measurements weighted by shape coefficient

x_1	−0.4635	+0.4635	−0.9270
x_2	+1.4391	−1.4391	+2.8782
x_3	+4.4541	−4.4541	+8.9082
x_4	+2.8450	−2.8450	+5.6900
Total	+8.2747	−8.2747	+16.5494
Variance	3.0912	3.0912	

(From Penrose.[20])

TABLE A 5

Combination of size and shape coefficients

	Size	Shape	Combined
x_1	1.4351	−2.3353	−0.9002
x_2	1.4351	−8.0664	−6.6313
x_3	1.4351	+5.9774	+7.4125
x_4	1.4351	+4.4243	+5.8594
	($R^2 = 0.96329$)		

(From Penrose.[20])

Example II. Calculations for manurial experiment (Bartlett.[4,5])

TABLE A 6

Analysis of variance and covariance of grain (x_2) and straw (x_1) yields in a manurial experiment on a cereal crop

	D.F.	Sum x_1^2	Sum x_1x_2	Sum x_2^2
Treatments	7	12,496.8	−6,786.6	32,985.0
Blocks	7	86,045.8	56,073.6	75,841.5
Residual	49	136,972.6	58,549.0	71,496.1
Total	63	235,515.2	107,836.0	180,322.6

TABLE A 7

Sums of squares and products excluding blocks (56 D.F.)

	x_1	x_2
x_1	149,469.4	51,762.4
x_2	51,762.4	104,481.1

TABLE A 8

Sums of squares and products between treatments (7 D.F.)

12,496.8	−6,786.6
−6,786.6	32,985.0

TABLE A 9

Canonical roots

$R_1^2 = 0.47698$	$R_2^2 = 0.05934$

TABLE A 10

Equations for first canonical variable $a_1x_1 + a_2x_2$

$$58,797.1a_1 + 31,477.2a_2 = 0$$
$$31,477.2a_1 + 16,850.4a_2 = 0$$
$$a_1/a_2 = -0.535$$

TABLE A 11

Approximate chi-square test of collinearity

	D.F.	χ^2
First root	8	33.06
Remainder	6	3.12
Total	14	36.18

TABLE A 12

Approximate chi-square test of hypothetical canonical variable $x_1 + x_2$

	D.F.	χ^2 (nonadditive)
Discrepancy with estimated variate	1	28.01
Noncollinearity	6	3.12
Total	7	31.10

Example III. Analysis of serological data (Bartlett,[5] Fisher.[12])

TABLE A 13

Two-way array of serological readings

		Blood samples											
		1	2	3	4	5	6	7	8	9	10	11	12
	a	W	?	W	W	W	W	(+)	W	W	?	W	W
	b	W	W	W	W	(+)	W	(+)	+	(+)	?	W	(+)
	c	W	?	W	W	W	(+)	(+)	(+)	(+)	W	(+)	+
	d	(+)	W	W	W	(+)	(+)	(+)	(+)	(+)	W	W	(+)
	e	W	W	W	W	W	W	+	W	W	W	W	(+)
	f	(+)	W	W	W	W	W	+	(+)	(+)	W	W	(+)
Sera	g	?	?	W	—	?	?	W	W	W	?	?	W
	h	W	W	W	W	(+)	W	(+)	(+)	(+)	W	W	(+)
	i	W	W	W	W	W	W	W	W	W	W	W	W
	j	(+)	W	W	W	(+)	(+)	(+)	(+)	(+)	W	W	(+)
	k	W	W	W	W	W	W	(+)	(+)	W	W	W	+
	l	W	?	W	?	W	W	W	W	W	?	W	W

(G. L. Taylor's data, from Fisher.[12])

TABLE A 14

Canonical roots

$$R_1^2 = 0.708659 \quad R_2^2 = 0.270323 \quad R_3^2 = 0.117181 \quad R_4^2 = 0.106235$$

TABLE A 15

Approximate chi-square test of linearity of scale

	D.F.	χ^2
First root	25	159.71
Remainder	63	71.49
Total	88	231.20

TABLE A 16

Approximate chi-square test of hypothetical linear scale $\frac{1}{4}y_1 + \frac{1}{2}y_2 + \frac{3}{4}y_3 + y_4$

	D.F.	χ^2 (nonadditive)
Discrepancy with estimated scale	3	13.81
Departure from linear scale	63	71.49
Total	66	85.03

Example IV. Canonical variables and psychiatric data (Maxwell.[17])

TABLE A 17

Psychiatric score data

Multiple state				Group				
a,	b,	c,	d	I	II	III	y_1	y_2
0,	0,	0,	0	38	69	6	0	0
0,	0,	0,	1	4	36	0	−0.06	−0.34
0,	0,	1,	0	29	0	0	+0.70	+0.06
0,	0,	1,	1	9	0	0	+0.64	−0.28
0,	1,	0,	0	22	8	1	+0.46	+0.03
0,	1,	0,	1	5	9	0	+0.40	−0.31
0,	1,	1,	0	35	0	0	+1.16	+0.09
0,	1,	1,	1	8	2	0	+1.10	−0.25
1,	0,	0,	0	14	80	92	−0.49	+0.29
1,	0,	0,	1	3	45	3	−0.55	−0.05
1,	0,	1,	0	11	1	0	+0.21	+0.35
1,	0,	1,	1	2	2	0	+0.15	+0.01
1,	1,	0,	0	9	10	14	−0.03	+0.32
1,	1,	0,	1	6	16	1	−0.09	−0.02
1,	1,	1,	0	19	0	0	+0.67	+0.38
1,	1,	1,	1	10	1	0	+0.61	+0.04

	Total	224	279	117
	Mean y_1	0.446	−0.205	−0.402
	Mean y_2	0.074	0.034	0.265

REFERENCES

1. Aitken, A. C. 1939. "Determinants and Matrices," 135 pp. Oliver and Boyd, Edinburgh.
2. Bailey, N. T. J. 1959. "Statistical Methods in Biology," 200 pp. Wiley, New York.
3. Barnard, M. M. 1935. The secular varieties of skull characters in four series of Egyptian skulls. *Ann. Eugen. London* 6: 352–371.
4. Bartlett, M. S. 1947. Multivariate analysis. *J. Roy. Statist. Soc.*, 9 (*Suppl.*): 176–197.
5. Bartlett, M. S. 1951. The goodness of fit of a single hypothetical discriminant function in the case of several groups. *Ann. Eugen. London* 16: 199–214.
6. Bartlett, M. S., and Please, N. W. 1963. Discrimination in the case of zero mean differences. *Biometrika* 50: 32–36.
7. Blackith, R. E. 1961. Multivariate statistical methods in human biology. *Med. Documentation* 5: 26–28.
8. Cochran, W. G. 1962. On the performance of the linear discriminant function. *Bull. Inst. Intern. Statist.*, 39(2): 435–447.
9. Cochran, W. G., and Hopkins, C. 1961. Some classification problems with multivariate qualitative data. *Biometrics* 17: 10–32.
10. Eysenck, H. J. 1955. Psychiatric diagnosis as a psychological and statistical problem. *Psychological Repts.* 1: 3–17.
11. Fisher, R. A. 1936. The use of multiple measurements in taxonomic problems. *Ann. Eugen. London* 7: 179–188.

12. Fisher, R. A. 1946. "Statistical Methods for Research Workers," 10th ed., 354 pp. Oliver and Boyd, Edinburgh.
13. Hotelling, H. 1936. Relations between two sets of variates. *Biometrika* **28**: 321–377.
14. James, G. S. 1954. Tests of linear hypotheses in univariate and multivariate analysis when the ratios of the population variances are unknown. *Biometrika* **41**: 19–43.
15. Karn, M. N., and Penrose, L. S. 1951. Birth weight and gestation time in relation to maternal age, parity and infant survival. *Ann. Eugen. London* **16**: 147–164.
16. Mahalanobis, P. C. 1936. On the generalised distance in statistics. *Proc. Natl. Inst. Sci. India, Pt. A* **2**: 49–55.
17. Maxwell, A. E. 1961. Canonical variate analysis when the variables are dichotomous. *Educational Psychol. Measurement* **21**: 259–271.
18. Maynard Smith, S. 1954. Discrimination between electro-encephalograph recordings of normal females and normal males. *Ann. Eugen. London* **18**: 344–350.
19. Maynard Smith, S., Penrose, L. S., and Smith, C. A. B. 1961. "Mathematical Tables for Research Workers in Human Genetics," 74 pp. Churchill, London.
20. Penrose, L. S. 1947. Some notes on discrimination. *Ann. Eugen. London* **13**: 228–237.
21. Penrose, L. S. 1954. Distance, size and shape. *Ann. Eugen. London* **18**: 337–343.
22. Rao, C. R. 1952. "Advanced Statistical Methods in Biometric Research," 390 pp. Wiley, New York.
23. Reyment, R. A. 1962. Observations on homogeneity of covariance matrices in paleontologic biometry. *Biometrics* **18**: 1–11.
24. Rogers, D. J., and Tanimoto, T. T. 1960. A computer program for classifying plants. *Science* **132**: 1115–1118.
25. Smith, C. A. B. 1947. Some examples of discrimination. *Ann. Eugen. London* **13**: 272–282.
26. Smith, H. F. 1936. A discriminant function for plant selection. *Ann. Eugen. London* **7**: 240–250.
27. Sneath, P. H. A. 1957. The application of computers to taxonomy. *J. Gen. Microbiol.* **17**: 201–226.
28. Sokal, R. R., and Michener, C. D. 1958. A statistical method for evaluating systematic relationships. *Kansas Univ. Sci. Bull.* **38**: 1409–1438.
29. Stocks, P. 1933. A biometric investigation of twins and their brothers and sisters, II. *Ann. Eugen. London* **5**: 1–55.

[9]

MORPHOMETRICS

Robert E. Blackith

I. INTRODUCTION

Morphometric analysis is a new technique in an old setting; it represents a quantitative approach to taxonomic problems. The practice of taxonomy involves the preparation and use of keys based on dichotomies, thus emphasizing the differences between the organisms. The theory of taxonomy is concerned primarily with the relationships between organisms, in particular the relationship between their forms. This apparent divorce between theory and practice is an artificial one, but of long standing.

The earliest attempts to compare the shapes of animals were made by the Pythagorean philosophers as early as the 5th century B.C. Although their mathematical techniques were inadequate for what we now know to be a highly sophisticated set of problems, they were essentially quantitative, seeking to describe the forms of animals numerically. The geometrical techniques they used did not prove rewarding, and a major advance was made in the 4th century B.C. by Aristotle who introduced a dichotomous classification based on syllogistic logic. Bertrand Russell has remarked that Aristotle was inept at quantitative work, and the advances which he made in taxonomic theory were achieved at heavy cost.

The Pythagoreans, by considering similarities of form, tried to understand the nature of the relationships between animals, whereas Aristotle was able to make his great strides forward in classification by sacrificing such an understanding, except at a superficial level. An essential property of a dichotomous classification is that the divisions within it are descriptive.

The empirical syllogistic classifications of Aristotle were taken over by Linnaeus.[12,13] The superficial level of the classification thus produced has ever since failed to meet the desire of taxonomists to understand, as well as to describe, the relationships involved. The Pythagorean line of thought has therefore persisted side by side with the Aristotelian, and is seen to emerge strongly in the work of D'Arcy Wentworth Thompson.[46] For similar reasons the evolutionary basis of any classification now seems to many workers so obviously necessary that a taxonomic system which ignores phylogenetic considerations is to them hardly worth having.

To resolve this taxonomic schizophrenia calls for bold action, and a new freedom of intellectual approach to the subject has thrown up some radical suggestions.[39] New intellectual tools have become available in the form of multivariate analysis at the same time that a major reconstruction of ideas has become necessary. It is expedient to consider, first, the use of these new tools; second, the new intellectual framework that is being built up with their aid; and third, the practical work of reconstruction within this framework of ideas.

Traditionally, and as a direct consequence of Pythagoras' view that in numerical relations lay the essence of taxonomy, the study of the shapes and sizes of organisms has held a pre-eminent position. For convenience we still speak of morphometric analysis, referring to the quantitative expression of morphological relationships, even though a much wider range of characters has become available. In the taxonomy of the lower organisms, where shape is too simple and too plastic an attribute upon which to found a comprehensive relational system, serological and biochemical characters are included. This trend is much to be welcomed, and is extending to the higher organisms, since the greater generality of the comparisons helps to ensure that they represent what is essential, rather than what is trivial, in biological relationships. Some authors instead of calling the subject morphometric analysis prefer to describe it as taxometrics or numerical taxonomy.[41,43b]

II. TECHNIQUES OF MORPHOMETRIC ANALYSES

A. *Detecting Contrasts of Shape*

1. *The choice of characters.* In conventional taxonomy, where single characters are used to split groups of organisms successively into hierarchical subgroups, the different levels of organization are denoted by the choice of characters which reflect, in the judgment of the taxonomist concerned, the generality of the contrast being made. Such judgments are usually tinged with phylogenetic speculations, and there are likely to be several possible systems of classification according to the different views concerning the "primitiveness" of the characters upon which the dichotomies are founded.

The first of the radical changes which morphometric analysis requires is the realization that this subjective element can be removed by the use of a constant suite of characters, as widely spread over the organism as is practicable, to measure all the various taxonomic contrasts. The different weights to be attached to the characters will be determined objectively in each contrast by some such process as the maximization of the separation between the groups.

2. *The generalized distance.* The suite of weighted characters then becomes the discriminant function linking the groups which are separated by an amount which is calculable for any given linear compound of the characters and is known as the generalized distance.[25,33] This generalized distance is the measure of the degree of resemblance between the groups of organism.

As a consequence of this new approach, the different kinds of contrast which a taxonomist wishes to make will be illuminated to an extent not clearly brought out by the conventional techniques. The amount of the separation afforded by the suite of characters, that is, the measure of the similarity of the two groups of organism being compared, affords a quantitative scale on which genetic, specific, and other criteria can be measured.[41] The nature of this similarity is also made clear, and it is in this respect that the new techniques score so heavily by comparison with the conventional ones.

3. *Discriminant functions.* The contrast between one species and another may be different in kind from the difference between one of the species and a third. Conventionally

this distinction is qualitative and cannot be measured. However, by concentration on the characters which are shared, the nature of the underlying comparisons can be investigated because it is easy to compute the extent to which any two discriminant functions are related by computing the angle between them. If two such functions are represented by

$$y_1 = \alpha_1 x_1 + \alpha_2 x_2 + \alpha_3 x_3 + \alpha_4 x_4 + \ldots \alpha_i x_i \ldots$$

and

$$y_2 = \beta_1 x_1 + \beta_2 x_2 + \beta_3 x_3 + \beta_4 x_4 + \ldots \beta_i x_i \ldots$$

then the angle θ between them is given by the expression

$$\cos \theta = \frac{\sum (\alpha_i \beta_i)}{\sqrt{\sum \alpha_i^2 \sum \beta_i^2}}$$

This ability to measure the extent to which two taxonomic comparisons resemble one another is the fruit of the greater generality of vector techniques as compared with the scalar techniques possible when only one character is used for defining contrast.[7] We are beginning to call into service the armory of multivariate techniques introduced in Chapter 8. Details of the computational routines are to be found in Rao.[33]

For two discriminant functions which represent distinct patterns of growth, or distinct contrasts of form, θ will approach 90°. A pair of discriminant functions which measure the orientation of essentially similar contrasts of form will be almost parallel. Hence θ will be only a few degrees in such cases. This angle thus measures objectively the extent to which the contrasts of form differ from one another.

4. *Multivariate comparisons.* There is no reason why more than two groups of organisms should not be compared simultaneously, and, indeed, charts showing the mutual orientation of several biologically distinct discriminant functions and their associated generalized distances have already been constructed.[2,9,10,45] When several discriminants are compared, there is usually found to be a small number of basic axes of variation along which most of the vectors are aligned. For instance, the discriminant functions representing sexual dimorphism in related species of insect are usually parallel, and whenever some other common source of variation can be traced in several related species, as with phase variation in the swarming species of locust, the vectors that represent that variation are parallel also[8] (see Figure 3).

Evidently, if it is possible to reduce the variation of a large number of various organisms to a relatively small number of underlying contrasts of form, the way is open to a considerable gain not only in simplicity, but also in providing some understanding of the factors which comprise the variation.

5. *Latent roots.* From the sources of variation latent in contrasts between numerous groups of organisms, it is convenient to turn to the discovery of components of variation in supposedly homogeneous batches of organisms. The word "supposedly" indicates that the concept of a homogeneous group of organisms is an abstraction that is probably never realized in nature. A homogeneous group has been defined as one in whose heterogeneity the experimenter has not yet become interested.

In such a homogeneous group the matrix of correlations (or, with slightly different results, the matrix of sums of squares and cross-products of deviations from the means) of the several characters measured in the investigation may be factorized to reveal the underlying components of variation. This process of factorization is intellectually, though not alge-braically, equivalent to the familiar decomposition of an algebraic expression such as

$$(x^2 + x - 2) \quad \text{into} \quad (x + 2)(x - 1)$$

To carry this out, each of these factors is made to take up successively the greatest fraction of the residual variation. Such vectors are generated from the latent roots of the charac-teristic equation of the matrix A; each of the roots being a value of the unknown, λ, for which there are as many solutions as there are measured characters. To each solution there is a corresponding latent vector of the matrix, and each of these vectors is orthogonal to all the others. The form of the characteristic equation is

$$|A - \lambda I| = 0$$

Here the matrix I is a unit matrix, of the same rank as A, but with unity in the leading diagonal, and zero elsewhere.

One can relax the condition that these latent vectors are at right angles to one another, and the vectors then become the "factors" of factor analysis. This relaxation seems to the

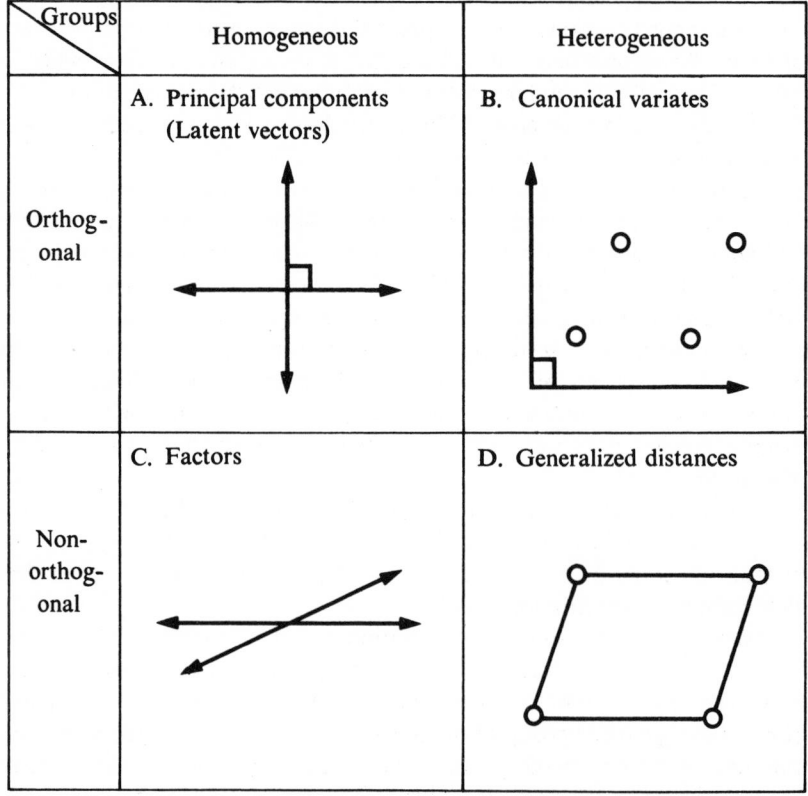

Groups	Homogeneous	Heterogeneous
Orthog-onal	A. Principal components (Latent vectors)	B. Canonical variates
Non-orthog-onal	C. Factors	D. Generalized distances

FIGURE 1. Formal relationships between the four main types of morphometric analysis. The organisms may be arranged in one group (homogeneous A, C), or several (heterogeneous B, D). The orthogonality of the axes of variation may be maintained (A, B) or relaxed (C, D).

writer to be unnecessary from a biological point of view and to entrain such further assumptions about the configuration of the underlying patterns of growth as essentially to beg the whole question.[27] This is, however, a highly controversial issue of secondary interest.

The relationships between these methods of analysis are summed up in Figure 1. The situation where the groups are separated by the discriminant functions between each pair is formally analogous to that in which the canonical variates, which serve to orient hetero-geneous material in the same way as latent vectors serve to orient homogeneous, are allowed to take up some configuration other than that of rectangularity; they do not, however, correspond to factors in practical analyses because no further assumptions are needed to perform the reorientation which is carried out by the calculation of the angles between the vectors as described above.

6. *Canonical analysis.* The presence of a multiplicity of groups, each containing several individuals, gives rise to the two sources of variation, whose matrices of correlations between the characters are denoted by A, as before, to indicate the dispersion within the various groups, and B, to indicate the dispersion between the groups. The equation to be solved in order to give the canonical roots, each of which describes the axes of variation known as canonical variates, is then

$$|B - \lambda A| = 0$$

Evidently, this process of creating hierarchies of organisms corresponds closely to that of conventional taxonomy, and one could conceive of a canonical analysis in which the "groups" were in fact groups of species, and the "individuals" the mean values for each species, which would leave individual measurements as a third level in the hierarchy.

Although no work has so far been done on these lines, attempts have in fact been made to compare the orientation of the latent vectors describing variation within any one group (or common to the variation within each of a set of groups) with the canonical vectors arrived at by factorizing the variation between groups.[6]

B. Reification

The discriminant functions which link any two of the groups being studied have an objective orientation which can be compared, again by the calculation of angles, with any of the factors, latent vectors, or canonical vectors in which one is interested. This process of referring to objectively oriented vectors, all those vectors which are somewhat arbitrarily computed on the basis of sets of assumptions of whose validity the experimenter is uncertain, is known to psychometricians as reification. An example of analysis by discriminant functions closely linked to the biological basis of the relevant experiments has been worked out in connection with the influence of nutrition on the form of the silkworm cocoon.[17] True reification outside the highly specialized field of psychometry is so rare that no published examples seem to be available.

One of the reasons for the writer's indifference to current controversies about the justification for factor analysis is simply that such arguments arise only when the factori-zation is conducted as a mathematical abstraction. In a real biological situation the correctness of the orientation of the vectors can in principle virtually always be verified by reification; even when a single group of organisms is under investigation, individuals having certain exaggerated characters can be found which will serve as objective landmarks from which to orient the computed vectors.

III. GROWTH PATTERNS AND CONTRASTS OF SHAPE

A. *Application to Patterns of Growth*

To tie all these ideas together in a biologically satisfying way is not easy because some of the ideas are abstractions and cut across the usual manner of thinking of those who have strong taxonomic interests. As a first step, it is helpful to remember that comparisons of shape in adult organisms represent cross-sections through a diagram in which the patterns of growth of each group are sufficiently distinct so that the resulting adult forms fall into clearly defined categories. Fortunately, there is one organism in which this interplay of patterns of growth is known to all, and that is man himself.

That normal growth is distinct from a tendency to fatness is immediately apparent, particularly since we know at least something about the physiological bases for these different patterns. In the same way the complex interplay of growth patterns giving rise to sexual dimorphism is distinct from those just mentioned. If a group of adults is subjected to a series of measurements, the matrix of correlations between the measurements may be factorized in various ways so as to uncover these three differential modes of growth.

Alternatively, the group could be split up into fat and thin people, tall and short people, and men and women. Suppose that the suite of measurements adopted includes the cranial width and length, the femoral length, the height, the girth around the chest and abdomen, and the weight and thickness of subepidermal adipose tissue as revealed by skinfold calliper measurements.

The skeletal measurements will be heavily weighted in the discriminant functions representing the differences of stature; the girths and adipose tissue will be heavily weighted in that representing the fatness-thinness polarity; and the chest girth will be strongly represented in the contrast between the sexes. In this way, the interplay of the three fundamentally distinct patterns of growth can be dissected from the adult measurements. We should expect to find that an analysis of the group as a whole would yield at least three latent vectors closely orientated along the discriminant functions specified above. Such an analysis would be an excellent example of reification.

B. *Application to Taxonomic Relations*

1. *Relational measurement.* A schematic representation of some taxonomic relationships is given in Figure 2. a) The distances between the groups and their mutual orientation are purely symbolic, but generic differences are understood to be more marked than, and perhaps different in kind from, specific differences of form. Species L and M belong to one genus; N and O to another in the same family. b) Representation of taxonomic affinity, showing the distance between groups as a measure of the similarity of form.

Lines joining the species L, M and N, O are vectors, the angle between which reflects the similarity of contrasts of form within either genus. The angles θ_1 and θ_2 are not necessarily the same, representing different degrees of divergence of the two sets of specific contrasts relative to the contrast between genera. The lengths of the lines joining L and M, or N and O, are reflections of the similarity of the members of each pair of species, and are not necessarily the same. Cross-sections of these "trees" are equivalent to generalized distance charts. c) Diagram representing the distinct effects of convergence by adaptation to a common habitat of species M and O cogeneric with the species L and N

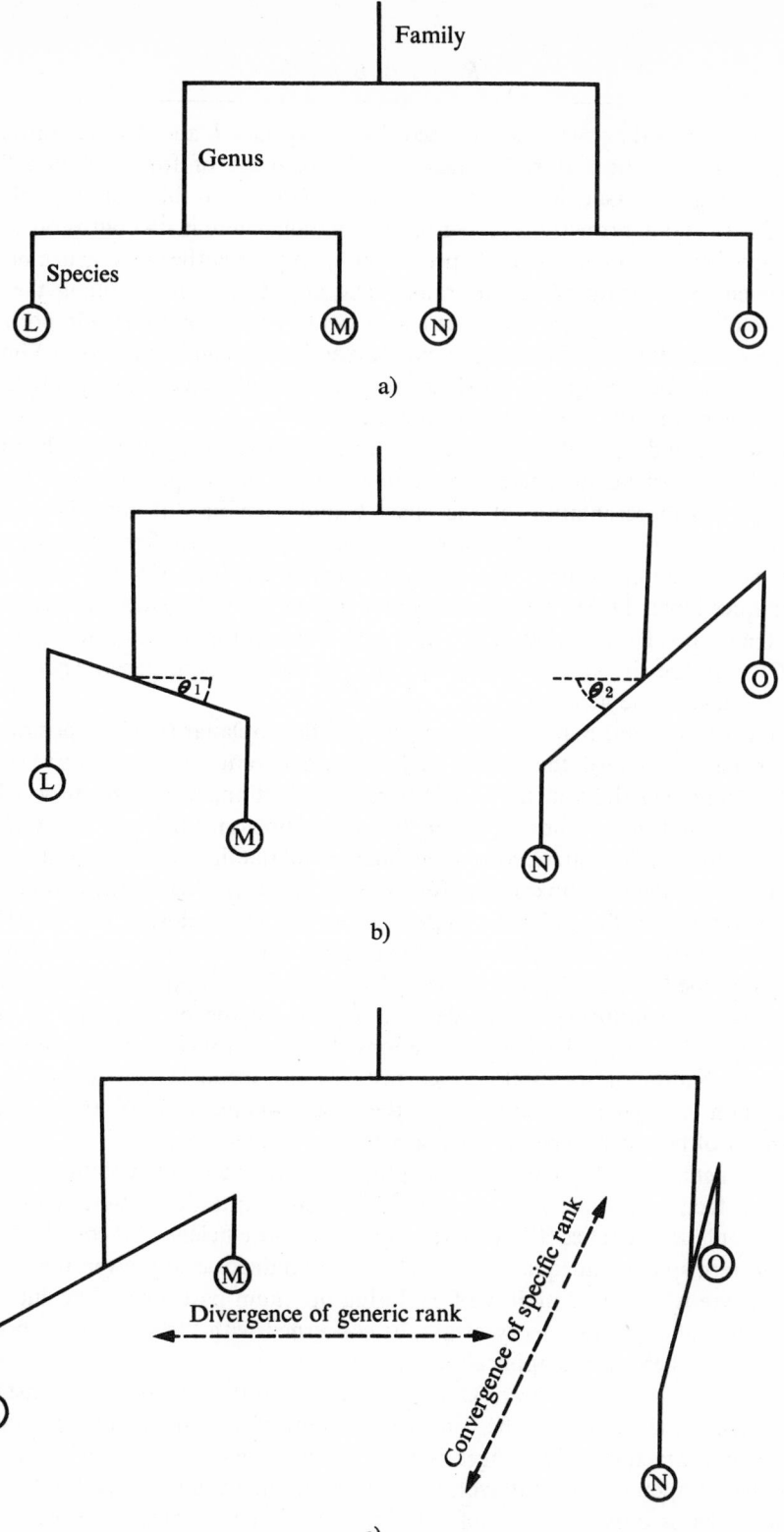

FIGURE 2. Conventional expressions of taxonomic relationships. (For explanation of symbols see text.)

respectively. In this diagram it is supposed that the species L and N have converged along a dimension of variation at right angles to the contrast of form between the genera.

Thus, although the fact that L has evolved (to M) in a fashion closely related to the change of N (to O) is properly reflected in the diagram, there is no confusion between this convergence, here supposed to be of specific rank, and the earlier divergence of L from N, here represented as being of generic rank. The objective of maintaining the systematic importance of the "divergence" without losing sight of the evolutionary importance of the "convergence" is attained. Whereas in the conventional diagrams (such as Figure 2a) the distances between the groups are purely symbolic, in quantitative taxonomy these distances are reflections of the affinities of the groups.

In Figures 2b and 2c, only the horizontal distances are of significance, but there is no reason why the vertical distances should not also be made quantitative; however, the two-dimensional representation of the chart would then be difficult. These figures are perhaps best regarded as multi-dimensional "mobiles" which are fixed once the intergroup distances have been computed. Conventional taxonomy does not take into account the following questions: 1) Are the specific differences in the first genus (that is, the contrast between the shape of L and that of M) similar to those in the second (the polarity between N and O)? 2) Are the specific differences, if common to both genera, parallel with the differences between the genera?

Questions of this kind reduce to a discussion of the coplanarity of the positions allotted to the four species. Indeed, they can be set in the wider context of quantitative evolutionary studies by expressing them in the form, "Are all evolutionary changes proceeding in the same direction and, if not, how many of these directions are there in any given taxon?" The answers to these questions are immediately available in terms of the angles between the discriminant functions linking the four groups, or, if preferred, the canonical variates along which the specific and generic differences are most closely aligned (Figure 2b).

2. *Genetic interpretation.* These questions have substantial genetical consequences; for one thing, the leakage of genes between two hybridizing populations living in habitats where the selective influences differ depends on the degree of similarity of the general direction of evolution in the two populations.[23] For another, the measurement of the relative contribution of parental species towards the mean shape of hybrid forms[16,48] depends upon a correct orientation of the discriminant, just as the detection and measurement of heterosis depends upon a proper choice of scale.

The construction of relational diagrams purporting to represent evolutionary diversification does, in fact, immediately pose a range of searching questions abutting on the general topics of population genetics (Chapter 15) and that of the efficiency, or cost, of evolutionary progress in terms of the adequacy of the structure attained at any given time (Chapters 3 and 16). There is also a possibility of exploring optimum pathways of evolution through that division of the general theory of graphs concerned with "trees" and "arborescences" (in the senses of these words applicable to set theory[5]).

3. *Recognition of convergence.* One argument is often advanced against relational systems which are not based on the background knowledge of the taxonomist in respect to his choice of characters; the danger is that the relational system will come to express similarity based upon convergent evolution. This argument presupposes that, since on the conventional bases only one kind of difference or similarity between organisms can be expressed, this one kind must represent the phylogenetic background of the classification rather than the degree of resemblance actually found.

The problem disappears when the possibility of giving effect to a multiplicity of kinds of difference is realized. The vectorial representation of the convergence will almost certainly be oriented in a different direction from that representing the phylogenetic relationship where this is known. These different sources of variation are represented diagrammatically in Figure 2c. The generalized distance between the two groups N and O, here supposed to have been rendered similar in form by convergence, is, as it should be, small. To render it large by neglecting the characters influenced by convergence, as conventional techniques of classification tend to do, is simply to falsify the record. That the organisms have converged in form is just as much a part of the biological situation as any past divergence, and the classificatory scheme should acknowledge this fact. Nevertheless, in Figure 2c there is no problem in distinguishing the effects of convergence from the absence of divergence when a sufficiently comprehensive suite of characters has been chosen.

Problems are much more likely to arise in quantitative morphometric analysis, just as they do in conventional taxonomy, from the difficulty of establishing homologies in organisms not closely related. This is, however, a problem which quantitative techniques do nothing to exacerbate even if they do nothing to resolve it.

C. Adansonian Taxonomy

Bacteriologists and mycologists have particular reason to be dissatisfied with the shortcomings of the dichotomous approach to taxonomy, and with the even more obviously archaic type concept of the species. Moreover, workers in these subjects have an urgent practical task of diagnosis since many of the organisms with which they have to deal are of medical importance. Arguments about the need for classification to wait upon phylogenetic considerations fall particularly flat when no fossil record is ever likely to be found. Sneath[39] has commented that "bacterial classification is in such confusion that it seems doubtful whether any nonsense can make it much worse than it is."

1. *The method.* Important advances in taxometrics have been made by taking at its face value the proposition that all conceivable characters are of equal potential worth as taxonomic discriminants. Large numbers of characters of the order of 100 are compounded together with equal weights, following an idea put forward by Adanson in 1763 and, probably independently, by Scopoli in 1777. Many of these characters are only pseudo-quantitative and are classified into "states" such as "presence/absence."

The relational diagrams ("dendrograms") which result from the Adansonian computation of resemblance bear a deceptive likeness to phylogenetic trees but carry information about the degree of similarity of the organisms represented and not about their descent.[41] The great merit of Adansonian taxonomy is its objectivity and the fact that the computational processes lend themselves to electronic processing.[40] However, the more elaborate calculations involved in the computation of generalized distances and discriminant functions, or latent and canonical vectors, can also be processed on electronic computers, although the preparation of and inversion of the dispersion or correlation matrix may exhaust the capacity of the machine if very large numbers of characters are employed (Chapter 10).

2. *Criticisms.* The weakness of Adansonian taxonomy as at present practiced seems to lie in the consequences of the fallacy that because all characters are potentially of equal worth in a discriminant they must have equal weights. The appropriate conclusion, if the proposition of equal potential worth is accepted, is that the weights of the characters should be determined objectively according to the biological nature of the discrimination which they are being called upon to perform. Such empirical determination of relative weights

permits the vector, along which the measure of resemblance is being made, to be oriented in a biologically meaningful direction.

In its present form, Adansonian taxonomy with equal weights imposes a constraint on the measure of similarity or resemblance by virtue of the fact that the equal weights themselves constitute a vector direction. Although it is true that with increasing numbers of characters the distance between the groups will tend to a limit, this limit will, in general, be biased.

To illustrate the point by taking an extreme example, let us consider two related segmented organisms with ellipsoidal segments; the essential difference between the two organisms we will suppose to lie in the eccentricity of the ellipsoids (their relative elongation). If the forms of these organisms are appreciated by means of the lengths of the major and minor axes of the ellipses, that is, the lengths and breadths of the segments, the optimal discriminant function will take the form of a series of coefficients in which the segment lengths have coefficients such as $+I$, whereas the segment breadths have coefficients such as $-I$. Equal weighting, on the other hand, will give a set of coefficients (say $+I$) throughout. This set is orthogonal to the first, so that the two groups would come out to have zero distance (complete resemblance) in such a calculation, even though they obviously differ.

There are also difficulties in the current practice of numerical taxonomy as defined by Sneath and Sokal[41] in that the covariance of the characters is not taken into account, so that the addition of redundant characters increases the distance between the groups, just as did the "coefficient of racial likeness" of Karl Pearson, to which the Adansonian distances bear a resemblance.[42]

It may well be true at present that to compute distances which do not suffer from this source of bias is impracticable because of the large number of characters which are currently employed. This is a purely technical limitation, however, which time will no doubt cure; there is a temporary reversal here of the general rule that computers grow faster than the biological theory needed to make intelligent use of them, as Levins has remarked. At present it seems preferable to use fewer characters and compute the generalized distance, which is known to provide the correct distance whatever the covariance of the characters, rather than to obtain a more general, but perhaps seriously biased, result by the Adanson approach.

To draw attention to these current controversies is not to suggest that Adansonian taxonomy should not be practiced; it represents an advance on conventional techniques of classification to which the further improvements suggested are secondary. There remain, however, desirable changes which will come about as soon as the fallacy noted above is recognized.

D. *Analysis of Phenotypic Plasticity*

1. *Types and variations.* The "type" concept in taxonomy enshrines the belief that animals and plants of a given species ought not to vary beyond limits which an experienced taxonomist can recognize. This concept seems to stem from a prescientific mode of thought in which variation represents a measure of imperfection in the specially created species. Thus, variation challenged what remained in natural philosophy of Plato's theory of forms (the archetype concept), in much the same way as the elliptical planetary orbits at one time challenged the theory that such orbits must be circular because only circles were perfect figures.

As the genetical heterogeneity of populations of a single species was uncovered, this concept of an ideal form was transferred to the idealized phenotype, latent in the much more easily idealized genotype. Even today, species are often described on the evidence afforded by a study of only a small part of the phenotypic range, and much confusion in nomenclature arises because of this limitation.

One useful service of morphometric analysis is the clear distinction which it offers between phenotypic plasticity and contrasts of form which have taxonomic consequence. In general, the phenotypic plasticity will be oriented along a vector distinct from those vectors along which the specific, generic, and other genotypic distinctions are oriented. In this way some difficult taxonomic problems have been resolved, but in this early stage of the development of the subject it is the promise, rather than the achievement, which stands out.

2. *Vector analysis of plasticity.* As illustrations of the possibility of describing phenotypic plasticity in terms of vectors, the following studies may serve.

a. "Plagiognathus albipennis *growing on different species of* Artemisia" (*T. R. E. Southwood and R. E. Blackith, unpublished*). There are several species of the mirid bug *Plagiognathus*, some of which live by sucking plants of the genus *Artemisia*. The form of the bug which is found on the salt-marsh *Artemisia maritima* runs down in a key[47] to *P. litoralis*. That found on the mugwort, *A. vulgaris*, runs down to *P. albipennis*. The two forms were originally regarded as good species because they differ in size, color (especially that of the antennae), body shape, and, most important of all, in the shape of the genitalia. This last character is critical in many insects because the lock and key nature of the hard parts of male and female genitalia prevents interspecific breeding.

To all appearances the case for two distinct species of *Plagiognathus* was clear. However, by transferring populations of the form collected from *A. maritima* to plants of *A. vulgaris*, we have found that the pale forms referable to *P. litoralis* give rise to dark progeny referable to *P. albipennis*. The reciprocal transfer converts the dark forms collected from the green-leaved mugwort to the pale forms characteristic of the silvery salt-marsh *A. maritima*.

The full story is not yet known, but by the analysis of the various forms of these and related bugs along canonical variates, three biologically distinct axes of variation have been disclosed: one axis represents sexual dimorphism and certain genuine specific distinctions; the second axis represents the influence of the host plant on the growth and adult form of the bugs; the third represents the influence of geographical factors on the form of the bugs, the relative amount of phenotypic and genotypic variation in this dimension being unknown at present. Thus the range of variation induced merely by transferring the bugs from one host plant to another is sufficiently large to span contrasts of form that have been regarded as of specific rank.

b. *Phase variation in locusts.* The story of the phases of locusts is well known and needs only to be briefly recapitulated. When locusts of several species are reared under crowded conditions they differ morphometrically and biochemically, as well as in color, behavior, and reproductive performance, from those reared in isolation. At one time the different phases, corresponding to densities of rearing, were given specific status, though this view has long since been abandoned. It has now been established that the change of shape which results from crowded larval life is represented by a vector quite distinct from any specific or generic distinctions of form.[2] Moreover, these phase vectors are oriented in the same direction for all the swarming species of acridians (true locusts) with the exception of one species which undergoes changes of shape on crowding but does not form true swarms; the phase vector in this case is orthogonal to the orientation found for it in all swarming species.[8]

E. Geographical Variation

In general, size variation in animals is more likely to respond to environmental changes than is shape, at least as far as skeletal structures are concerned.[16,22,36] For this reason, special attention is paid to the size components of geographical and other types of environmental variation. However, the almost universal occurrence of allometric growth entrains certain differences of shape along with the differences of size. It is not unknown for these allometric forms to be described as distinct species.[23] Multivariate analyses of geographic variation have concerned frogs,[35] turtles,[22] and wolves.[21]

Vectors may be used to illustrate the nature of such geographical variation (Figure 3). The generalized distances between six groups of the grasshopper *Chorthippus parallelus* have been computed. Five morphometric characters were used for the appreciation of shape and size, namely, the widths of the head and thorax, and the lengths of the tegmen, the pronotum, and the hind femur. Three of the groups represented males, the other three, females. Two groups, consisting of 25 specimens each, were collected and measured by Spett[44] in the Ukraine at Dorf Kasarowitschi, Kreis Kiev, during the summer of 1929. Some closely affine material, which would not now be identified as *C. parallelus*, may have been included in Spett's measured specimens, but this possibility does not alter the illustrative value of the example.

The other groups, each consisting of 100 individuals, were collected and measured by the writer at Sunninghill, Berkshire, in the summer of 1955. Previous analyses of the Berkshire material had shown that the two color polymorphs "green, with brown legs" and "dorsal stripe" were most clearly distinct in body shape. For simplicity only these two polymorphs, of the five that this species exhibits, are shown in Figure 3.

When all the generalized distances had been computed, the chart was found to be capable of a three-dimensional representation, of which Figure 3 is a two-dimensional projection. The drawing of the chart is a simple matter of ruler-and-compass geometry in which the generalized distances make up the sides of triangles. If the chart is two-dimensional, the triangles will "close up" on plane paper; if a three-dimensional model is made, they will close up when represented by rods cut to lengths proportional to the generalized distances and inserted in flexible holders (rubber toy golf balls serve well for this purpose). If these

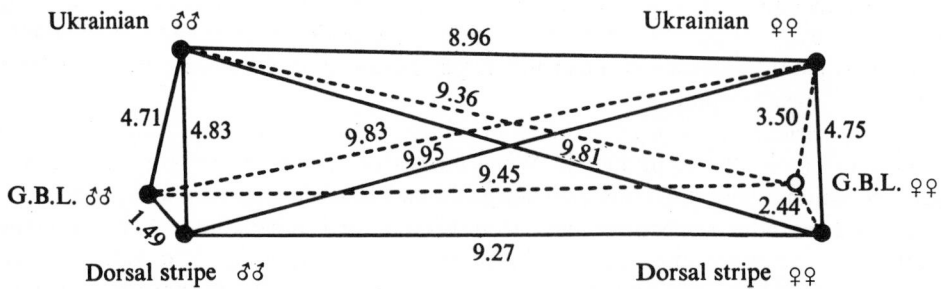

FIGURE 3. Generalized distance chart showing three of the basic axes of morphometric variation in the grasshopper *Chorthippus parallelus*. The three axes are: 1) sexual dimorphism (horizontal), 2) geographical variation contrasting Ukrainian with British specimens (vertical), 3) color polymorphism (parallel lines to the vanishing point). "G.B.L." (green body with brown legs) and "Dorsal Stripe" are the two color polymorphs of the species in Britain which most clearly differ morphometrically. This two-dimensional projection of the original three-dimensional mode shows the generalized distances in figures.

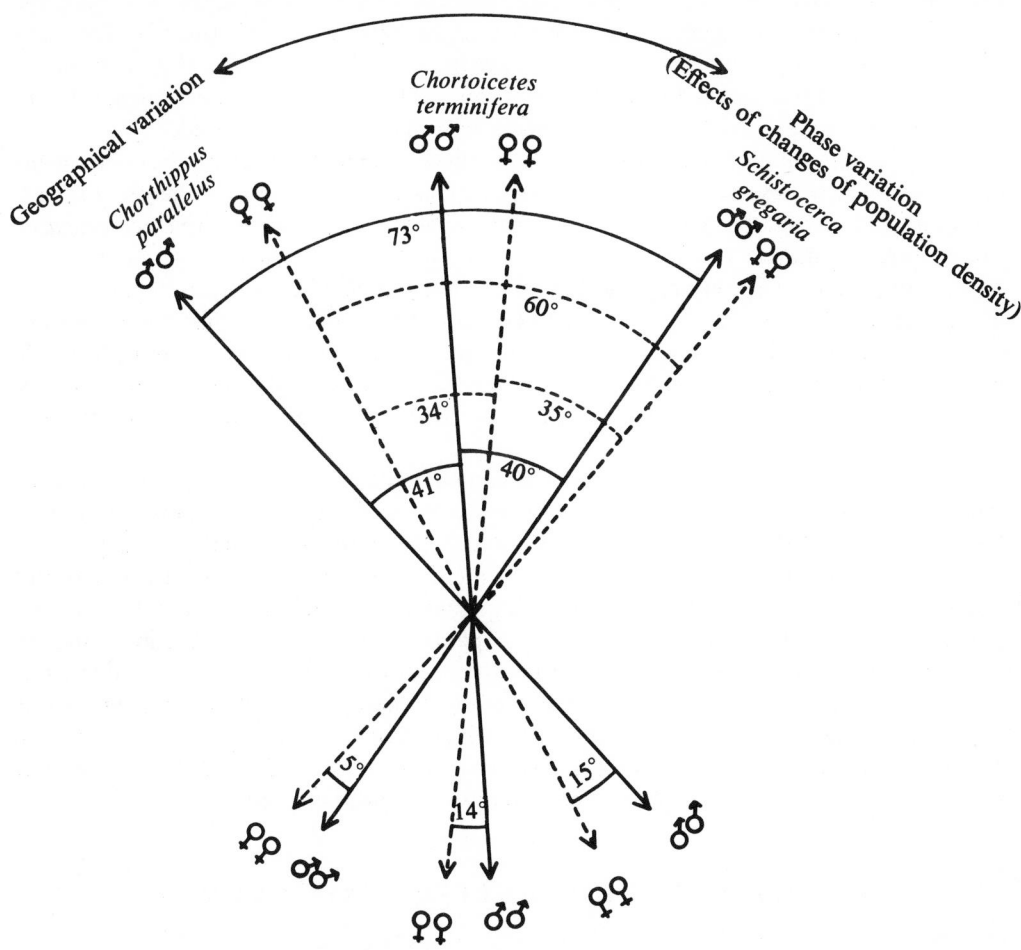

FIGURE 4. Comparisons of geographical variation in *Chorthippus parallelus* with phase variation (shape changes due to crowding during the larval stages) in two species of swarming locust, the Australian plague locust, *Chortoicetes terminifera*, and the desert locust, *Schistocerca gregaria.* The vectors are coplanar, as is shown by the fact that there is only a modest discrepancy between the sums of the constituent angles, such as 41° and 40°, and the over-all divergence (73°) between the extreme species in a tripartite contrast. Such discrepancies are attributable to sampling variation.

lengths cannot be made to fit in three dimensions, then more than three fundamental sources of variation are concerned and an analysis along canonical variates is indicated.

In this instance, however, a solid model is adequate. This fact is in itself interesting because it shows that although five characters have been measured, so that the hyperspace is potentially five-dimensional, an accurate representation is possible in a three-dimensional space, the fundamental coordinates of which are readily seen in the figure. The first of these basic axes of variation is marked sexual dimorphism; the second is the "vertical" axis representing geographical variation in body shape; the third is the contrast of body shape between the color varieties.

The geographical variation already examined in the nonswarming grasshopper, *C. parallelus,* may be compared with phase variation in the swarming locusts (Figure 4).

The same five characters are used for this comparison, but instead of obtaining the generalized distances between the groups, the angles between the discriminant functions representing the different kinds of variations have been calculated. Details of the calculation of the "phase" discriminant functions have been published, together with the sources of data.[8] From a simple chart of this kind, much information can be gleaned.

Despite the pronounced sexual dimorphism in these acridian Orthoptera, the components of variation are represented by vectors closely aligned in the two sexes. The geographical variation in *C. parallelus* is quite distinct from phase variation in *Schistocerca gregaria*, since the representative vectors are at angles of some 75°. *Chortoicetes terminifera*, the Australian plague locust, has a phase vector which is intermediate between the orientation of the vectors for the other species, but there is a strong possibility that the samples of crowded and isolated *Chortoicetes* differ by virtue of the fact that they were collected in climatically distinct regions of Australia, as well as by virtue of the population densities. In other words, the intermediate orientation of *Chortoicetes* probably reflects both geographical and phase variation.

The last point to note from Figure 4 is the coplanarity of the six vectors, as indicated by the fact that the angles between the *Chortoicetes* vectors and those outside them add up to the angles between the vectors for *Chorthippus* and *Schistocerca*. Sometimes this property of coplanarity can be used to break down the different levels of similarity between patterns of growth. The phase vector for the swarming locusts is roughly orthogonal to that for a nonswarming locust, for instance, but still coplanar with it. When the cotton stainer, *Dysdercus fasciatus*, an insect belonging to a different order yet showing shape differences as a consequence of larval crowding, is compared with these locusts, the vector representing the shape change is found to be not merely distinct from those for swarming locusts, but not even coplanar with them. This indicates an even greater disparity of the genetic mechanisms which render the phenotypic response to crowding possible.[8]

IV. INTERLOCKING PATTERNS OF GROWTH

The idea that it is possible to associate a large number of morphological characters into a much smaller number of biologically meaningful patterns of growth entrains certain consequences from the point of view of systematic biology which should be briefly considered. First, such an analysis disposes of the major argument that has been used to support saltatory evolution. Many workers have found it difficult to believe that complicated structures such as the mammalian eye could have arisen as a consequence of the fortuitous and simultaneous mutation of the many parts of which it is composed. Therefore, such structures have been supposed to arise as major evolutionary leaps which were not part of the slow progress by random mutation, although this concept is devoid of explanatory value because it has never been much more than a redescription of the result.

When one realizes that the multiplicity of characters in the organism are associated together in a relatively small number of patterns of growth, the problem of molding the mutations influencing any one pattern into a coherent modification disappears. There is indeed direct evidence that genetic control of growth operates directly on these patterns of growth rather than on the individual characters. Kraus and Choi[24] in 1958 extracted the latent vectors describing the independent patterns of growth in the human fetus. They found that twelve skeletal characters reduced to four patterns of growth. Moreover, they found some evidence to suggest that each pattern of growth could fail as a consequence of a single genetic mutation proper to that particular pattern, and by a reasonable inference, controlling it as a whole.

A. Natural Selection and Patterns of Growth

A major consequence of the shift of emphasis from individual characters to compound patterns of growth is that we may expect natural selection to operate on the degree of interlocking of these patterns, rather than on their individual elements. An immediate result is that the need for a concept of "nonadaptive" characters disappears, and with it the justification for much of the conventional systematic arrangement of animal and plant life based on what are supposed to be nonadaptive characters. For we can hardly assume that patterns of growth as such are nonadaptive, and whether any particular constituent character is of obviously selective value to the organism is in consequence trivial since it presumably forms part of the ensemble upon which the genotype is acting. The concept that selection acts upon suites of characters taken as entities is favored by the multivariate analyses of Sokal[43a] and has also been supported by work using conventional techniques in the fields of morphology[20,29] and physiology.[38]

If natural selection does indeed act upon the interlocking of patterns of growth, characters which are not closely associated in contrasts between the individuals of a single species should show much more close association when these contrasts of form are extended to cover groups of substantially different genotypic constitution, such as different species within a genus or related genera within a family. Such indeed proves to be the case, as the following examples demonstrate.

1. *Color pattern in* Cepaea. In this highly polymorphic snail the pattern of the shell, although once regarded as an example of a character of no adaptive consequence, has been shown to have a marked effect on the predatory activities of thrushes. As a result the predominant color of the body and pattern of the whorls on the shell are distinct according to whether the snails are living in woodland litter or open grassland. Furthermore, the predominant genotypes in the different habitats are not the same. Within any one habitat, however, there is little or no association between the body color and the shell pattern, even though these independent factors are associated in contrasts across the different habitats in such a way that the resultant appearance of the snail harmonizes it with the surroundings.[14]

In most problems where the selective value of a character is in question, individuals removed from a population by natural selection are lost to the investigator; in contrast, the snails that are removed by thrushes have their shells discarded around the "anvils" where the birds break them open, and in this way the results of the thrushes' disregard for dogma are open to inspection.

2. *Grasshopper growth patterns.* The comparison of the latent vectors describing variation within each of the British species of grasshopper *Stenobothrus lineatus* and *Omocestus viridulus* with the canonical variates describing the contrasts of form between these two genera confirms that patterns of growth which are independent within any one population are interlocked when comparison is carried across the genera.[6] It so happens that the first three latent vectors are practically unit vectors, since they are dominated by the dry weight, the antennal segmentation, and the tegmen length, respectively. However, the discriminants linking the corresponding color polymorphs of the same sex, which happen to be parallel to those linking the genera, are certainly not unit vectors. Neither is the discriminant linking the sexes which is common to all the Acrididae for which data have been obtained.

Thus in contrasts between the genetically determined color polymorphs, or between the genera, the three characters, dry weight, antennal segment number, and tegminal length are bound together even though their growth is virtually independent in the individual insects.

3. *Ostracod evolution.*   There is an even more striking instance of the persistence of patterns of growth in the course of the evolution of carapace shape in the ostracod *Buntonia* from the Maestrichtian beds of Nigeria.[34]   During the transition from the Maestrichtian to the Paleocene, the carapaces gradually became more elongate and generally larger.   In the Upper Paleocene, however, *Buntonia (Protobuntonia) ioruba* gave way in a relatively short period to *Buntonia (Buntonia) beninensis*, which evolved from the preceding species as this was itself extinguished.   The succeeding species *B. beninensis* was a reversion to the size and shape of *B. ioruba* at the time of *B. ioruba*'s early evolutionary history in the Maestrichtian.

This marked change of subgeneric status corresponds to the fact that allometric growth cannot proceed too long in one direction without either the extinction of the organism or its mutation to a form more closely resembling an earlier evolutionary stage.   Notwithstanding the drastic reduction of size accompanying the mutation, the pattern of growth remained essentially the same.   At a time when the carapaces had become inconveniently needle-shaped the mutation had the effect of temporarily restoring the *status quo ante*. The extent to which the growth of different parts of the body is integrated so closely, and along the same vector, in the two successive subgenera demonstrates the persistence of this pattern.

Close associations of characters in persistent patterns of growth are widespread and have given rise to deeply rooted misunderstanding of evolutionary processes.   In particular, these associations formed the basis of theories of orthogenesis.   Such theories were based on a confusion between the persistent association of characters into patterns of growth and the more flexible interlocking of these growth patterns as evolutionary entities.

B.   Form Variation in Geological Time

If it is true that natural selection operates on the degree of interlocking between patterns of growth rather than upon individual characters (save for some special cases), the study of the changes of form of related species through the geological record stands in particular need of multivariate morphometric analysis.   There is probably no application of the principles of Linnean taxonomy so unsatisfactory as the attempt to describe the essentially continuous process of evolution by a set of categories initially conceived to accommodate specially created, and essentially discrete, forms.   As a recent comment puts it, "the enshrined Linnean nomenclature . . . is the emblem of affinities determined by reference to the categories of an Aristotelian blue-print: it is totally inappropriate in conception as an instrument for expressing evolutionary relationships."[18]

Against this Procrustean classification, morphometric analysis sets the possibility of a flexible description of observable evolutionary changes, both qualitatively and quantitatively. Where the affinities between groups of organisms need to be studied in time as well as in space, the advantage of this more flexible approach is considerable and has been utilized effectively in attempts to sort out the relations of fossil man,[4,26,28] coyotes,[19] ostracods,[34] and brachiopods.[11]

Nevertheless the penetration of paleontological research by multivariate morphometric analysis is likely to be slower than in the zoology or botany of living organisms because the tradition of the subject has been less able to accommodate itself to quantitative distinctions. However, such penetration may well prove to be more rewarding in the long run since the ferment of dissatisfaction with the conventional techniques is higher in paleontology than perhaps in any other branch of biology.

V. PROBLEMS OF ORIENTED VARIATION OF SHAPE

A. Variation in "Homogeneous" Samples

Even when a group of organisms appears to be homogeneous, there are special problems connected with the variation of shape within the sample, which have not received the attention they deserve; their existence renders the ordinary multivariate significance tests, such as Wilk's criterion,[33] irrelevant to the examination of differences of form in living material.

If the correlation matrix, representing the mutual variation of the various characters in the sample, is factorized, in all cases of which the writer is aware, some latent roots prove to be significant, that is, the form variation is not isotropic. The existence of these roots implies that there are certain preferred directions along which the residual variation is oriented.[30] As a general rule, the most important of these roots is associated with the vector describing pure size fluctuations. The fact that this root is usually the most important quantitatively (in the sense that it takes up the largest fraction of the residual variance) is very far from implying that it is the most important to the biologist studying the organisms. The second and perhaps subsequent roots are likely to be carrying information about the shape variations of the material which is the main concern of the taxonomist.

B. The Oriented Significance Test

Any multivariate significance test is necessarily oriented in the direction of some linear compound of the characters that are being measured. The usual tests give an assessment of the separation afforded by the discriminant function which links the two groups and which is oriented along this vector. This discriminant function, however, is likely to be strongly affected by the direction of the numerically most important of the components of random variation within the groups which, as noted above, is usually the vector describing size variation.

What the biologist and, in particular, the taxonomist require, however, is a test of the shape differences between the groups, and for this purpose the significance test must be oriented along the appropriate axis of variation.[31,32] Only in this way can a relevant test be made, for it is quite possible for two groups to differ significantly in some aspect of shape, and yet for a conventional multivariate test along the discriminant function to indicate that no significant differences exist.

An analogous situation may be found in the analysis of an agricultural field trial. The vector representing size variation in the morphometric analysis is essentially comparable to general soil heterogeneity in the agricultural plot experiment. In turn, segregation of size variation along an independent axis of variation, taking up a calculable fraction of the total variance in the analysis, is analogous to the segregation of components of soil heterogeneity by block contrasts or, even more appositely, by covariance.

One can well imagine an agricultural trial whose analysis failed to denote significant effects because proper precautions had not been taken in its design. Similar precautions are just as necessary in morphometric analysis, but the theory is as yet undeveloped. Until such theory is available, it seems justifiable to compute the scores of the individual organisms along the appropriate vector by serial multiplication of the measurements of the organisms by the vector coefficients, followed by summation of the products. These scores may then be used in a conventional univariate analysis of variance.

C. Symbatic Patterns of Growth

Generally we have seen that despite the multiplicity of characters that can be measured, their mutual interrelationships can be described in terms of a much smaller number of fundamentally distinct patterns of growth. This situation is not surprising in the light of the rather small number of hormonal and other growth-regulating devices known to be at the disposal of the animal body. Such a neat and economical method of representing the interlocking patterns of growth does, unfortunately, also suggest that any given contrast between the various patterns of growth will sometimes be elicited by quite distinct stimuli.

There is no reason to suppose that a particular contrast between the forms of two distinct species shall not also be produced by differences in the environment, though perhaps not to the same extent. As an illustration, the red locust, *Nomadacris septemfasciata*, has two distinct forms, one of which passes through six molts, bearing seven eyestripes in the adult, the other passing through seven molts, bearing eight eyestripes. These forms differ morphometrically, but the differences of form are represented by a vector which is parallel with that which describes phase variation in this species.[9] Again, the temperature at which the desert locust, *Schistocerca gregaria*, is reared influences its growth so that the contrast between insects reared in hot or in cool surroundings parallels the phase difference for the species.[45] Parallel changes of form of this kind have been called "symbatic."[9]

Such symbatic shape changes are a nuisance because they often superimpose environmental effects on differences of systematic importance. There is little doubt that much of the confusion into which the study of the pyrgomorphine grasshopper genus *Chrotogonus* has fallen stems from the fact that the two canonical variates which most clearly describe the differences of form of taxonomic rank have, superimposed on them, other contrasts of form of no systematic importance (Kevan and Blackith, unpublished). This situation reinforces the need for even the conventional taxonomist to study the whole range of variation of his material, for characters that may be "good" for distinguishing species also may be greatly influenced by certain types of environmental variation.

VI. THE FUTURE OF QUANTITATIVE TAXONOMY AND MORPHOMETRICS

Morphometric analysis is being taken up within the general framework of taxonomic studies with a rapidity which suggests that it represents a way of clarifying the prevailing confused theoretical situation. One consequence of this flux of new ideas is that many of the new techniques of analysis, which bear a general resemblance both in intent and in execution, are competitors. The element of competition which exists is, however, secondary to the contrast between the conventional techniques of taxonomy and any of the newer quantitative ones.

At the present stage of development there is room for this wide variety of analytical methods, each of which emphasizes some of the varied considerations that the experimenter may have in mind. They include, indeed, methods which involve factorization of the matrix of correlations between taxa with respect to their characters (Q-techniques) as opposed to the factorization of correlations between characters with respect to the taxa (R-techniques). The former, although hardly morphometric analyses, are highly relevant to the broader problems of quantitative taxonomy.[37]

The most encouraging feature of all these methods of attack is that their results agree quite closely when compared with one another. In general, these techniques also agree with the consensus of opinion in conventional taxonomy, so far as the broad outlines of classification are concerned. In view of these facts there is some justification for supposing that quantitative methods may take over at the point where conventional methods begin to fail.

A. Nomenclatorial Stability

One helpful result, which is now foreseeable, for the application of quantitative techniques is that the nomenclature will be stabilized. At present a potent source of instability is the discovery that the differences of form once thought to be only of specific rank now seem sufficiently great to be elevated to generic rank. This is a problem which should be resolved by quantitative work.[41] A second source of instability arises from the differences of opinion among taxonomists as to the appropriate characters to choose for differentiation at various categorical levels; this difficulty should not survive the choice of a suitably comprehensive suite of characters.

Quantitative comparisons should also help to diminish a discrepancy which is at present masked by the intensive specialization by taxonomists, leading to the creation of genera in, say, anthropology on the basis of dissimilarities that would hardly be accorded subspecific status in other branches of the subject. Some nomenclatorial instability is the inevitable result of progress in understanding systematic relationships, but much of the present instability seems unnecessary; almost every important insect pest of stored products has had its name changed in the last three decades for one of the two sets of reasons just noted, and the old as well as the new names have to be remembered.

B. Generality of the Techniques

For predicting the likely survivors from the plethora of new quantitative techniques now available, their degree of generality has an obvious survival value. Those outlined above are particularly general in character and may serve a multiplicity of purposes. This generality stems from the fact that methods of computing generalized distances are, in fact, exploitations of the proposition that whenever one is faced with correlated variates in a rectangular flat space one can transform to a curved hyperspace having uncorrelated variates.

One well-known application of this proposition is the general theory of relativity. The fact that the generalized distance technique was related to the special theory of relativity has long been known,[25] but analogy with the general theory is even more apparent. The length of a geodesic in general theory is given by the expression

$$ds^2 = \sum g_{ij} \, dx_i \, dx_j$$

where the dx_i, dx_j represent the differences along the axes x_i, x_j, and the fundamental tensor g_{ij} describes the curvature of the hyperspace in which the geodesic is being measured.

The analogous expression for the generalized distance between two groups of organisms is

$$D^2 = |d_i| \, A^{-1} \, |d_i| \quad \text{or} \quad D^2 = A^{-1} \, |d_i| \cdot |d_j|$$

where A is the matrix of correlations between the characters and $|d_i|_{i,j}$ represents the vector of the mean differences of the characters for the two groups.

Thus the inverse of the dispersion or correlation matrix plays essentially the same role as does the fundamental tensor $g_{i,j}$ in describing the extent to which the Riemannian hyperspace has to be distorted in order to accommodate the interrelationships existing between the characters when measured in the Euclidean space.[1] This relationship is illuminated by replacing the fundamental tensor g_{ij} by the Kronecker delta δ_{ij}, which is a unit matrix having each term in the leading diagonal unity, to represent standardized variances, and all pre- and postdiagonal terms zero, to represent the absence of correlation between the characters.

The expression for the generalized distance then becomes the well-known result of the theorem of Pythagoras

$$D^2 = d_i^2 + d_j^2 + \ldots$$

for a Euclidean space of the same number of dimensions as there are characters. This expression has been suggested as a measure of distance in taxonomic work,[42] but is particularly biased where the characters do not vary much from individual to individual within a group. In that case the covariances and the correlations become not vanishingly small, as do the variances, but indeterminate. It is in such instances, unfortunately, that the use of the crude Pythagorean distance has been recommended.

C. *Experimental Taxonomy*

The use of quantitative methods of morphometric analysis is closely bound up with the experimental approach to taxonomy. Conventional methods still retain traces of the attitude of mind that limited permissible characters to those visible in museum specimens, and even, in entomology for example, to features of the upper side of such material.

An important unifying concept emerges from the appreciation that, just as no characters are nonadaptive, so none are intrinsically unsuited for inclusion in a comprehensive suite of taxonomic attributes. Application of this concept permits, and indeed compels, us to recognize that the manifold contrasts of form which animals and plants can exhibit are accompanied by changes in their physiology,[3] in their reproductive performance,[3,15] and in their survival value.[3] Morphometric analysis thus falls into place in the general framework of biological studies.

Many of the problems of classification, at the specific and infraspecific levels particularly, are not likely to be resolved without direct experimental tests of the hypotheses suggested by comparisons of relevant collected material. Breeding experiments may help to reveal the environmental influences on growth,[50] host-transfer experiments to establish the nature of parasitic species, and estimates of survival or of reproductive potential to illuminate the selective value of different forms (Chapters 15 and 16). The capacity of plants to orient growth to one or other of the limits of the phenotypic plasticity may well prove to have survival value;[50] the existence of such marked phenotypic plasticity in itself calls for multivariate methods of analysis as an aid in clarifying the situation.[49]

In all these, and many other experiments, there is implicit recognition that slight contrasts of form are often external accompaniments for far-reaching contrasts of function. The

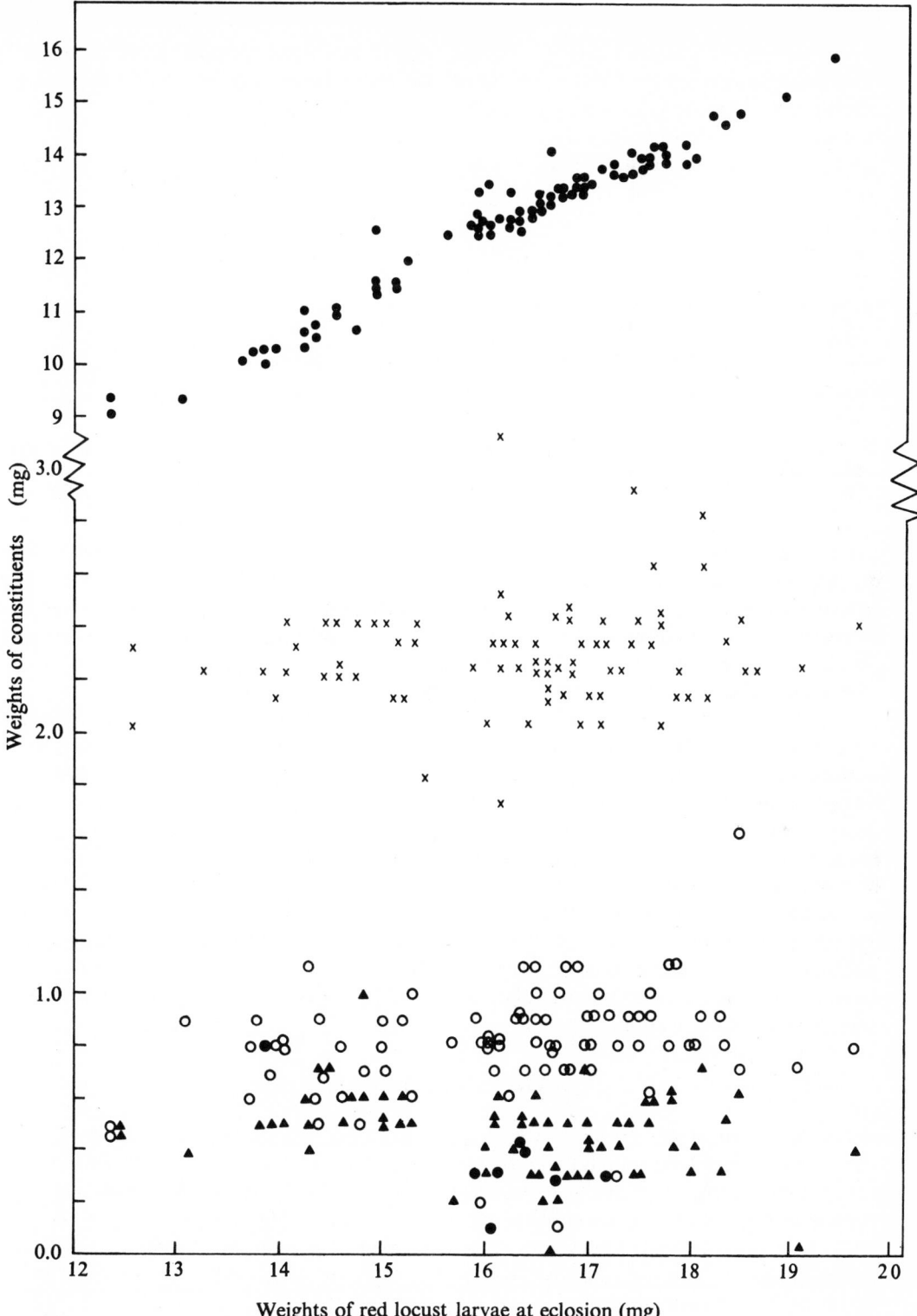

FIGURE 5. Physiological grouping of the newly hatched red locust larva, *Nomadacris septem-fasciata*. All the 80 larvae (analyzed individually) came from two oothecae laid by the same female. ○, chitin; ●, water content; ×, water-soluble solids; ▲, fat.

study of these associations of form and function is in its infancy; more often than not the present level of progress is due to the stimulus of applied research. The broad sweep of biological attributes now included in the criteria for the classification of bacteria and yeasts illustrates this point, as does the evaluation of the substantial differences of reproductive potential and larval survival which accompany the changes of phase, defined morphometrically, in locusts.[3]

The temptation to discount the contrasts of form within a species as too small to have serious biological consequences is strong; the stronger, in fact, the weaker is our knowledge of the biology of the organism. Variation of size and shape in adult red locusts is slight, and might seem trivial. However, growth studies on these animals show that the earliest instars are markedly different in size, and growth is so rigidly controlled that the initially smaller individuals pass through an additional molt so as to catch up to those which are initially larger. Moreover, even within a group of locusts having a constant number of molts, those that exceed the mean size grow a little more slowly, those below the mean size a little faster, so that all finish within a narrow range of sizes.

To dismiss as being trivial any character so closely controlled as is size in the red locust seems unwise; and so it proves to be in nature. Albrecht[2] has shown that in East Africa during the long dry season when these locusts remain in an adult diapause, unable to develop their reproductive organs, there is a marked selective mortality of the population, so that those individuals which in the earliest larval stages were the smaller, suffer the most severe mortality. Undoubtedly this selection does not directly depend on the residual differences of size, but it is certainly associated with them.

The general concept of size can be broken down in various ways: conventionally into the sizes of the various parts of the body of the organism, but this is far from being the only meaningful breakdown. A division on a physiological rather than on a morphological basis is also useful. By this means, the differential survival of the widely variable earliest stages[2] of the red locust has been investigated. With these very small larvae, survival depends on the capacity to resist dehydration until food can be found.[3] A physiological breakdown of the "size" contrasts in the first instar of the insects is shown in Figure 5. The differences of size are evidently almost entirely differences of water content, which places the morphometric contrasts in a new light, directly interpretable in terms of the ecological needs of the organism. There is no substitute for experimental work, in fact, when exploring the association of form and function, nor can one suppose that morphological contrasts are on a different plane from, say, physiological or behavioral ones, in constructing a classification.

VII. SUMMARY

The development of morphometric analysis represents a synthesis of two trends in taxonomy, each of long standing. One trend is particularly concerned with the differences between organisms, the other with their similarities. Vector methods of representing the contrasts of form in animals and plants reconcile these superficially conflicting approaches by making possible a quantitative assessment of these "qualitative" differences. This is accomplished in terms of the mutual orientation of the discriminant functions which represent the contrasts of form.

The formal relationships between the various methods of morphometric analysis are outlined, and within this framework Adansonian taxonomy is examined. The basic biological proposition of Adansonian taxonomy, that all characters are intrinsically of equal worth for classificatory purposes, is upheld; the currently practiced applications which give equal weight to each character in the discriminants are shown to be based on a fallacy but readily capable of sound development. Given the new flexibility of morphometric analysis, the conventional trees, or dendrograms, used to represent the relationships of organisms, may be modified so that more than one fundamentally distinct type of variation can be effectively represented.

These distinct axes of variation can be extracted directly from the matrix of correlations between the multiplicity of characters measured; in general, practical illustrations of the application of morphometric analysis to classificatory problems show that variation which at first sight requires many characters for its proper representation can in fact be reduced to a much smaller number of basic patterns of development. The problem of interpreting in biologically meaningful terms these patterns which emerge from the statistical analysis as a series of vectors is discussed, and a solution of general applicability advocated. There is evidence that it is upon the interlocking of these patterns of growth rather than upon their constituent characters that natural selection operates.

The rapid development of morphometric analysis is closely associated with the experimental approach to taxonomic problems. Such an approach seeks by experiment and analysis to break down the abstract conception of contrasts of form into components, such as size, and the various components of shape changes corresponding to the distinct axes of variation extracted from the multivariate analyses. These components may then be considered further; size, for instance, may be regarded as an assemblage of measures of the development of different parts of the body, or it may be broken down into components of primarily physiological interest, such as the amounts of water, proteins, fats, et cetera, in the body. By associating the objectively determined contrasts of form with these physiological contrasts, the relevance of morphometric analysis to ecological studies may be greatly enhanced.

REFERENCES

1. Adke, S. R. 1958. A note on the distance between two populations. *Sankhyā* **19:** 195–200.
2. Albrecht, F. O., and Blackith, R. E. 1957. Phase and moulting polymorphism in locusts. *Evolution* **11:** 166–177.
3. Albrecht, F. O., and Blackith, R. E. 1960. Poids et delai de survie des larves nouveau-nées chez les acridiens migrateurs. *Compt. Rend.* **250:** 3388–3390.
4. Ashton, E. H., Healy, M. J. R., and Lipton, S. 1957. The descriptive uses of discriminant functions in physical anthropology. *Proc. Roy. Soc.* (*London*) *Ser. B* **146:** 552–572.
5. Berge, C. 1962. "The Theory of Graphs and Its Applications," 247 pp., Methuen, London; Wiley, New York.
6. Blackith, R. E. 1960. A synthesis of multivariate techniques to distinguish patterns of growth in grasshoppers. *Biometrics* **16:** 28–40.
7. Blackith, R. E. 1961. Multivariate statistical methods in human biology. *Med. Documentation* **5:** 26–28.
8. Blackith, R. E. 1962. L'identité des manifestations phasaires chez les acridiens migrateurs. *Colloq. Intern. Centre Nat. Rech. Sci.* (*Paris*) **114:** 299–310.
9. Blackith, R. E., and Albrecht, F. O. 1959. Morphometric differences between the eye-stripe polymorphs of the Red Locust. *Sci. J. Roy. Coll. Sci.* **27:** 13–27.
10. Blackith, R. E., and Roberts, M. I. 1958. Farbenpolymorphismus bei einigen Feldheuschrecken. *Z. Vererbungslehre* **89:** 328–337.

11. Burma, B. H. 1949. Studies in quantitative paleontology. II. Multivariate analysis—a new analytical tool for paleontology and geology. *J. Paleontol.* **23:** 95–103.

12. Cain, A. J. 1958. Logic and memory in Linnaeus' system of taxonomy. *Proc. Linnean Soc.* (*London*) **170:** 185–217.

13. Cain, A. J. 1962. The evolution of taxonomic principles. *In:* "Microbial Classification," (G. C. Ainsworth and P. H. A. Sneath, eds.), pp. 1–13. Cambridge Univ. Press, London.

14. Cain, A. J., and Sheppard, P. M. 1952. The effects of natural selection on body colour in the land snail, *Cepaea nemoralis. Heredity* **6:** 217–231.

15. Clark, P. J., and Spuhler, J. N. 1959. Differential fertility in relation to body dimensions. *Human Biol.* **31:** 131–137.

16. Cousin, G. 1956. Intérêt de la zoologie quantitative pour la systématique. *Bull. Soc. Zool. France* **81:** 2–8.

17. Fraisse, R., and Arnoux, J. 1954. Les caractères biométriques du cocon chez *Bombyx mori* L. et leurs variations sous l'influence de l'alimentation. *Rev. Ver à Soie* (*Paris*) **6:** 43–62.

18. George, T. N. 1962. The concept of homeomorphy. *Proc. Geologists' Assoc.* (*Engl.*) **73:** 9–54.

19. Giles, E. 1960. Multivariate analysis of pleistocene and recent coyotes (*Canis latrans*) from California. *Univ. Calif.* (*Berkeley*) *Publ. Geol. Sci.* **36:** 369–390.

20. Grafius, E. J. 1961. The complex trait as a geometric construct. *Heredity* **16:** 225–228.

21. Jolicoeur, P. 1959. Multivariate geographical variation in the wolf, *Canis lupus* L. *Evolution* **13:** 283–299.

22. Jolicoeur, P., and Mosimann, J. E. 1960. Size and shape variation in the painted turtle. A principal component analysis. *Growth* **24:** 339–354.

23. Kermack, K. A. 1954. A biometrical study of *Micraster coranguinum* and *M.* (*Isomicraster*) *senonensis. Phil. Trans. Roy. Soc.* (*London*) *Ser. B.* **237:** 375–428.

24. Kraus, B. S., and Choi, S. C. 1958. A factorial analysis of the prenatal growth of the human skeleton. *Growth* **22:** 231–242.

25. Mahalanobis, P. C. 1936. On the generalised distance in statistics. *Proc. Natl. Inst. Sci. India, Pt. A* **2:** 49–55.

26. Mahalanobis, P. C., Majumdar, D. N., and Rao, C. R. 1949. Anthropometric survey of the United Provinces. *Sankhyā* **2:** 89–360.

27. Maxwell, A. E. 1961. Recent trends in factor analysis. *J. Roy. Statist. Soc.* **A23:** 49–55.

28. Mukherjee, R., Rao, C. R., and Trevor, J. C. 1955. "The Ancient Inhabitants of the Jebel Moya," 123 pp. Cambridge Univ. Press, London.

29. Olson, E. C., and Miller, R. L. 1958. "Morphological Integration," 317 pp. Univ. of Chicago Press, Chicago.

30. Pearce, S. C. 1959. Some recent applications of multivariate analysis to data from fruit trees. *Ann. Rept. East Malling Res. Sta. Kent*, pp. 73–76.

31. Pearce, S. C., and Holland, D. A. 1960. Some applications of multivariate methods in botany. *Appl. Statist.* **9:** 1–7.

32. Pearce, S. C., and Holland, D. A. 1961. Analyse des composantes, outil en recherche biométrique. *Biométrie-Praximétrie* **2:** 159–177.

33. Rao, C. R. 1952. "Advanced Statistical Methods in Biometric Research," 390 pp., Wiley, New York.

34. Reyment, R. A. 1960. Notes on the study of evolutionary changes in ostracods. *Proc. Intern. Geol. Congr. Copenhagen* **6:** 7–17.

35. Reyment, R. A. 1961a. Kvantitativ biologi. *Svensk Naturvetenskap* **14:** 97–104.

36. Reyment, R. A. 1961b. Quadrivariate principal component analysis of *Globigerina yeguaensis. Stockholm Contribs. Geol.* **8:** 17–26.

37. Rohlf, F. J., and Sokal, R. R. 1962. The description of taxonomic relationships by factor analysis. *Syst. Zool.* **11:** 1–16.

38. Schreider, E. 1960. "La Biométrie," Collection "Que Sais-Je?" No. 871, 126 pp. Presses Univ. France, Paris.
39. Sneath, P. H. A. 1957. Some thoughts on bacterial classification. *J. Gen. Microbiol.* **17:** 184–200.
40. Sneath, P. H. A. 1962. The construction of taxonomic groups. *In:* "Microbial Classification," (G. C. Ainsworth and P. H. A. Sneath, eds.), pp. 289–332. Cambridge Univ. Press, London.
41. Sneath, P. H. A., and Sokal, R. R. 1962. Numerical taxonomy. *Nature* **193:** 855–860.
42. Sokal, R. R. 1961. Distance as a measure of taxonomic similarity. *Syst. Zool.* **10:** 70–79.
43a. Sokal, R. R. 1962. Variation and co-variation of characters of alate *Pemphigus populi-transversus* in Eastern North America. *Evolution* **16:** 227–245.
43b. Sokal, R. R., and Sneath, P. H. A. 1963. "Principles of Numerical Taxonomy." 359 pp. Freeman, San Francisco.
44. Spett, G. 1930. Entwicklung der sekundären Geschlechtsmerkmale in der Ontogenese des *Chorthippus parallelus* Zett. (Orthoptera). *Arch. Entwicklungsmech. Organ.* **122:** 593–628.
45. Stower, W. J., Davies, D. E., and Jones, I. B. 1961. Morphometric studies of the desert locust *Schistocerca gregaria* (Forsk.) *J. Animal Ecology* **29:** 309–339.
46. Thompson, D'A. W. 1942. "On Growth and Form," 2nd rev. ed., 1116 pp. Cambridge Univ. Press, London.
47. Wagner, E. 1961. "Die Tierwelt Mitteleuropas," Vol. IV, No. 3, Pt. 10a (Heteroptera, Hemiptera), 173 pp. Quelle and Meyer, Leipzig.
48. Weber, E. 1959. The genetical analysis of characters with continuous variability on a Mendelian basis. I. Monohybrid segregation. *Genetics* **44:** 1131–1139.
49. Whitehead, F. H. 1954. An example of taxonomic discrimination by biometric methods. *New Phytologist* **53:** 496–510.
50. Whitehead, F. H. 1956. Preliminary investigation of factors determining the growth form of *Cerastium tetrandrum* Curt. *J. Ecology* **44:** 334–340.

[10]

SCOPE OF COMPUTER
APPLICATIONS*

Robert S. Ledley

I. INTRODUCTION

One of the most remarkable aspects of modern technology is the rapidity with which the field of high-speed digital electronic computers has developed. Within a single decade this entirely new field has penetrated almost all phases of modern civilization, from nuclear energy production and missile design to the processing of bank checks and business inventory control. In research stages there already are components that might make feasible computers many-fold more complex than present-day computers. Now we have available machines that vastly increase man's "thinking" capabilities, using "thinking" in the sense of planning, analyzing, computing, and controlling. Not only will their influence be directly marked on the economic, political, and social aspects of our civilization, but they will have a tremendous effect in the physical, biological, and medical sciences as well.

In the biomedical sciences, the use of computers has barely begun. In the future, however, perhaps the greatest utilization of computers will actually be in the biomedical sciences.[3,5] The problems that arise here characteristically involve large masses of data and many complicated interrelated factors, and it is just these types of problems for which computers are primarily suited. Also of great significance are the recent dynamic changes taking place in the biomedical fields themselves. For example, biological processes are now being examined in terms of atomic structures, energy levels, binding forces, molecular configurations, and the kinetic and thermodynamic details of biochemical reactions. Increasing quantization, with concurrent emphasis on the biophysical and physicochemical basis of biological systems, is rapidly bringing a large portion of biomedical science to a point where complicated mathematical manipulations and mass data reduction and analysis are absolute prerequisites to further progress.

At the present, however, only about 5% of digital computer time in university laboratories is devoted to biomedical research. For example, the Cooperating Colleges of New England, comprising about forty universities and colleges which utilize the computer laboratory at the Massachusetts Institute of Technology, report[1] that only 5.6% of the computer time is spent in the biological sciences, and of this 0.8% is used in the crystallography of organic

* This chapter is based on work performed under National Institutes of Health research grants RG-5626 to the National Academy of Sciences and RG-7844 to the National Biomedical Research Foundation.

substances, 1.4% in psychology, 1.0% in agriculture, 1.5% in medicine, leaving only 0.9% for use in what might be called "pure" biomedical research.*

Currently, of course, many hundreds of applications of computers are being studied throughout the country in the biomedical sciences. Many of these applications utilize the computer as a rapid calculator that can perform complex mathematical and logical operations more conveniently and often more economically than could be done by manual means. However useful computers may be for such jobs, their greatest advantage does not derive merely from ability to calculate rapidly. Rather, electronic computers are significant because they *can make feasible the solutions to problems that could not otherwise be approached.* Thus computers can enable theories to be explored, experiments to be performed, and data to be collected which would otherwise be impracticable; computers greatly extend the biomedical research worker's range of capabilities.

This chapter attempts to indicate the scope of computer applications in the biomedical sciences through the presentation of brief descriptions of specific examples. The examples are chosen to give some idea of the range of problems that can be approached and the variety of methods that can be used in computer applications.

Computers handle numbers or numerical representations of symbols. There are two basic types of computers, *analog* computers and *digital* computers, classified according to the mode in which the numbers appear in the electronic circuitry. In the analog computer, a number is represented by some analog quantity, such as a voltage level. The most common analog computer is the differential analyzer, which is primarily used for the rapid solution of ordinary differential equations, most often linear differential equations. The digital computer, on the other hand, handles numbers actually in the form of digits, and has a vastly greater capability for including alternative decisions in the computation. The analog computer is usually of a more specific nature, not as capable of performing generalized computational procedures as a digital computer.

This chapter is organized into four sections, the first two of which deal with the "programming" of the analog computer and of the digital computer, respectively. The section after these is devoted to computer applications associated with the analysis of biomedical systems, and the last section discusses some problems in biomedical data processing, including the use of computers in medical diagnosis.

II. INTRODUCTION TO ANALOG COMPUTERS

A. Components

This section first considers the components that make up the analog computer. Next, the method by which these components are connected to each other for solving specific equations is described; this constitutes the *programming* of such computers. Finally we shall consider an example of the solution of simultaneous equations for simulating the heart and circulatory system.

Five important types of components of an analog computer are the *adder*, the *integrator*, the *constant multiplier*, the *function multiplier*, and the *function former*. If the output

* The most recent Report, No. 13, July, 1963, showed 4.5% of computer time used in biomedical research, with a breakdown of 0.3% in medicine, 1.1% in psychology, 1.3% in crystallography, 0.2% in agriculture, and 1.6% in biology.

Name	Symbol	Effect
Adder	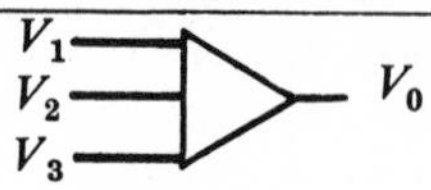 V_1 V_2 V_3 V_0	$V_0 = -(V_1 + V_2 + V_3)$
Integrator	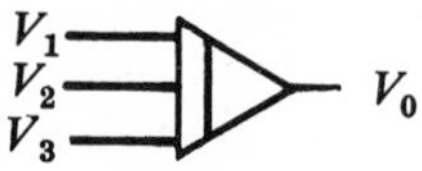 V_1 V_2 V_3 V_0	$V_0 = -\int_0^t (V_1 + V_2 + V_3)\,dt + V_K$
Constant multiplier	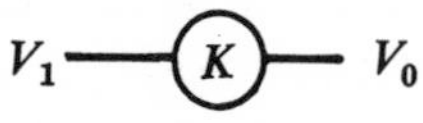 $V_1 \!-\!\!\bigcirc\!\!K\!\!-\! V_0$	$V_0 = KV_1 (-1 \leq K \leq +1)$
Function multiplier	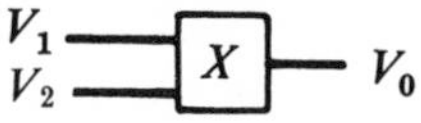 V_1 V_2 $\boxed{X}$ V_0	$V_0 = V_1 \times V_2$
Function former	 $\boxed{\diagup}\!-\! V_0$ $y = f(t)$	$V_0 = f(t)$

FIGURE 1. Symbols for, and effect of, some types of analog computer Components. Here K is a constant, and V_K is the initial condition of the component, i.e., the voltage output at $t = 0$.

voltage is V_0, and the input voltages are, say, V_1, V_2, and V_3, then Figure 1 illustrates the different types of components and the conventional symbols used to designate each. For an analog computer the *independent variable is the time*, and the *dependent variable the voltage level value*. Note from Figure 1 that in the case of the adder and integrator, the sign of the output is the opposite of the input. This is due to the fact that a high gain negative feedback amplifier, called an *operational amplifier*, is used in each component. Modern transistorized operational amplifiers may not produce this sign reversing effect. Analog function multiplication is difficult to perform accurately and rapidly, and many

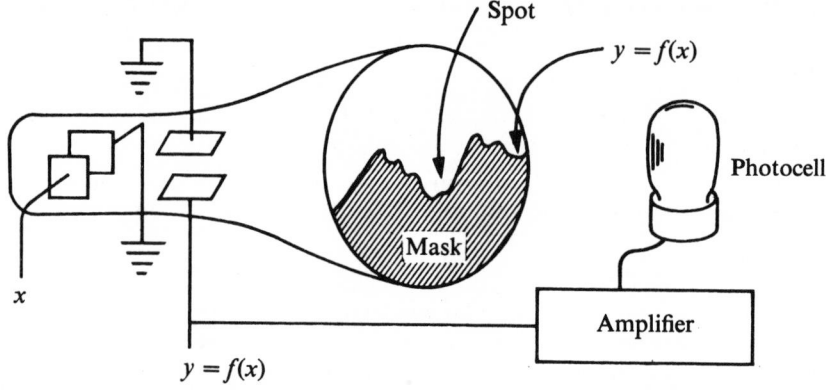

FIGURE 2. Photoformer for generating $y = f(x)$, as described by the upper edge of the mask.

types of devices have been invented for this purpose. On the other hand, multiplication by a constant simply utilizes a resistor or *potentiometer*, and for inversion of the sign, an operational amplifier.

Of particular interest is the *photoformer* type of function former. Here a cathode ray tube is utilized, and upon it is placed a mask that has been cut to the desired shape of the function, $y = f(t)$ (see Figure 2). A bright spot is formed on the face of the tube; this is "seen" by a photocell attached through an amplifier to the vertical deflecting plates. At the same time, the voltage representing t is applied to the horizontal deflection plates. If the spot is seen by the phototube, a voltage is generated that tends to bring the spot down behind the mask. If the spot goes behind the mask, the phototube is not activated, and the spot rises above the mask. The result is that the spot is kept just at the edge of the mask for every t or horizontal deflection. Thus $V = f(t)$ is generated across the vertical deflection plates of the cathode ray tube.

B. Programming the General-Purpose Analog Computer

A general-purpose analog computer or differential analyzer consists of racks of operational amplifiers that can be used for adding (or subtracting), integrating, multiplying by constants greater than one, and for changing sign; also racks of potentiometers that can be used for multiplying by constants less than one, positive or negative, servo-motor-driven potentiometers used for multiplying and dividing, and racks of special-function generators. The inputs and outputs of these components are terminated in appropriately labeled plug boards and rows of knobs for the potentiometers that can be set by hand. Connecting wires are supplied so that the required components can be conveniently plugged together. The output of such a computer is, typically, a plot of the function that is the solution to the differential equation, made by an automatic plotter.

Let us consider, first, programming the solution to the ordinary differential equation:

$$A\frac{d^2x}{dt^2} + B\frac{dx}{dt} - Cx - D = 0 \tag{1}$$

It should be noted that time is always the actual independent variable (that is, t) for analog computers. The *first step* is to *solve the given equation for the highest derivative:*

$$\frac{d^2x}{dt^2} = -\frac{B}{A}\frac{dx}{dt} + \frac{C}{A}x + \frac{D}{A}$$

$$= -R\frac{dx}{dt} + Sx + T \tag{2}$$

Now observe that if we know $\dfrac{d^2x}{dt^2}$, then we can find $\dfrac{dx}{dt}$ and x by integration. However, from Equation (2), if we multiply $\dfrac{dx}{dt}$ by R and subtract it from the product of S and x and add T, we shall have just $\dfrac{d^2x}{dt^2}$ at some small increment of time later. In this way the *loop* of electronic circuit components of the computer progressively develops the solution $x(t)$ of Equation (1).

A *flow chart* indicating the connections of the components representing the *second step* is shown in Figure 3. We start in the upper left-hand corner with $\dfrac{d^2x}{dt^2}$, send it through an

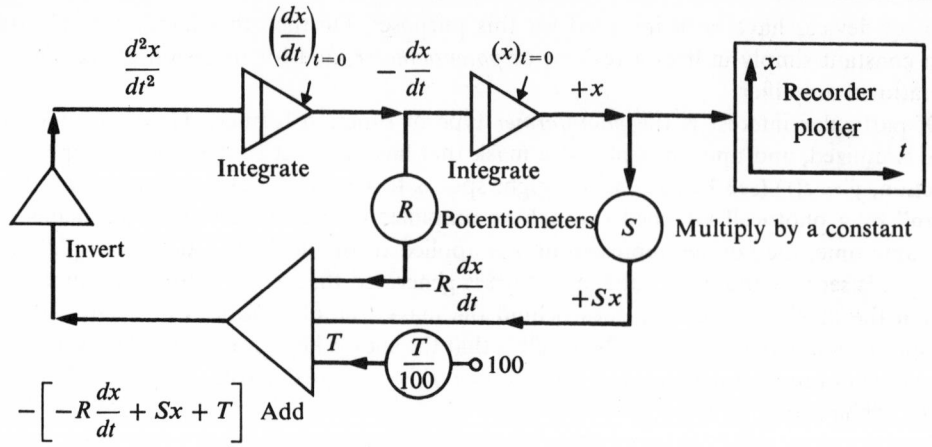

FIGURE 3.   Flow chart for solution to Equation (1).

integrator to obtain $-\dfrac{dx}{dt}$ (note the sign inversion obtained by the operational amplifier), send this through an integrator to obtain x. Next, we multiply $-\dfrac{dx}{dt}$ by R through the potentiometer to form $-R\dfrac{dx}{dt}$; similarly, we form Sx by means of another potentiometer; finally, we form T by multiplying a standard voltage source of 100 volts by $\dfrac{T}{100}$ in a potentiometer.

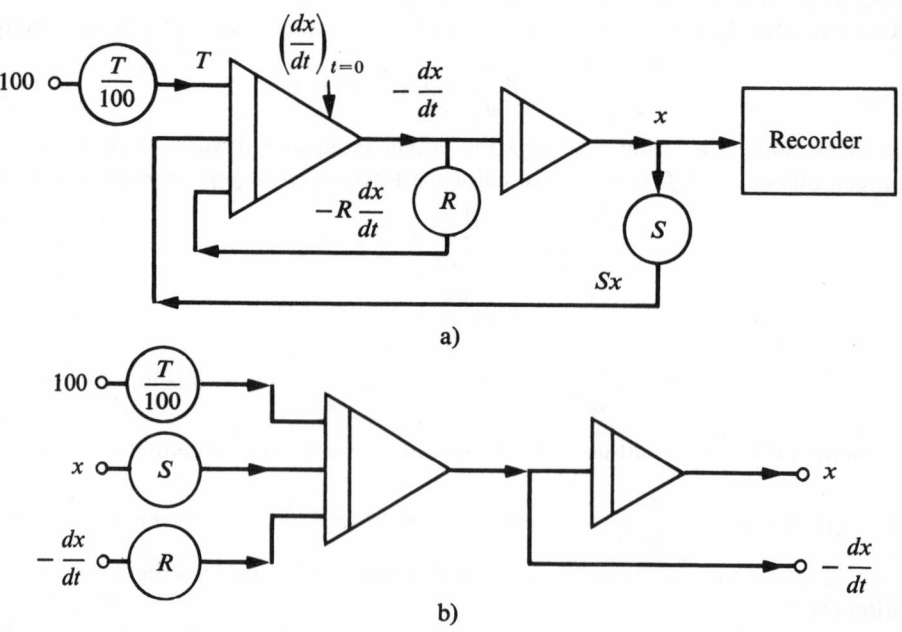

FIGURE 4.   Simplified flow chart for Equation (1). The feedback connections of a) are just indicated in b) rather than drawn completely.

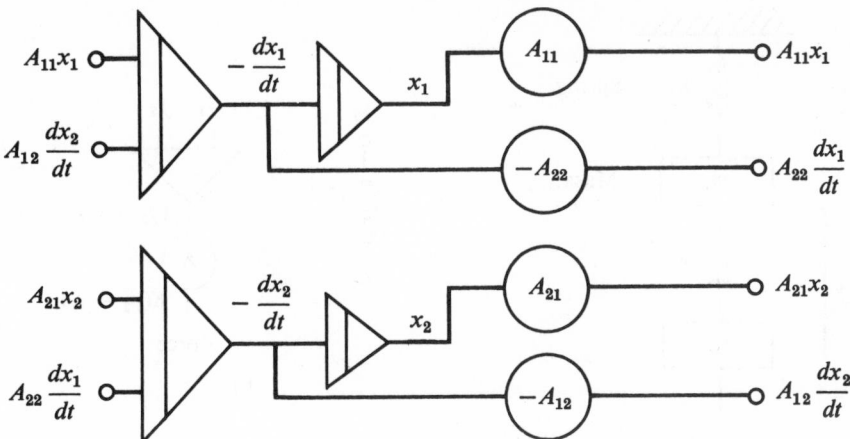

FIGURE 5. Flow chart for the solution to Equation (3).

The sum of these terms, formed in the adder, results in $-\left[-R\dfrac{dx}{dt} + Sx + T\right]$ which, when sent through an operational amplifier for inversion only, becomes just the desired $\dfrac{d^2x}{dt^2}$, and the cycle continues. The cycle is initiated after *the initial conditions are set into the integrators*, i.e., the values of $\left(\dfrac{dx}{dt}\right)_{t=0}$ and $(x)_{t=0}$. The recorder plots the value of $x(t)$ as it is generated in time. The *third step*, of course, is to plug in the components and adjust potentiometer settings and initial conditions as indicated in the flow chart. We can simplify the flow chart of Figure 3 by observing that the inverter can be eliminated by changing the signs of the potentiometers, forming $(-R)\left(-\dfrac{dx}{dt}\right) = +R\left(\dfrac{dx}{dt}\right)$ and $-Sx$ and $-T$. However, we can actually use the integrator to add, eliminating the adder and its inversion. The potentiometer signs are changed back, and Figure 4a is a simplified version of the flow chart for Equation (2). Sometimes the feedback connections are not actually drawn but simply indicated, as shown in Figure 4b.

Simultaneous differential equations can be solved by these means. For example, let us consider the following growth-rate equations:

$$\frac{d^2x_1}{dt^2} = A_{11}x_1 + A_{12}\frac{dx_2}{dt}$$
$$\frac{d^2x_2}{dt^2} = A_{21}x_2 + A_{22}\frac{dx_1}{dt}$$
(3)

Since these are already solved for the highest derivatives, the solution can be drawn as shown in Figure 5.

C. Direct Simulation

Constructing flow charts by direct simulation, without ever writing the differential equations, is an important method for utilizing analog computers. This method is most easily illustrated by means of a mechanical problem that can be clearly visualized. Let us

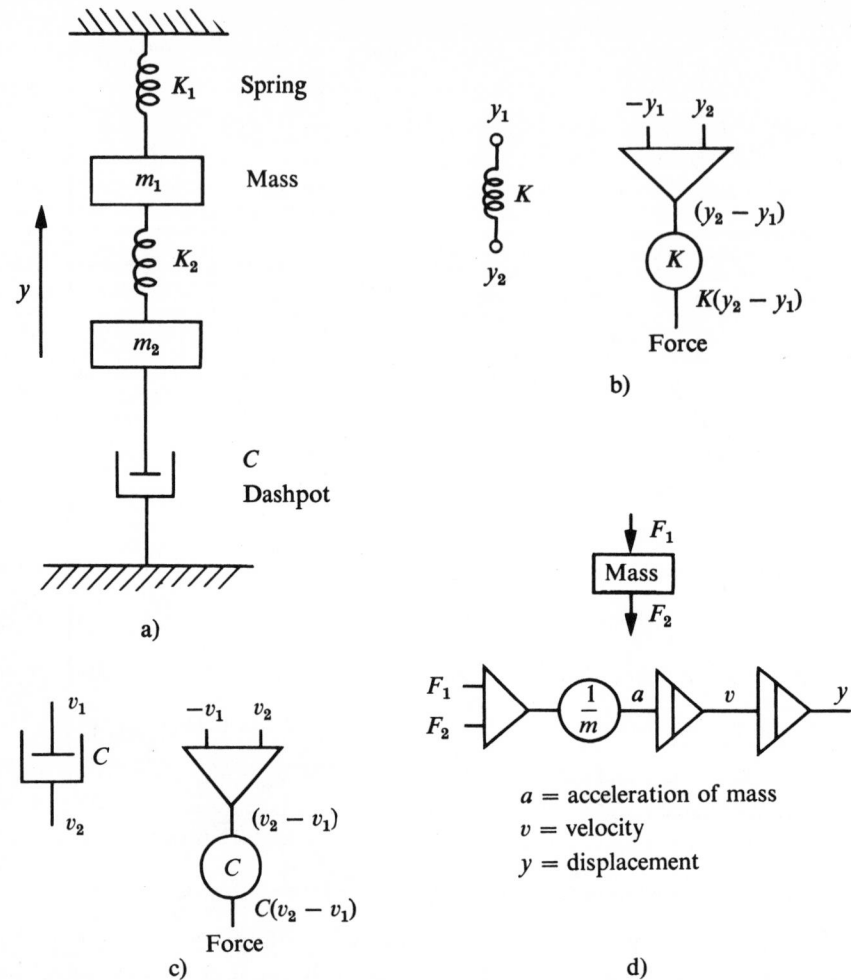

FIGURE 6. Direct simulation of the dynamic situation of a) by means of analog representation of a spring b), a dashpot c), and a mass d).

consider Figure 6a, showing a spring K_1 attached to a mass m_1, attached through spring K_2 to a mass m_2, which is attached through a dashpot (that is, resistance cylinder and plunger) to the floor. The problem is to describe the motion of the masses as a function of the time, given some initial displacement of the masses. In Figure 6b we note that a spring can be represented by two inputs, the displacements of its two ends, and one output, a force $F = K(y_1 - y_2)$. In Figure 6c we note that a dashpot is represented by two inputs, the velocities of its ends, and one output, a force $F = C(v_2 - v_1)$. In Figure 6d we note that a mass is represented by several inputs, the forces acting on it, and three outputs, an accelera-tion $a = \dfrac{1}{m} \sum_i F_i$, velocity $v = \displaystyle\int_0^t a\, dt$, and a displacement $y = \displaystyle\int_0^t v\, dt$ $\left(\text{since, of course,} \right.$ $a = \dfrac{d^2y}{dt^2}$, and $v = \dfrac{dy}{dt}\Big)$. Figure 7 represents the direct simulation flow chart of this dynamic problem of Figure 6a, wherein unnecessary components have been eliminated and the signs have been appropriately adjusted.

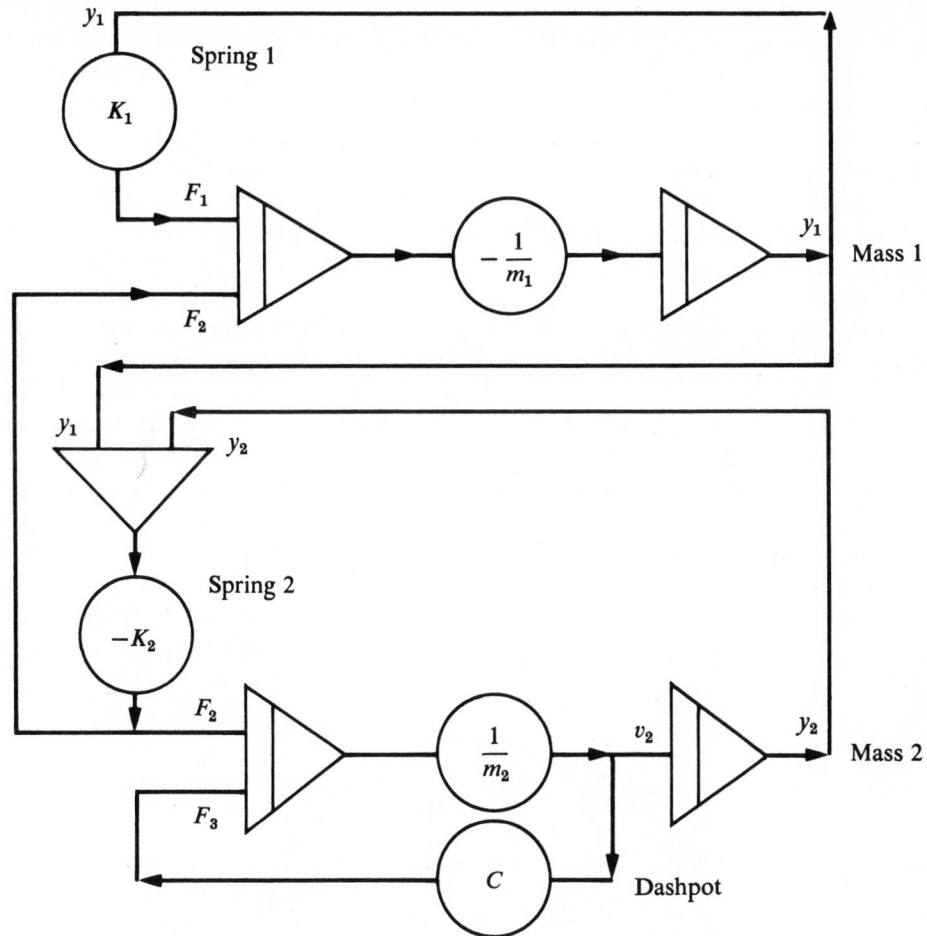

FIGURE 7. Direct simulation flow chart of dynamic situation of Figure 6a on eliminating unnecessary components and adjusting signs appropriately.

The important feature about this example is the illustration of how, by specifying the inputs and outputs of the parts of a complicated problem in terms of a literal interpretation of the analog computer components, the flow chart of the problem may be formulated without any explicit recourse to the governing equations. Not only does this procedure result in a better intuitive understanding of the parts of the flow chart in relation to the actual specific aspects of the problem under consideration, but the resulting flow chart will, in general, be simpler to interpret and often simpler in programming than if the equations were explicitly written out, particularly with regard to the placement and character of the constants.

D. *Analog Simulation of Heart and Circulatory System*

As an illustration of the use of an analog computer, consider a simulation of the heart and circulatory system suggested by H. Warner.[12] The simulation itself consists of a hypothesis in the form of simultaneous differential equations about the interrelationships between the heart and the rest of the circulatory system. In order to test the validity of the simulation, a particular functional relationship, as for example the pressure as a function of time in the right and left ventricles, is measured in the experimental animal. This measurement is inserted into the simulation equations, and the equations are used to predict certain other aspects of circulatory regulation. These aspects are measured on the experimental animal and then compared with the results predicted by the simulation equations. If the simulation appears adequate, then it can be used to study, predict, or "explain" various complicated effects of the interrelations of the circulatory system components.

The equations utilized for our illustration are perhaps the simplest that may be initially used in this connection. The division of the heart and circulatory system into six compartments for the purposes of this particular simulation is shown in Figure 8. These compartments are 1) right ventricle, 2) pulmonary arteries, 3) pulmonary veins and left atrium, 4) left ventricle, 5) aorta and arterial bed, 6) body system veins and right atrium. The order in which these compartments were named is also the order in which the blood passes through them. In the simulation to be described, relationships between the blood pressure and volume within each compartment and the flow of blood from one compartment to the next will be of prime interest.

In order that the notation be clear, let P_i represent pressure in the ith compartment, V_i represent volume in the ith compartment, and F_i represent the flow *into* the ith compartment

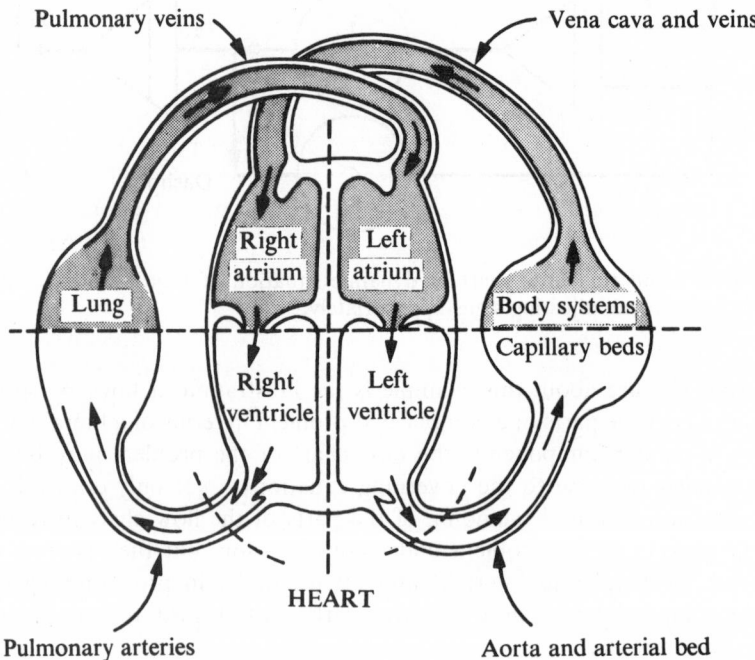

FIGURE 8. The heart and circulatory system. Diagrammatic illustration of the six compartments of the heart and circulatory system used for the purposes of this simulation. Dashed lines show separation of compartments; arrows show direction of blood flow.

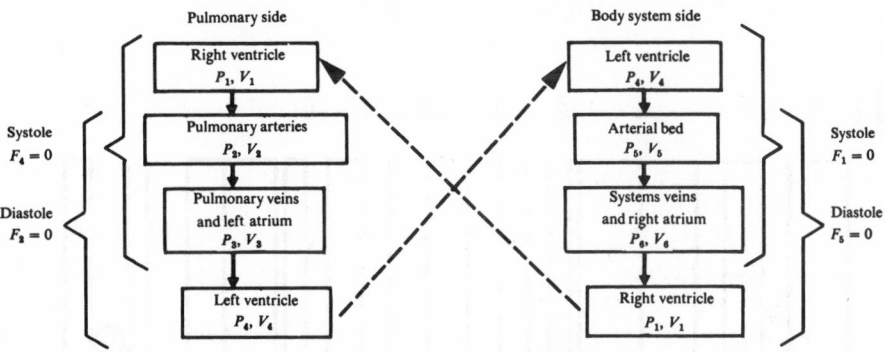

FIGURE 9. Relationships between blood pressure and volume. Summary of conditions during systole and diastole, indicating that $F_1 = F_4 = 0$ during systole, and that $F_5 = F_2 = 0$ during diastole. The dashed lines indicate the direction of blood flow.

(that is, $i + 1$ represents the flow *out of* the ith compartment). This notation is summarized in Figure 9.

There is one additional consideration that must be discussed concerning the different roles played by the ventricles during systole and diastole, that is, contraction and subsequent expansion of the heart, pumping blood out and being refilled, respectively. This is illustrated in Figure 9, where the ventricles have been repeated, once for systole and once for diastole, since different sets of equations will govern them at those times. The initial conditions at P_1 and V_1 for systole are the final values of P_1 and V_1 resulting from diastole, and conversely, the initial conditions at P_1 and V_1 for diastole are the final values of P_1 and V_1 resulting from systole. Similar remarks apply to P_4 and V_4.

There are twenty-two equations in this illustrative simulation, as given in Table 1. The pulmonary and body-system sides of the table are directly analogous; hence we shall only discuss the pulmonary side. During the systole, the heart is pumping blood out of the right ventricle into the pulmonary arteries, where we assume that the pressure, P_1, at any instant of time is primarily a function of the volume, V_1, at that instant and of the time, t (Table 1, Equation [T-1]). The rate of change of volume of the right ventricle is, by definition, proportional to the flow, F_2, and is negative (that is, decreasing) (Table 1, Equation [T-2]). However, the flow from the right ventricle into the pulmonary arteries is a function of the pressure gradient $(P_1 - P_2)$ across the valve and a time lag, τ_1, which depends on the inertia of the blood and heart, together with a coefficient of friction R_1, so to speak, that depends on the flow value at that time (Table 1, Equation [T-3]). For Equation [T-4] we have assumed a particular form for the pressure volume relation between the pressure P_2 and the volume V_2 of the pulmonary arteries. Similarly the rest of the equations of the simulation can be discussed. The analog program is shown in Figure 10.

Now recall that we have not specified the functions $f_S(V, t)$ and $f_D(V, t)$ that give the relation of pressure to volume in the right and left ventricles during systole and diastole. These functions could be measured on the experimental animal (that is, by heart probe and flow-meter) and put into the computer by means of magnetic tape. The method for switching in the animal recording is shown in Figure 10. The recording will then be used by the computer network for P_1 and P_4 instead of the computed P_1 and P_4. Note also that it is the recording that determines when change from systole to diastole and diastole to systole is to take place in the simulator.

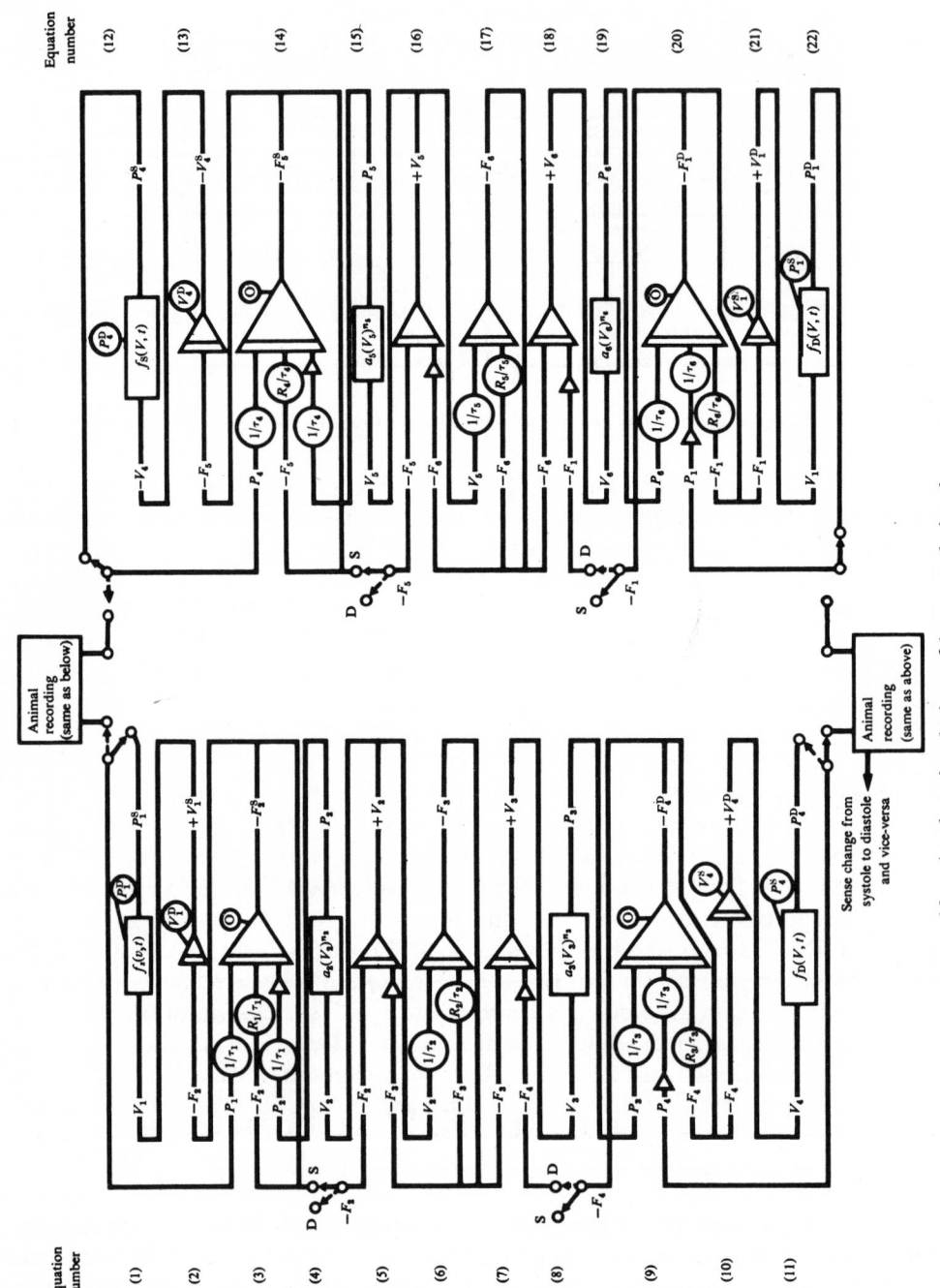

FIGURE 10. Analog simulation of heart and circulatory system.

TABLE 1

Twenty-two equations relating elementary aspects of the heart and circulatory system
set up for an analog simulation

Pulmonary side	Body system side
Right ventricle	**Left ventricle**
$P_1 = f_S(V_1, t)$ [T-1] or recording $\dfrac{dV_1}{dt} = -F_2$ [T-2] $\dfrac{dF_2}{dt} = \dfrac{1}{\tau_1}[(P_1 - P_2) - R_1F_2]$ [T-3]	$P_4 = f_S(V_1, t)$ [T-12] or recording $\dfrac{dV_4}{dt} = -F_5$ [T-13] $\dfrac{dF_5}{dt} = \dfrac{1}{\tau_4}[(P_4 - P_5) - R_4F_5]$ [T-14]
Pulmonary arteries	**Arterial bed**
$P_2 = a_2(V_2)^{n_2}$ [T-4] $\dfrac{dV_2}{dt} = F_2 - F_3$ [T-5] $\dfrac{dF_3}{dt} = \dfrac{1}{\tau_2}[V_2 - R_2F_3]$ [T-6]	$P_5 = a_5(V_5)^{n_5}$ [T-15] $\dfrac{dV_5}{dt} = F_5 - F_6$ [T-16] $\dfrac{dF_6}{dt} = \dfrac{1}{\tau_5}[V_5 - R_5F_6]$ [T-17]
Pulmonary veins and left atrium	**System veins and right atrium**
$\dfrac{dV_3}{dt} = F_3 - F_4$ [T-7] $P_3 = a_3(V_3)^{n_3}$ [T-8]	$\dfrac{dV_6}{dt} = F_6 - F_1$ [T-18] $P_6 = a_6(V_6)^{n_6}$ [T-19]
Left ventricle	**Right ventricle**
$\dfrac{dF_4}{dt} = \dfrac{1}{\tau_3}[(P_3 - P_4) - R_3F_4]$ [T-9] $\dfrac{dV_4}{dt} = F_4$ [T-10] $P_4 = f_D(V_4, t)$ [T-11] or recording	$\dfrac{dF_1}{dt} = \dfrac{1}{\tau_6}[(P_6 - P_1) - R_6F_1]$ [T-20] $\dfrac{dV_1}{dt} = F_1$ [T-21] $P_1 = f_D(V_1, t)$ [T-22] or recording

III. INTRODUCTION TO DIGITAL COMPUTERS

A. *General Capabilities*

The general capabilities of a digital computer can be most easily seen by the analogy between hand computation and the functions performed by the parts of a digital computer. A general rule for evaluating the capabilities of a digital computer is: if the steps in the solution of a problem can be broken down into sequences of unambiguous instructions that conceptually could be performed by a very patient secretary who has no knowledge of the subject matter but who has infinite perseverance and can follow instructions

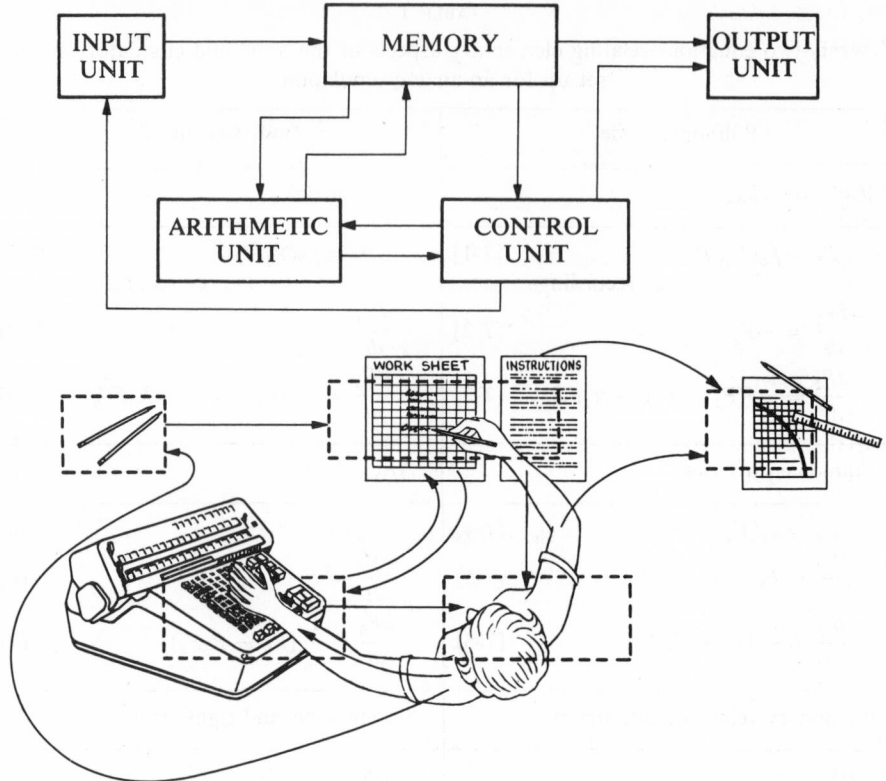

<small>FIGURE</small> 11.   Analogy between manual computing and an electronic digital computer.

precisely, never making an error, then the problem can be solved on a digital computer. This rule is an oversimplification only insofar as the necessary computation time on the computer and the cost of this time are also restrictions.

It is, in fact, instructive to carry our analogy still further, describing the functions of the various parts of the computer (see Figure 11). These are the input and output units, the memory, the control unit, and the arithmetic unit. The computer memory is analogous to the work sheet and instruction list of the hand computation: the memory stores the initial data to be operated on, the intermediate results and the final results, and also the instructions themselves. The control unit interprets the instructions regarding the operation to be performed, the arguments to be operated upon, and the instruction to be chosen next; this is analogous to the computing secretary's mind. The actual operations indicated by the instructions are performed in the arithmetic unit, analogous to the secretary's desk calculator. The input and output units, which for the computer can be punched paper tape, or card readers and punchers, or magnetic-tape readers and writers, or character-reading machines and high-speed printers, and so forth, are analogous to the secretary's pencils and graph paper.

Besides the great speed with which arithmetical and other operations can be performed (for example, modern computers can perform close to a half million additions per second) the computer derives its unique logical powers from its instruction-handling capabilities. These are basically of four types.

First, there is the chain instruction-sequencing capability of the computer to execute a list of instructions in sequence. For example, if

$$(ab + c)/d$$

is to be computed for given values of a, b, c, and d, the computer could be made to execute a sequence of instructions that formed the product ab, then added c to this result, and finally divided the sum by d.

Second, there is the decision capability of the computer to choose between alternative sequences of instructions for subsequent computations, depending upon the outcome of some previous computation. For example, suppose several different statistical procedures were to be applied to each set of input data, depending upon certain characteristics. In such a case the computer would be made to evaluate these characteristics for each set of data as it is received, and thence would choose the appropriate computational procedure to perform.

Third, there is the recursive computational capability of the computer to execute iteratively a sequence of instructions. For example, if a power series is being evaluated to a particular accuracy, each time a successive term of the series is computed its value is compared with the allowed error; if the term is smaller, the computer goes on to another part of the program, but if the term is larger, the computer adds it to the partial sum, adjusting certain constants, and repeats the general sequence of instructions to evaluate the next term.

Fourth, there is the instruction modification capability of the computer to change some of the instructions in its memory and then go on to compute with these modified instructions. In this way, for example, the computer itself can be made to write a sequence of instructions. This capability, and the other three as well, has implications more important and far-reaching than the mere ability to compute at high speed.

B. Flow Charting

The first step in programming for a digital computer is to draw a flow chart of the computation. A flow chart is a diagram that is helpful for visualizing interrelationships between various parts of a code or program. Such a diagram is almost always made before the specific instructions are written. There are essentially three kinds of symbols used in a flow chart (see Figure 12). The first represents function calculation; the second represents decisions and the various associated alternatives, and the third, called a (variable) connector, is simply a way to eliminate too many crossing lines in the picture. For example, to calculate $Y = V_{0v}t - \frac{1}{2}gt^2$ we would have the flow chart of Figure 13. Note that the symbols representing intermediate results appearing on the left-hand side of the equations, namely x and y, appear later in the chart on the right-hand side of an equation. Only symbols that signify end results, like Y, will not appear on the right-hand side of an equation.

An important type of flow chart is that of a loop, used to perform a repeating or recursive operation. There are four basic elements to such a loop. It must contain: 1) a set of

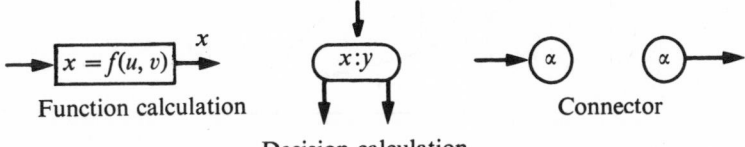

Function calculation   Decision calculation   Connector

FIGURE 12. Flow-chart symbols.

FIGURE 13.   Simple flow chart.

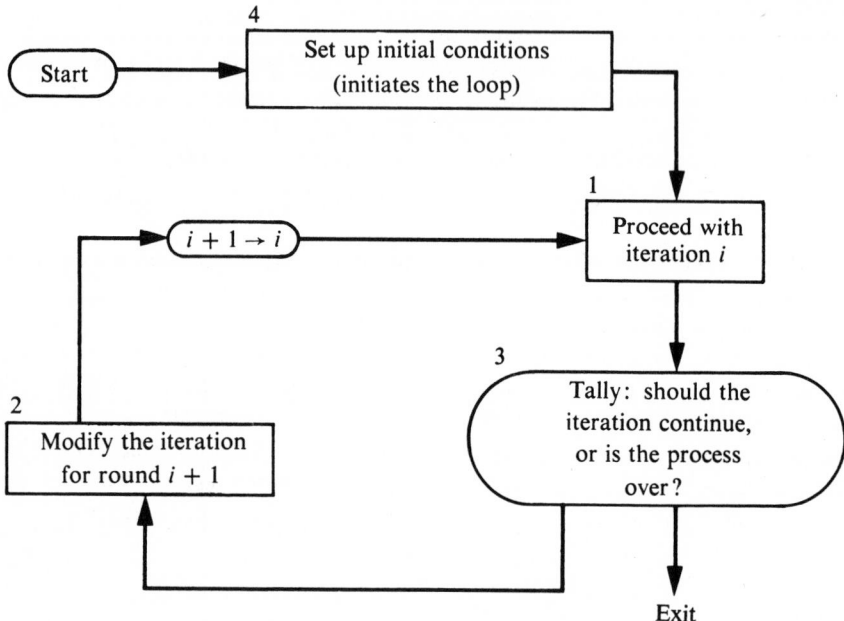

FIGURE 14.   Flow chart of generalized loop.

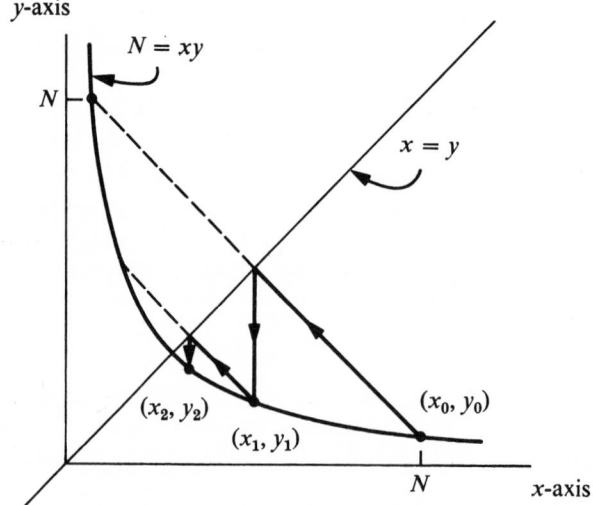

FIGURE 15.   Computation of $\sqrt{N}$.

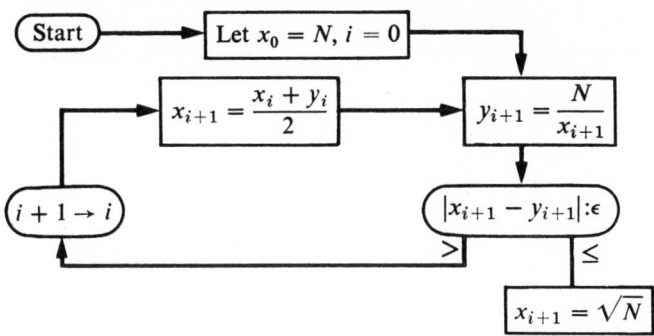

FIGURE 16. Flow chart for computation of $\sqrt{N}$.

instructions, called the iteration to be reused each time around; 2) another set of instructions that modifies the original set each time around; 3) a set of instructions, called the tally, that determines when to exit, or break out of the loop; and 4) a set of instructions that sets up the initial conditions and starts the loop (Figure 14). The "$i + 1 \rightarrow i$" means that for the next iteration we replace the old ith values with the new $i + 1$st values for the next time around.

As an example consider the computation of $\sqrt{N}$ to within an error of ϵ as follows (Figure 15). First note that $\sqrt{N}$ is the x (and the y) coordinate where the curves $x = y$ and $N = xy$ intersect. We approach this point by successive approximations, starting from (x_0, y_0), where $x_0 = N$, $y_0 = 1$, moving along a perpendicular to $x = y$, dropping an altitude to point (x_1, y_1) on $N = xy$, moving from this point along a perpendicular to $x = y$, dropping an altitude, et cetera, et cetera. The next point (x_{i+1}, y_{i+1}) is found in terms of the present point (x_i, y_i) as follows:

$$x_{i+1} = \frac{x_i + y_i}{2} \qquad y_{i+1} = \frac{N}{x_{i+1}}$$

When $|x_i - y_i| < \epsilon$, the desired accuracy has been obtained. The flow diagram for this loop is shown in Figure 16.

C. Programming Languages

Automatic programming techniques have been developed which can significantly aid in the programming of digital computers. These techniques, or languages as they are called, can enable computer instructions to be written in a format that is somewhat more familiar to the user than is the actual machine language itself. These automatic languages accept instructions for the computer in general terms and compile from them the specific list of instructions that the computer will actually perform step by step. Machine programs have to be written to transform from the automatic language to the machine's language; such programs are called compilers (see also Chapter 11). The automatic language itself may be designed for ease in programming special problems; in such a case it is often called a problem-oriented language. In this section, we shall briefly attempt to describe one particular automatic programming language called ALGOL (algorithmic language).[4,10]

We will begin by describing in general what an ALGOL instruction or statement looks like. Since the purpose of ALGOL is to describe computational processes, arithmetic expressions will be involved and an instruction or statement of the language, called the assignment statement, will be illustrated. The arithmetic expression is composed of combinations of the arithmetic operations with numbers, variables, and functions; the assignment statement, containing within it an arithmetic expression, tells the computer to proceed with the performance of the computations indicated by that arithmetic expression. As an illustration of how the language works, consider the following simple example of a code to compute a root of $Ax^2 + Bx + C = 0$ for $A = +3$, $B = +1.7$, and $C = -0.31$. One of the two roots is given by the well-known formula

$$x = \frac{-B + \sqrt{B^2 - 4AC}}{2A}$$

The code to evaluate the right-hand side of this equation becomes*

    A := 3;
    B := 1.7;
    C := −0.31;
    root := (−B + sqrt (B ↑ 2 − 4 × A × C))/(2 × A);
    stop;

The meaning of this jumble of symbols becomes more or less obvious with the following explanation. First the symbols demarcated by semicolons are *statements*. Statements are normally executed in sequence. The first three statements record the desired values of A, B, and C; the fourth statement computes the root; the last statement stops the routine. In this example, the *expressions* are A, 3, B, 1.7, C, −0.31, root, sqrt $(B \uparrow 2 − 4 × A × C)$, and stop; here $B \uparrow 2 − 4 × A × C$ is an arithmetic expression, or the whole collection

$$(−B + \text{sqrt}\ (B \uparrow 2 − 4 × A × C))/(2 × A)$$

can be considered an arithmetic expression. The numbers involved are 3, 1.7, −0.31, 2, and 4; the variables are A, B, root, and C; the function involved is sqrt; −, +, ↑, /, and × are the arithmetic operations. The automatic program that is to interpret this language compiles the appropriate instructions and, for the square root (sqrt), refers to the appropriate subroutine.

D. Description of the Language

Having given a brief illustration of what an ALGOL code looks like, we will now proceed to describe the language itself. Computer programming languages are "what to do" or "cookbook" languages. They are built up in a logical fashion by first describing the allowable letters, digits, punctuation marks, and so forth; symbols not included in the description of the language will not be recognized by the computer. These allowable *characters* can then be put together to form numbers, words, or phrases which are the *expressions* utilized in the language as illustrated above. The rules for forming these expressions must be adhered to strictly or again the computer will not be able to understand them. Finally, we come to the instructions, called *statements*, which involve the expressions. ALGOL includes only five basic types of statements which, when put together appropriately into a *program*, are sufficient to carry out any possible computational procedure. These

* Although ALGOL does not have a *stop* statement, we shall use it for pedagogical reasons.

statements are: 1) the *assignment* statement (as illustrated above); 2) the *go to* statement; 3) the *conditional* statement; 4) the *for* statement; and 5) the *procedure* statement.

1) The assignment statement is of the form

$$VAR := EXPR$$

where VAR represents a variable and EXPR can be an arithmetic or Boolean expression. This statement tells the computer to compute the value of the right-hand side and store that value (for example, a number) in the storage location designated by the left part, that is, to assign the value of the expression to the variable. The coloned equal sign, $:=$, is used to indicate that the left part is to be the name of the value of the right-hand side. If the expression is in terms of numbers, then the indicated operations will be performed. If the expression is in terms of letters, i.e., variables, the values of the variables will be first found by the computer and then the expression evaluated.

2) A *go to* statement interrupts the normal sequence of execution of successive statements by explicitly defining the label of the next statement to be executed. For example, if the next desired statement is not in normal sequence, and if its label or name* is L, then we would simply write

$$go\ to\ L$$

3) The purpose of the *conditional statement* is to enable the computer to make a decision based upon previously computed circumstances. The form of the conditional statement is

$$if\ BEXP\ then\ S$$

where BEXP is a Boolean expression, that is, can have the value true or false. For example, we could have a conditional statement of the form as

$$if\ (a > b),\ then\ S1;$$

$$S2;$$

This would mean that if the value of a was indeed greater than the value of b, then the next statement to be executed will be statement labeled S1. Otherwise, the next statement to be executed will be the next statement in natural order, labeled S2. This illustrates the basic means by which the computer makes decisions. The decision is really a branch point where the computer will execute one set of statements under one condition and another set of statements under another condition. If several statements are to be executed after *then*, we write: *then begin* S1; S2; ... ; SM *end*.

4) The purpose of the *for statement* is to enable iterations to be indicated in a simple but effective manner. The form of the statement is

$$for\ INDX := J\ step\ \Delta\ until\ T\ do\ S$$

where J, Δ, and T are arithmetic expressions, and S is a statement. Here the initial value of INDX is set to the value of J; the statement S is executed. Next a new value of J is computed as $J + \Delta$; if this new $J \leq T$, S is executed again using the new value of J; otherwise the statement following the *for* statement is executed next. If several statements are to be executed after *do*, then we write: *do begin* S1; S2; ... ; SM *end*. As an example of the use

---

* Statements themselves can be named. If the statement $A := 3$ is named L we would write L: $A := 3$.

of the *for* statement, suppose we desire to find the largest of three given (positive) numbers, N1, N2, and N3. We could write

$$LNC := 0;$$

$$for\ J\ :=\ 1\ step\ 1\ until\ 3\ do\ if\ LNC < N[J]\ then\ LNC := N[J];$$

$$stop;$$

Here LNC will be the name of the largest of the three numbers when it has finally been determined. We first try N1 as the largest of the three numbers (i.e., J = 1). Next (when J = 2) we try N2 by comparing it with N1 and replacing N1 by N2 if N1 < N2. Finally when J = 3 we try N3 to see if it is greater than the larger of N1 and N2.

5) A *procedure statement* tells the computer to execute a subroutine, i.e., another program which has been given a name. The form of the procedure statement is for example

$$PROCDR\ (DV,\ IV1,\ IV2)$$

where PROCDR is the name of the subroutine, DV is the dependent variable, and IV1, IV2 are the independent variables. If we had written a subroutine to evaluate $\sin \theta$ to an accuracy of ϵ, we might write

$$\sin\ (Y,\ \theta,\ \epsilon)$$

and the computer would execute the program to evaluate the $\sin \theta$ to an accuracy of ϵ and assign the result as the value of Y. This statement is important since it enables the use of *building blocks* when writing a complicated program. Small parts or pieces of the entire program can be written, and then all put together to comprise the final program.

Of course we have given here only a greatly oversimplified version of the language ALGOL. However, the concepts involved are those utilized in many automatic programming languages including FORTRAN.

E. *Simulation of Colloidal Sediment*

Colloids occur frequently among biological materials. As an example of a digital computer program, let us consider the program for the study of the sediment volume and sediment structure from dilute dispersions of spherical particles with strong interaction. A simplified description of the program will be presented here. This example has many characteristics frequently encountered in a biomedically oriented digital computer program as it necessarily involves a great number of detailed considerations; many variations of the initial assumptions must be tried (such as differences in the interaction forces assumed, shapes of particles considered, and so forth). It is a simulation of a system that involves random variables.

The problem is to simulate the formation of the sediment.[11] This is accomplished as follows: one particle at a time is "dropped" vertically into a container. For each particle the x and y coordinates from which it is dropped are chosen at random. The first few particles will come to rest on the bottom of the container. Other particles will come in contact with a previously dropped particle; and according to the assumed short-range large forces of our simple illustration, the one particle will cohere to the other on contact.

Figure 17 illustrates (in two dimensions) an example of the results of such a process, the

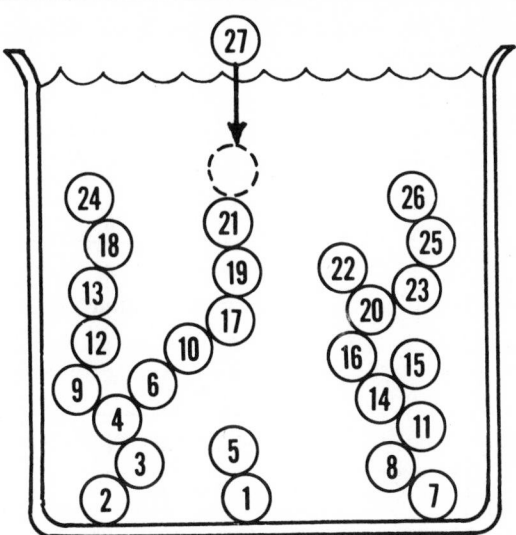

FIGURE 17. Diagrammatic illustration of results computed in a two-dimensional space, with circled numbers representing order in which sedimentating particles were "dropped" into solution.

number in each circle representing the order in which the particle was dropped. The figure illustrates the dropping of the 27th particle, which will cohere to the 21st particle in the position illustrated by the respective dotted circle. This is a physical model or picture of the formation of the sediment; the entire process is computed by the machine, with the final coordinates of each particle recorded (see discussion of flow chart below). When the process is completed an evaluation of the results must be made, a process also carried out by the computer. For example, the packing density, or volume per cent, of spheres in the formed sediment is calculated; the number of contacts that each particle makes with others can be calculated, and so forth. These results are compared with experiment.

A simplified flow chart appears in Figure 18. We start with a single particle of radius r placed at the bottom of the container: i.e., $z_0 = 0$ at $x_0 = 0$ and $y_0 = 0$. Within the loop, the x_k and y_k coordinates of the kth particle and its radius R_k are chosen at random from given distribution functions. As this particle falls through the solution, we desire to determine its final z coordinate when its motion is arrested as it coheres to the first particle it touches.

The first particle it touches on the way down will have two attributes: First, its x, y coordinates must be sufficiently close to the x, y coordinates of the kth particle for it to be hit by the kth particle; that is, the ith particle could be hit by the kth particle provided that $T^2 > D^2$, where $T^2 = R_i^2 + R_k^2$, and $D^2 = (x_k - x_i)^2 + (y_k - y_i)^2$. If the kth particle hits the ith particle, then the z coordinate of the kth particle will be $z' = z_i + (T^2 - D^2)^{1/2}$.

The second attribute is that, of all the particles satisfying the first attribute, the first particle touched must result in the largest z'. Naturally, for each k we need only try all particles already in solution, that is, all particles i for $i < k$, which accounts for the inner loop of the flow chart. The process stops when all n particles are dropped and their arrested positions recorded. The program must now evaluate the various properties of the resulting sediment. This is accomplished in a results-summary program, which we shall not describe here.

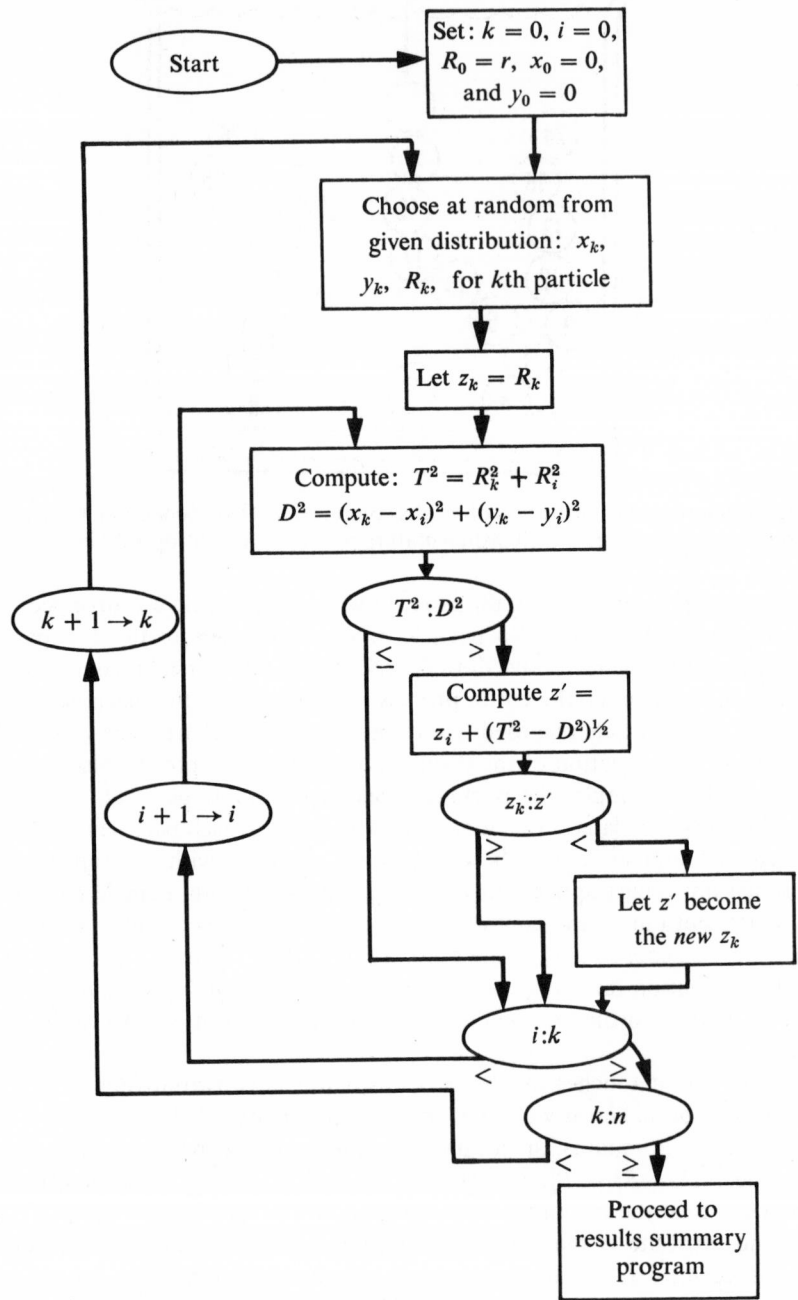

FIGURE 18. Flow chart for digital-computer simulation program to determine sediment volume and structure from dilute dispersions of spherical particles which cohere on first contact.

The ALGOL code for the diagram is as follows:

```
1  X[0] := 0,  Y[0] := 0;

2  For K := 0 step 1 until N do
3  begin X[K] := RAND;  Y[K] := RAND;  R[K] := RSPH
4  Z[K] := R[K]

5  for I := 0 step 1 until K do
6  begin TSQ := R[K]↑2 + R[I]↑2;
7  DSQ := (X[K] − X[I])↑2 + (Y[K] − Y[I])↑2;
8  if TSQ > DSQ then
9  begin ZE = Z[I] + sqrt(TSQ − DSQ);
10 if Z[K] < ZE then Z[K] := ZE end
11 end

12 end
```

For convenience in discussion we have numbered the different lines. Line 1 sets the initial conditions, where the number in the square brackets is the index. The K loop starts at line 2 and ends at line 12. The inside I loop starts at line 5 and ends at line 11. Note that the *begin* on line 3 corresponds to the *end* on line 12; the *begin* on line 6 corresponds to the *end* on line 11; and the *begin* on line 9 corresponds to the end on line 10. Note that, for example, R_k^2 is written as R[K]↑2, and so forth. Also we denote T^2 by DSQ, since T and D themselves are never explicitly utilized. The reader will greatly gain by tracing the loops of the code in conjunction with the flow diagram of Figure 18.

IV. APPLICATION OF COMPUTERS TO BIOMEDICAL SYSTEMS

A. Computer Aid to Primary Protein Structure Determination[2a,2b]

Finding the amino acid order of a protein chain has proved a time-consuming process for the biochemist; in fact, only a very few complete or almost complete protein orderings have thus far been found, e.g., those of insulin, hemoglobin, ribonuclease, tobacco mosaic virus protein, myoglobin, and cytochrome c. The basic technique used on all these proteins (with the exception of myoglobin) was to break down the long chain chemically into smaller fragment chains at several different points, to analyze the amino acids in each fragment chemically, and then to try to reconstruct the entire protein chain by a logical and combinatorial examination of overlapping fragments from the different breakdowns. It is in this reconstruction of the protein that the computer finds its application.

As a trivial example, suppose that for a protein one chemical breakdown produced the fragment chains of known ordering,

Breakdown P: AB,   CD,   and E

where A, B, C, D, and E each occurs once and only once in the protein. Let us call this a complete breakdown, and let another breakdown, this time incomplete, produce the fragments

Breakdown Q: BC   and   DE

where A, B, C, D, and E represent amino acids. Here fragment BC in Breakdown Q clearly overlaps the two fragments AB and CD of Breakdown P, and DE overlaps CD and E of breakdown P, giving as the reconstructed protein

ABCDE.

As another example, consider the more common case, where the amino acid components of a fragment are known, but the order of these within the fragment is unknown. Let parentheses indicate that the order they enclose is unknown (for example, (A,B,C) represents the six permutations of A, B, C; (D,E) represents either DE or ED; (A,B,C) (D,E) represents the 6 × 2 = 12 fragments of each of the six permutations in (A,B,C) followed by DE or ED, etc.), and suppose that one complete breakdown is

Breakdown P: (A,B,C)   and   (D,E)

and that another, incomplete, breakdown is

Breakdown Q: (A,B)   and   (C,D)

Clearly (C,D) of breakdown Q overlaps (A,B,C) and (D,E) of breakdown P, but (A,B) is contained within (A,B,C). Hence, since each amino acid has distinct "left" and "right" ends, two possible protein reconstructions result, namely

(A,B)(C)(D)(E)   and   (E)(D)(C)(A,B)

where in each possibility the order of A,B still remains unknown. Such partial reconstructions frequently occur, and pinpoint for the biochemist that portion of the molecule on which further effort is required.

Unfortunately, however, the problems involved in reconstructing proteins are not as simple as in the examples just given. Among the largest proteins analyzed, the tobacco mosaic virus protein has only 158 amino acids, whereas proteins usually have chains of many hundreds of amino acid links. Since the number of combinations on n things taken r at a time $(1 < r < n)$ increases more rapidly than does n itself, it is to be expected that the difficulties in piecing together the fragments of a protein will increase proportionally faster than the number of amino acids in the protein. In addition, there may be occasional errors in the fragments reported by the biochemist, as well as other aberrations in the data. Hence the logical and combinatorial problems can become severe, and a computer is then required to assist in the analysis.

The advantage of computer aid is that it may help significantly to extend the current chemical analysis methods of determining the amino acid sequences of proteins to many more and much larger proteins. By exhaustively analyzing the possibilities of protein reconstructions, the computer may assist in determining the best next step to try in the chemical analysis processes. In addition, it should be noted that presently the chemical analysis is carefully planned to produce results that will be logically simple for mental analysis. The use of a computer to perform the logical analysis may thus allow significant simplification and further systematization of the chemical experimental procedures by placing more of the burden on the automated logical and combinatorial analysis and less on the experimental procedures.

Discussion of the programming methods utilized can best be illustrated by a simple example. Suppose a complete breakdown P is made by the biochemist as in Figure 19, and that another breakdown Q is also known but not complete (see Figure 19). In Figure 20

	Complete breakdown	Incomplete breakdown
	P LIST	Q LIST
	p_1 (R)(A,B)	q_1 (A)(B,B,D)
	p_2 (D)(B)(C,A)	q_2 (A)(C,A,C)
	p_3 (A)(C)(D)(X,A)(C)	q_3 (X)(A,C,B)
	p_4 (B)(D)(B)(D)(A,B,D)	q_4 (B)(A,A,C,D)
	p_5 (C)(A)(Z)	q_5 (A)(B,C,D)

FIGURE 19. Breakdowns of protein fragments for the example given in the text. (From Dayhoff and Ledley.[2a])

we show how such breakdowns P and Q can occur from our hypothetical protein, but the problem is to reconstruct this from the fragments given in Figure 19. Since each fragment q_i of breakdown Q must either overlap several fragments of P, or else be included within some fragment of P, let us start by making a list for each q_i of all possible such associated P fragments; Figure 21 shows such lists for our illustration. As an example of how each entry in a list is found, consider the test of whether or not q_4 overlaps p_4p_5 (see Figure 19).

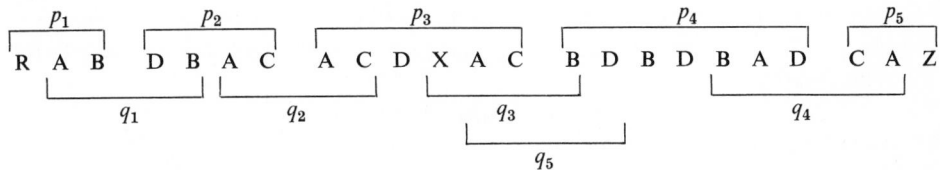

FIGURE 20. Illustration of sources of peptide fragments from protein molecule discussed in the text. (From Dayhoff and Ledley.[2a])

q_1	q_2	q_3	q_4	q_5
p_1p_2	p_2p_3	p_3p_4	p_1p_3	p_1p_2
p_1p_4	p_2p_5		p_4p_3	p_2p_4
p_2p_4	p_3p_5		p_4p_5	p_3p_2
p_4p_2				p_3p_4
				p_4p_2
				p_4p_5

FIGURE 21. The q list for the example in the text. (From Dayhoff and Ledley.[2a])

The problem is to determine if each acid of q_4 can be accounted for in p_4 and p_5. First note that the maximum overlap between q_4 and p_4 is (B,A,D), on the right of p_4. This leaves (A,C) of q_4 "hanging over" on the right of q_4, to be accounted for in p_5. This is clearly possible, resulting in the overlap:

p_4	p_5
(B)(D)(B)(D)(B)(A,D)	(C)(A)(Z)
(B)(A,D)	(C)(A)

$$q_4$$

In order to determine all the entries in all the lists, such trials must be made by the computer for every pair of fragments p_ip_j, for each q_k.

However, just forming the lists is but the first step in reconstructing the protein chain. The next step is an elimination process to leave only the consistent possibilities. For instance, q_3 can only arise from p_3p_4; hence p_3 must be followed by p_4, and p_4 must be preceded by p_3, and therefore all other possibilities in other lists involving p_3 and p_4 can be eliminated—such as pairs p_1p_4 and p_2p_4 in the q_1 list of Figure 21, p_3p_5 in the q_2 list, p_4p_3 in the q_4 list, and p_2p_4 and p_3p_2 in the q_5 list.* This leaves in the list for q_1 only p_1p_2 and p_4p_2. If we first assume that p_1p_2 is overlapped by q_1, then in the q_4 list only p_4p_5 remains, and hence in the q_2 list only p_2p_3 remains, giving altogether these adjacent fragments

$$p_3p_4 \quad p_1p_2 \quad p_4p_5 \quad \text{and} \quad p_2p_3$$

which determine the structure as

$$p_1p_2p_3p_4p_5$$

On utilizing p_1, p_2, p_3, and p_4 we find as the final structure:

$$(R)(A)(B)(D)(B)(A)(C)(A)(C)(D)(X)(A)(C)(B)(D)(B)(D)(B)(A,D)(C)(A)(Z)$$

If we return to the second possibility in the q_1 overlap list, namely p_4p_2, this leaves only p_1p_3 in the q_4 list, which in turn leaves only p_2p_5 in the q_2 list. Hence a second possibility for adjacent fragments is

$$p_3p_4 \quad p_4p_2 \quad p_1p_3 \quad \text{and} \quad p_2p_5$$

which gives the structure

$$p_1p_3p_4p_2p_5$$

On utilizing q_3, q_2, q_4, and q_2, the structure is found to be

$$(R)(B)(A)(A)(C)(D)(X)(A)(C)(B)(D)(B)(D)(D)(A)(B)(D)(B)(A)(C)(C)(A)(Z)$$

The problems involved in writing a computer program, however, are not as straightforward as the above illustration might indicate. The biochemist utilizes enzymes to break up (hydrolyze) the protein into the fragments that we have been considering; these fragments are called peptides by the biochemist. The enzymes commonly used, such as subtilisin and chymotrypsin, produce an assortment of peptides which may overlap each other. Hence a problem arises in actually arriving at a complete set of peptide fragments, as illustrated above in the breakdown P. In addition, for several reasons, the biochemical experiments very often do not result in integral values for the number of amino acids of a particular kind that occur in a peptide fragment. This second uncertainty problem must also be taken into account by the computer program. Furthermore, there may be experimental errors in the amino acid composition and ordering of some peptides.

In the case of overlapping peptide fragments from a hydrolytic breakdown, the computer program tries to reconstruct a complete set of fragments from overlapping subsets of fragments. The procedure of accomplishing this is to look for every group of two, three, or four acids known to be adjacent in some peptide. Then, for each such group, the probability that this particular group will occur again in the protein chain is computed

---

* Actually, it is also necessary to eliminate the occurrence of p_4 in the lists by replacing it with p_3^*, which stands for p_3p_4. This is to insure that an impossible succession of conditions such as p_1p_2, p_2p_3, p_3p_1 is not produced.

from the amino acid frequency data. For instance, if the ordered pair *LYS-PHE* occurs, and it is known that there are five *LYS* residues and four *PHE* residues in the entire protein chain of, say, 150 amino acid links altogether, then the probability that another such *LYS-PHE* pair will occur is approximately $4 \times 3/150$.

If the probability is small that another such group occurs, it is most likely that all of the peptides containing this group would arise from the same part of the protein; hence these peptides are sorted out. All possible fragments that can be reconstructed from these (overlapping) peptides are then determined.

It may happen, however, that all these peptides cannot "fit" into any reconstructed fragment; this indicates either that some peptide must arise from a different place on the protein or that there may be an experimental error. In such a case the experimental results are reconsidered from a chemical point of view.

Of course, there is a small but finite probability that a misinterpretation can be made at this point and an erroneous peptide constructed, such as could happen if a highly unlikely configuration actually occurred more than once in the protein or if there were lost peptides from a particular region but the existing peptides fortuitously fit. However, in any case, it is likely that in a later building up of the protein, an inconsistency would arise, leading to the rejection of this erroneously constructed peptide.

Further details must be taken into consideration by the program; the set of fragments may still not be complete; there may exist alternative possibilities for a fragment; and there may be gaps in the chain where all the peptides were lost.

After obtaining a complete, or almost complete, set of fragments by iteration of the searching procedure, the program can continue toward reconstructing the entire protein utilizing the remaining peptides not used in the building up of the complete set P as the Q set of peptides (see example above).

Note that in the various phases of the reconstruction of the protein the assumption is made that the total amino acid content of the entire protein and of the fragments is known. There is always, however, some experimental uncertainty in the number of amino acids of each type in the protein, to within a fraction of one amino acid. As a rule, the larger number of amino acids is always chosen initially. If an extra acid is thereby included in the computations, it may be eliminated at the end, by an additional procedure.

The programming system is based on the following six programs:

1) MAXLAP: Program to find the maximum possible overlap between any two peptides with any amount of ordering information known.

2) MERGE: Program to find all possible overlapping configurations of two peptides.

3) PEPT: Program to find all possible fragments that are consistent with the overlapping of any number of peptides.

4) SEARCH: Program to search on probabilistic considerations all peptides which contain an unusual group of amino acids.

5) QLIST: Program to generate the Q-lists of possible associated sets of P peptides over which q_i fragment can fit.

6) LOGRED: Program to perform the logical reduction of the Q-lists to obtain all possible protein structures that are consistent with the data.

The computer programming system to aid protein analysis has been written in a flexible manner. The computer input and output is in terms of three-letter abbreviations for the amino acids, with the parentheses notation for ordered and unordered sets as described above. Intermediate results are printed out for examination by the biochemist; in fact, the entire process is geared for a close cooperative effort between the computer and the biochemist during the entire analysis. This is necessary in order to take advantage of the special conditions presented by any particular protein and type of chemical experimental procedures.

B.   Computer Analysis of Photographic Data*

A large amount of important biological data is recorded in the form of pictures, such as photomicrographs, electromicrographs, cineradiographs, et cetera.   Although   much

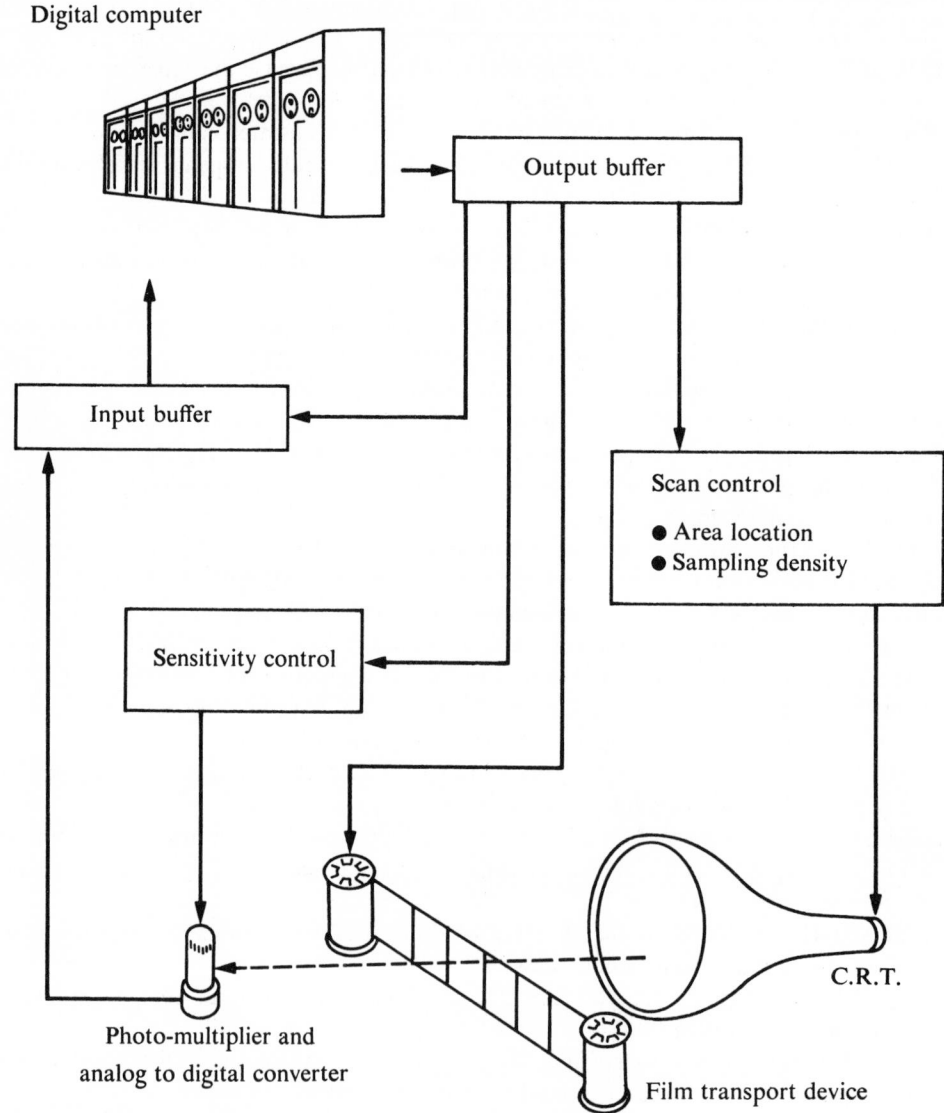

FIGURE 22.   Film scanning device.

* Developed at the National Biomedical Research Foundation by R. S. Ledley, L. S. Rotolo, J. B. Wilson, and G. Cheng, under National Institutes of Health Grants GM–10789, GM–10797, and NB–04472.

quantitative data is embodied in these photographs, until the present time methods for extracting such data have not been entirely successful. The reason for this is that manual methods are so slow and tedious that they limit the extent to which the analyses can be made. Examples of such attempts to extract biological data from pictures are analyzing chromosome photographs, tracing axons and dendrites of nerves, studying the flow of red blood cells through capillaries, and analyzing patterns in electronmicrographs.[6a,6b]

To make the quantitative processing of such pictorial data automatic, a so-called "picture scanner" can be utilized, in conjunction with a computer, in a closed-loop system as shown in Figure 22. The purpose of such a setup is to enable a computer program to direct the analysis of pictorial information in successively more detailed stages, in order more effectively to extract the required quantitative data. As an example, let us suppose we wish to determine the area of a particle in the nucleus of a cell, as shown in Figure 23. The computer program first would direct the picture scanner to make a gross scan to determine the location of the nucleus of the cell in the picture. Next, a finer, more detailed scan would be made of the nucleus to determine the location of the particle of interest. Finally, the computer program would direct the picture scanner to make a fine scan over the particle, from which the area of the particle would be determined.

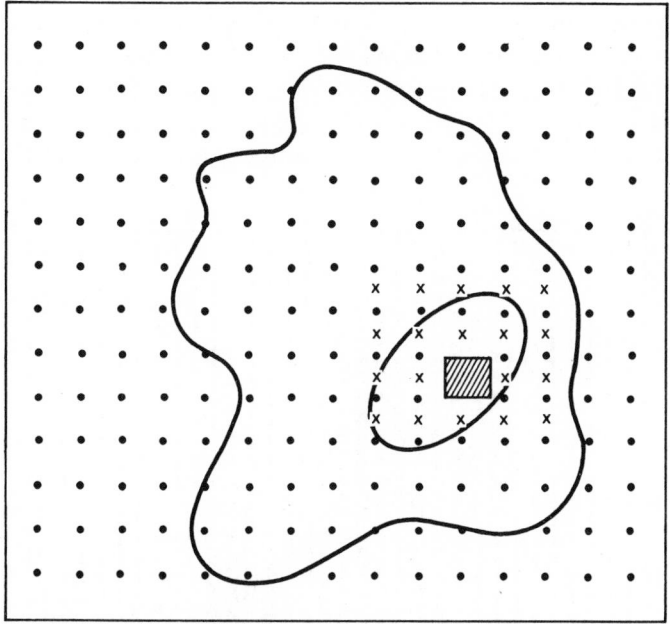

• • • Thin scan

x x x Particular area

▨ Detailed examination

FIGURE 23. Frame scanning of several sorts.

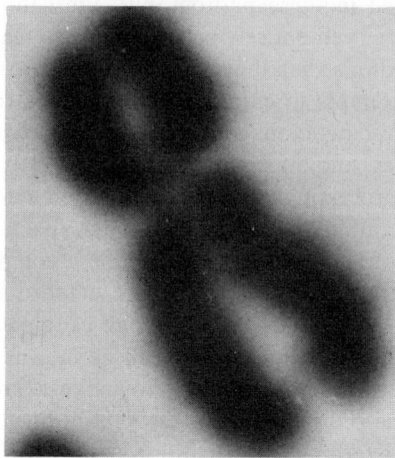

FIGURE 24.   Picture of a chromosome.

The reason for using successive scans, rather than recording the entire picture in the computer's memory, is that the number of bits required to record the film frames would saturate the computer's memory. Alternatively, only about ten frames of film could be recorded on a magnetic tape, and then access to different parts of the picture in its magnetic-tape representation would be very time-consuming. Hence the technique of using the picture itself as a memory and successively scanning appropriate parts will lead to greater efficiency.

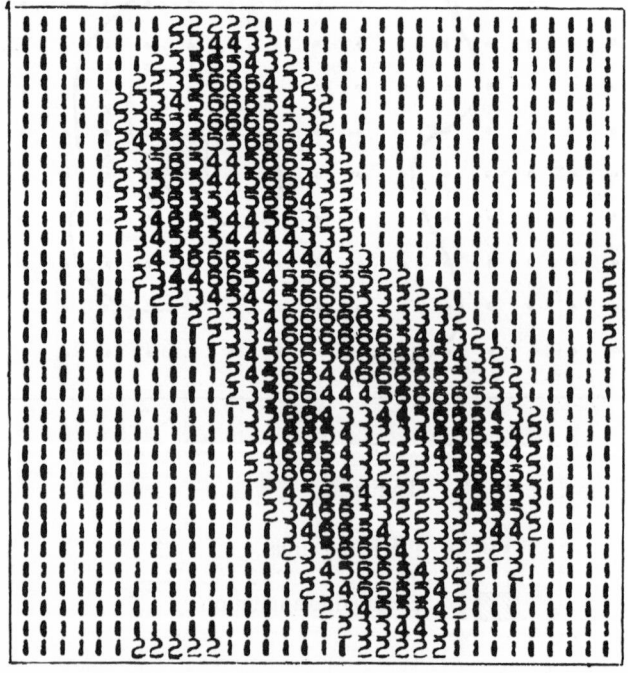

FIGURE 25.   Representation of Figure 24 in computer memory.

Type A   Type B   Type C   Type D   Type E

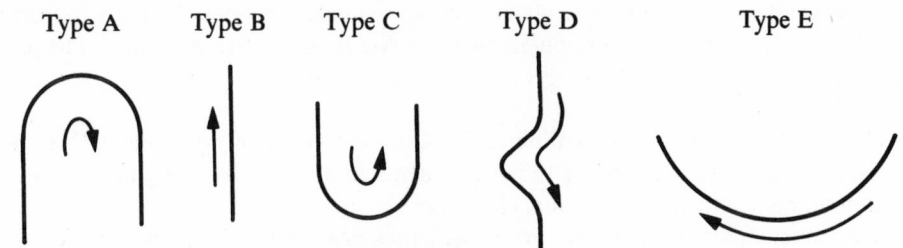

FIGURE 26. Five types of lines that may be recognized by the "bug."

To be more specific, consider the problem of analyzing chromosomes. After a scan, the picture is recorded in the computer memory as a large array of numbers which denote the density of the pictures at the position of the number. Figure 24 overlaid on Figure 25 illustrates a picture of a chromosome and its representation in the memory. The problem then becomes one of interpreting this array of numbers to elicit facts about the chromosomes. For simplicity in discussion, we have distinguished only black (a unit) and white (a zero), although the picture-scanning device can in general distinguish eight different gray levels.

One approach to the picture analysis makes use of a so-called bug that can walk from number to number and remember all it has seen, but can only see in advance one number at a time. This is called the line analysis technique. Another approach makes use of so-called globs in which areas of the picture are analyzed. Both techniques have their applications; however, here we will limit our illustration of picture analysis only to the line or bug analysis technique.

The picture processing actually occurs in two conceptual steps. In the first step, component shapes such as curved lines, straight lines, et cetera, are recognized. In the second step, relationships between these component parts are recognized. For example in Figure 26 we show five types of lines that may be followed and then recognized by the bug. Figure 27 illustrates schematically how two chromosome configurations can be thought of as composed of these five types of curves, where the bug walks around the boundary always

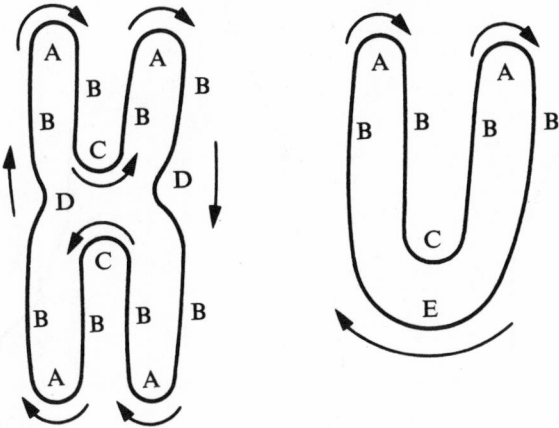

FIGURE 27. Composition of chromosomes from the five types of lines.

in a clockwise direction. We have illustrated the sequence of symbols that would characterize the relationships of the component parts for two types of chromosomes. The problem is therefore reduced to the following sequence of operations:

1) Locate a chromosome.
2) Have the bug follow the outline and record the types of component lines it sees.
3) Examine the relationships of the components and recognize the chromosome type.
4) Determine length measurements, et cetera.

As a component part is identified, its coordinates are recorded. Hence, once we have recognized the type of chromosome, we have already identified the location of its different parts, and therefore all measurements and other information that may be required can now be obtained, such as chromosome arm lengths, arm length ratios, et cetera.

To locate a chromosome the bug walks systematically across the rows of numbers starting on the top, until it finds a nonzero cell. The bug then begins to walk around the object along successive boundary points. The basic concept utilized in the recognition of the component curves along the boundary is that of observing successive chords. As the bug progresses these chords are drawn along the boundary, each chord spanning three boundary points. Since the bug is moving around the object in a clockwise direction, the chords are directed—that is, they can be represented by arrows (see Figure 27).

When successive chords turn on a curve of Type A, some chord will eventually be in a direction approximately opposite to some previous chord (see Figures 26 and 28). This will also be true of curves of Type C, the only difference between curves of Types A and C being that the arrows will turn in a clockwise direction for Type A, and a counterclockwise direction for Type C. Lines of Type B will be recognized when successive arrows are approximately parallel in the same direction. As each component curve is recognized, its name is added to the list of symbols that will characterize the chromosome.

After a chromosome is bordered by the bug, recognized, and its measurements computed and recorded, the chromosome is erased from the computer's memory. This erasing process is necessary so that this chromosome will not be examined again by mistake. The technique for erasing an already processed chromosome is as follows. During the processing, the bug follows the boundary of the chromosome, and changes the value of these

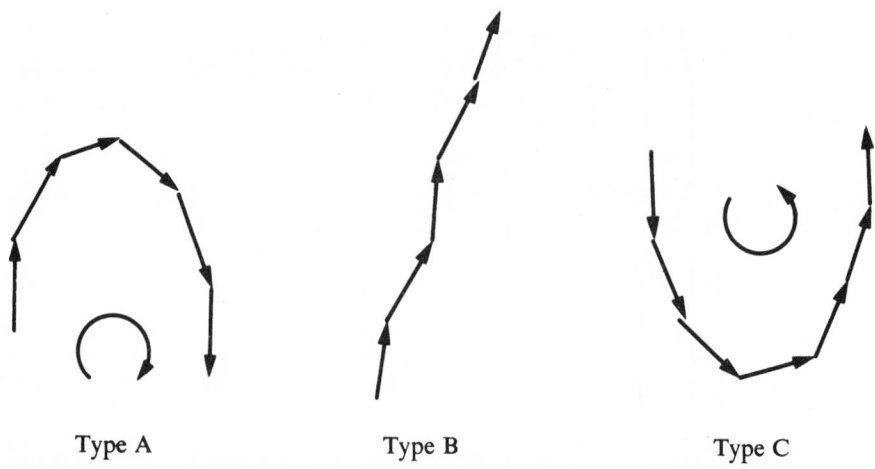

Type A   Type B   Type C

FIGURE 28.   Chords as arrows following boundary.

boundary points to seven. By the time the entire boundary has been traversed, all of the boundary points will have value seven. Next all members in a row between sevens are erased, including the sevens, where by "erased" we mean that these points are changed to value zero. A little reflection will show that this technique can only be used for figures that have no holes.

We have briefly illustrated but a few of the many concepts that were developed for the processing of photomicrographs of chromosomes. By these means the computer program can count, recognize, determine arm length ratios, find the coordinates, and otherwise discriminate among all chromosomes in a photomicrograph. The program will work even if there is dirt on the slide or other artifacts in the chromosome picture. Once the component curve types have been recognized, the procedure for recognizing the chromosome itself is a simple analysis according to flexible criteria. Many different kinds and shapes of chromosomes can be recognized by the same program simply by adding further definitions of component-part relationships to the list.

C. *Computer Aids to Medical Diagnosis*[8,9]

1. *Symptom-disease complexes and medical knowledge.* Before using a computer to aid in various aspects of making a medical diagnosis, the medical diagnosis process itself must first be systematically analyzed and formalized so that a computer program can be written. We will here consider such an analysis or systematic formalization of the reasoning that enters into a medical diagnosis. This analysis is an example of a sequential decision theory that utilizes several different mathematical disciplines, integrated into an over-all, self-consistent, stage-by-stage method of deductive inference. The methods described here represent a general approach to problems involving identification of a system as a representative of one or more already defined classes. The method of solution to this type of problem can have wide application to such biological sciences as taxonomy, virology, agronomy, ecology, and so forth.

In our medical diagnostic context, mathematical logic (the propositional calculus) may be employed in order to make a computer list diagnostic possibilities for the symptoms presented by a patient. The use of logic for this purpose is closely related to the concept of symptom-disease complexes (sdc's). A symptom complex is a list of the symptoms that a patient does and does not have; a disease complex is a similar list of diseases. A symptom-disease complex is a list of both symptoms and diseases that a patient does and does not have. For example, consider Figure 29, where for simplicity our attention is limited to two symptoms, $S(1)$ and $S(2)$, and two diseases, $D(1)$ and $D(2)$. Each column represents a symptom-disease complex: a unit in the row signifies that the patient has the corresponding symptom or disease, and a zero signifies that the patient does not have the symptom or disease. The columns represent all conceivable sdc's that can be formed from

$$
\begin{array}{llllll}
S(1) & 1111 & 1111 & 0000 & 0000 \\
S(2) & 1111 & 0000 & 1111 & 0000 \\
D(1) & 1100 & 1100 & 1100 & 1100 \\
D(2) & 1010 & 1010 & 1010 & 1010 \\
\end{array}
$$

FIGURE 29. Logical basis for two symptoms, $S(1)$ and $S(2)$, and two diseases, $D(1)$ and $D(2)$. (From Ledley and Lusted.[7])

two symptoms and two diseases. Thus the outlined column represents the symptom-disease complex of the patient having symptom $S(1)$, not having $S(2)$, having $D(1)$, and having $D(2)$.

We use the phrase "all conceivable sdc's," but not all of these are possible, or actually occur. It is medical knowledge that informs us of which sdc's do or do not occur. For example, suppose that for the particular symptoms and diseases under consideration, medical knowledge informs us that if a patient does not have $D(1)$ and does not have $D(2)$, then he cannot have $S(1)$ and he cannot have $S(2)$, or conversely. Such a statement can be symbolized in terms of mathematical logic as

$$\overline{D(1)} \cdot \overline{D(2)} = \overline{S(1)} \cdot \overline{S(2)}$$

where the bar "$\overline{}$" represents *not* and the dot "$\cdot$" represents *and*. The effect of such a statement of medical knowledge is to eliminate from consideration some of the conceivable sdc's which are not possible. For example, the following columns

$S(1)$	110	000
$S(2)$	101	000
$D(1)$	000	110
$D(2)$	000	101

represent the sdc's that cannot happen according to our rule of medical knowledge; the left-hand three columns represent sdc's for which the patient has no diseases but does have the symptoms, and the right-hand three columns represent sdc's for which the patient has no symptoms but does have the diseases. In Figure 30 these columns have been crossed off.

Suppose, for example, that another assertion of medical knowledge is that if the patient has disease $D(2)$, then he must have symptom $S(1)$, which can be symbolized as

$$D(2) \rightarrow S(1)$$

This means that in addition the sdc's having $D(2)$ but not having $S(1)$ cannot occur, for they are contrary to the assertion of medical knowledge. These columns have also been crossed off in Figure 30.

The logical effect of medical knowledge is to reduce the totality of all conceivable sdc's to those which are possible or compatible with the assertions embodied in medical knowledge. Figure 31 represents all possible sdc's for our illustrative situation. In general

$S(1)$	1111	1111	0000	0000
$S(2)$	1111	0000	1111	0000
$D(1)$	1100	1100	1100	1100
$D(2)$	1010	1010	1010	1010

FIGURE 30. Reduced logical basis resulting from the application of medical knowledge. (From Ledley and Lusted.[7])

S(1)	111	111	0	0
S(2)	111	000	1	0
D(1)	110	110	1	0
D(2)	101	101	0	0

FIGURE 31. Reduced logical basis. Column in the rectangle represents the case of a patient's having symptom S(2) but not symptom S(1). (From Ledley and Lusted.[7])

medical knowledge is stated in the form of our second assertion: if the patient has a certain disease complex, then he can have some set of symptom complexes. This is why most medical textbooks are organized by diseases and discuss symptoms associated with each disease.

2. *Listing diagnostic possibilities.* Suppose a particular patient presents a symptom complex as follows: the patient does not have symptom $S(1)$ but does have symptom $S(2)$. Written symbolically, this is $\overline{S(1)} \cdot S(2)$. To make the diagnosis, we look at Figure 31, which contains all possible sdc's, for those columns which contain the symptom complex $\overline{S(1)} \cdot S(2)$. There is only one such column, namely, the seventh.

Thus, the logical analysis informs us that the patient with symptom complex $\overline{S(1)} \cdot S(2)$ has disease complex $D(1) \cdot \overline{D(2)}$, i.e., the diagnosis is that the patient has disease $D(1)$ but not disease $D(2)$. Suppose another patient presents $S(1) \cdot S(2)$. Columns 3, 4, and 5 contain this symptom complex.

Thus the patient may have both $D(1)$ and $D(2)$, or only one of them. This means that the symptoms considered in this case are insufficient to distinguish between $D(1)$, $D(2)$, or both $D(1)$ and $D(2)$. Therefore, the logical analysis can result in a list of possible diagnoses consistent with the symptoms presented by the patient.

A more formal statement of our logical analysis is as follows: Let $D(1)$, $D(2)$, . . . , $D(n)$ be the diseases under consideration, and let $S(1)$, $S(2)$, . . . , $S(m)$ be the symptoms under consideration. Then medical knowledge appears as a Boolean function

$$E = E[D(1), \ldots, D(n), S(1), \ldots, S(m)]$$

The symptom complex of the patient is the Boolean function

$$P = P[S(1), \ldots, S(m)],$$

and the logical aspect of the medical diagnostic problem is to determine a function

$$f = [D(1), \ldots, D(n)]$$

of the list of diagnostic possibilities such that the following Boolean equation is satisfied:

$$E \rightarrow (P \rightarrow f)$$

where $\rightarrow$ indicates *implies*.

3. *Probability in medical diagnosis.* Frequently it is unfeasible or undesirable to make further tests to distinguish between alternative possible diagnoses. The problem then resolves itself into answering the question: In the light of the patient's present symptom complex, what is the probability that he has a particular disease complex? We are asking

for a conditional probability: Given the patient's symptom complex s_j, what is the probability of his having a disease complex d_i? This is frequently denoted by $P(d_i \mid s_j)$, where the symbol to the right of the bar is the condition, and the symbol to the left of the slash is the occurrence whose conditional probability is desired.

The well-known Bayes' formula offers important information concerning the composition of $P(d_i \mid s_j)$:

$$P(d_i \mid s_j) = \frac{P(d_i)P(s_j \mid d_i)}{\sum\limits_{\substack{\text{all} \\ k}} P(d_k)P(s_j \mid d_k)}$$

where $\sum\limits_{\text{all } k}$ indicates a summation over all possible disease complexes d_k. Since the denominator merely acts as a normalization factor, let us focus our attention on the two terms in the numerator, namely,

$$P(d_i)P(s_j \mid d_i)$$

The term $P(s_j \mid d_i)$ is the probability of having the symptom complex s_j when it is known that the patient has the particular disease complex d_i. This is precisely what is described in medical textbooks when a particular disease is under consideration. Of course, textbooks do not at the present time assign numerical values to $P(s_j \mid d_i)$, but they do state that associated with a certain disease particular symptoms are common, frequent, rare, etc. The reason for discussing $P(s_j \mid d_i)$ rather than $P(d_i \mid s_j)$ is that the etiology of the symptoms is related to, or stems from, the disease. Thus $P(s_j \mid d_i)$, that is, the symptoms resulting from a disease, is a constant for the particular disease complex under consideration, being relatively independent of other circumstantial factors.

On the other hand, consider the term $P(d_i)$. This is the probability that of the particular population of patients involved, any particular patient has this disease complex d_i. By "particular population of patients," we mean that population from which the patients can be considered as chosen at random in the technical sense. For example, the population may be that of the entire United States, or that of a particular clinic in a particular hospital, etc.; in each case, $P(d_i)$ will, in general, be different. This term relates the influence of geographical, seasonal, epidemiological, social, and other such factors to the diagnosis. Thus in the tropics one is more apt to find tropical disease; during an Asian flu epidemic, the symptoms of a cold are more likely to be relegated to Asian flu; some diseases, like poliomyelitis, have a seasonal variation, et cetera. A little reflection indicates clearly that both these factors—the circumstantial or local, and the constant relating to the disease-symptom syndrome—influence the diagnosis.

As we have noted, the statistics in which we are interested, for instance, $P(d_i \mid s_j)$, reflect local changes in place and time, and therefore must be collected locally. In order to be valid, however, "sufficiently large" samples must be used, which may not be available locally. Bayes' formula comes to our aid under such circumstances, for it is clearly not necessary to have as large a sample to determine $P(d_i)$ as to determine $P(d_i \mid s_j)$. Thus, since $P(s_j \mid d_i)$ is a constant, independent of local conditions and time, nationwide statistics collected over a long period of time can be used for this purpose. Then, locally, only $P(d_i)$ need be derived from collected data, and Bayes' formula used to determine $P(d_i \mid s_j)$. Notice also that the collection of statistics locally to calculate $P(d_i)$, where no symptoms enter, is a relatively simple process. Thus the use of Bayes' formula presents important practical advantages.

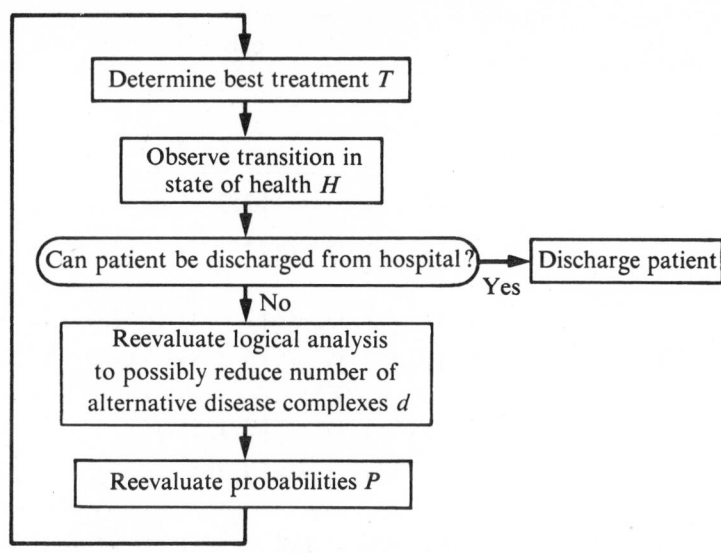

FIGURE 32. Flow chart of the dynamic diagnostic-treatment cycle. (From Ledley.[4])

4. *The diagnostic-treatment cycle.* A medical diagnosis and treatment plan is usually provisional; that is, a tentative diagnosis is made and a possible treatment plan initiated. Then after an appropriate time the effect of the treatment is noted, as well as any additional symptoms, and a new diagnosis with a modified treatment plan is instituted. The cycle continues until the patient is cured (see Figure 32). The reasons for such an iterative method are three-fold. First, rarely is a definite unequivocal diagnosis made initially, and hence as more information is gathered in the form of further symptoms or more test results, the diagnosis can be re-evaluated and made more precise. Second, the effect of the treatment on the patient can itself be an important symptom and can lead to further restriction of the possible diagnostic alternatives. Third, and perhaps most important, a single course of therapeutic measures often will be insufficient; rather, a treatment plan is formulated which may involve a sequence of therapeutic measures with periodic re-evaluation as new information is obtained.

Four types of factors are involved in this dynamic diagnostic-treatment cycle. First, there is the patient's state of health, which is to be described as one of several possible health states, each characterized by values of the patient's various physiological indexes. Second, there is the possible choice of treatments. Third, there is the probability of transition from one state of health to another under the applied treatment. And fourth, there is the value to the patient of the state of health transition. For example, suppose that four states of health of the patient can be distinguished: H_1, cured; H_2, good; H_3, poor; H_4, critical. Suppose also that there are two possible treatments T_1 and T_2 that can be given for each state of health. For each of the possible diseases d_r that the patient may have, let $p(j \mid i, k, r)$ and $v(j \mid i, k, r)$ be the transition probability and value, respectively, of going from state of health H_i to state H_j under treatment T_k. If we are concerned with only two diseases, say d_1 and d_2, then we would have the table of Figure 33 for each disease.

5. *Application of dynamic programming.* An optimum treatment plan is one that maximizes the value to the patient of the treatment sequence. The introduction of values into the problem is important, because it is not necessarily true that the treatment sequence that

State of Health	Treatments	Probabilities and values			
		to H_1	to H_2	to H_3	to H_4
H_1: cured					
H_2: good	T_1	$p(1\mid2,1,1)$ $p(2\mid2,1,1)$ $p(3\mid2,1,1)$ $p(4\mid2,1,1)$ $v(1\mid2,1,1)$ $v(2\mid2,1,1)$ $v(3\mid2,1,1)$ $v(4\mid2,1,1)$			
	T_2	$p(1\mid2,2,1)$ $p(2\mid2,2,1)$ $p(3\mid2,2,1)$ $p(4\mid2,2,1)$ $v(1\mid2,2,1)$ $v(2\mid2,2,1)$ $v(3\mid2,2,1)$ $v(4\mid2,2,1)$			
H_3: poor	T_1	$p(1\mid3,1,1)$ $p(2\mid3,1,1)$ $p(3\mid3,1,1)$ $p(4\mid3,1,1)$ $v(1\mid3,1,1)$ $v(2\mid3,1,1)$ $v(3\mid3,1,1)$ $v(4\mid3,1,1)$			
	T_2	$p(1\mid3,2,1)$ $p(2\mid3,2,1)$ $p(3\mid3,2,1)$ $p(4\mid3,2,1)$ $v(1\mid3,2,1)$ $v(2\mid3,2,1)$ $v(3\mid3,2,1)$ $v(4\mid3,2,1)$			
H_4: critical					

FIGURE 33. Table of factors required for disease d_1, four states of health, and two possible treatments.

will cure the patient most quickly, or most economically, et cetera, is the best. Clearly the optimum treatment plan can depend on intangible as well as tangible values, and rests on the patient's particular circumstances. Also, almost all treatments involve certain risks; and hence a greater risk may be of greater value for a patient in a very poor state of health than for a patient not so critically ill. In any event, if we know the probability of transition from one health state to another under alternative treatments, and if we also know the alternative values, then we can try for a sequence of treatments that will optimize the expected value of the cure to the patient.

To do this we apply R. Bellman's "principle of optimality," which is as follows: Let $V_i(n)$ be the total expected value obtained in n cycles, starting from H_i, if an optimum sequence of treatments is chosen at each cycle; then

$$V_i(n-1) = \max_k \sum_j p(j\mid i, k, r)[v(j\mid i, k, r) + V_j(n)]$$

Thus if an optimum sequence of treatments has already been chosen for the final n cycles, then the principle describes how to choose the optimum treatment for the previous cycle, that is, how to choose that treatment T_k which results in the maximum $V_i(n-1)$.

Two problems remain. First, how many cycles do we plan for? And second, we have only stated the result for d_r; what about the other diagnostic possibilities? To solve the first of these problems, numerical calculations show that for a single diagnosis d_r, as the treatment is computed for earlier cycles, in most cases one treatment choice will predominate over all others; the cycle at which this predominance takes place determines an appropriate N, or number of cycles to plan for. If we do this for each of the alternative possible diagnoses d_r we obtain a collection of numbers N_r; the number of cycles to plan for is then

$$N = \min_r N_r$$

To solve the second problem, let p_r be the probability that the patient has disease d_r. Then we compute expected value $E_i^k(n)$ as

$$E_i^k(n) = \sum_r \{ p_r \sum_j p(j \mid i, k, r)[v(j \mid i, k, r) + V_i^r(n)] \}$$

The $V_i^r(n)$ are computed for d_r, as described above. Then the treatment of choice in the nth cycle is that T_k for which $E_i^k(n)$ is a maximum. At the next cycle, a re-evaluation of the p_r is made; and

$$E_i^k(n + 1) = \sum_r p_r \sum_j p(j \mid i, k, r)[v(j \mid i, k, r) + V_i^r(n + 1)]$$

is evaluated for each T_k to determine the next treatment, and so forth.

6. *Treatment evaluation.* Our above discussion implies that to make a treatment plan the probabilities $p(j \mid i, k, r)$ and $v(j \mid i, k, r)$ must be known. Of course, such probabilities and values currently are rarely known in quantitative form; but we believe that they are now taken into account qualitatively, even if not in as systematic a procedure as dynamic programming dictates. However, if a treatment is to be evaluated, then the theory indicates that the first step is to determine $p(j \mid i, k, r)$, that is, to evaluate statistically how effective the treatment is with respect to the disease process, irrespective of the value problems involved. If the treatment proves effective then the second step is to evolve guides for estimating $v(j \mid i, k, r)$, that is, to classify circumstances as advantageous and disadvantageous to the use of the treatment, through clinical experience.

Consider in more detail the meaning of $p(j \mid i, k, r)$. If the patient is now in health state H_i, then $p(j \mid i, k, r)$ is the probability that the patient will move to state H_j. That is, $p(j \mid i, k, r)$ is the conditional probability of the patient's moving to health state H_j, given that he is now in health state H_i, will receive T_k, and has disease d_r. Thus $p(j \mid i, k, r)$ is a predictive probability which is used directly in evaluating the treatment. However, consider the meaning of $p(i \mid j, k, r)$. If the patient is now in health state H_j, then $p(i \mid j, k, r)$ is the probability that the patient was in health state H_i. That is, $p(i \mid j, k, r)$ is the conditional probability that the patient was in state H_i, given that he is now in state H_j, has received treatment T_k, and has disease d_r. Thus $p(i \mid j, k, r)$ is an *a posteriori* probability, which, since it can be calculated after the fact, is easier to determine statistically. Again using Bayes' formula, namely

$$p(j \mid i, k, r) = \frac{p(j \mid k, r)p(i \mid j, k, r)}{\sum\limits_{\substack{\text{all} \\ j}} p(j \mid k, r)p(i \mid j, k, r)}$$

permits the desired probabilities to be calculated from those that are easier to obtain. Here $p(j \mid k, r)$ is the ratio of the number of patients in health state H_j after receiving the treatment T_k to the total number of patients who have received the same treatment (all of whom have disease d_r, of course).

Conditional probabilities can also be utilized for a comparison of two treatments, say, T_k and $T_{\hat{k}}$. For example, let H_j be a cured state of health, and $H_{\hat{j}}$ be a sick state. Then the two ratios

$$\frac{p(j \mid i, k, r)}{p(j \mid i, \hat{k}, r)} \quad \text{and} \quad \frac{p(\hat{j} \mid i, \hat{k}, r)}{p(\hat{j} \mid i, k, r)}$$

will be much larger than unity if the treatment T_k is better than $T_{\hat{k}}$. Here $\hat{k}$ refers to the other treatment, and $\hat{j}$ means that the patient will not move to health state j. However, since it is easier to compile *a posteriori* probabilities, we can use the following formulas:

$$\frac{p(j \mid i, k, r)}{p(j \mid i, \hat{k}, r)} = \frac{p(j \mid k, r)p(i \mid \hat{k}, r)p(i \mid j, k, r)}{p(j \mid \hat{k}, r)p(i \mid k, r)p(i \mid j, \hat{k}, r)}$$

$$\frac{p(\hat{j} \mid i, \hat{k}, r)}{p(\hat{j} \mid i, k, r)} = \frac{p(\hat{j} \mid \hat{k}, r)p(i \mid k, r)p(i \mid \hat{j}, \hat{k}, r)}{p(\hat{j} \mid k, r)p(i \mid \hat{k}, r)p(i \mid \hat{j}, k, r)}$$

V. ROLE OF COMPUTERS IN BIOMEDICAL RESEARCH

The use of computers will undoubtedly revolutionize the theoretical approaches, the experimental methods, and indeed the very nature of biomedical research. Quantitative theoretical techniques that heretofore were limited almost exclusively to the physical sciences will now become feasible through the aid of computers. Complicated experimental procedures that involve measurement and control of a large number of factors and inter-relationships now can be formulated by including the computer in the experimental design. Thus biomedical problems, which until recently were far beyond the reach of realistic consideration, can now be studied.

For convenience we can discuss the role of computers in biomedical research in terms of five basic (but inevitably overlapping) categories; in our above discussions we have presented a concrete illustration for each of these categories. The categories (and the illustrations presented above, are these:

1) Solution to rate equations associated with biomedical processes (for example, flow equations for heart and circulatory system).

2) Simulation of biomedical systems (for example, simulation of colloid sedimentation).

3) Nonnumerical biomedical data analysis (for example, aids to the analysis of primary protein structure).

4) Biomedical picture-data processing (for example, analysis of chromosome preparations).

5) Processing biomedical data (for example, aids to medical diagnosis).

Rate equations arise in many diverse aspects of biological and medical research. Initial approximation studies of many systems can be made by means of linear differential rate equations, as was illustrated for the heart and circulatory system. Multiple reaction rate problems arise in the exploration of certain metabolic processes: here sets of equations are used to determine intermediate reactions from a knowledge of experimentally determined final rates. Radioactive tracing techniques for metabolic studies depend on solutions to rate equations: here the amount of radioactive substance would be measured, as a function of the time, in such "compartments" as the blood, body organs, feces, and excreted urine; from such data appropriate fractional-turnover rate equations are solved for the rate constants themselves.

The analysis of genetic control mechanisms is an important example of the use of rate equations in biological research: here the equations express the relationships between the synthesis of protein enzymes by the genetic material and the feedback effects of these enzymes in inhibiting protein production, and also in inhibiting the production of the inhibitory enzymes themselves. In all such cases the use of computers is almost always mandatory if numerical results and over-all systems behavior are to be critically studied.

The technique of system simulation frequently presents the only approach to the study of highly involved biological phenomena. For example, even in the apparently simple problem of predicting the properties of a colloid sediment, a detailed molecule-by-molecule simulation, as described above, presented the only accurate method of approach. In general, computer simulations are required in cases where a great deal is known about the local-component aspects of a large system and it is desired to study how these many complicated parts combine to produce the behavior of the whole system; hence the purposes and uses of a computer simulation are to enable 1) the study of a complicated system as an integrated result of many individual, interacting component parts, 2) the evaluation of the relative influence of each small component on the whole system, 3) the testing of hypotheses about a part of a system for consistency with known data about the whole system, and 4) the designing and planning of future, more critical experiments concerning still unknown components of the system.

In particular, many of the physical and chemical characteristics of biological phenomena can be studied only by considering individual molecular reactions. An important method for studying such complicated phenomena is the so-called Monte Carlo simulation, which in most instances can only be carried out on an electronic digital computer. With the Monte Carlo method, the random effects of individual molecular motions, of collisions, and of chemical reactions and force interactions can be simulated, according to some assumed model, and the over-all statistical responses of the system can be predicted, to be compared with experimental results. Our above colloid-sedimentation example illustrated the Monte Carlo technique. It has also been used to analyze enzyme systems, cell division, tumor growth, migration patterns, the spread of disease, self-organizing neural nets, and other diverse aspects of biomedical research.

Biomedical research frequently presents problems of a nature not generally found in other sciences. An example is nonnumerical data-processing problems. Here the biological problems being attacked can be structured only by abstract logical or qualitative relationships, and the system must be handled in these nonnumerical terms. In referring to "logical" or "qualitative" relationships, we do not mean to imply "imprecision" or "variability"; on the contrary, the relationships involve operations that are logical or qualitative rather than numerical, but these operations and the structures developed with them are precisely defined. The aids to protein structure determination discussed above are one example of nonnumerical data processing. Many other problems of this type arise—for example, in exploring possible three-dimensional molecular configurations of proteins or other polymers, in constructing molecular models by computer-aided synthesis, in characterizing functional-behavior relationships in terms of factors of brain capabilities, in understanding the pattern-recognition and concept-formation mechanisms of organisms, and so forth.

The technique for computer analysis of pictorial information of biomedical importance, which we described briefly above, can, we believe, open up entirely new fields in biological and medical research. The method presents a new tool for the biomedical research worker, which can be likened to, say, the electron microscope, in that new areas of research now become feasible, new experimental approaches can be planned, and new methods of analysis can be attacked. In the case of the electron microscope, it is perhaps not too bold to state that none of its present-day applications were predicted by its original inventors; carrying our analogy a bit further, it is similarly almost impossible to foresee the eventual applications in biomedical research of computer-aided picture-data processing. However, it can be predicted that one of the most important applications of computers in biomedical research will be in this area of pictorial analysis.

Biomedical data processing is a large field for computer applications. Of these applications, many are in the straightforward statistical analysis of medical records, experimental results, and other such information. Computers are aiding in the evaluation of new drugs, in the correlation of diseases with various possible etiologies, in studies of the effectiveness of new cures and preventatives, and so forth. However, a large number of data-processing problems in biomedical science require the development of new methods of approach. For example, computer aids to taxonomy require new techniques for eliciting "clustering" tendencies of large masses of data on characteristics of certain animals or plants (Chapters 8 and 9 discuss this from a statistical point of view); the analysis of electroencephalograms requires new correlative procedures for isolating the signals from background noise; and ecological research on marine-life requires new techniques for systematically organizing and retrieving large masses of collected data for studying environmental effects on evolution. Similarly, the problem of making a medical diagnosis and formulating a treatment plan requires a new synthesis of analytic methods, as described above.

VI. CONCLUSIONS

The use of computers in biomedical science vastly increases the researcher's capabilities in approaching the exceedingly complicated and extensive computations so frequently required for investigation of the more modern mathematical, biochemical, and biophysical concepts. The computer makes feasible approaches to problems that could not otherwise be solved; it opens up entirely new methods of biomedical investigation; and it holds promise for assisting in the more efficient utilization of research results. Although there presently exists great interest in the use of computers among biomedical research workers, we are only on the threshold of understanding their full potential capabilities.

REFERENCES

1. Computer Center Research and Educational Activities, MIT, Cooperating Colleges of New England, Semi-Annual Report, No. 10, Jan. 1, 1962.
2a. Dayhoff, M. O., and Ledley, R. S. 1962. Comprotein: A computer program to aid primary protein structure determination. *In:* "Proc. Fall Joint Computer Conf.," *AFIPS Conf. Proc.* **22:** 262–274.
2b. Dayhoff, M. O. 1964. Computer aids to primary structure determination. *J. Theoret. Biol.* (In press.)

3. Ledley, R. S. 1959. Digital electronic computers in biomedical science. *Science* **130:** 1225–1234.

4. Ledley, R. S. 1962. "Programming and Utilizing Digital Computers," Chapter 6, pp. 193–239. McGraw-Hill, New York.

5. Ledley, R. S. 1965. "Use of Computers in Biology and Medicine," McGraw-Hill, New York. (In press.)

6a. Ledley, R. S., et al. 1963. Digest of Papers Presented to the 16th Annual Conference on Engineering in Medicine and Biology.

6b. Ledley, R. S. 1964. High-speed automatic analysis of biomedical pictures. *Science* **146:** 216–223.

7. Ledley, R. S., and Lusted, L. B. 1951. The role of computers in medical diagnosis. *Med. Documentation* **5:** 70–78.

8. Ledley, R. S., and Lusted, L. B. 1959. Reasoning foundations of medical diagnosis. *Science* **130:** 9–21.

9. Ledley, R. S., and Lusted, L. B. 1962. Medical diagnosis and modern decision making. *In:* "Proc. Symp. Applied Math., 14th, 1961," (R. Bellman, ed.), pp. 117–158.

10. Naur, P. (ed.) 1960. Report on the algorithmic language ALGOL. *Commun. Assoc. Computing Machines* **3:** 299–314.

11. Vold, M. 1959. Sediment volume and structure in dispersions of anisometric particles. *J. Phys. Chem.* **63:** 1608–1612.

12. Warner, H. 1959. The use of an analog computer for analysis of control mechanisms in the circulation. *Proc. IRE* **47:** 1913–1916.

[11]

COMPUTER SIMULATION IN BIOCHEMISTRY AND ECOLOGY

David Garfinkel*

I. INTRODUCTION

Biological systems are extremely complex almost by definition, and predicting their quantitative behavior is often a difficult undertaking, as we have already seen in many of the preceding chapters. When the prediction required is of behavior as a function of time, it is often necessary to solve a system of differential equations. If such a system of equations represents any but the simplest biological system, it will probably be too complicated to solve with pencil and paper (either exactly—to yield an analytical solution—or by approximation methods), and must accordingly be solved by some type of computer.

In the case of relatively simple systems (for instance, biochemical systems involving a few enzymes) it has been feasible to conduct such studies with analog computers. Analog computation applied to biochemistry has led to results of importance in the theory of enzyme kinetics,[18,19a] and a useful model of photosynthesis has been constructed.[9] Specialized analog computers have been constructed to represent alveolar ventilation,[1] for instance.

An analog computer has two serious limitations (see also Chapter 10). It is limited by the fact that differential equations are physically represented in the hardware of the computer (integrators, multipliers, et cetera). Adding an additional equation to a system requires assigning additional hardware for it. As the systems studied become more complex, the amount of hardware available soon becomes limiting. It is limited also in that the user himself must perform the necessary information conversions; first he must describe the biochemical system he is studying in terms of differential equations, and then he must physically wire the analog computer to represent those differential equations. Between these two limitations the analog computer cannot represent biological systems of any real complexity. Probably the largest analog computers presently in existence would have difficulty in simulating in detail an enzymatic pathway such as glycolysis.

It has proved necessary to use digital computers to represent the behavior as a function of time of biochemical systems complex enough to have biological significance.[21] The two disadvantages of the analog computer can be overcome here. As a digital computer is not merely a faster adding machine and does much more than calculate, it can easily be made to

* This chapter was prepared during the tenure of a Research Career Development Award from the U.S. Public Health Service.

write almost all of its own detailed program. The memory size of existing digital computers is far greater than that of existing analog computers, and still is increasing rapidly; it can also be extended by the use of auxiliary memory devices, such as disc files, much more easily than the size of an analog computer can be increased by multiplexing.

The following is a description of methods that have been evolved for using digital computers to simulate biological systems and their behavior, as well as some of the results obtained by these methods.

II. DIGITAL COMPUTER METHODS

A. *Application to the Law of Mass Action*

One of the fundamental laws of chemistry is the law of mass action which states that the rate of a reaction

$$A + B \rightarrow C + D$$

is proportional to the concentrations of A and B, with a proportionality constant which is usually called a rate constant (Chapter 4). From this law one can derive a system of differential equations describing the behavior, as a function of time, of a system defined by such a set of chemical equations. In order to write these equations, solve them, and manipulate the results automatically, a series of computer programs has been prepared which collectively may be described as a *problem-oriented language*. These permit a chemist to state a problem in approximately his own language, except for some necessary artificial requirements, have the computer solve it, and return an answer which is readily comprehensible to him.

The computer must translate the chemist's problem into its own language in order to perform the necessary calculations, and this task is performed by a *compiler*. The general definition of a compiler is "a computer program which accepts its input information in some language other than that of the computer in question and not closely resembling it and translates it into computer instructions which are subsequently executed." Detailed descriptions of the system of compilers and other programs which make up this problem-oriented language have been published[12,13a,22] and only a brief exposition is necessary here.

To the chemical reaction

$$A + B \rightarrow C + D$$

correspond the differential equations

$$-\frac{d(A)}{dt} = -\frac{d(B)}{dt} = \frac{d(C)}{dt} = \frac{d(D)}{dt} = k(A)(B)$$

where (A) is the concentration of A, et cetera.

The compiler upon receiving chemical equations will prepare a list of all the chemicals mentioned, in the order in which they are mentioned, and assign each an address in memory. It will then prepare a set of instructions to evaluate the product or *flux*, $k(A)(B)$, for each reaction in the system. The machine then goes through the list of chemicals; for each chemical it will check through all the reactions, and upon finding one in which that chemical appears or disappears, it will write instructions to add in, or subtract out, the flux product for that reaction. These last two sets of instructions together give the relationship between the chemical concentrations and their derivatives, and in effect define the differential equations, one for each chemical.

This subprogram is accompanied by other programs to read in the initial values for rate constants, concentrations, et cetera, put them in their proper places in memory, normalize them by dividing by scale factors (this is a method of treating all concentrations as if they had values less than one because the Univac I and II computers employed cannot easily represent numbers greater than one), solve the differential equations, translate the results into a graphical plot of concentration against time, and perform further analysis with the results. In the actual process of solving differential equations the emphasis has been on simplicity and speed rather than accuracy, since one is in general simulating systems whose behavior can be measured only to within 2–3%. In order to use computer time effectively, the size of the integration steps is varied so as to keep the error of computation constant. Thus the steps are made much larger when the curves of concentration against time approach straight lines.

Some stress has been laid upon analysis of the presence and extent of steady states. This is important in the theory of enzyme kinetics[18] and is of great physiological importance, as living organisms spend most of their lives in steady states and come to equilibrium only at death. Recognizing steady states is a form of "pattern recognition," presently a subject of great interest in the computer field. The basic pattern of the steady state is that although chemical concentrations may change, the second derivatives (rate of change) of the concentrations are small. At equilibrium, all derivatives become zero.

This is not a sufficiently precise definition to be useful to a computer, and several more explicit criteria have been developed[12] to enable the computer to determine when a steady state exists. Two of these are illustrated in Figures 1 and 2 which represent graphs of

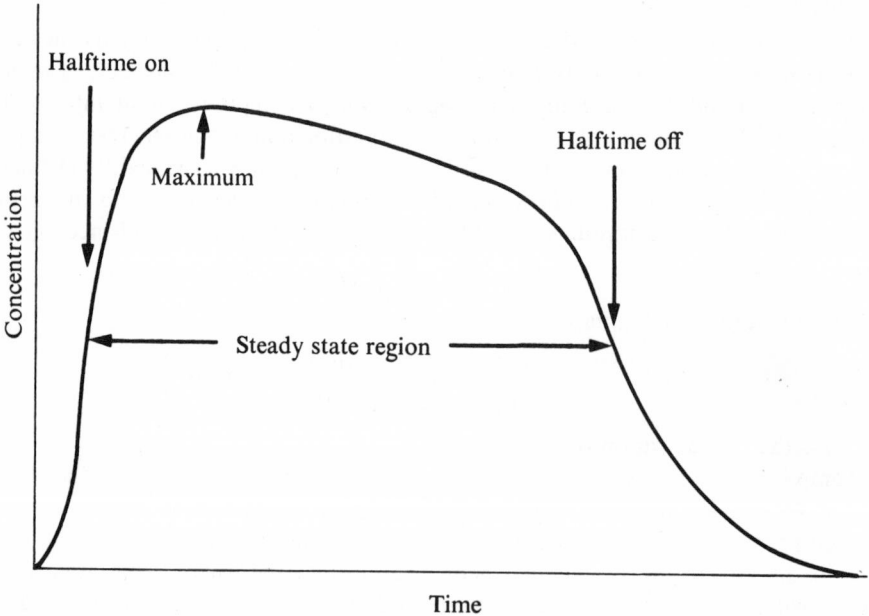

FIGURE 1. Method of defining steady states from halftimes. For one chemical the steady state region is the region between the times when the concentration has risen to half its maximum value and when it has fallen to half its maximum value again. For the entire system the steady state region is the logical intersection of the regions for the several chemicals. (From Garfinkel, et al.[12])

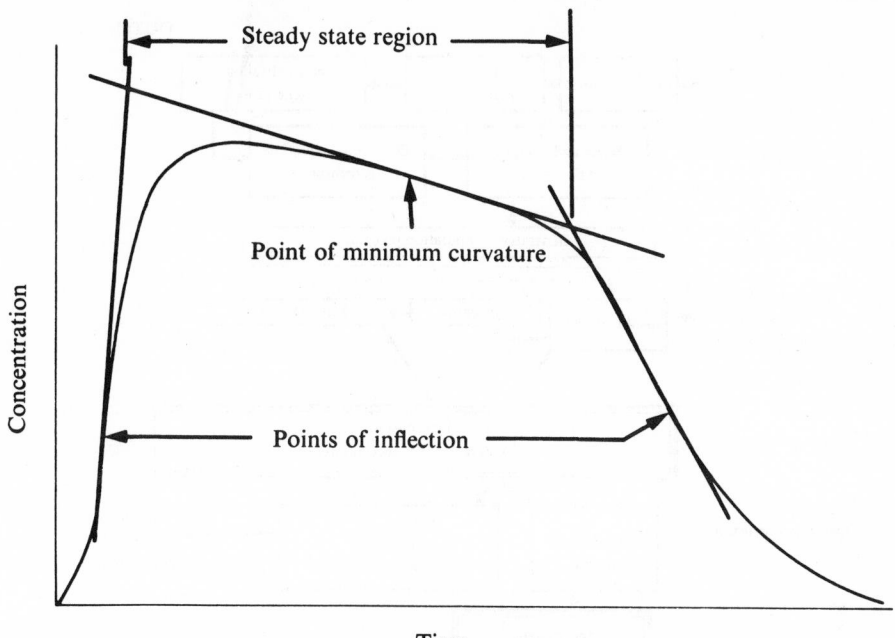

FIGURE 2. Method of finding steady states from intersection of tangents drawn at the inflection points and minimum curvature point. Their two points of intersection mark the beginning and end of the steady state for the chemical in question. These are combined as for the halftime method. (From Garfinkel, et al.[12])

concentration against time for an enzyme-substrate complex in a typical enzymatic system. Such a system as usually studied initially contains only free enzymes; when substrate is added, an enzyme-substrate complex is formed, increases in amount with time, reaches a maximum, and then decreases, slowly at first and then faster. The steady state region is approximately the region of the maximum and slow decrease.

An over-all *flow chart* for the entire system of programs which have been prepared for the Univac I and II is shown in Figure 3.

B. Monte Carlo Application to Bound Systems

Real systems, unfortunately, do not necessarily obey the mass action law, as this law applies only to systems that are in true solution, and not always then. For instance, there are biochemical systems that are bound to membranes or exist as solid structures; the cytochrome systems are an important example. A program to deal with this situation has been prepared by J. D. Rutledge, P. Markstein, and D. Irving (unpublished). It represents individual molecules in the memory of the computer, and in this case the IBM 7090 was used instead of the Univac I and II because of the limited memory of the latter. This program is similar to the other one in that it constitutes a problem-oriented language, although it does not include as great an array of result-processing routines. In this case the compilation and computation steps are not separate as they are in the Univac program; both the chemical equations and the initial conditions are fed in together.

Instead of writing differential equations this program sets up in the memory of the computer itself an array of numbers representing molecules, each duplicated a sufficient number

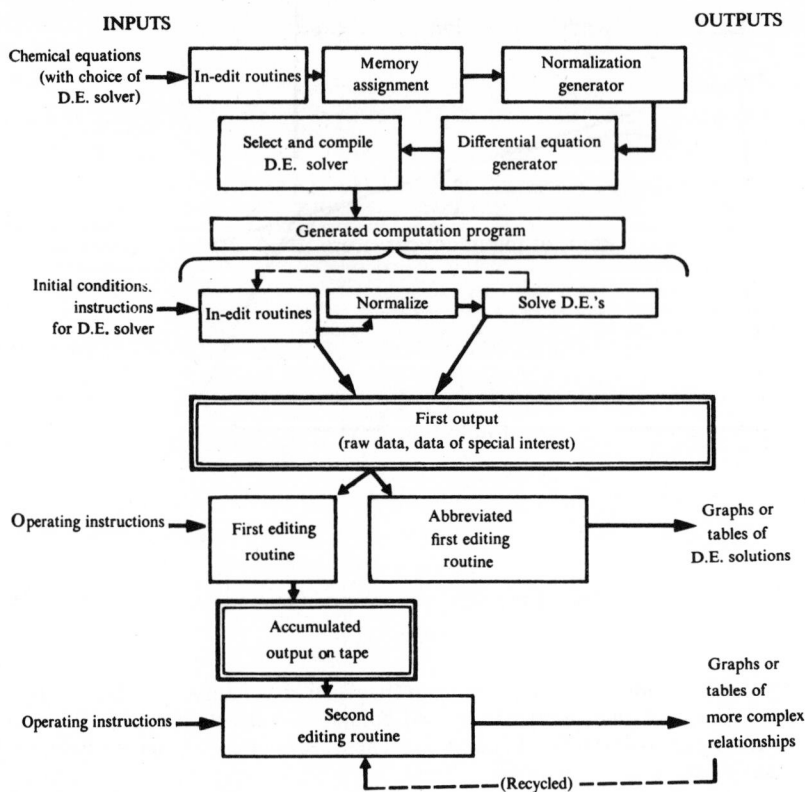

FIGURE 3.   Over-all chart of the Univac I program.   (From Garfinkel, et al.[13a])

of times, usually about 1000, to smooth out statistical noise.   Each of these "molecules" may exist in as many possible states as are needed for the particular problem, up to a maximum of thirty-two.   When a molecule is changed in a chemical reaction, the state number in the memory is changed correspondingly.   From the conditions existing at any time, the machine calculates out the probabilities of all reactions and transitions, and then determines whether each one took place by taking a random number.   It records all changes made as a result and then proceeds to the next iteration, to calculate probabilities, take random numbers, et cetera.   This routine will handle reactions of molecules purely in solution which do obey the mass action law as described above, and also reactions of molecules which are in solutions with molecules which are not.   This type of computation is designated "Monte Carlo," and was originally invented for studies of neutron diffraction.

These two methods of representing biochemical systems are not mutually exclusive.   The Monte Carlo routine can represent systems which do obey the mass action law; in effect, the computation degenerates to an inefficient process of solving differential equations.   And it has been shown[20] that bound chemical systems can be represented in terms of differential equations, but the number of equations required is large.

The principal application of the Monte Carlo routine thus far has been to cytochrome systems, especially the mitochondrial cytochrome complex.   This system as it exists in reality is quite similar to its representation in the computer, as it has been found[7] that each mitochondrion contains about 17,000 cytochrome chains, each consisting of the several cytochromes and associated molecules, such as flavoprotein. Electrons are transmitted down these chains. In the computer representation, each chain is represented as a series of cytochrome "molecules" which are allowed to react with each other and which may assume "oxidized," "reduced," and "inhibited" states. Such a representation transmits electrons down the chain, and differences in behavior from the true solution (mass-action) system have been observed.

Perhaps the most thorough study[6] using this method has been of the simplest of the bound cytochrome systems, microsomal cytochrome b_5. In this case the mechanisms of the reactions involved have been worked out in detail[26,27] and accordingly a reasonable representation of the entire system is possible. It has been found experimentally (M. Klingenberg, unpublished observations) that the bound cytochrome system behaves like a membrane-bound system rather than a mass-action system. The difference is most easily shown in a Lineweaver-Burk type plot (1/reaction velocity against 1/substrate concentration), as illustrated in Figure 4. A mass-action system yields nearly a straight line whereas the bound system yields a curved line similar to that obtained experimentally.

At present the Monte Carlo computer program described above has not been used nearly as much as the program for studying soluble reactions. It can be applied not only to further

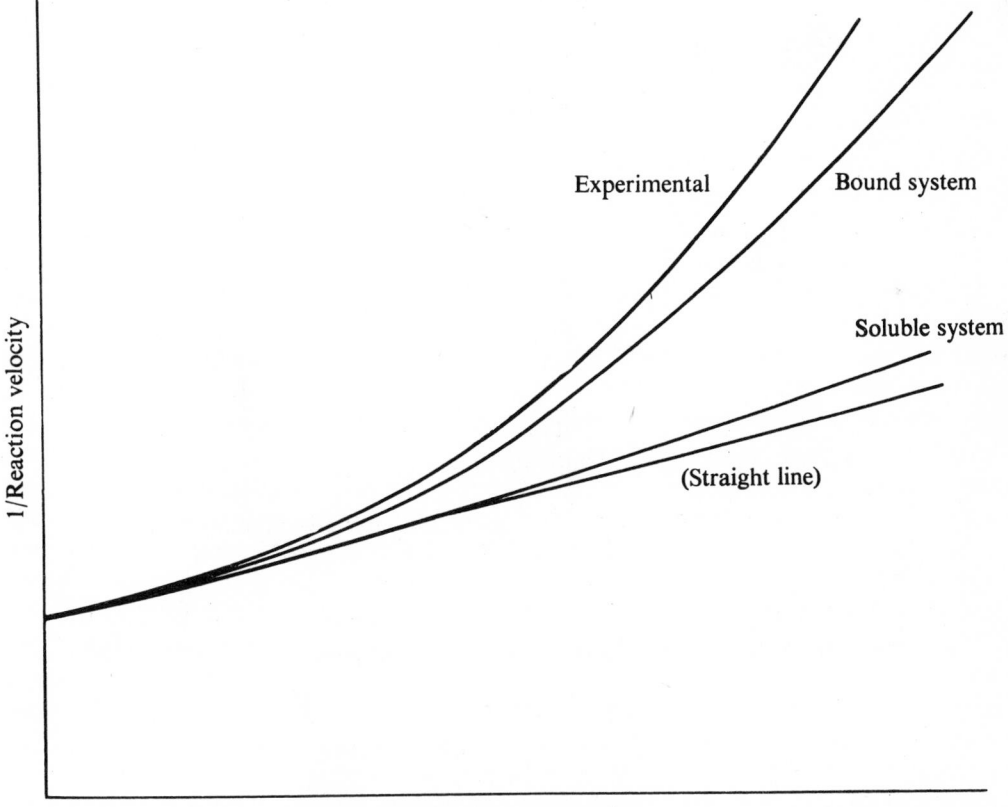

FIGURE 4. Lineweaver-Burk plot for the microsomal DPNH-cytochrome c reductase system. The "soluble" curve was calculated with paper and pencil, the "bound" curve with the IBM 7090.

studies of bound cytochrome systems, but to such systems as chromosomes interacting with soluble proteins and small molecules.

III. BIOCHEMICAL APPLICATIONS

Recent developments in biology, especially biochemistry, are leading to the accumulation of large amounts of quantitative data. This information is in many forms and from many sources. Although systems analysis and related fields (Chapter 12) are moves in this direction, there is no presently existing body of theory of the organization of biological systems which permits assembling this information into a coherent whole. Furthermore, the amount of information on any given item of interest may easily be too large for the unaided human mind to handle readily. As a computer can manipulate a larger amount of information than a man, but in a limited number of ways only, it may be able to give valuable assistance here. Hence the current interest in the construction of models of biological systems with computers.

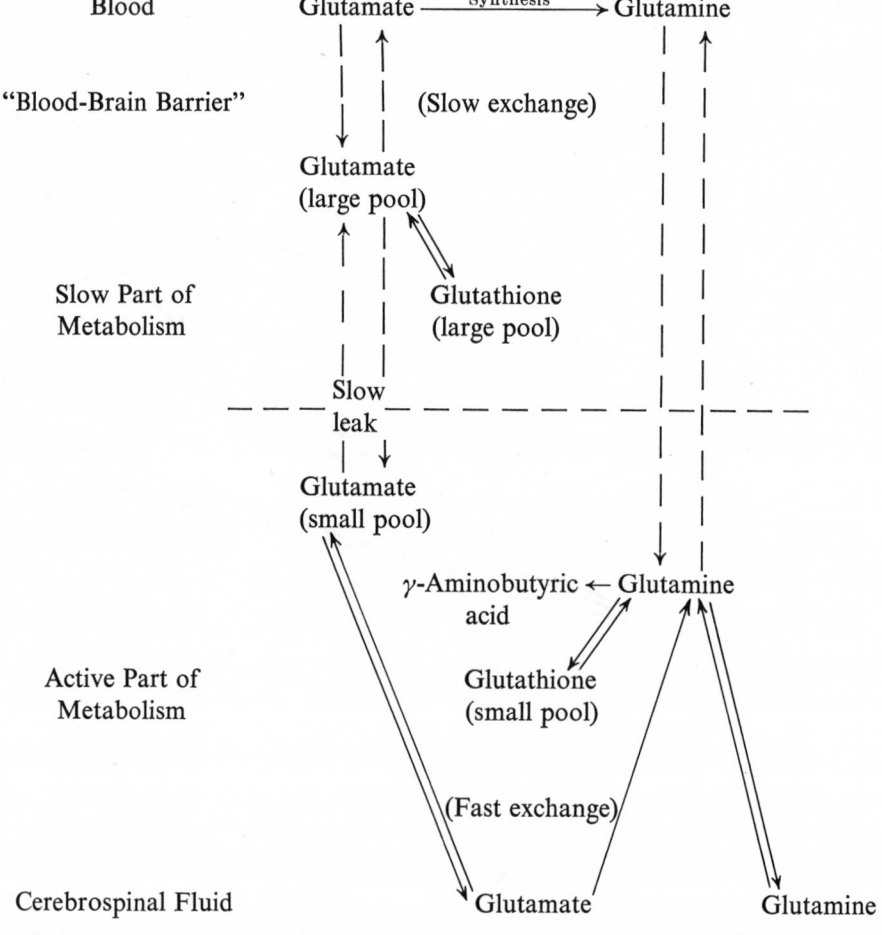

FIGURE 5.   Organization of the brain glutamate model.

Biochemical applications of the computer program for studying reactions in solution include detailed studies of the kinetics of single enzymes, studies of complex enzyme systems, studies of compartmentations where the flow of material from one physical location to another is of comparable importance with its transformation from one chemical form to another,[25] and studies of systems involving both diffusion and metabolism.

A. Brain Glutamate Metabolism

In the course of a study on the metabolism of amino acids by the rat brain,[2] it was found that tagged glutamic acid injected into the cerebrospinal fluid yielded brain glutamine whose specific radioactivity was five times as great as that of the brain glutamic acid isolated simultaneously. This led to the conclusion that at least two pools or compartments of glutamic acid were present in the brain, with the glutamine being synthesized from the more radioactive one.

A model involving both compartmentation and chemical reactions was constructed to represent this system.[11a] The organization of this model is shown in Figure 5; the more active glutamate pool is one-fifth the size of the other. In order to match the experimental data it was necessary to postulate both that there are two pools of glutathione and that glutamine is synthesized at the membrane separating the cerebrospinal fluid from the brain proper. The fit of the model to the experimental data is shown in Figure 6, and it is seen to be within experimental error with one or two exceptions.

A principal finding of this study was that the metabolism of glutamic acid seems to be divided into two parts, one of which is highly active and the other comparatively inert. The highly active part, including the small glutamate pool and the glutamine, exchanges readily with the cerebrospinal fluid, whereas the inert part, including the large glutamate and glutathione pools, effectively does not. Neither interacts rapidly with the blood, perhaps

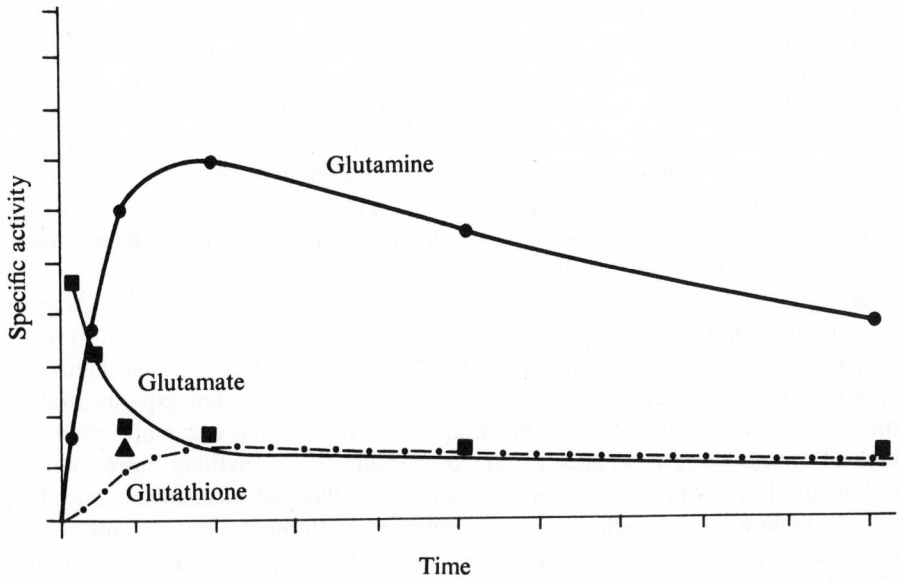

FIGURE 6. Fit of the brain glutamate model predictions (curves) to the experimental data (points) of Berl, Lajtha, and Waelsch.[2]

owing to the "blood-brain barrier." A method of histologically localizing these two portions of the brain glutamate metabolism was also suggested by the model. In addition, some indications were found that the observed compartmentations serve as a stability mechanism for brain glutamate metabolism. Although this model is based on experiments on amino acid metabolism in the brain, it could not be carried much further than has been described without also considering such things as carbohydrate metabolism, the blood-brain barrier, and oxidative metabolism of the brain.

In working with systems of this kind a technique has been developed for simulating radioactivity. Experimental results are often obtained in the form of specific activity, which has the dimensions of an amount of radioactivity (in counts/minute or in microcuries) divided by an amount of chemical (in moles). The computer calculates these two separately, and the amount of radioactivity at any given time is divided by the amount of corresponding inert chemical to yield a specific activity. In the event that the system is in a physiological steady state, that is, the amount of the inert chemical is constant, this can be done quite easily by using the constant amount of the inert chemical as a scaling factor in the calculations, which was done in studying the above model. When the amount of inert material varies with time, two separate and distinct sets of solutions must be obtained, one for the radioactivity and the other for the inert chemical.

B. *Ascites Cell Metabolism*

It is of course possible to construct a biochemical model that is based on chemical transformations alone, but this has been thus far done only in the case of isolated and pure enzymes. A system primarily involving chemical transformation, but with some compartmentation, which has been studied thoroughly is the glycolysis system, especially for the Ehrlich mouse ascites cell, a type of cell easily obtained, pure, and in large quantities, and therefore a favorite for biochemical study.

A first study of this system has been published.[5] This required twenty-two chemical reactions to represent the system, even though much was omitted. A moderately complete representation of this system (including only the enzymes, the coenzymes, and the substrates themselves, together with very crude representations of mitochondrial oxidative phosphorylation, and of the systems within the cell that use the ATP generated by the glycolysis and oxidative phosphorylation systems) required eighty-nine reactions involving sixty-five chemicals.[11b] If such other substances of regulatory importance as magnesium ion and hydrogen ion are included, the number of differential equations rises to several hundred, well beyond the capacity of the Univac I and II computers.

In working with a system of this sort, the enzymatic mechanisms, where known, can be taken essentially from the appropriate textbooks or research publications. In other cases the mechanisms are not known and it has been necessary to postulate mechanisms that would fit the available experimental data. For this purpose even a few experimental points will offer some strong suggestions concerning the nature of the enzymatic mechanisms, although of course these postulates cannot be considered as anything more than strong suggestions until confirmed by experiment. Such hypothesized mechanisms may be particularly valuable when it is difficult to do experiments with the isolated enzyme because of instability or problems in isolation, since one can use the computer study to make the best use of hard-to-get experimental data.

Ascites cells when fed glucose take it up rapidly at first and then more slowly; they likewise take up oxygen rapidly when glucose is first added but then slow down. There has

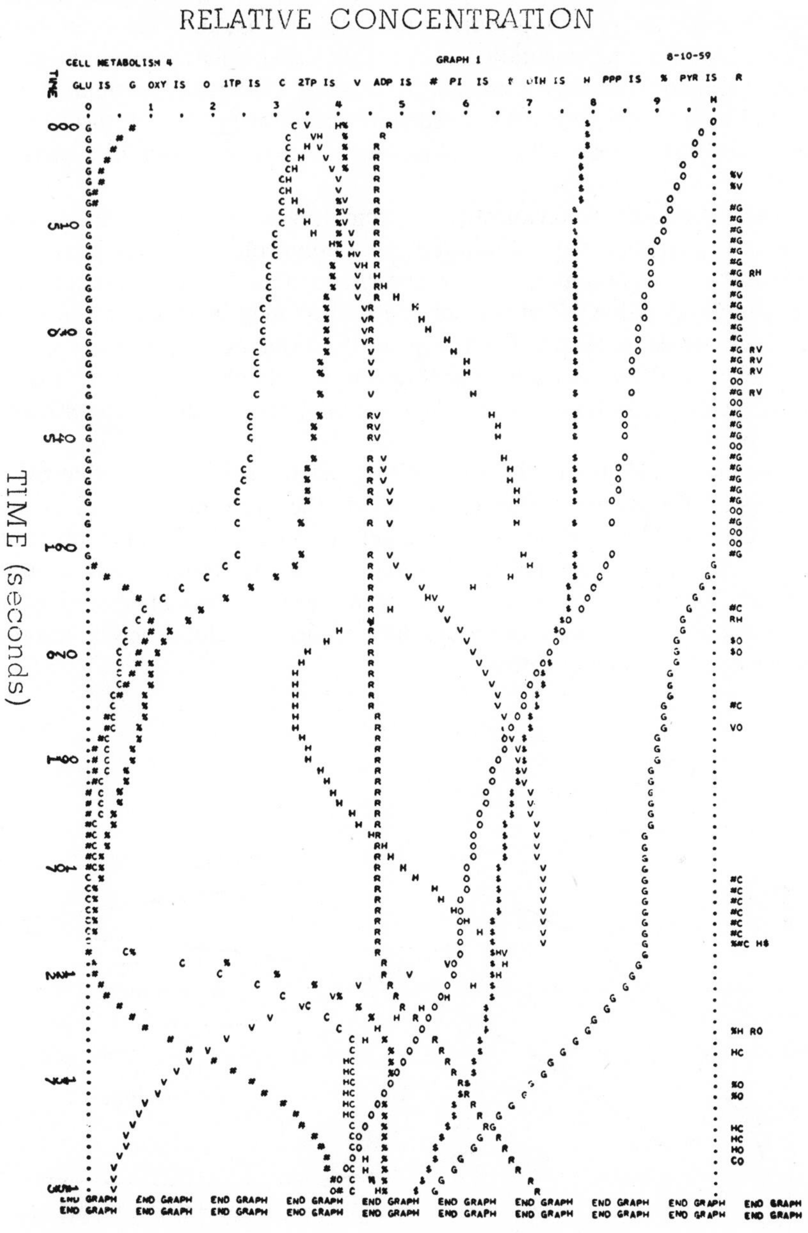

FIGURE 7. Behavior of selected metabolites in the first ascites glycolysis model as shown in the actual computer print-out. Time is plotted in seconds along the ordinate, and the relative concentrations of various components on the ordinate. Symbols for these metabolites are as follows: G = glucose, O = oxygen, C = cytoplasmic ATP, V = mitochondrial ATP, # = ADP, $ = inorganic phosphate, H = mitochondrial DPNH (NADH), % = phosphatase-phosphate-complex, R = pyruvate. Initially this system is in a resting state (000–064); the effect of adding glucose is shown from 064–119; at 119, the addition of dibromophenol as an uncoupling agent relieved the oxygen and glucose inhibition. (From Chance, et al.[5])

been much speculation regarding the cause of this glucose inhibition. Since oxidative phosphorylation is more active than glycolytic phosphorylation, this inhibition in the present model is ascribed to compartmentation of ATP, such that some of it is contained within the mitochondria and does not readily escape. As a result ATP would accumulate in the mitochondria, and both cytoplasmic ATP (needed for glycolysis) and ADP (needed for respiration) would be exhausted. This is illustrated in Figure 7 and discussed further in Chapter 13.

When one examines the behavior of this system in more detail,[17] some interesting points are observed. In particular the amount of glucose-6-phosphate, the first intermediate in the chain, increases to a maximum, decreases, and rises again. This may be explained in terms of a control by ATP and ADP of the enzyme immediately involved in the synthesis and conversion of glucose-6-phosphate, as well as the product inhibition of hexokinase by glycose-6-phosphate.[14,15,16] A study of a more complete model including detailed enzymatic mechanisms yielded calculated results shown in Figure 8 with the experimental points plotted for comparison.

Among the findings from model studies of this system are indications that the activity of most enzymes is affected by substances other than the substrates: this effect usually, but not always, takes the form of negative feedback (the product of a reaction tends to slow down that reaction or the reactions leading to it); and it is often difficult to designate any one substance or enzyme as *the* substance or *the* enzyme regulating a given metabolic pathway. A model of this type can of course be extended to include the synthesis of enzymes with repression, adaptation, et cetera.

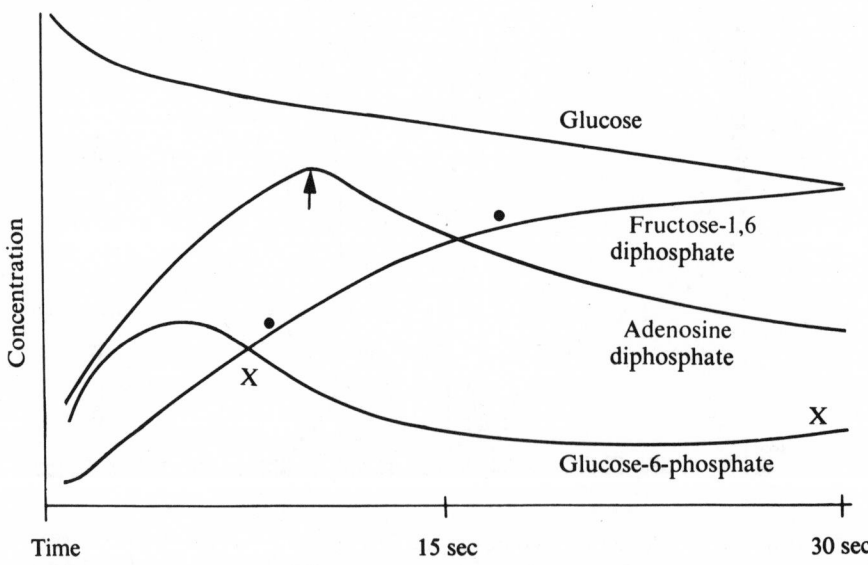

FIGURE 8. Behavior of chemicals as a function of time in a more detailed glycolysis model which includes the reactions through aldolase and a crude oxidative phosphorylation mechanism which is "turned on" at the arrow. Experimental points: X, glucose-6-phosphate; ●, fructose-1,6-diphosphate.

IV. ECOLOGICAL SYSTEMS*

A. *Applications of Simulation to Ecology*

The same computer program described above for studying metabolism can be used to simulate biological systems that are not composed of chemicals, since there is no real need that the things called "chemicals" actually be chemicals. The only assumption required thus far is that the biological system obey the mass action law and, indeed, if one carries a computer program of this type to its limits, the only real requirement is that the system be describable in ordinary differential equations which are reasonably well-behaved when solved by numerical methods.

The mass action law has been shown by Volterra, Lotka, and others to apply also to ecological systems;[23,29] consequently, such systems may be represented in this way. This was first tried[10] with a simple ecological situation consisting of a prey (grass), a predator (rabbits), and a second predator (foxes) which preys on the first predator. It was found that the behavior of this system depends on the efficiency with which the predators attack their appropriate prey. Hence it is possible to have situations 1) in which the first predator will exterminate its prey, 2) in which they will coexist in a steady state (as shown in Figure 9), and 3) in which a cycling process occurs with the prey and predator alternately increasing and decreasing (Figure 10). The relationship between two of the species may be affected by the presence of the third: when the system of Figure 9, in which rabbits and grass had reached a steady state, had foxes added to it (Figure 11), the system went into wild oscillations and ultimately the rabbits became extinct, within the error of calculation.

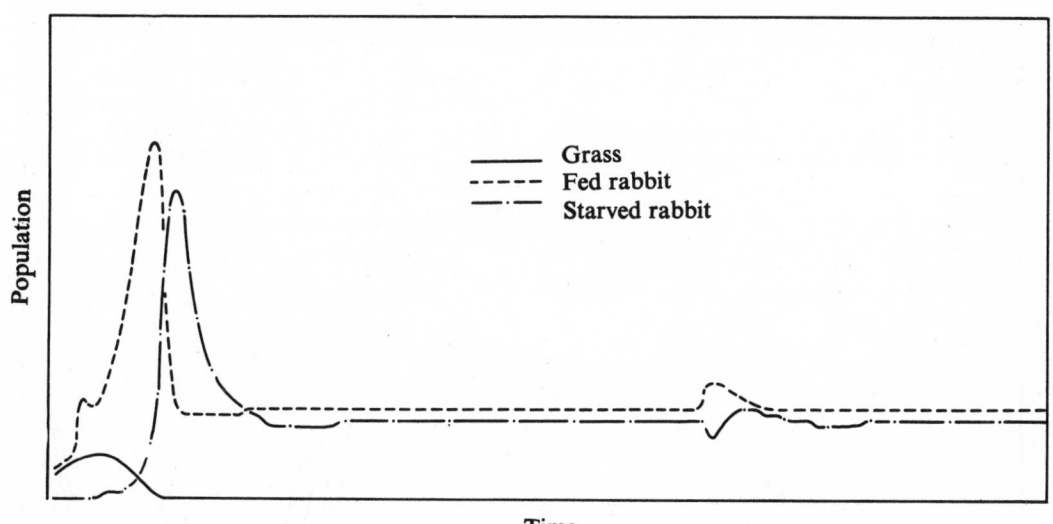

FIGURE 9. Behavior of ecological computer model. Rabbits and grass coexisting in a steady state. (From Garfinkel.[10])

---

* These are also treated from genetic and evolutionary points of view in Chapters 15 and 16.

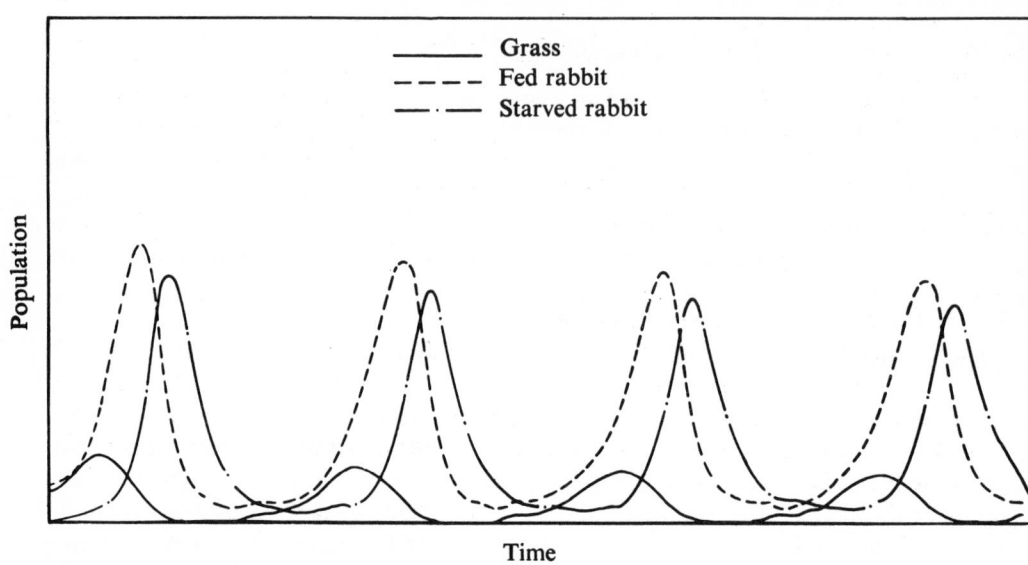

FIGURE 10. Output of ecological computer model with rabbits and grass cyclically increasing and decreasing. The only difference from the system of Figure 9 is in one rate constant. (From Garfinkel.[10])

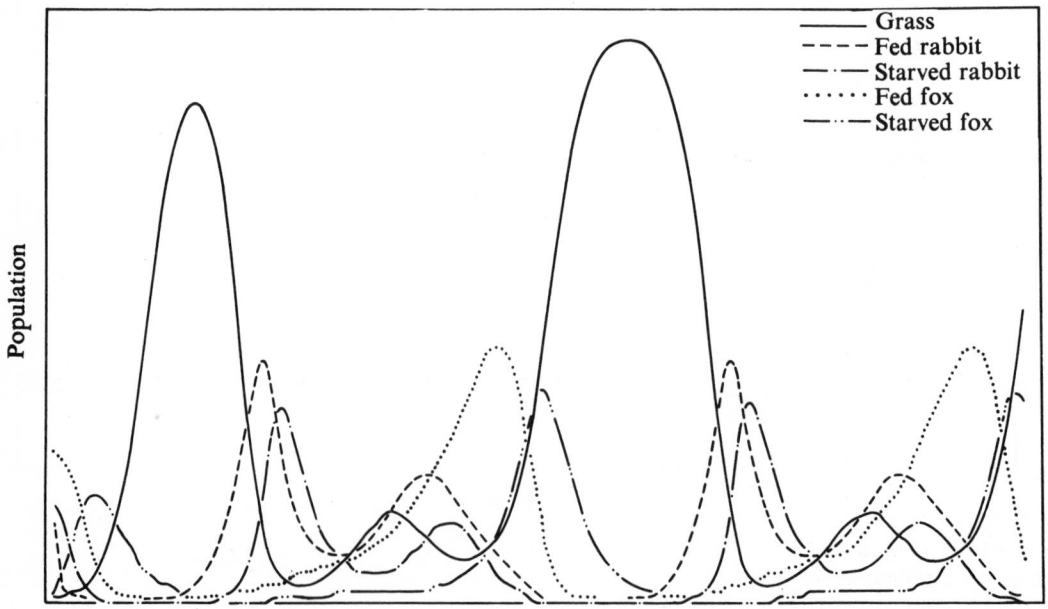

FIGURE 11. Output of ecological computer model with foxes added to the system shown in Figure 9. (From Garfinkel.[10])

In the above study the animals had only two nutritional states, fed and starved, with the fed animals going starved and the starved animals dying if they did not return to a fed status. Both of these are first-order reactions of the form

$$FED \rightarrow STARVED$$

with the reverse pathway being

$$STARVED + FOOD \rightarrow FED$$

It is possible to introduce finer nutritional distinctions, such as fed, hungry, malnourished, and starved, where appropriate. One may also include effects of disease. Seasonal factors may be introduced by varying the rate "constants" appropriately. The organisms can be made to reproduce; in the above system the grass was allowed to reproduce only up to a limiting density. Mass-balance and energy-balance conditions may also be included.[13b] The possibility exists of building a model as complex as desired; the larger computers now available will permit representing systems of real-life complexity.

It may be somewhat open to question to what extent the mass-action law applies to ecosystems on land[28] where many animals display a distinct territorial behavior and there is an appreciable difference in behavior between an animal that has a territory of its own and one that does not. A situation more closely analogous to the chemical one can be described in the field of marine biology.

If one were to construct a model of the life in a cubic mile of ocean, as a first assumption one could have all life forms distributed equally throughout it and therefore write "concentrations" in organisms per cubic mile. This first approximation is not very good because it is known that many marine organisms stratify themselves at characteristic depths. A better approximation is one in which this cubic mile of ocean is sliced into layers, each of which contains a characteristic animal and plant population (Figure 12). As the computer

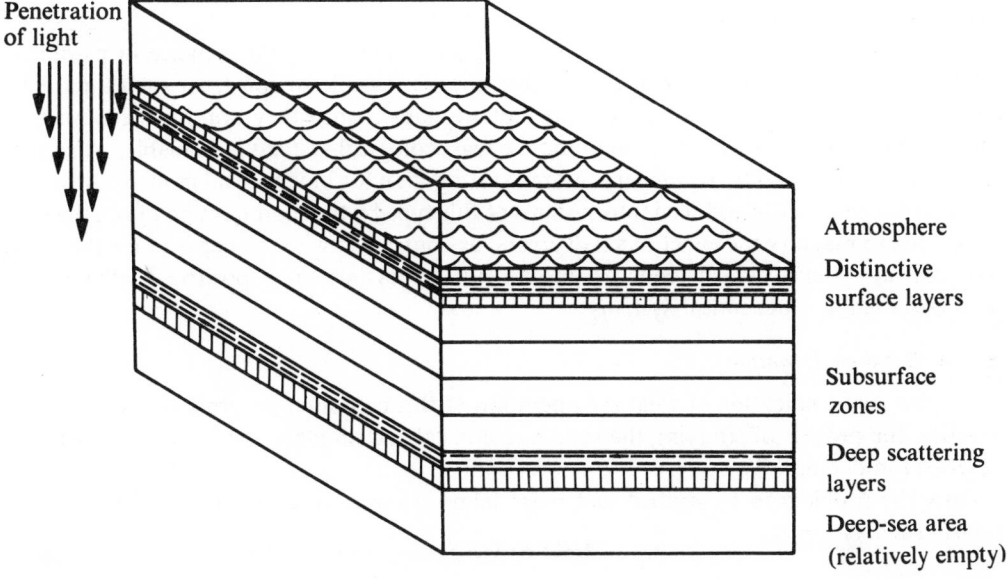

FIGURE 12. Basic organization of a model of oceanic life. The depth zones having large populations of living organisms are indicated by hatching.

sees it, this involves introducing a compartmentation since a given organism may be the same in the topmost zone as in the zone below it, but in order to distinguish them it is necessary to give them different names. In some cases they will also behave differently in different locations. It is not necessary to have the zones into which this cubic mile of ocean is divided be equal in size; a number of tricks are available to permit representations of zones of unequal size.

For various components of this over-all system one may write reactions of the form:

Species A (hungry) + Species B → Species A (fed)

Species A (fed) → more species A (with limiting conditions as desired)

Species A (fed) → larval or immature Species A (if this behaves appreciably differently from the adult, as is commonly the case), and

Larval Species A + Species C → juvenile Species A

Species A + Species B (a parasite) → Species D (parasitized Species A) → parasite young, et cetera.

Species B (a plant) → more species B, or in more detail

Species B + light + nutrients (i.e., phosphate, magnesium) → more species B

Species A (top zone) → Species A (next lower zone) (This can be arranged to take care of massive vertical migrations as well as movements of individual organisms and can be made a function of either light intensity or the time of day.)

The amount of light is not a constant since it shows both daily and seasonal variations; however, it is possible to treat it formally as if it were a chemical and to obtain a suitable approximation to the amount of light that is actually present. As a first approximation one may take a sine curve; as a second, one may take a more accurately shaped step function. Temperature may also be treated in the same way. In view of the fact that birds may interact with fish in the top layer, one would have to represent the atmosphere above this cubic mile of ocean in the model also. Probably for most purposes the effect of a large school of fish swimming through the volume in question could be represented as if the fish were more or less evenly distributed in the appropriate depth zone.

A functioning model of this sort might be of economic value, for instance in planning fishery management. However, it is probably not yet feasible to construct such a model; not because the necessary computers are not available, since they are, but because not enough quantitative information regarding the real ecological systems is available. Also the technique of constructing the model is more exacting than for biochemical models, owing to the positive feedback introduced into systems of this type by the reproduction of organisms. This tends to magnify the effect of small errors, as contrasted with the negative feedback of biochemical systems, which tends to smooth out errors (although positive feedback has been observed in biochemical systems[24,13c,19b]).

B. A Detailed Example

To give some indication of what the operation of this computer program is like in actual practice, the process of studying the simple ecological system mentioned first above will be described in detail.

Once the problem to be studied had been defined, it was described in "chemical equations," such as

$$GRS \rightarrow GRS$$

$$RTS \rightarrow GRS$$

$$GRS + GRS \rightarrow DUM - GRS$$

where *GRS* is the amount of grass, *RTS* indicates roots for the grass which herbivores cannot dig up, and *DUM* is a dummy variable, required by the grammatical rules of the computer language, which state that something must always appear on the right side of an equation. This set of chemical equations amounts to stating that the rate at which grass grows is given by an expression of the form

$$\frac{d(GRS)}{dt} = c_1 + c_2(GRS) - c_3(GRS)^2,$$

where c_1, c_2, and c_3 are constants. The first term of this equation represents the constant growth of the grass from the roots; the second, the ordinary reproduction of grass. The third term limits the amount of grass to the maximum value that can grow in the land area available to the system.

A total of nine such equations were required to describe the system of rabbits and grass, and these correspond to three differential equations. In order to have the computer perform the conversion, the equations, together with specifications as to how the differential equations were to be solved, were typed on magnetic tape and fed into the computer. It would be more convenient to punch the equations on cards, one to a card, but the Univac I does not easily receive card input. The computer required about five minutes to convert the taped equations into the instructions for solving the differential equations. These are in the form of a program on tape called the "running tape."

A set of "rate constants" for the "chemical reactions" was then prepared from the known lifespan and reproduction rates of the species involved, and reasonable initial numbers of the species involved were assumed. These were also typed on tape in a format which requires a five-letter identifier and a seven-digit numerical value, together with instructions on what graphical output was desired. When this was fed to the computer together with the "running tape" instructions, a set of solutions to the differential equations was obtained. The computer solves the differential equations simultaneously, one time-step at a time, and writes the concentrations after each step on magnetic tape. When the solution is terminated, either by some time or concentration exceeding a preset limit or by the user's intervention, the computer reads back through the magnetic tape containing the stored solutions and constructs a graph. This is also written on tape, and is then printed out on a high-speed (line-at-a-time) printer. As the graphs so prepared are not easy to reproduce by photo-engraving methods, it is sometimes necessary to make tracings of them for publication. For this ecological system about twenty minutes is required by the computer to solve the equations and about five minutes to construct the graph.

When the first calculation was made for this system, the results of course bore little resemblance to the biological system being simulated. In the author's experience, in several years of this type of work only one problem behaved correctly the first time it was tried. A process of correcting the initial mistakes and adjusting the rate constants to make the system behave properly was then carried out; some fifteen to twenty calculations of the type described were required. The real biological study begins after satisfactory machine behavior is obtained.

V. FUTURE PROSPECTS

A. *Economic Limits*

The principal limitation on what can be accomplished with this type of procedure is presently an economic one. Thus, the construction of the first model of glycolysis[5] required the expenditure of about $5,000 worth of computer time in addition to the time and labor of the individuals involved. As the model system comes to resemble the real system more closely, the economics become worse, both because there are more equations to solve and because the numbers which accurately represent real enzymatic systems make the equations more difficult to solve.

To some extent this situation can be mitigated by the availability of more economical computers; it is estimated that the most economical computers available as of this time of writing will effect a savings of at least 200-fold over the expenditure required on the Univac I to do a given problem. Also, the computer may offer greater assistance in the construction of models, both in finding errors made by the user and in obtaining initial conditions which yield a better fit to the experimental data. Indeed, for the special case of compartmentation systems describable entirely by linear differential equations, a computer program has been prepared[3,4] to calculate the rate constants which give the best fit to a given set of points when the organization of a model has been given also. By the use of such techniques, and undoubtedly others can be found, it is hoped to decrease greatly the expense of constructing a model, perhaps to the point where the principal expense is simply that of the time and labor of the persons doing the work.

B. Theoretical Limits

Once it is possible to construct models easily and inexpensively, what ultimately may be expected from working with them? It must first be stressed that experiments with models are in no way substitutes for experiments with real systems, and that any finding postulated on the basis of model experiments must ultimately be confirmed by real experiments. However, a model can be quite useful in clearing away untenable theories, since inability to construct a model in agreement with a given theory can be considered as strong evidence against that theory. A computer model can be used to organize large masses of material into a workable whole, or to give a better understanding of how a given system fits together, particularly in terms of the quantitative interactions that make it behave as it does. Models can also be used to pinpoint crucial experiments that can distinguish among several theories; it may be cheaper or easier to construct models based on the theories under test and do experiments with them than to do an equivalent number of real experiments. Once a workable model has been constructed for a given system, one can of course use experiments with that model as a high-probability prediction of the behavior of the real system being modeled. This may ultimately be of economic importance, at least for ecological models.

It is accordingly to be expected that with the advent of more economical computers and better techniques the construction of models will come to be a tool of great value in biological investigation, although it will probably never be entirely complete in itself.

REFERENCES

1. Bellville, J. W., and Seed, J. C. 1959. Respiratory carbon dioxide response curve computer. *Science* **130**: 1079–1083.
2. Berl, S., Lajtha, A., and Waelsch, H. 1961. Amino acid protein metabolism VI. Cerebral compartments of glutamic acid metabolism. *J. Neurochem.* **7**: 186–197.
3. Berman, M., Shahn, E., and Weiss, M. F. 1962. The routine fitting of kinetic data to models: A mathematical formalism for digital computers. *Biophys. J.* **2**: 275–288.

4. Berman, M., Weiss, M. F., and Shahn, E. 1962. Some formal approaches to the analysis of kinetic data in terms of linear compartmental systems. *Biophys. J.* **2:** 289–302.

5. Chance, B., Garfinkel, D., Higgins, J. J., and Hess, B. 1960. Metabolic control mechanisms V. A solution for the equations representing interaction between glycolysis and respiration in ascites tumor cells. *J. Biol. Chem.* **235:** 2426–2439.

6. Chance, B., Higgins, J. J., and Garfinkel, D. 1962. Analogue and digital computer representations of biochemical processes. *Federation Proc.* **21** (1): 75–86.

7. Estabrook, R. W., and Holowinsky, A. 1961. Studies on the content and organization of the respiratory enzymes of mitochondria. *J. Biophys. Biochem. Cytol.* **9:** 19–28.

8. FitzHugh, R. 1962. Computation of impulse initiation and saltatory conduction in a myelinated nerve fiber. *Biophys. J.* **2:** 11–21.

9. French, C. S., and Fork, D. C. 1961. Computer solutions for photosynthesis rates from a two pigment model. *Biophys. J.* **1:** 669–681.

10. Garfinkel, D. 1962a. Digital computer simulation of ecological systems. *Nature* **194:** 856–857.

11a. Garfinkel, D. 1962b. Computer simulation of steady-state glutamate metabolism in rat brain. *J. Theoret. Biol.* **3:** 412–422.

11b. Garfinkel, D., and Hess, B. 1964. Metabolic control mechanisms. VII. A detailed computer model of the glycolytic pathway in ascites cells. *J. Biol. Chem.* **239:** 971–983.

12. Garfinkel, D., Polk, W., Higgins, J. J., and Ochser, R. T. 1962. Simulation and analysis of biochemical systems III. Analysis and pattern recognition. *Comm. Assoc. Computing Machinery* **5:** 115–118.

13a. Garfinkel, D., Rutledge, J. D., and Higgins, J. J. 1961. Simulation and analysis of biochemical systems I. Representation of chemical kinetics. *Comm. Assoc. Computing Machinery* **4:** 559–562.

13b. Garfinkel, D., and Sack, R. 1964. Digital computer simulation of an ecological system, based on a modified mass action law. *Ecology* **45:** 502–507.

13c. Ghosh, A., and Chance, B. 1964. Oscillations of glycolytic intermediates in yeast cells. *Biochem. Biophys. Res. Comm.* **16:** 174–181.

14. Hammes, G. G., and Kochavi, D. 1962a. Studies of the enzyme hexokinase I. Steady state kinetics at pH 8. *J. Am. Chem. Soc.* **84:** 2069–2073.

15. Hammes, G. G., and Kochavi, D. 1962b. Studies of the enzyme hexokinase II. Kinetic inhibition by products. *J. Am. Chem. Soc.* **84:** 2073–2076.

16. Hammes, G. G., and Kochavi, D. 1962c. Studies of the enzyme hexokinase III. The role of the metal ion. *J. Am. Chem. Soc.* **84:** 2076–2079.

17. Hess, B., and Chance, B. 1961. Metabolic control mechanisms VI. Chemical events after glucose addition to ascites tumor cells. *J. Biol. Chem.* **236:** 239–246.

18. Higgins, J. J. 1959. "Kinetic Properties of Sequential Enzyme Systems," 244 pp. Ph.D. Thesis, University of Pennsylvania.

19a. Higgins, J. J. 1961. Use of computers. *In:* "Technique of Organic Chemistry," (S. L. Friess, E. S. Lewis, and A. Weissberger, eds.), 2nd rev. ed., Vol. VIII, pp. 285–341. Interscience, New York.

19b. Higgins, J. J. 1964. A chemical mechanism for the oscillation of glycolytic intermediates in yeast cells. *Proc. Natl. Acad. Sci.* **51:** 989–994.

20. Holmes, W. F. 1960. "Rate Law of Interactions between Bound Chemicals," 115 pp. Ph.D. Thesis, University of Pennsylvania.

21. Kavanau, J. L. 1961. Predictions of the growth model for normal chicken growth. *Science* **134:** 1627–1628.

22. Larson, R., Sellers, P., and Meyer, R. 1962. Simulation and analysis of biochemical systems II. Solution of differential equations. *Comm. Assoc. Computing Machinery* **5:** 63–65.

23. Lotka, A. J. 1956. "Elements of Mathematical Biology," 465 pp. Dover, New York.

(Originally published 1925 as "Elements of Physical Biology," 460 pp. Williams and Wilkins, Baltimore.)

24. Nakao, M., Motegi, T., Nakao, T., Yamazoe, S., and Yoshikawa, H. 1961. A positive feed-back mechanism of adenosine triphosphate synthesis in erythrocytes. *Nature* **191:** 283–284.
25. Robertson, J. S. 1957. Theory and use of tracers in determining transfer rates in biological systems. *Physiol. Rev.* **37:** 133–154.
26. Strittmatter, P. 1958. The interaction of nucleotides with microsomal cytochrome reductase. *J. Biol. Chem.* **233:** 748–753.
27. Strittmatter, P. 1959. The properties of nucleotide complexes with microsomal cytochrome reductase. *J. Biol. Chem.* **234:** 2665–2669.
28. Watt, K. E. F. 1959. A mathematical model for the effect of densities of attacked and attacking species on the number attacked. *Can. Entomologist* **91:** 129–144.
29. Volterra, V. 1931. "Leçons sur la Théorie Mathématique de la Lutte pour la Vie," 214 pp. Gauthier-Villars, Paris.

$$\left[\quad \text{SECTION V} \quad\right]$$

Systems Analysis

The notion that the whole is greater than the sum of its parts is familiar to biologists. The modern statement of this idea is tied up with the concept of systems and systems theory. Within this framework the notion cited would be formulated as follows: a system of interacting entities has certain properties which are not obvious properties of the component entities themselves. Throughout biology we encounter sets of interacting entities; they may be networks of neurons, cycles of metabolites, pools of genes, individuals in a group, species in a population, or any of a great variety of other systems.

The primary problem in studying such entities theoretically has been to predict the properties of the whole from the rules of interaction between its components. No general mathematics is available for this sort of analysis. Hence each problem must be separately treated by the best methods available, whether they be analytical or empirical. The following five chapters discuss a series of biological problems that are systems oriented.

Quastler first introduces certain general properties of systems and then examines four relevant general theories that have been developed (Chapter 12). He then analyzes some features of biological organization in terms of these theories. Next, Chance (Chapter 13) discusses some highly specific cycles of reactions involved in energy production in living systems. His chief concern is in developing a theory for the control of such systems. The computer approach to part of this problem has been dealt with above by Garfinkel in Chapter 11. In going to Chapter 14 we move from collections of molecules to collections of neurons. To begin with, Reichardt reviews the experimental evidence for neural inhibition in the *Limulus* eye and then formulates a model which he compares with the experimental data. In the final section he discusses a model for the visual perception of motion by insects.

Levins and Mac Arthur both deal with systems of genes and systems of species. Levins' analysis is aimed primarily at the gene distribution and Mac Arthur's is oriented toward the species distribution, but there is in fact a strong overlap between these points of view. In both papers mathematical models are developed to study the properties of the biological situation. Predictions made with such particular models are then tested against fresh data, and the model altered as required.

[12]

GENERAL PRINCIPLES OF SYSTEMS ANALYSIS*

H. Quastler

I. INTRODUCTION

This chapter deals with formal theories of organization. The presentation will make much use of the semiformal devices of black boxes and white boxes. Four of the major theories of organization will be considered: cybernetics, game theory, decision theory, and communication theory. A common structure underlying all of them will be demonstrated. The same structure will be extracted from an analysis of biological systems, and the significance of the analogies thus suggested, discussed. A general feature common to many biological acts is shown to be operation according to the Signature Principle. The importance of this principle in biological organization and its evolution will be considered.

A. The Black Box Concept

In formal treatments of organization, much use is made of a simple conceptual device called the *black box*. This name designates an object about which the following is known: it can sense a certain repertory of inputs, generate a certain repertory of outputs, and associate outputs to inputs according to one of a repertory of admissible laws. In a more abstract way, a black box can be considered as the embodiment of a class of events each of which involves the concrescence into a unit—be it ever so fleeting—of a particular input, a particular output, and a particular rule of association (Figure 1).

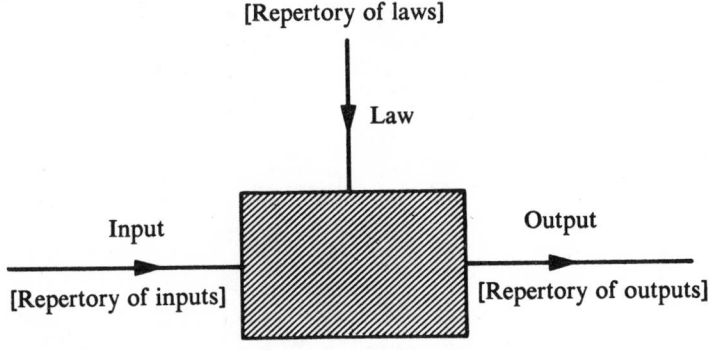

FIGURE 1. Black box representation.

* Research carried out at Brookhaven National Laboratory under the auspices of the U.S. Atomic Energy Commission.

In	Out
A	+
non A	−

FIGURE 2.   Simplest input-output law.

The laws can be stated in many different forms. They can be defined by lists of associated input-output pairs, such as a telephone directory or a dictionary. In the simplest case, say, there are just two significantly different inputs, A and *not-A*, and two outputs, *plus* and *minus* (Figure 2).

Such might be the law of a highly specific enzyme which accepts only one substrate, A, and rejects any substrate which is not A. A more complicated black box can be described

$y =$

	1	2	3	•	•	•	j	•	•
x = 1	.89	.01	.00	•	•	•	•		
2	.04	.80	.01	•	•	•	•		
3	•	•	•	•	•	•	•		
•	•	•	•	•	•	•	•		
•	•	•	•	•	•	•	•		
•	•	•	•	•	•	•	•		
i	•	•	•	•	•	•	$p(j/i)$		
•									
•									

FIGURE 3.   Input-output conditional probability matrix.

by a probability matrix which states for each input, x_i, and each output, y_j, the conditional probability that y_j will be generated in response to x_i (Figure 3). This might be the description of a system of moderately specific enzymes, some of which can react with different substrates although with different probabilities.

Some of the abstractions of systems theory are customarily described by probability matrices, for example, communication channels and detector performance. If any given input always generates one particular output, and each output is produced by only one input, then the probability matrix becomes diagonal and equivalent to a list of rigidly associated input-output pairs.

Input-output laws can sometimes be stated in analytical form. For example, if a population responds to some agent with exponential survival:

$$S_D = S_0 e^{-D/D_0}$$

(where D is the dose of the agent measured in units D_0; S_D, the number of units surviving a dose D; S_0, the initial size of the population, and e the exponential base); then the response can be pictured as a black box, characterized by the exponential law and the two parameters S_0 and D_0. The box takes in an input D and produces an output S_D (Figure 4).

The black box concept had its origin in systems engineering. If one wants to design a complicated system it is difficult to consider all parts at the same time. One thus tries to cut up the function of the entire system into independent component functions, each of which is represented by a black box. This done, one can consider separately the problem of how to replace each black box by some real object which will yield the desired function. Now, biologists are not interested in designing systems but in analyzing them. In this task, too, the black box concept is useful: in studying any particular function of a living system, it is not necessary to analyze the nature of every single factor which enters into the function; some can be replaced by black boxes and the analytic effort concentrated on one or a few factors. In either context, the black box is nothing but a symbolic representation of functions associated with a given object or a given class of events. It is useful because it exhibits essential features in a simple and lucid fashion.

B. Black Boxes and White Boxes

The progress of both systems design and systems analysis can be symbolically represented by a progressive replacement of black boxes by *white boxes*. A white box[18] is a system of

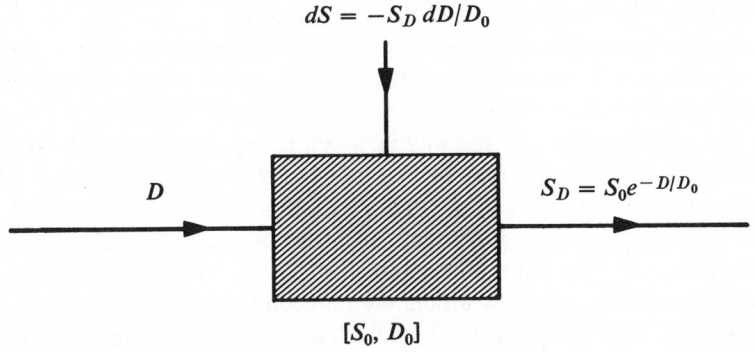

$$dS = -S_D \, dD/D_0$$

D

$$S_D = S_0 e^{-D/D_0}$$

$$[S_0, D_0]$$

FIGURE 4. Exponential input-output law. D, input dose; S, survivors; D_0 and S_0, constants.

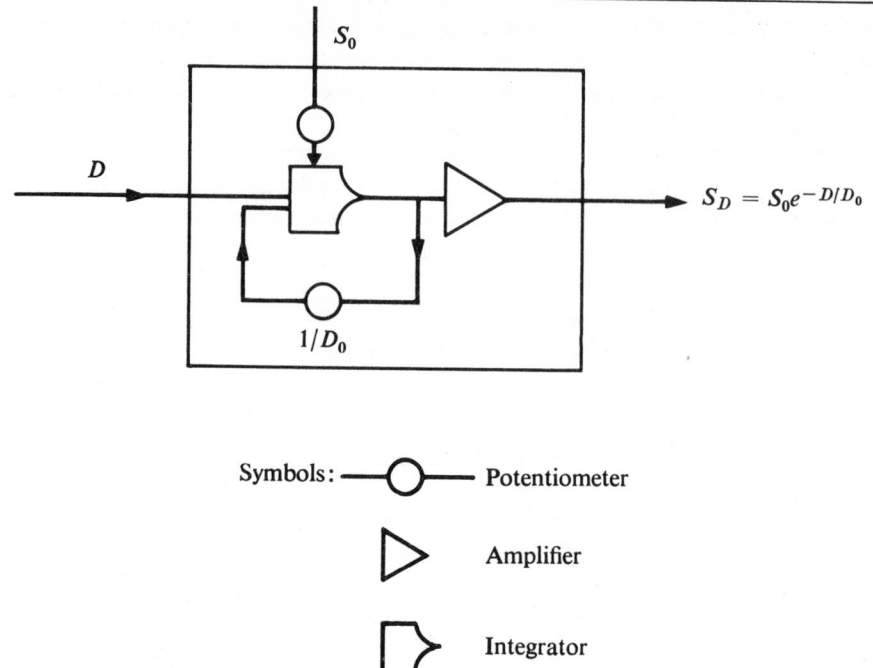

$$S_D = S_0 e^{-D/D_0}$$

Symbols: ──O── Potentiometer

▷ Amplifier

Integrator

FIGURE 5. White box representation (for analog computers) of exponential dose-response behavior. Other symbols as in Figure 4.

known components, put together in a known fashion so as to produce a given input-output law. The replacement of every black box by a white box is a possible solution of the task. For instance, the white box below (Figure 5) is a realization of the "exponential law" black box in terms of analog computer components.

For the user of an analog computer, the task is completed by some white box like that shown. For the designer and the manufacturer of analog computers, each component shown is itself a black box which must be replaced by some real system consisting of available components. Another step of this regression involves the design and manufacture of the components of components; in complex systems, many black box-white box transitions occur between the final system and the raw materials.

Systems analysis progresses through an analogous sequence of steps. Thus a model ascribing the limitation of growth of some organ to some substance elaborated by its constituent cells immediately invites questions concerning the nature of the substance, the way in which it is elaborated, and the way in which its presence is sensed. The regression from explanation to explanation may or may not be infinite but it certainly takes periods of time which are long compared to the lifetime of a biologist.

Neither in systems design nor in systems analysis will every possible solution be automatically accepted. At this point, the parallelism stops. In systems design, the choice between possible solutions depends ultimately on economic factors; in systems analysis, on the extension of the black box-white box relation beyond the domain originally considered. The process of validation consists in extracting from the structure of a proposed white box predictions on thus far unknown features of the black box, or vice versa, in extracting from a given black box relations which the white box must fulfill and which have not yet been tested. In either case, a successful prediction is a gain in validity. The basic operation in systems analysis is thus a complete circle; it is not important whether the circle starts at the white or the black box.[1]

II. FORMAL THEORIES OF ORGANIZATION

In this section some of the principal mathematical theories of systems, namely, cybernetics, decision and detection theory, game theory, and communication theory, will be introduced by means of simple black box diagrams. It need hardly be mentioned that a simple diagram can show no more than a few superficial aspects of any of these theories, and that the diagrams given here are not the only ones that could be used. Indeed, every one of the four theories could be represented more elegantly than is done here; the particular diagrams used have been designed to bring out some elements common to all four mathematical theories of organization.

In every case, the system is represented by a white box, the surroundings are left as a black box. The system interacts with the surroundings, and the surroundings are also acted upon by influences outside the system. The components of the system are represented by three kinds of black boxes: one kind, drawn as long rectangles, represents *motivators*, the generators of systems needs, including both immediate (or tactical) and long-range (or strategic) needs. A second kind of element is represented by square boxes; they are the *sensor* and *effector* elements which receive tactical information or generate tactical action. The *laws* or *strategies*, by which sensor and effector elements operate, are generated by a third kind of element which is drawn as diamonds.

A. Cybernetics[3,17,18]

The diagram below (Figure 6) shows a scheme of a cybernetic system; the specific illustration is that well-used example, the thermostat. The significant feature of the surroundings, in this case, is the temperature in a room; it is regulated by the system through a heater and modified by factors such as fluctuations in outside temperature, wind, et cetera. Information about the temperature is fed back to the heater and serves to control its activity. Two acts of motivation are concerned. One, M_1, represented by the lower rectangle, is the choosing of a desired temperature. This information is used to produce a thermostat setting θ_0. Experience teaches which setting of θ_0 is likely to produce the desired temperature; with the cheap thermostats commonly used, the two are rarely identical. The choice of θ_0 is represented by the lower diamond-shaped box, S_1.

The sensing element, the thermometer (square box, T_1) in this case converts temperature information into a difference between actual temperature and standard, and this becomes the object of the second act of motivation. The difference is checked against two criteria: an excess, ϵ_1, of actual temperature over θ_0 at which the heater will be turned off, and a deficit, ϵ_2, at which it will be turned on; the checking is represented by the box T_2, the heater by T_3. The two criteria are arrived at as a result of a compromise: one wishes to keep the actual temperature within narrow ranges, which means small ϵ, but the other does not wish to have the heater go on and off very frequently, which suggests large ϵ. The computation of the compromise, S_2, depends on the relative values of temperature fluctuations and changes in heater activity represented by M_2, and on long-range experience of the results of

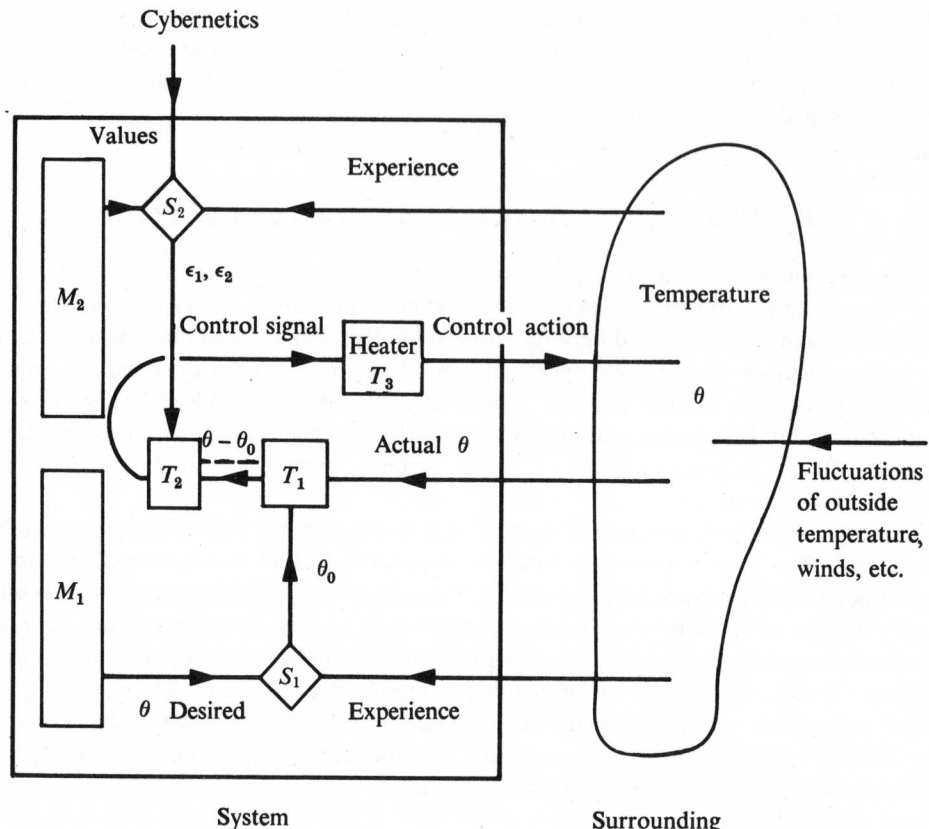

FIGURE 6. A cybernetic system. Symbols explained in text.

heater activity. This computation (or something resembling it) is performed by the electrician who would probably be surprised to find himself referred to as a cybernetician; however, where the values at stake are high, a great deal of cybernetic skill may have to go into the calculation of satisfactory compromises.

Cybernetic analysis, due to Norbert Wiener,[17] has many merits, three of which are particularly relevant to this discussion. One is precisely the development of the general scheme which allows the partition of systems analysis (or synthesis) into clearly separated black boxes. The second is the recognition of the general importance of feedback, that is, the steering of control actions through sensing their results; in the thermostat for example, the action of the heater is controlled by the temperature which it produces. Feedback was known to engineers, particularly to those working with servomechanisms, long before cybernetics was formulated. However, it was left to Wiener to bring out the general prevalence of feedback.

A great comfort to the theoretical biologist is the recognition that any feedback system is automatically goal-oriented, and that the difference between an automatically oriented system and one which pursues a goal because of an effort of will is a purely internal one; it cannot be assessed with certainty by any external criterion. In this way cybernetics disposes of the old fear of teleology in biology; one now may safely talk of goal-oriented systems without having to add the embarrassed "as if."

A third point of great importance is this: what flows along the arrows connecting the various black boxes must be energy or matter, but the flow always contains a certain element of choice, a choice of one particular mode of flow out of a set of possible modes which might have occurred instead. The choice represents information, and the flow of information can be treated independently of the particular physical processes which carry the information. The information aspect of feedback is easily realized from the diagram, Figure 6. A single accurately computed control signal to the heater could restore the desired temperature without any feedback, but the requirements for accuracy of the control signal would be considerable.

With feedback, the temperature information is first converted into information on a temperature difference and thus reduced to a much narrower range of choice; this difference, in turn, is compared with standard differences and the result of this comparison is a conversion into a non- or off-signal. Hence, no single phase of the actual operation involves processing of much information; however, a great deal of information-processing may be needed (in complex cases) by the computer elements which determine how temperature information is to be converted into control signals.

B. Game Theory[16,19]

The structure of *game theory* is diagramed in Figure 7. This theory, due to the late John von Neumann,[16] deals with situations of conflict between two or more persons or organizations. The games come in as such only in highly formalized types of conflict. Input and output repertories, often difficult to specify in natural situations, are replaced by a repertory of well-defined possible moves. The surroundings become the game, acted upon by the system (the player), the opponent, and by random events (such as the result of throwing dice). The "player" is analyzed into four components: a sensor T_1, an effector T_2, a motivator

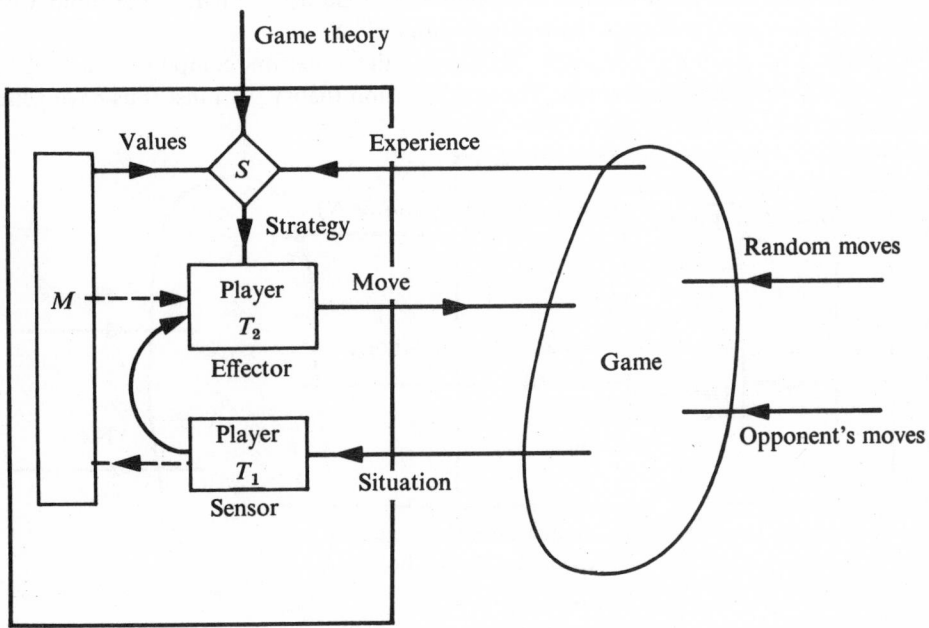

FIGURE 7. A game theory system.

M, and a strategy computer *S*. The situation of the game may be fed to the "motivator" component, *M*, which generates the "tactical needs" which are communicated into the effector component; or one may think of the situation being directly communicated to the effector. The effector, acquainted with the general strategy and the tactical needs, or the situation itself, generates a "move."

The generation of a move may be technically difficult, but this kind of difficulty is not considered in game theory; here the mathematically difficult problem is that of generating the strategy, or the law which prescribes a move for every possible situation. The strategy computer is endowed with comprehensive experience in the kind of game played, that is, with knowledge of all possible games and their outcomes. In addition, the strategy computer receives, from the motivator, a set of values for all possible outcomes. Given this information, a strategy can be computed according to the rules of game theory. The basic rule is to design a strategy such that the expected gain is maximized (or losses minimized) if the opponent follows what is for him an optimum strategy. As in the cybernetic situation, the computation of an optimum strategy can be a difficult and highly sophisticated job.

C. Decision Theory[14]

The same general organization prevails in *decision theory* (Figure 8). The diagram illustrates a particular class of decisions, namely, signal detection. The system is analyzed into a detector, T_1, an effector, T_2, a motivator, *M*, and a criterion computer, *S*. Into the surrounding are fed signals; it is assumed that a single-type signal is present or absent. Also into the surrounding is fed "noise," a variety of events with traits similar to or identical with the signal. Into the detector T_1 is fed information from the surrounding; this can be either pure noise, or a mixture of signal plus noise. The detector has to make a decision and generate a response which may be either "signal" or "noise"; no other response is admitted. The determination of the response is made by comparing the input with a criterion which emanates from a "criterion computer," *S*.

As in the organizations previously discussed, the criterion computer must operate according to given rules—in this case, those of decision theory. It must thus have general

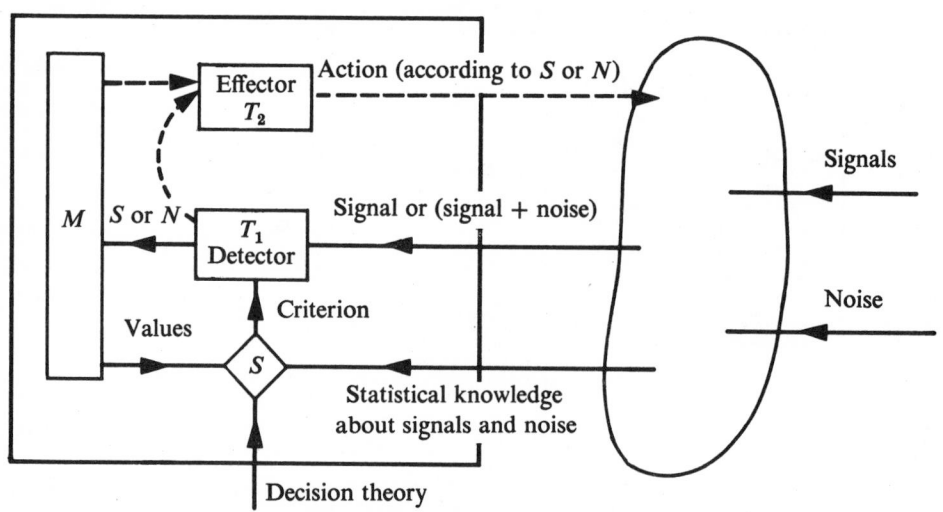

FIGURE 8. A decision theory system.

experience with the surrounding, i.e., information as to the respective properties of signals and noise, and of the probability of a signal occurring; and, it must have information on the *values* of the possible outcomes. In the simple case considered, the possible outcomes are four: a signal can be correctly recognized; it can be missed; the absence of a signal can be correctly diagnosed; or a false alarm can be given. To compute the decision criterion according to the rules, definite values must be assigned to each of the four contingencies, and a principle of evaluation must be stated. In general, one maximizes the expected value of decisions; other principles are equally possible, for example, there may be a particular contingency which it is very important to avoid. The effector part of the system is not explicitly treated but is implicit: the values depend on the action that will be taken in response to whether or not a signal is judged to have occurred.

D.   *Communication Theory*[6,13]

The formal analysis of the process of communication reveals, once more, the same structure (Figure 9). This time, it consists of two symmetrical parts. In one, the motivator, M_1, is a *source of messages*. Mathematically, a source is defined by stating the repertory

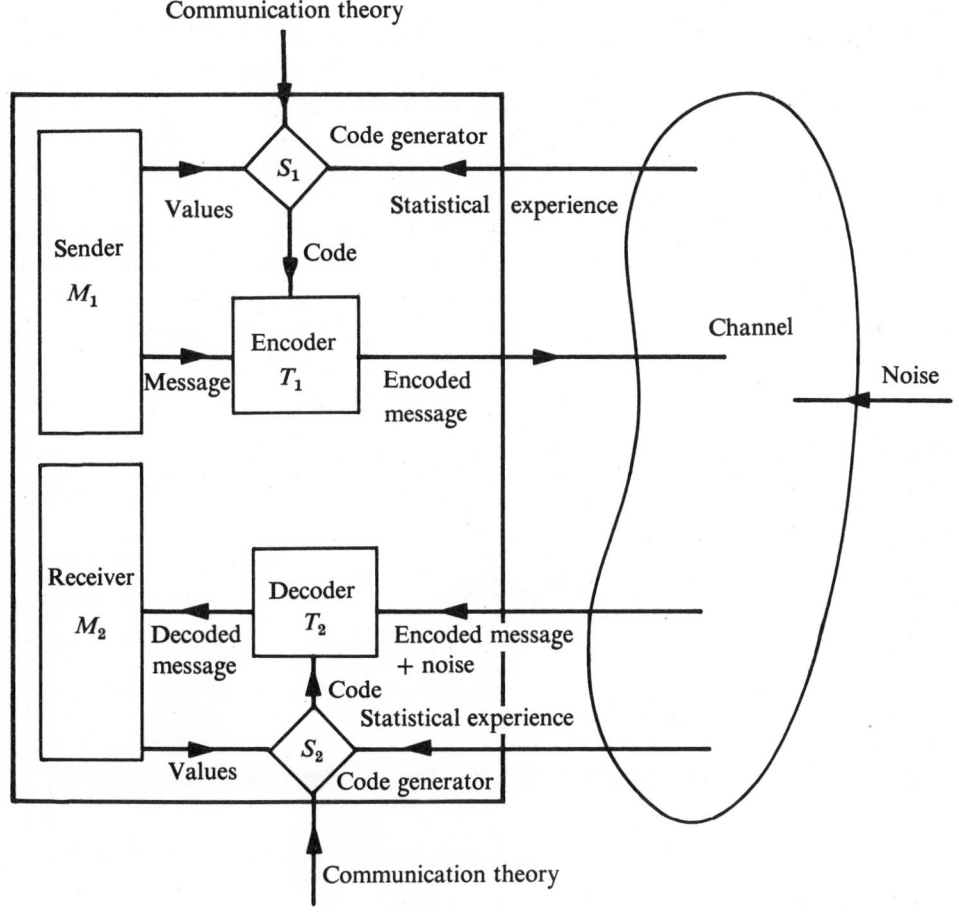

FIGURE 9.   A communication theory system.

of messages it can generate, and, for each message, the probability that it will occur. These messages are not directly communicated but fed into an effector organ, T_1, called an *encoder* which modifies, or *codes*, the message to make it compatible with the process of communication. The surrounding into which encoded messages are fed is here called a *channel*. Also fed into the channel, and mixed with the message, are perturbations generated outside the system; they are called *noise*. Mathematically, the channel is specified by the repertory of messages it can receive, by the repertory of messages it can pass on, and by a matrix of conditional probabilities stating the likelihood of any given output message resulting from any given input message. The mixture of message and noise is transmitted in a *decoder*, T_2, which feeds into the *receiver*, M_2. In general, the message repertories of sender and receiver are the same, and the function of encoder and decoder is to make the message received the same as the message sent. In principle, however, encoder and decoder can be different organs, and each may consist of a whole string of different elements.

Communication is the flow of information. With each piece of information can be associated a quantity called its amount which is independent of its semantic nature. The *amount of information* in a message is defined as the mean number of binary choices (or statements) by which one of a given set of messages is selected, with the proviso that the sequence of binary choices be such that the average number of steps per message is minimized. Thus the amount of input information is a function not of a specific message but of the whole repertory of messages which the source can produce, and their associated probabilities. The output information is determined in the same way.

For each communication event, the joint amount of information in source and receiver is that number of binary statements which indentifies both the message sent and the message received. It can be partitioned into three parts. 1) The amount of coherent information, that is, output information which can be directly deduced when the input is known, and vice versa; this portion is called amount of *information transmitted*. 2) Input information which fails to be transmitted, and thus represents uncertainty concerning the input if the output is known; it is called amount of *equivocation*. 3) Output information which is not

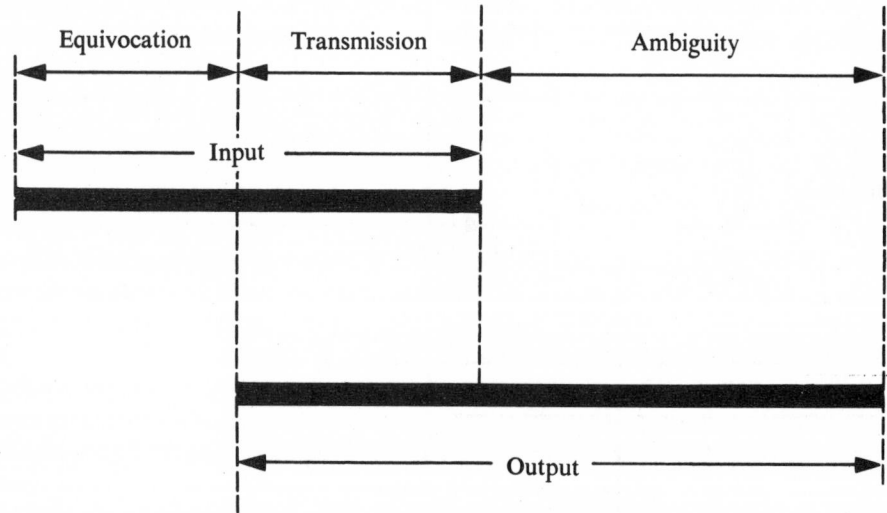

FIGURE 10.   Information analysis of communication process.

due to the input, and hence is uncertain if the input is known; it is called amount of *ambiguity*. The relation between these quantities is diagramed in Figure 10; amounts of information are represented as length of bars, corresponding to the mean lengths of tapes if the defining binary choices were written so that each choice corresponds to an equal length of tape.[8]

Like the other systems, the communication system has one component which is charged with a subtle job: it is the component which generates a code. *The code generator, S*, must have statistical information about the transmission of all messages in the repertory; it must also have directives from the motivators which serve to assess the relative values of the effort spent in communication and the risks of faulty decoding. Given these items, plus knowledge of communication technology and the mathematical theory of information and communication, an optimum code can be designed. This tends to be a lengthy and difficult procedure.

E. Comments

The four theories of systems organization sketched above do not exhaust the range of systems theories, and each of the sketches given does no more than hint at the nature of the theory. Even so, a few useful generalizations emerge. All theories of organization are formally similar; this formal similarity is based on conceptual homology. The four systems considered are simply different types of abstractions or formalizations of the same type of situation. A criterion which determines the decision to be taken in response to a given report from the sensor elements is not basically different from the strategy which prescribes a given move for a given situation, or from the code which, upon transmission of a mixture of message and noise, decides which message was the one presumably sent. Equally, the standard temperature and the standard temperature differences of the cybernetic scheme are codes which transform the incoming temperature information in successive steps into an error signal and a control action; a criterion in a detection system is a code which translates a report of the sensory elements into one of the admissible responses; a game strategy is a code by which situations perceived are converted into moves to be made.

In all theories of organization, the system is found to contain three kinds of components. One kind comprises the various components which appear as sensor and effector elements, the elements operating on the tactical level. These are the classical black boxes defined by a repertory of inputs, a repertory of outputs, and a repertory of laws associating outputs to inputs.

The second kind of components are the computers which generate the laws: standards for producing control signals, game strategies, decision criteria, and codes. In a way, these are also black boxes, but they operate on a strategic level rather than on that of the tactical immediate contingency. The inputs for these black boxes are over-all experience on systems and surroundings as well as a set of values; the outputs are the laws governing the operations of the components of the first kind, and these outputs are generated from the inputs by sophisticated mathematical methods.

The third type of components, called "motivators," are not treated as black boxes. On the strategic level, the motivators embody the setting of values which are necessary ingredients for the operation of the computers. The theory says nothing about how these values are arrived at, and this indeed is a weak point in many applications of systems theories. Consider, for instance, the situation of a purchasing agent who has to decide whether to accept or reject a given lot of goods after having inspected a sample. The sample, even if drawn impartially from the lot, will not necessarily reflect the true composition; it may happen to be better or worse than the whole of the lot. Consequently, the purchasing agent is bound sometimes to reject a good lot, or accept a bad one. The modern statistician, equipped with the tools of decision theory, can help; he can set criteria of acceptance and rejection; he can even assist in devising efficient sampling procedures. However, he won't do anything until he is informed precisely what loss of value will arise if a good lot is wrongly rejected, and what if a bad lot is wrongly accepted. Unfortunately, it is usually difficult or impossible to make a rational estimate of the precise values in either case. The result tends to be a somewhat haphazard guess which is then fed into a precise and impeccably rational computing mechanism.

On the tactical level, the motivators can receive inputs and generate outputs; for instance, in the communication analysis, receive and send messages. The theory says nothing about why a particular source generates a particular message, and about what motivates the reception. Indeed, in the mathematical theory of communication a source of messages is treated as a generator of a random sequence of signals, modified only by a set of probabilities.[6,13] In more elaborate treatments, sequential probabilities are taken into account, that is, the probability that a particular message follows a given antecedent or even a given string of antecedents. In no case, however, does the theory inquire into the rationale of sending a particular message rather than another. It is seen that the "motivators" play a curious role in systems theory: in some way, they represent the innermost core of the system, that which makes it go; but they also serve as receptacles for features that remain unexplained and which the theory fails to rationalize.

III. SOME PRINCIPLES OF BIOLOGICAL ORGANIZATION

Cybernetics and the theories of games, decisions, and communications are excellent tools for the design engineer. They yield normative statements: how one should go about setting up a control system, how to plan a rational strategy in organized conflict, how to set up a pattern of decisions that will satisfy certain conditions, and how to achieve optimum communication in the presence of noise. All these schemes have been developed with patterns of human behavior in mind; they are vivid and appealing renderings of certain aspects of human activity, and can be applied to the study of conscious behavior. However, since the schemes are paradigms rather than descriptions of actual happenings, any application to naive everyday behavior requires much caution.[4,9] Even more circumspection is needed in application to nonconscious activities on the physiological, cellular, or biochemical level.[8,10,11,22] Used with the proper caution, however, organization theory is an interesting and promising tool for biological research.

A.   An Example of Biological Organization: The Organization of Enzyme Synthesis[5,7]

1. *A model.* Enzymes are proteins with catalytic functions; they are the tools of the metabolic activities of the cell, and presumably mediate the expression of any character of a living thing. The blueprints which say what enzymes a cell can produce are presumably embodied in very different kinds of macromolecules, namely, nucleic acids. One of the basic problems of biology is how a particular part of the blueprint becomes actuated at the right time. The diagram below (Figure 11) shows how this may happen. It is based on the model developed by Jacob and Monod.[7] The scheme is not quite complete. It may be

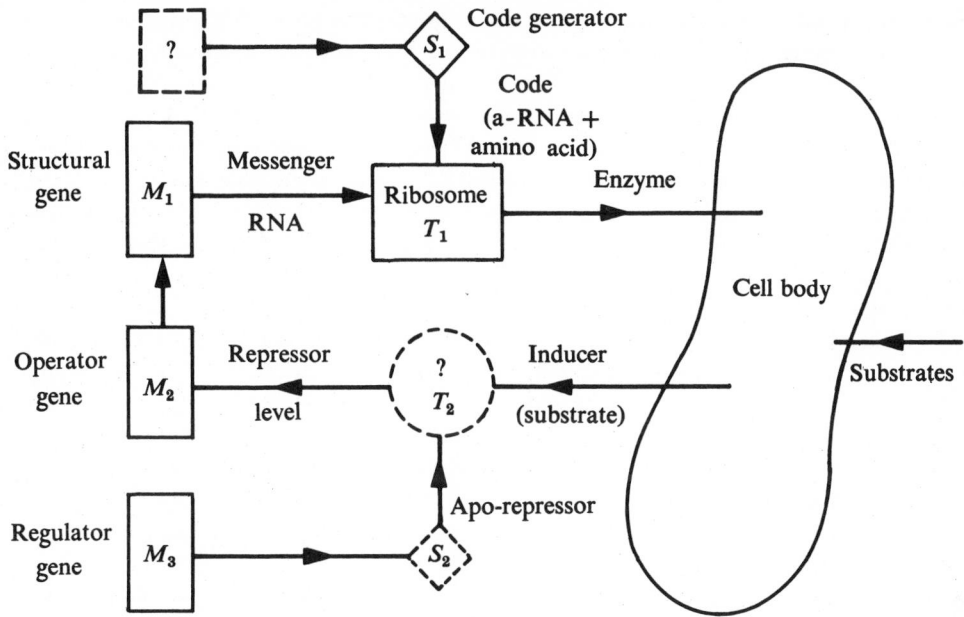

FIGURE 11. A model of the organization of enzyme synthesis. Symbols explained in text.

wrong in detail. It is almost certainly not of general validity. But the fact that a fairly comprehensive molecular scheme of gene activity could be formulated at all, even tentatively, is one of the major triumphs of modern biology.

Proteins are polymers with a primary structure consisting of a sequence of amino acids, and secondary and tertiary structures. By the so-called Crick's "central dogma," the primary structure determines automatically the secondary and tertiary structures and thereby all functional properties of the polymer. The primary structure is imparted to the enzyme in the process of its synthesis, which takes place on a ribosome (the upper square box, T_1, of the diagram); for a specific model of T_2 see reference[12]. The specification of the sequence of amino acids is mediated through a gene product, the *messenger RNA*, which combines with the ribosome to form a *template*. The unit process of specification involves a single amino acid, and is controlled by a group of nucleotides on the messenger RNA molecule. The mapping relation between groups of nucleotides and amino acids is the *code* of protein specification.

The physical embodiment of this code is a collection of a particular type of RNA molecules called *adapter RNA* (also transfer RNA, soluble RNA). They are thought to be stiff rods, about 100 A long, which carry on one end an amino acid, on the other a group of nucleotides which is effectively a description of the amino acid in a language compatible with the messenger RNA.[23] The physical production of the code consists of the combination of free amino acids with the appropriate molecules of transfer RNA; it is mediated by a set of *activating enzymes*; this process is indicated by the upper diamond-shaped box, S_1, of the diagram.

The messenger RNA itself is produced by a part of the genome called the *structural gene*; it is represented by the upper rectangular box, M_1. The sequence "production of messenger RNA---synthesis of enzyme" corresponds to the sequence "control signal---control action" of the cybernetic scheme, to the sequence "message emitted---message encoded" of the communication scheme. The enzyme embodies a control action, an encoded message from the genome, which will operate upon the metabolic pool of the cell body.

The receptor part of the organization is less well worked out. The stimulus emanating from the cell body is the presence, in excess, of the *substrate* the enzyme can catalyze (or some substance which is similar to this substrate). The ultimate recipient of this message is a part of the genome called the *operator gene*, M_2; however, the message goes first through a decoder, T_2. The decoded message at the operator is defined as the level of specific *repressor* molecules, presumably also RNA, which prevent the activity of the operator. The repressor molecules are produced in still another part of the genome, called the *regulator gene*, M_3. The decoding operation consists of inactivation of the repressor molecule by the prospective enzyme substrate; this inactivation may take place at the gene itself, or involve only the gene product. If no repressor molecule ties up the operator gene, it will produce a signal (of unknown nature) which activates the structural gene, which in turn produces a messenger, which specifies the synthesis of the appropriate enzyme, which then operates on the substrate. As the substrate disappears, the repression process is unleashed, the operator, the structural gene, and, ultimately, the enzyme synthesis are blocked; the cycle of control action is closed.

2. *Comments.* The similarity between the diagram representing enzyme induction and the various schemes of system theory is not a fortuitous one. One may note that the system uses two means of communication, or languages, of rather different character. Between genome and encoder and, presumably, decoder, messages are originated and carried by means of essentially linear nucleic acid molecules. Activities within the body of the cell, and messages coming from and to the coding devices, rest largely on interactions of protein molecules with other molecules, interactions involving surfaces and volumes. The encoding device is a typical black box (of the "tactical" type) operating on two levels of organization: the input repertory probably consists of a set of nucleotide triplets, the output repertory of the set of amino acids which participate in protein synthesis, and the law is the code which associates a given triplet with a given amino acid. For the purpose of this discussion, it does not matter whether this analysis will stand as is or be modified.

On a higher level of organization, the encoder accepts not single inputs but whole linear sequences of inputs. There does not seem to be any restriction as to what input sequences are acceptable. The sequences are determined elsewhere: in the genome, in the virus, or in the test tube of a biochemist. Hence the encoder acts, as an encoder should, as a transcription device which will translate any message in the appropriate input language into a message in the output language. Much less is known about the decoder but it may be assumed that it acts along similar lines. It probably translates "inducer" into "repressor RNA" which, incidentally, calls for a repertory some ten times larger than that of the encoder.

The generator which produces the code for translating nucleic acid into proteins has the properties of a strategy computer (the diamond-shaped box S of Figures 6–9). It was mentioned that the physical embodiment of the code is a collection of rods which carry an amino acid on one end, its equivalent in nucleic acid language on the other. The manufacture of any given element of this collection is a tactical operation, consisting of the enzymatic attachment of an amino acid to an RNA molecule. The strategic functions are the manufacture of a code such that every one of about fifty inputs is associated with a particular one of at least nineteen outputs, and the preparation of a set of activating enzymes which will execute this code. This involves a great deal more planning than one would like to ascribe to a cell constituent.

Whenever a living structure functions in a way which to a conscious mind would result from a good deal of deliberation, Darwinian evolution is invoked. The "value input" to the strategy computer is then the drive to live and to reproduce (unexplained by the theory, as are other value inputs); the "experience input," the selection of the fittest; and the mode of operation is the method of trial and error.* Now, organization by trial and error works only in situations where there is a reasonable expectation that a solution will be arrived at within the time available. Hence the main general problem associated with strategy computers is that of finding strategies which can be computed by the trial and error method within the length of time allowed for evolution.

The identification of the genes with the "motivating" components of systems is an obvious step. Genes are at the core of all (or at least most) biological activities; they presumably are the source of unexplained value messages such as the order "live and reproduce." Like people who are the true models of the "motivator" components, genes can respond in a predictable manner to tactical needs; the enzyme induction diagram (Figure 11) pictures such a situation. The subtle problem arises if one asks how it is possible that the messenger RNA, which is released in response to the presence of a given substrate, will result in the synthesis of an enzyme which is capable of catalyzing that substrate. The extraordinary difficulty of this job becomes manifest when one considers that the elements of an associated triplet of substrate, enzyme, and messenger RNA, while carrying the same information, have no physical similarity to each other, and that there must be a few hundred such systems working concomitantly in the same space without interfering much with each other.

Most of biological research is concerned with problems of tactical operations. The problems raised by the strategic operations are vast, probably more difficult, and certainly less popular; these problems are the proper domain of theories of biological organization. General solutions to these problems are out of reach at this time. However, consideration of existing biological organizations vaguely suggests some principles which may, in the not too far future, help in establishing a sound theory. In the following sections, some such principles will be roughly, very roughly, sketched.

B. The Signature Principle

1. *Some facts.* In accepting an amino acid from a transfer RNA, the template does not react with every portion of the molecule; for instance, the template was shown not to respond to the amino acid directly attached to the transfer RNA. This was demonstrated in an ingenious experiment where an amino acid was enzymatically attached to its transfer RNA and subsequently chemically changed to another; this resulted in the fraudulent amino acid being incorporated. Thus the chemical recognition process which directs the specification of an amino acid sequence by the RNA template involves recognition not of the entire molecule but only of a *signature*, presumably the nucleotide triplet at one end of the molecule. The nucleic acid portion adjacent to the amino acid itself could not possibly be used in specifying the amino acid since it has the same sequence in all transfer RNA's so far studied. Conceivably, this portion of the molecule could permit the polymerase to distinguish a duly activated amino acid from many other objects with which it might collide.

* These matters are discussed in detail in Chapters 15 and 16.

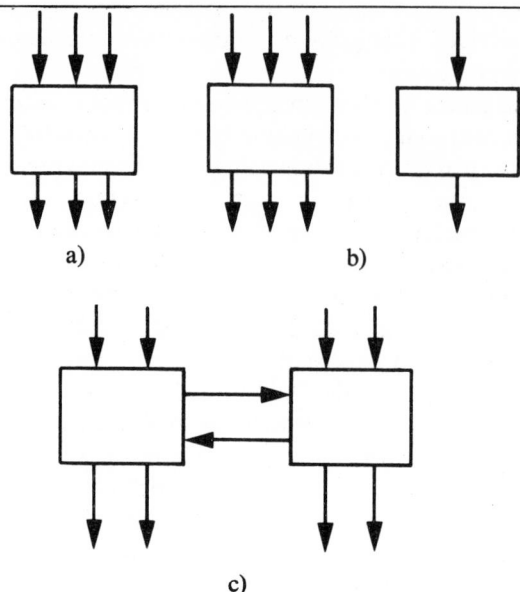

FIGURE 12.   Design for information processing.

Recognition by signature is a common phenomenon in metabolic processes. It underlies the effect of antimetabolites, substances which are combined with normal metabolites because of partial similarity. Some antimetabolites are active in some cells and inactive in other cells which depend on the same metabolite; this suggests that not all cells necessarily register the same signature of a given metabolite.[20]

A molecule, particularly a large one, may have more than one signature. A protein may have one or more signatures which determine its metabolic activity, and other signatures for serological specificity. The transfer RNA, as mentioned before, has one signature which is acted upon by the template, probably another one recognized by the peptide polymerase, and quite possibly still another one for interaction with the activating enzyme.

The signature principle extends beyond biochemical processes to all levels of biological organization. To give an example from mammalian physiology: a low oxygen level causes a variety of changes in bodily functions. The signature of this condition which affects short-range regulation via the respiratory center is increased CO_2 tension; a signature for long-range regulation through increased proliferation of red cells is a substance, erythro-poietine, which the kidney produces if oxygen is low. In neither case is the primary factor directly operative in the control system. To skip to the psychological level, the signature principle is met with in just about every recognition process. We may recognize a given person by several different signatures (for example, a combination of visual features, a pattern of movement, the sound of the voice), and different observers will recognize the same person by different signatures, illustrating the phenomenon of multiple signa-tures.

2. *Need for operating with signatures.* If one referent has two or more signatures, its effects will be ambiguous. If two or more signatures have the same referent, equivocation of referents results. For instance, since the RNA-protein code is degenerate, two or more nucleotide triplets may spell the same amino acid; this causes no damage (it has, in fact, a small protective value since a few possible errors at or on the template result in no amino

acid change). On the other hand, antimetabolite effects due to equivocal signatures can cause much damage. Ambiguity and equivocation mean less than perfect communication. This is compatible with perfect control if the lost information was not needed, as in the case of the degenerate code. In general, however, imperfect communication causes imperfect control; hence, signature recognition is basically an evil, and since it is common it may be a necessary evil.

The following consideration of a model system (Figure 12) will illustrate conditions which lead to the establishment of operation through signature. Let the world in which a system lives consist of pieces of information each containing the same amount of information, and the components of the system be such that each can process three such pieces per unit time. Thus a single element can operate as a channel passing three units of information per unit time (Figure 12a).

Two elements are needed if four items of information must be processed (Figure 12b). In the arrangement shown, one element is partly idle, and since neither element knows what the other sees, no coherent action is possible. The arrangement of Figure 12c is better. The system is now coherent, and both components operate at capacity. This is bought at the price of using two of the available units of information processing for internal communication which does not contribute to the payload of interaction with the surrounding. Furthermore, the coherence cannot be perfect. Each component receives two units of information and passes on one unit to its neighbor. This one unit may contain parts of the information in both input units; the information passed from each element to the other is a signature of the total information it has received. As long as the signature is all that is needed for successful cooperation, the system is all right. If an occasion arises where the signature yields misleading or insufficient information, the system will be in danger.

As the ratio of total task to component capability increases, the system grows more complex, a larger fraction of informational capabilities is used for internal information traffic, and signature recognition must become more and more prevalent. For instance, nine units of information could be handled by six components such that half the information capability is used for internal communication, and each of the three effects of elements has some of all the input information (of course, not more than one-third of the total amount).

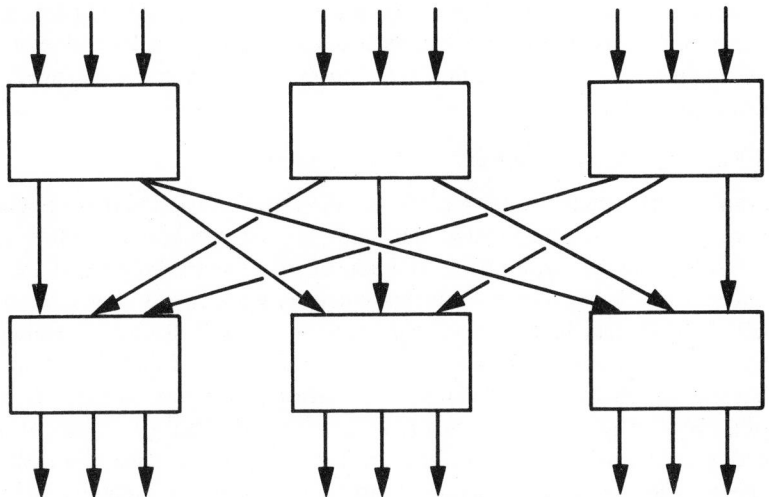

FIGURE 13. More complex design for information processing system.

3. *Informational limitations of biological processes.* A discrepancy between informational challenge and informational capability can be met, to a degree, by operating with signatures. Living systems seem to operate very largely with signatures; they also have to cope with informational challenges which transcend the informational capabilities of elementary acts. Every single discrete act of control, communication, or decision involves a choice. Whatever the discrete physical event that underlies the act of choice, there will always be a limitation on the number of choices available at any one time. This kind of informational limitation is conspicuously present in all elementary biological acts.

Consider, for example, the information limitations in a chemical system of control and communication, like that outlined in Section III-A.[8] Chemical communication relies on specificity of chemical reactions, and the forces involved in chemical reactions are myopic and have an effective range measured in angstroms. Hence a single molecule can effectively "see" only an area of some 100 A^2 in the course of a collision. Suppose the reactive partner is a protein. Then the reactive surface is made up of amino acids, and there are not many of these which can be accommodated within the limited area. Hence, there are just so many independently different reactive spots on protein molecules, possibly only a few hundred kinds, hardly as many as 10,000.

The limitations in the amount of choice or information which can be crammed into a single elementary process extend through all levels of biological organization. Skipping intermediate levels and going right through to mental activity, a good example of the limitation is the amount of information which can be grasped at a single glance; it corresponds to a choice of one in about a million possibilities.[9]

A second type of informational limitation is a temporal one: for any elementary act of communication and control, there is a minimum time of realization, and a maximum time during which all components can remain gathered for the final interaction.

4. *Comments.* The *Signature Principle* of biological organization has been sketched in a rough and heuristic manner. The events to which it applies have in common that only a fraction of the features (the signatures) of the components become ingredients of the process of concrescence; the concrescence into a unity of an input, a law, and an output, in one form or another underlies all acts of control, communication, and decision. As a rule, the signature is a small fraction of the features; a given object, or event, can have more than one functional signature, and a given signature can be equivocal. From this, harmful confusion can result; this characterizes signature operations as potentially evil. They are, thus, a necessary evil, a way of dealing with large informational challenges in spite of limited informational capabilities.

C. Remarks on Self-Organization[2,11,15]

In the paradigms of systems organization, the development of codes, strategies, or rules of decision involves using sophisticated reasoning on a large body of data. In the cell, comparable results must be achieved by trial and error. The probability of success in this procedure depends on the fraction of strategies which are workable, and on the time available for trials before the system breaks down for want of a usable strategy.[2] Hence the trial-and-error procedure is highly adequate for exploring a restricted neighborhood, that is, in complex systems, for gradual adjustments; in creating a complex strategy *de novo*, it has no chance of success unless it starts from a fairly good approximation. Now, even the most basic operations of life, like protein synthesis, depend on the existence of a rather complex strategy. The question of how this came about is of formidable difficulty. However, we propose to show that any system that operates by the signature principle has a chance of easily finding a strategy not far from optimum.

Consider the problem of setting up a code to transmit messages through a noisy channel. In the presence of ambiguity and equivocation, some of the message information is bound to be lost. It can be retrieved only if the message contains some *redundant* information, that is, information about itself which can be used to spot and correct errors which have occurred in transmission. The simplest application of redundancy is repetition of the message; this fails if there are particular difficulties with some parts of the message language. It is, therefore, more effective to couch the repetition in a different language. The most sophisticated method is to translate the original message into one containing more (and thus, redundant) information in such a way that all parts of the message are interrelated so that each part of the message contains some information about all the rest of it. The minimum amount of information which is needed to make transmission free from error through a noisy channel can be computed.[13] The problem of working out a code to translate the original message into one protected by a minimum amount of information is very difficult, and can be solved only for a fraction of the possible contingencies.[6,21] However, if the system is large enough, then a translation code based on random selection will turn out to be not far from optimal.

This is a somewhat startling statement; the following consideration will serve to make it plausible. A well-constructed message containing redundant information will contain a maximum number of relations which can be used for checking purposes. Thus, if the message consists of a string of numbers, it will be useful to ensure that each number occurs with equal frequency; then, upon reception, a count of the total number of zeros, ones, twos, threes, etc., may reveal that there is one zero too many and one five too few, and thus suggest the presence of an error as well as a number of possible locations for it. A further check can be made if the relative frequencies of all number pairs (i.e., sequences 0,0; 0,1; 0,2; 0,3; ... 1,0; 1,1; etc.) are kept equal; similarly for number triplets, quadruplets, etc. So we arrive at the conclusion that the ideal numerical message will be one that shows no bias for any number or combination of numbers; but this is precisely the criterion used to check a sequence of numbers for randomness. To put this result into more concrete terms: suppose messages are to be expressed in terms of decimal digits. The number of digits originally needed depends on the number of messages which are to be sent. Thus with one digit one can transmit ten different messages, with two digits 100, with three digits 1000, etc. If redundancy is to be added, then an r-digit message must be replaced by one with $r + s$ digits, for example, a three-digit message by one with six. A good way of choosing a particular set of 1000 out of the 1,000,000 possible six-digit messages is to rely on random selection.

To get the full benefit of redundant information, the entire message as received must be decoded. For more modest requirements, it may be sufficient to start with a portion of the received message. For instance in the example given, one may start with any four digits and see whether these identify any of the possible 1000 messages with satisfactory certainty; if not, one can look at the fifth digit, et cetera.[21] A general principle emerges: it is good strategy to encode a set of messages by a highly redundant, randomly selected set, to use in decoding only a random sample of the total information received, and to read out only as much as is necessary for recognition.

But this is precisely the signature principle. The set of messages corresponds to the set of factors relevant for particular kinds of events; the signatures are the portions of the messages which are read out. The problem of arriving at a satisfactory strategy is, then, reduced to that of adjusting the *size* of the signature to the needs. In principle, and so far only in principle, this appears to be a performance which should be within the informational capabilities of a cell.

IV. OUTLOOK

Many authors have observed that the foremost characteristic of living things is their great complexity. Systems of very great complexity, whether living or not, may well exhibit phenomena which either do not occur at all or are inconsequential in the relatively simple objects dealt with by chemistry and physics. This kind of circumspect vitalism is a noble principle which intuitively appeals to many biologists. However, not much has been done to apply it to the everyday work of the scientist. Almost all experiments and most theories aim at explaining biological phenomena by ultimate reduction to ordinary physics and chemistry, and our education is such that we are not really quite satisfied until such a reduction is successfully accomplished.

A very proper marriage of recognition of the complexity of living systems with reduction to orthodox physics and chemistry has been accomplished in the X-ray analysis of biological macromolecules. The principles are familiar to chemists and physicists; the complexity is acknowledged by not even trying to solve the problem through conventional computations or approximations, but by feeding the experimental results into large computers. This type of investigation deals with complex systems in a way specific for complex systems, yet without the slightest deviation from strict mechanistic reductionism; the results are greatly and unreservedly admired.

One may wonder, though, whether all kinds of biological complexity can be dealt with by simple recourse to large computers. It will not work for systems that are not or need not be completely known. This is where systems theories of one kind or another allow a direct approach. They have been used with great success in the analysis and synthesis of neural and quasi-neural networks. These studies have been very useful to engineers who design systems; the application to biology proceeds at a slow rate, presumably because the results of a systems-theoretical approach are not easily amalgamated with the results of the older physical-chemical approaches. It is for this reason that systems-theoretical investigations of biochemical systems are particularly attractive, since some specific aspects of a proposed structure should be readily translatable into experimental approaches of the conventional kind. Specific aspects are to be tested, but not every aspect, since if a system is well enough known to be analyzable in every respect by physical and chemical methods, then a systems theory approach does not seem to be necessary or rewarding. What we must learn, though, is not to regard every part of a model or a theory that is not or cannot be subjected to physical experimentation as a weak part of the whole. We have to accept the fact that results of systems theory approaches can be meaningful and interesting even if some of them are not amenable to analysis with the established methods.

REFERENCES

1. Aronow, S. 1959. A theory of analogs. *In:* "Proc. First Natl. Biophys. Conf." (H. Quastler and H. J. Morowitz, eds.), pp. 27–34. Yale Univ. Press, New Haven.
2. Ashby, W. R. 1954. "Design for a Brain," 2nd ed., 260 pp. Chapman and Hall, London.

3. Ashby, W. R. 1957. "Cybernetics," 295 pp. Chapman and Hall, London.
4. Attneave, F. 1959. "Applications of Information Theory to Psychology," 120 pp. Holt, New York.
5. Chovnik, A., ed. 1961. Cellular regulatory mechanisms. *Cold Spring Harbor Symp. Quant. Biol.* **26:** 1–408.
6. Fano, R. M. 1961. "Transmission of Information," 389 pp. M.I.T. Press, Wiley, New York.
7. Jacob, F., and Monod, J. 1961. Genetic regulatory mechanisms in the synthesis of proteins. *J. Mol. Biol.* **3:** 318–356.
8. Quastler, H., ed. 1953. "Essays on the Use of Information Theory in Biology," 273 pp. Univ. Illinois Press, Urbana.
9. Quastler, H., ed. 1955. "Information Theory in Psychology," 436 pp. Free Press, Glencoe, Ill.
10. Quastler, H. 1958. Information theory in radiobiology. *Ann. Rev. Nuc. Sci.* **8:** 387–400.
11. Quastler, H. 1959. Information theory of biological integration. *Am. Naturalist.* **93:** 245–254.
12. Quastler, H. 1963. Chemical communication systems in the cell. *Trans. N.Y. Acad. Sci.* **25:** 382–385.
13. Shannon, C. E., and Weaver, W. 1949. "The Mathematical Theory of Communication," 117 pp. Univ. Illinois Press, Urbana.
14. Thrall, R. M., Coombs, C. H., and Davis, R. L., eds. 1954. "Decision Processes," 332 pp. Wiley, New York.
15. von Neumann, J. 1958. "The Computer and the Brain," 82 pp. Yale Univ. Press, New Haven.
16. von Neumann, J., and Morgenstern, O. 1947. "Theory of Games and Economic Behavior," 641 pp. Princeton Univ. Press, Princeton.
17. Wiener, N. 1948. "Cybernetics," 1st ed., 194 pp. M.I.T. Press, Wiley, New York.
18. Wiener, N. 1961. "Cybernetics," 2nd ed., 212 pp. M.I.T. Press, Wiley, New York.
19. Williams, J. D. 1954. "The Compleat Strategyst," 1st ed., 234 pp. McGraw-Hill, New York.
20. Woolley, D. W. 1952. "A Study of Antimetabolites," 269 pp. Wiley, New York.
21. Wozencraft, J. M., and Reiffen, B. 1961. "Sequential Decoding," 74 pp. M.I.T. Press, Wiley, New York.
22. Yockey, H. P., Platzman, R. L., and Quastler, H., eds. 1958. "Symposium on Information Theory in Biology," 418 pp. Pergamon, New York.
23. Zubay, G. 1963. Molecular model for protein synthesis. *Science* **140:** 1092–1095.

[13]

TRANSIENTS IN METABOLISM:
An Approach to the Chemical Mechanisms of Metabolic Control

Britton Chance

I. INTRODUCTION

The simple theorem of reaction kinetics, that a chemical change which occurs in time prior to another must indeed be located in a preceding chemical sequence, has been used time and again in ordering the sequence of chemical reactions in biological systems. A particular example is the ordering of Complexes I and II in peroxidase kinetics.[1-3] Another example is represented by the application of reaction kinetics to the ordering of cytochromes in the respiratory chain.[4,5] In fact, it is possible to develop ordering theorems for the sequence of enzymatic reactions which can be of general use and significance in enzymology.[15]

The application of kinetic studies to the ordering of metabolic control processes which occur in living cells was considered briefly in 1954[5,6] and in more detail in connection with the suspension of ascites tumor cells.[11]

The particular problem in studying the living cell is the inability of the experimenter to alter the steady state over wide ranges by an imposed transient without causing severe and perhaps irreversible damage to the enzymatic systems. Experimental studies indicate that there are approximately three types of transients which may be imposed upon the metabolism of a cell and which may yield useful information on the nature and the time sequence of the metabolic control phenomena. They are:

1) energy dissipation in muscle

$$ATP \xrightarrow{\text{Myofibriles}} ADP + P_i,$$

where P_i is inorganic phosphate

2) starved-fed transition in yeast

$$P_i + \text{substrate} + ADP \xrightarrow{\text{oxidative phosphorylation + glycolysis}} ATP + \text{product}$$

3) energy demands of glucose loading

$$ATP + \text{glucose} \xrightarrow{\text{hexokinase}} \text{glucose} - 6P + ADP$$

It is important to note that only in the case of the third is a metabolic transient imposed exclusively in terms of ADP. The first gives equal amounts of ADP and P_i.

II. MUSCLE CONTRACTION AND METABOLISM

A flow chart for metabolic control phenomena in contractile tissue is shown in Figure 1. Initiation of contraction converts ATP or creatine phosphate to ADP and phosphate. These can be recombined to form ATP by the respiratory chain, by glycolysis, or by the creatine phosphate store. Glycolysis is less likely in aerobic muscle which produces very little lactate. In any case, the response of oxidative phosphorylation to a step increase of ADP and phosphate differs from that of glycolysis. In oxidative phosphorylation, an increased concentration of ADP and phosphate causes an oxidation of reduced pyridine nucleotide[14b] whereas in glycolytic activity an increased concentration of ADP and phosphate causes a reduction of DPN at the triose phosphate dehydrogenase stage. Thus, a study of intracellular kinetics immediately following muscular contraction will permit a time sequence study of the oxidation and reduction of the total intracellular pyridine nucleotide, and will thus identify the pathway of oxidative resynthesis of ATP. In addition, such a study will tell us a great deal about the time relations of the contractile mechanism and the control of glycogenolysis. If, for example, glycogenolysis were a main source of energy in muscular contraction, the primary metabolic event would have to be DPN reduction in the triose phosphate dehydrogenase step.

An experimental study of the transient response of the pyridine nucleotide component of excised sartorius muscle is given in Figure 2. The experimental record shows the time relations of tension development, heat production, and increased mitochondrial metabolism. It is seen that the two endergonic phenomena, tension development and heat production, activate the exergonic process of ATP hydrolysis for restitution of the energy balance of the muscle. Note the important fact that even one twitch exerts a clearly discernible control over energy metabolism (the small step of fluorescence change following a single contraction is readily reproducible and can easily be magnified for accurate measurement.[8,12] There are regular steps in the trace of fluorescence decrease which we interpret to represent the step-wise build-up of ADP concentration at the mitochondrial level. This is supported by the fact that recovery of the pyridine nucleotide trace parallels recovery of the heat production (remembering that a steady deflection of the temperature trace, after the transients due to the single contraction, represents roughly the rate of energy utilization in oxidative metabolism).

Response of respiratory carriers to muscle contraction

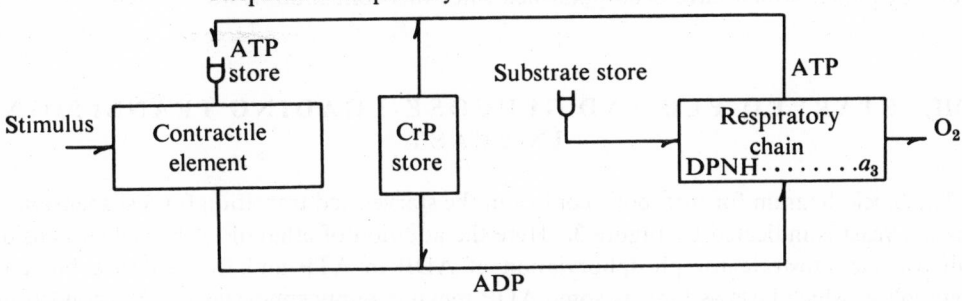

FIGURE 1. Diagram of chemical feedback connections involved in the response of oxidative enzymes to ADP formation in a muscular contraction. CrP = creatine phosphate; a_3 = cytochrome a_3.

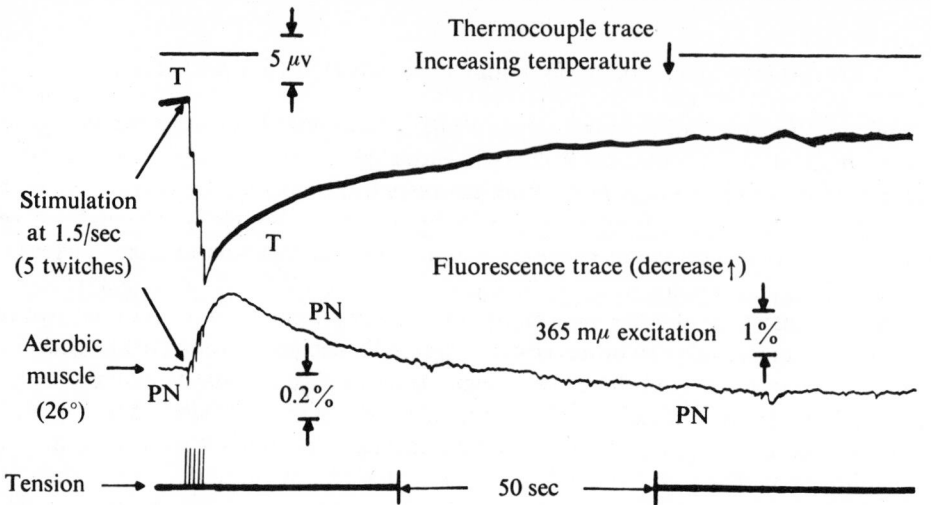

FIGURE 2. Physical and chemical responses of a frog sartorius muscle to a series of five contractions. Top trace (T) records heat production by downward deflection; middle trace (PN) indicates increased mitochondrial metabolism (measured by pyridine nucleotide fluorescence) by upward response; and bottom trace indicates tension development by upward deflection. Deflection calibrations are indicated. (Redrawn from Chance, Mauriello, and Aubert.[13]) (50E45A)

Referring back to Figure 1, we find the metabolic control phenomena as observed in terms of the oxidation-reduction level of DPNH in the muscle mitochondria to indicate an ADP control of oxidative metabolism following muscle contraction. Calculations of the ADP level formed from the known affinity of muscle mitochondria[8] and from the estimated equilibrium point of the creatine phosphokinase system[13] appear to be in reasonable agreement.

It is possible also that mitochondrial metabolism could have been activated by the phosphate release from the contractile element as well as by ADP release. At the present time, the phosphate assays of the intact muscle[18] indicate that the level of phosphate in the resting muscle is sufficiently large compared to the K_m, Michaelis-Menten constant, of the mitochondria for phosphate to make this unlikely.[9] A much more detailed discussion of the metabolic response of toad and frog sartorius muscles to electrical stimulation is provided by papers which have been published since this contribution was written.[14a,16b]

III. STARVED-FED AND GLUCOSE-LOADING TRANSITION IN YEAST

The block diagram for metabolic control in the starved-fed transition for a suspension of baker's yeast is indicated by Figure 3. Here the addition of ethanol to the cell suspension will provide substrate for phosphorylation of ADP to ATP and thus cause a burst of metabolism which lasts as long as some ADP remains unphosphorylated. A second transient can also be supplied by subsequently adding glucose to the cell which has just been "fed" with ethanol. This will cause a momentary depletion of ATP in Store(1) with reactivation of oxidative metabolism, due to ADP formation and the feedback of ATP for the phosphorylation of more glucose.

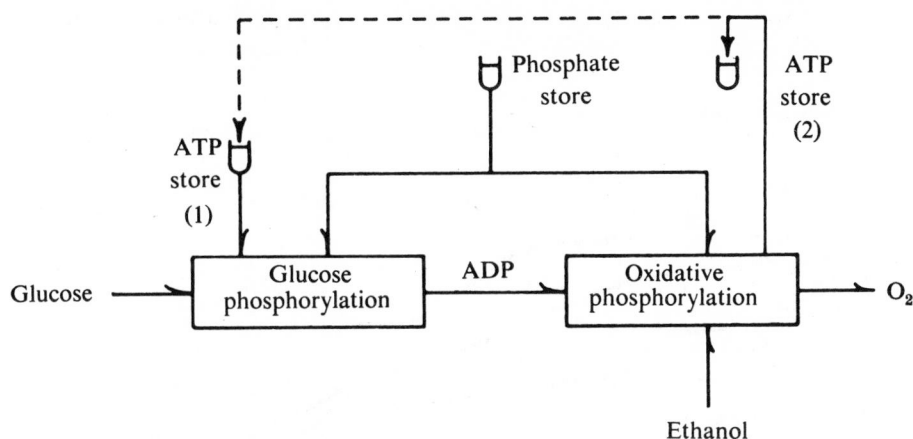

FIGURE 3. Block diagram of chemical feedbacks involved in the starved-fed transition and the glucose-loading transition of baker's yeast cells.

An experimental record illustrating the metabolic response of a suspension of baker's yeast cells to the starved-fed and the glucose-loading transition is indicated in Figure 4. In this experiment the cells are suspended in an 0.05 M acid phosphate buffer; after a steady base line has been established, the respiratory rate of the system is 0.55 μM O_2 per sec which characterizes the starved suspension (State 2). The addition of ethanol (EtOH) causes an abrupt reduction of DPN because of alcohol dehydrogenase activation, a reduction of cytochrome b by electron transfer, and an increased respiratory rate. A steady state is reached in about 15 sec, but this can last only as long as ADP is available (see Figure 3).

Thus at the end of 40 sec cytochrome b and pyridine nucleotide become more reduced and respiration slackens from 1.9 to 1.3 μM O_2 per sec. This represents the transition from the actively metabolizing State 3 to one in which the rate of metabolism is controlled by the availability of ATP (State 4).

The metabolic control cycle can now be repeated if an energy load is imposed by glucose addition, the phosphorylation of which releases intracellular ADP. Thus, 10 mM glucose added at the point marked by the arrow doubles the respiratory activity (2.7 μM O_2 per sec) and causes oxidation of cytochrome b. A mitochondrial response to ADP (just the reverse of the response observed when ADP is exhausted) is also an oxidation of pyridine nucleotide. As mentioned above, the pyridine nucleotide measured consists of both mitochondrial and cytoplasmic effects, and the expected oxidation is obscured by the large response of pyridine nucleotide at the triose phosphate dehydrogenase step.

Note that there is an overshoot in the response of cytochrome b to the glucose loading; the ADP level immediately following glucose addition is higher and causes a larger deflection of the cytochrome b trace than is obtained about half a minute later when the steady state has been established. Under these circumstances glycolytic phosphorylation may share a portion of the ADP load with the mitochondria. The record is terminated abruptly by the exhaustion of oxygen dissolved in the suspension, and the cytochrome b and pyridine nucleotide traces deflect abruptly off scale as the anaerobic state is reached.

Yeast is an organism which has classically been used for studies of glycolytic pathways and indeed is still found to be extremely useful for the analysis of all the metabolic intermediates that must interact in the pathways. Such analyses are now being carried on in this laboratory by my colleague, P. K. Maitra, and have been reported in preliminary

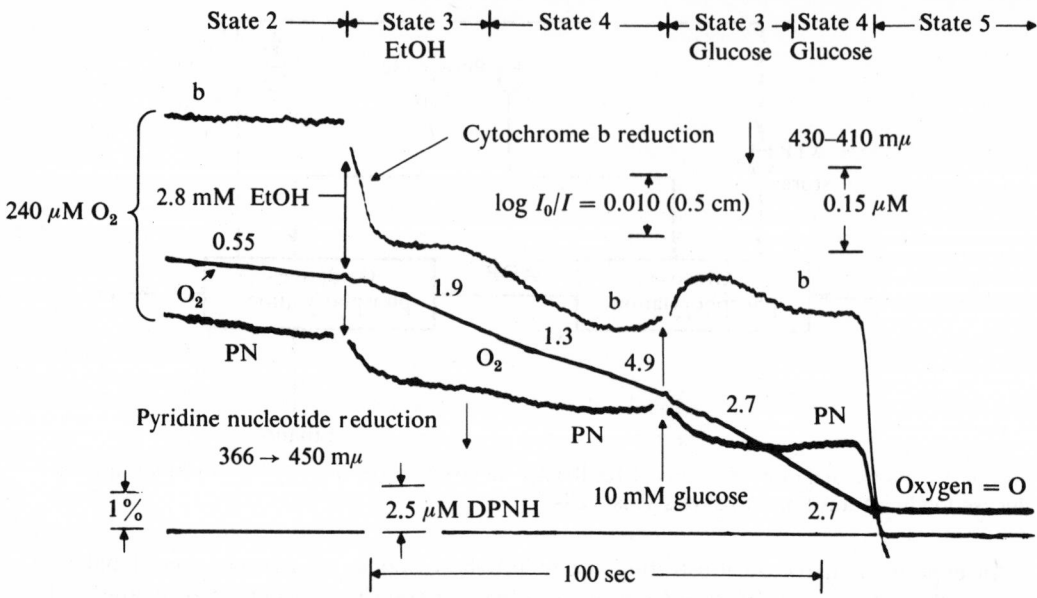

State 2 ——————— State 3 ——————— State 4 ——————— State 3 ——|State 4|—— State 5 ——→
                    EtOH   Glucose Glucose

FIGURE 4. Metabolic response of a suspension of baker's yeast cells to starved-fed and glucose-loading transitions. From top to bottom the three traces are: 1) oxidized cytochrome b (reduction indicated downward), marked with b; 2) amount of O_2 present (curve O_2) with 240 μM O_2 being the initial amount and the figures along the curve (0.55, 1.9, etc.) representing the respiratory rate in μM O_2 per sec; and 3) amount of oxidized pyridine nucleotide shown in curve PN with reduction to DPNH indicated downward. Calibrations for the ordinate of curves b and PN are shown. At the beginning of the first State 3, 2.8 mM of EtOH was added, and at the beginning of the second State 3, 10 mM glucose was added. (436-3)

form elsewhere.[17a,17b] It is sufficient to say that metabolic assays have now been perfected to the point where they can directly show the changes of metabolite and nucleotide concentrations which the continuous registration method had indicated. One difficulty with the analysis of total cell metabolites is, however, the possibility that components may not diffuse freely throughout the cell, and the average concentration of the metabolite may be a poor indication of its local concentration.

IV. GLUCOSE-LOADING IN THE ASCITES TUMOR CELL

In suspensions of ascites tumor cells, the starved-fed transition has not been feasible since the cells extracted from the mouse contain ample amounts of lactate and pyruvate. And even if these substrates are washed out, breakdown of other energy reserves in the cells (possibly fatty acids) provides substrate for them to maintain their respiration for long periods of time, so long in fact that cell deterioration may have occurred by the time an appreciably starved state is reached. Therefore, we study metabolic control patterns in the ascites tumor cell in terms of the glucose-loading transition.

Here the flow diagram for metabolic control is more comprehensive than that used for yeast. In order to represent the endogenous substrate, there is a "pyruvate store" which maintains respiratory activity and is, of course, in equilibrium with the lactate store. Thus, oxidative phosphorylation has a continuously available supply of substrate. The respiration rate during the oxidative metabolism of endogenous substrate is set by the rate of ATP utilization for purposes of synthesis and transport (see Figure 5) which feeds back ADP and phosphate into the oxidative phosphorylation system. Since these cells have a negligible glycogen supply, glycolytic phosphorylation of ADP is of little importance for exergonic purposes during the oxidation of lactate and pyruvate by the mitochondria.

Under such conditions of endogenous metabolism, the ATP level is high; addition of glucose to such a system will cause the formation of hexose phosphates and ADP and triose phosphate. The formation of ADP can increase the load on the mitochondrial oxidations and thereby increase respiratory activity. The formation of triose phosphates can also activate glycolysis, and a competition between glycolytic and mitochondrial energy-conserving reactions may ensue to determine which systems get the "lion's share" of the ADP formed from glucose loading. Finally, the feedback of ATP from oxidative and glycolytic phosphorylations will determine, among other things, the time interval over which the very rapid glucose phosphorylation can be maintained. In baker's yeast cells, we observed that the cell maintained a respiratory activity for an interval of over 40 sec. Longer experiments indicated that the glucose-activated respiration would continue at a steady rate for longer intervals as well. But in the ascites tumor cell, we have found an abrupt discontinuity in the glucose-activated respiratory activity occurring about one minute after adding glucose.[10]

The kinetics of these metabolic control phenomena are illustrated in Figure 6 in which pyridine nucleotide, cytochrome b, and oxygen are recorded as in Figure 4. Here the ascites tumor cells suspended in an aerobic reaction medium are pretreated with 3 mM malonate in order to block succinate oxidation in the citric acid cycle and enable us to observe the response of the mitochondria oxidizing a DPNH-linked substrate. The respiratory activity is very little affected by the malonate. The rate of oxidation of endogenous substrate is 1.0 μM O_2 per sec.

After a brief interval of observation to establish this rate and to observe the base line of the cytochrome b and pyridine nucleotide traces, 3.3 mM glucose is added. There is an almost immediate response of cytochrome b corresponding to an oxidation of this component and indicative of an increase of concentration of ADP in the mitochondria. Respiratory rate is more than doubled, apparently as soon as the platinum electrode is capable of recording the change. The response of pyridine nucleotide is similar to that observed with yeast. There are opposing changes in the mitochondria and the cytoplasm in which the cytoplasmic changes preponderate, and a net reduction of pyridine nucleotide is observed.

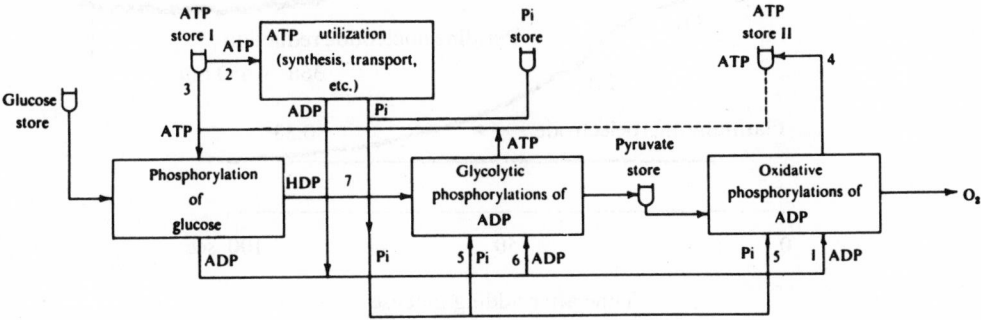

FIGURE 5. Block diagram of chemical feedbacks involved in the glucose-loading of oxidative and glycolytic metabolism in ascites tumor cells. The numbered pathways indicate key phosphate transfer reactions.

Shortly thereafter a reduction of pyridine nucleotide is observed and respiratory activity diminishes down to a level of 0.33 μM O_2 per sec below the activated rate by a factor of roughly 7, and 3 below the endogenous rate.

Not only is the respiratory metabolism inhibited in the 70-sec interval after glucose addition, but glucose metabolism is also inhibited in contradistinction to the situation observed with baker's yeast. Chemical evidence for such an inhibition of glucose utilization is provided by Figure 7, which represents chemical assays of glucose disappearance in another sample of ascites tumor cells. A break in the graph occurs at approximately 100 sec.

In referring to Figure 5, a correlation can be seen between the chemical flux in this diagram with the changes observed in Figures 6 and 7. We can see displayed some of the basic regulatory phenomena of the ascites tumor cell, and can apply the kinetic principles mentioned in the introduction to the characteristic activation of energy metabolism in response to the energy load of glucose phosphorylation. A rapid response of the mitochondrial components to this energy load is in accordance with measurements of their high affinity for ADP, their rapid phosphorylative activity, and even their possible special relationship to hexokinase.[17a]

The fact that rapid respiration and glucose utilization are not sustained phenomena in ascites tumor cells provided the first conclusive experimental evidence for a type of metabolic control which finds as its simplest explanation the compartmentation of adenine nucleotides.[11] Chemical assays show that both oxygen and glucose utilization are inhibited, and furthermore that 1) the ATP level averaged over the whole cell is high, and 2) glucose

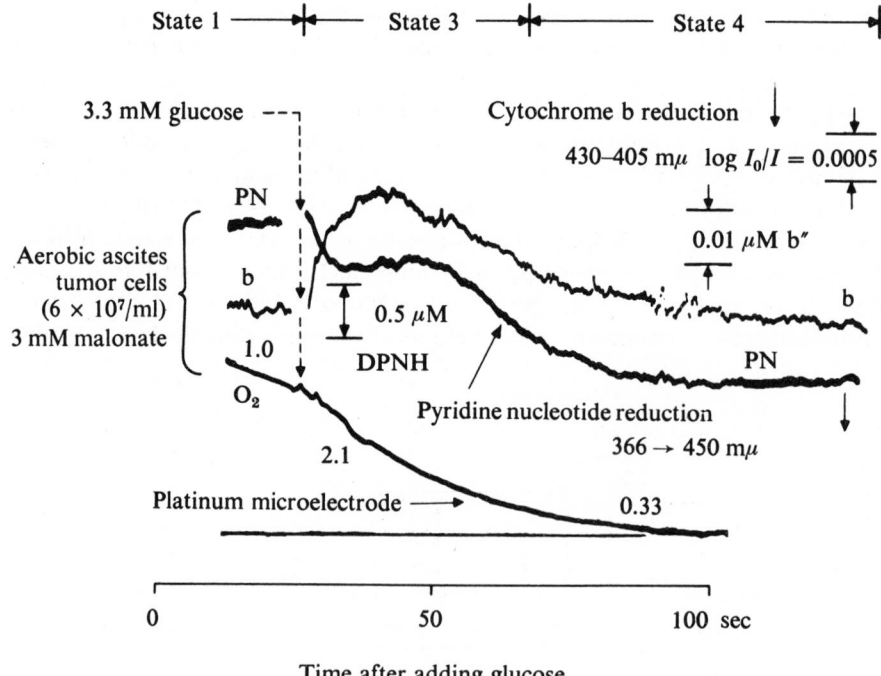

FIGURE 6. Experimental record of intracellular responses of a suspension of ascites tumor cells to glucose-loading. Top trace, pyridine nucleotide; middle trace, cytochrome b; bottom trace, respiratory activity. Details similar to those of Figure 4. (476-10)

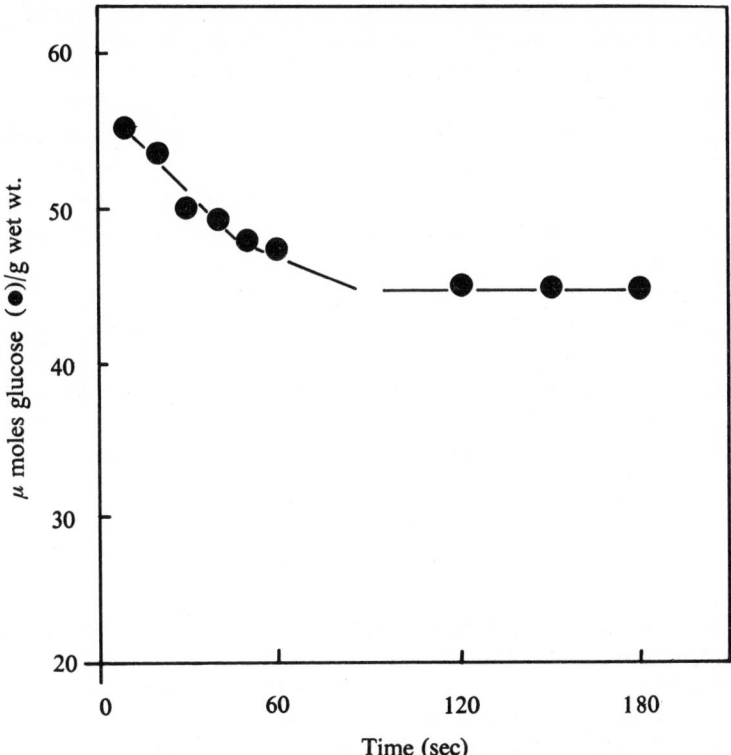

FIGURE 7. Kinetics of glucose disappearance in the glucose-loading phenomenon of ascites tumor cells. (H9)

utilization can immediately be restarted by the addition of an uncoupling agent which activates mitochondrial ATPase. For these and other reasons[11] we have proposed as the simplest hypothesis a barrier to chemical feedback of newly formed mitochondrial ATP to the needs of glucose phosphorylation.[7] This appears to be the most direct hypothesis, and one that is in accord with independent studies of the feedback of ADP from a system consisting of isolated mitochondria and added hexokinase.[16a] However, the localization of metabolic control in a single site of the multi-enzyme system is unlikely; undoubtedly many sites cooperate to control the activities of the systems.

V. CONCLUSION

Since this manuscript was originally prepared, two new methods for causing metabolic transients in intact tissues have been studied by direct continuous optical methods. The first is the response of cytoplasmic DPNH to electrical stimulation in slices of the main organ of *Electrophorus electricus*. Here the kinetics of the mobilization of glycolytic energy metabolism would be followed in terms of the activation of DPN reduction at the triose phosphate dehydrogenase step. Results are reported elsewhere in detail.[16c,17c]

More recently, the temperature jump method of Czerlinski[14c] has been employed to cause a rapid displacement of the steady state of metabolism of the sartorius muscle of the tropical toad, *Bufo marinus*. With this method, jump heating of the tissue is achieved in a half millisecond with a localized 1.5 joule flash at 694 mμ from a ruby maser. The consequent step function in glycolytic metabolism causes a fluorescence increase to occur with a time constant of roughly 100 msec. This is tentatively attributed to increased flow through the glycolytic train caused in general by increased flux for steps on the substrate side of triose phosphate glyceraldehyde dehydrogenase. The specific site of activation is not identified, although the temperature sensitivity of the aldolase step or an increase in glycogen breakdown may be a factor in this metabolic transient.[7b] These two methods greatly extend the time range of metabolic transients.

Obviously, chemical assays of intermediates are necessary to support in more detail the kind of conclusions reached by the *in vivo* observations of metabolic control phenomena. However, the advantages of the continuous following of the metabolic process, combined with the extraordinary speed of response of these optical methods in relation to the chemical assay methods, makes them of key importance in the study of intracellular kinetics, and, in particular, in the resolution of the time sequence of competing activities.

REFERENCES

1. Chance, B. 1943. The kinetics of the enzyme-substrate compound of peroxidase. *J. Biol. Chem.* **151**: 553–577.
2. Chance, B. 1949a. Horse-radish peroxidases and peroxides II. Kinetics and decomposition. *Arch. Biochem. Biophys.* **22**: 224–252.
3. Chance, B. 1949b. The properties of the enzyme-substrate compounds of horse-radish and lacto peroxidase. *Science* **109**: 204–208.
4. Chance, B. 1952. Spectra and reaction kinetics of respiratory pigments of homogenized and intact cells. *Nature* **169**: 215–221.
5. Chance, B. 1954. Enzyme mechanisms in living cells. *In:* "The Mechanism of Enzyme Action" (W. H. McElroy and B. Glass, eds.), pp. 399–453. John Hopkins Press, Baltimore.
6. Chance, B. 1955. Enzymes in action in living cells: The steady state of reduced pyridine nucleotide. *Harvey Lectures Ser.* **49** (*1953–1954*): 145–175.
7a. Chance, B. 1961. Control characteristics of enzyme systems. *Cold Spring Harbor Symp. Quant. Biol.* **26**: 288–299.
7b. Chance, B., Schoener, B., and DeVault, D. 1964. An attempt to apply the temperature jump technique to enzyme reactions in tissues. *Science* **144**: 561.
8. Chance, B., and Connelly, C. M. 1957. A method for the estimation of the increase of concentration of ADP in muscle sarcosomes following a contraction. *Nature* **179**: 1235–1237.
9. Chance, B., and Hagihara, B. 1963. Direct spectroscopic measurements of interaction of components of the respiratory chain with ATP, ADP, Phosphate, or uncoupling agents. *Proc. Intern. Congr. Biochem., 5th. Moscow, 1961*, p. 3. Pergamon Press, New York.
10. Chance, B., and Hess, B. 1956. On the control of metabolism in ascites tumor cell suspensions. *Ann. N.Y. Acad. Sci.* **63**: 1008–1016.
11. Chance, B., and Hess, B. 1959. Metabolic control mechanisms. *J. Biol. Chem.* **234**: 2404–2412.
12. Chance, B., and Jöbsis, F. F. 1959. Changes in fluorescence in a frog sartorius muscle following a twitch. *Nature* **184**: 195–196.
13. Chance, B., Mauriello, G., and Aubert, X. M. 1962. ADP arrival at muscle mitochondria following a twitch. *In:* "Muscle as a Tissue" (K. Rodahl and S. Horvath, eds.), pp. 128–145. McGraw-Hill, New York.
14a. Chance, B., and Weber, A. 1964. The steady state of cytochrome b during rest and after contraction in frog sartorius. *J. Physiol.* **169**: 263–277.

14b. Chance, B., and Williams, G. 1955. A method for the localization of sites for oxidative phosphorylation. *Nature* **176**: 250–254.

14c. Czerlinski, G. 1959. A temperature jump method for the investigation of chemical relaxation. (In German.) Ph.D. Dissertation, Göttingen, 1958. *Z. Elektrochem.* **63**: 652. 1959.

15. Higgins, J. J. 1961. Use of computers. *In:* "Technique of Organic Chemistry" (S. L. Friess, E. S. Lewis, and A. Weissberger, eds.), 2nd rev. ed., pp. 285–341. Interscience, New York.

16a. Hommes, F. A. 1962. The existence of an ATP barrier in isolated rat liver mitochondria. (Abstr.) *Federation Proc.* **21**: 142.

16b. Jöbsis, F. F. 1963. Spectrophotometric studies on intact muscle. II. Recovery from contractile activity. *J. Gen. Physiol.* **46**: 929–969.

16c. Keynes, R. D., Aubert, X. M., and Chance, B. 1964. Optical studies of biochemical events in the electric organ of electrophorus. *Proc. Roy. Soc. London. Ser. B,* **160**: 211.

17a. Maitra, P. K., and Estabrook, R. W. 1962. The ADP and phosphate control of ethanol oxidation in baker's yeast. *Biochem. Biophys. Res. Commun.* **9**: 1–6.

17b. Maitra, P. K., Estabrook, R. W., and Chance, B. 1964. Yeast as a model for the study of the regulation of cellular metabolism. *In:* C.N.R.S. Symposium on the Mechanism of Regulation of Cellular Activities in Micro-organisms, Marseilles, France, July, 1963. In press.

17c. Maitra, P. K., Ghosh, A., Schoener, B., and Chance, B. 1964. Transients in glycolytic metabolism following electrical activity in electrophorus. *Biochim. Biophys. Acta.* **88**: 112.

18. Mommaerts, W. F. H. M., Serydarian, K., and Wallner, A. 1962. Demonstration of phosphocreatine splitting as an early reaction in contracting frog sartorius muscle. *Biochim. Biophys. Acta* **63**: 75–81.

[14]

NERVOUS PROCESSING OF SENSORY INFORMATION

Werner Reichardt

I. INTRODUCTION

The functional principles on which the nervous system processes sensory information may be analyzed by two quite different experimental approaches. One of these makes use of electrophysiological recording techniques and is particularly applicable to nervous structures with isotropic functional properties such as the retina of *Limulus*. The other approach is based on the methods of behavioral physiology. Here the data consist of quantitatively measurable graded responses of a whole organism to particular stimulus patterns.

In the first case the input-output relations of various neurosensory components of the system in question are determined, whereas in the second the input-output relations of the whole animal are measured. Either method may permit the nervous mechanisms involved to be analyzed in terms of a minimal mathematical model. The present chapter gives an example of each of these approaches. In Section II, neural inhibition in the lateral eye of the horseshoe crab, *Limulus*, is considered on the basis of electrophysiological data;[41] in Section III, movement perception in insects is analyzed on the basis of optomotor behavior patterns.[42]

II. NEURAL INHIBITION IN THE LATERAL EYE OF *LIMULUS*

A. Introduction

In recent years inhibitory processes have been studied in many physiological systems by a number of investigators.[6,45] Several peripheral afferent systems are included in such work. For example, complex inhibitory phenomena are known to interact with excitatory ones in vertebrate retinas.[2,3,9-13,30] In human vision such interactions are responsible for simultaneous contrast and the existence of Mach bands.[32] Inhibitory phenomena are also important in the auditory system[48] (see also Chapter 7) for which electrophysiological evidence was obtained in single fibers of the cat by Galambos and Davis.[8a] Similar processes seem also to play an essential role in the functioning of touch receptors[29,49] and in the abdominal stretch receptors of macruran crustaceans (review in reference[5a]).

However, such sensory inhibitory interactions have been investigated most precisely in the compound eye of *Limulus*.[7,15-17,33-39,52] In this case the experimental findings have

344

reached a point where the first draft of a theory of lateral inhibition has appeared to be possible;[41-43] such a construct may well serve as a model for inhibitory interactions in other systems. The theory reviewed below is derived from an analysis both of neural inhibition in *Limulus* and of the dioptric properties of its compound eye. These two factors are related to lateral inhibition in an intricate way and are therefore considered first.

B. Dioptric Properties of Compound Eyes

1. *Diffraction and resolution.*   Because of diffraction, all image-forming optical devices, including both the compound eyes and the camera eyes of animals, possess limited resolving power. This property, measured in terms of the diameter d of the diffraction disk produced on the retina by a point source of light, is given by

$$d = 1.22 \frac{2f\lambda}{\delta n} \tag{1}$$

where f = focal length of the lens, λ = wavelength of light, δ = diameter of the aperture, and n = refractive index of the lens.

This equation has been applied to compound eyes by Barlow,[1] making use of previous experimental findings on the bee[28] and the beetle *Chlorophanus*.[20]   In the earlier work Hecht and Wolf[28] had shown that for the bee the best resolving power of the compound eye corresponds to the minimal angles between the optical axes of neighboring ommatidia; Hassenstein[20] had demonstrated quantitatively that for optomotor movement perception in *Chlorophanus* the ommatidia represented the basic functional units. Subsequently, the resolving power of the *Chlorophanus* eye was also shown to depend on the angle φ between neighboring ommatidia.[47]

Generalizing these results, one may say that the resolution of an apposition eye would be determined by φ. Overlap of visual fields may be assumed to occur when the edge of the diffraction disks of neighboring ommatidia just touch, which would happen when

$$\varphi = 1.22 \frac{2\lambda}{\delta} \tag{2a}$$

at the corneal surface. Hence if there are two distant point sources of light located respectively on the optical axis of two ommatidia A and C, separated by an intervening facet B, B receives no light when

$$\varphi > 1.22 \frac{2\lambda}{\delta} \tag{2b}$$

However, if

$$0 < \varphi \leq 1.22 \frac{2\lambda}{\delta} \tag{2c}$$

some rays from both light sources will enter Ommatidium B.

Now Barlow[1] calculated from available data on the bee[4] that in fact for the central area of its eye φ lies in the range determined by Equation (2c). Therefore the phenomena of diffraction alone predict that overlap occurs in the fields of neighboring ommatidia. Similar conclusions were reached on the basis of measurements and calculations for 27 other hymenopterans.

2. *Limulus* lateral eyes.   In the case of *Limulus* we must now inquire whether the optical geometry of the ommatidia are such as to reach the limit of resolution set by

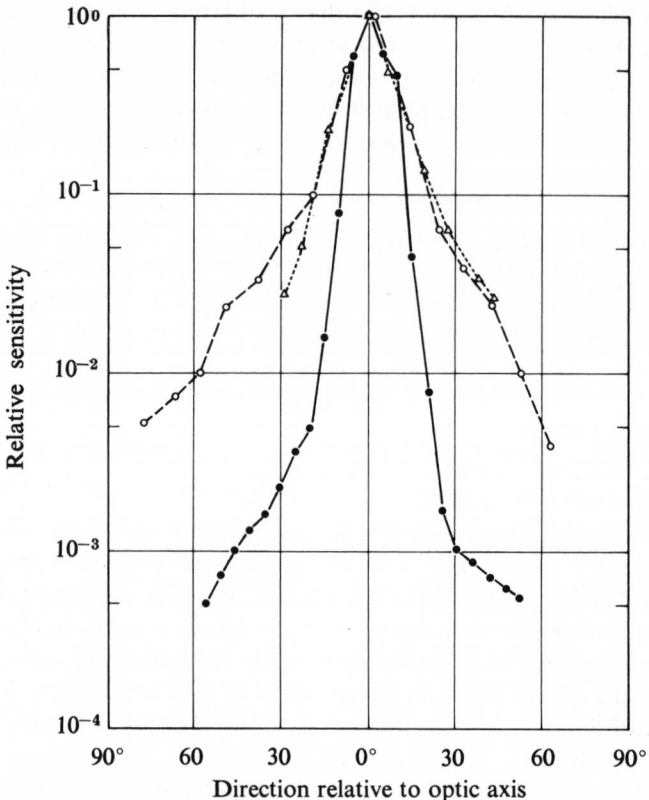

FIGURE 1. Directional sensitivity of three ommatidia from the central area of the *Limulus* lateral eye plotted relative to their optical axes at 0° for various angles of stimulus incidence in the dorso-ventral plane. Replotted from threshold measurements by Waterman.[50] (Redrawn from Reichardt.[41])

diffraction. For young specimens of *Limulus polyphemus*[50] the mean diameter of an ommatidium at the corneal surface is 160μ.* For $\lambda = 6 \times 10^{-5}$ cm the diffraction disk for a point source of light would subtend an angle of 0.52° for such an optical system. Now in these eyes φ varies between 4 near the center to 15° near the margin.[50] Consequently, diffraction would not be expected to produce any overlap in the visual fields of neighboring ommatidia.

Nevertheless, Waterman[50] found by recording from single optic nerve fibers that the overlap of visual fields in the *Limulus* eye is remarkably extensive. Measurements were made of the intensities of a point light source required to produce a standard spike response in a single eccentric cell axon when the light was directed onto the eye at various angles relative to the axis of the corresponding ommatidium. These data (replotted in Figures 1 and 2) show that considerable sensitivity still occurs at stimulus angles of 20° or more to the optical axis. Hence individual ommatidia possess relatively large apertures. Since these significantly exceed the measured values of φ (4–15°), the overlap in the visual fields of neighboring ommatidia is considerable. When the mean angular sensitivity distribution is

* Average diameters range from 50 μ in an individual of 15 mm prosoma length to 300 μ in one with an 180 mm prosoma length,[51] depending on the size of the animal.

calculated from these data (Figure 3), the value is seen to fall to 50% when the stimulus makes an angle of 8° with the ommatidial axis.

On the basis of this mean curve (Figure 3) the influence of visual field overlap on contrast may be estimated. To do so, two point sources of light on the axes of ommatidia (O_A) and (O_C) may be reconsidered. If φ is large relative to width of the angular sensitivity function at the 50% level, the intermediate O_B would receive no effective illumination. But if φ is smaller, then O_B may be illuminated and the contrast in the stimulation of O_A, O_B, and O_C becomes less. The calculated result of such overlapping illumination on contrast (Figure 4) indicates among other things that when $\varphi = 11.5°$, contrast is only 50%, and when $0 < \varphi < 6°$, contrast even changes sign since in this range B receives more light than either O_A or O_C. These calculations clearly indicate that, over much of the *Limulus* retina, overlap of ommatidial fields must cause considerable loss of the eye's potential resolving power; this is especially so in the central parts of the eye where small values of φ make the problem particularly severe.

Before this seemingly maladaptive optical situation is accepted as evidence for an over-all visual system with poor resolving power, the functional organization of its other components must be considered. Obviously the optical information entering the eye is processed by

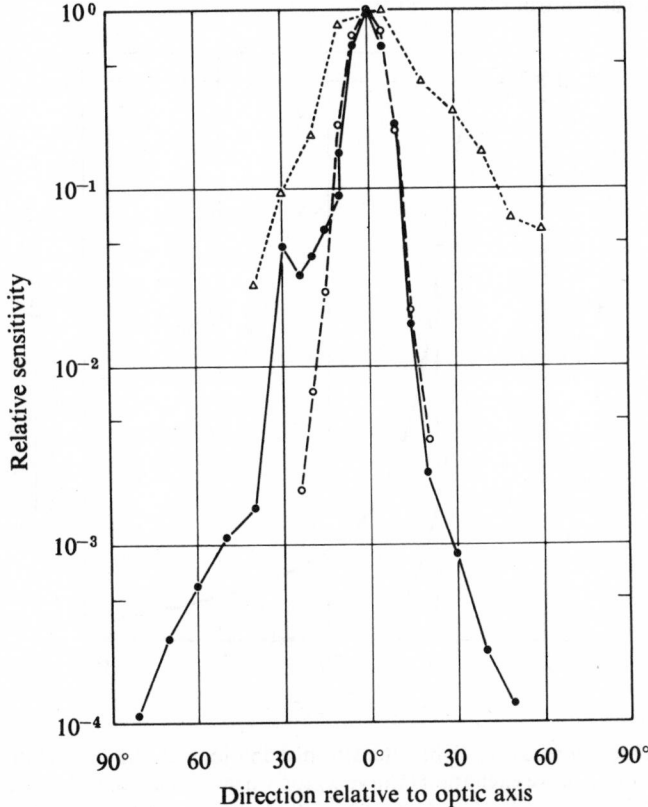

FIGURE 2. Directional sensitivity of three ommatidia of *Limulus* plotted for various stimulus angles in the anteroposterior plane of the lateral eye. Other details as in Figure 1. (Redrawn from Reichardt.[41])

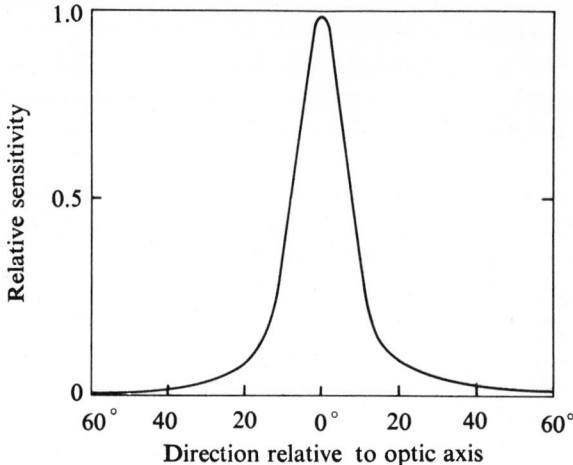

FIGURE 3. Mean directional sensitivity for an ommatidium in the central area of the *Limulus* lateral eye, obtained by averaging the data in Figures 1 and 2 and plotting them with a linear ordinate scale. (Redrawn from Reichardt.[41])

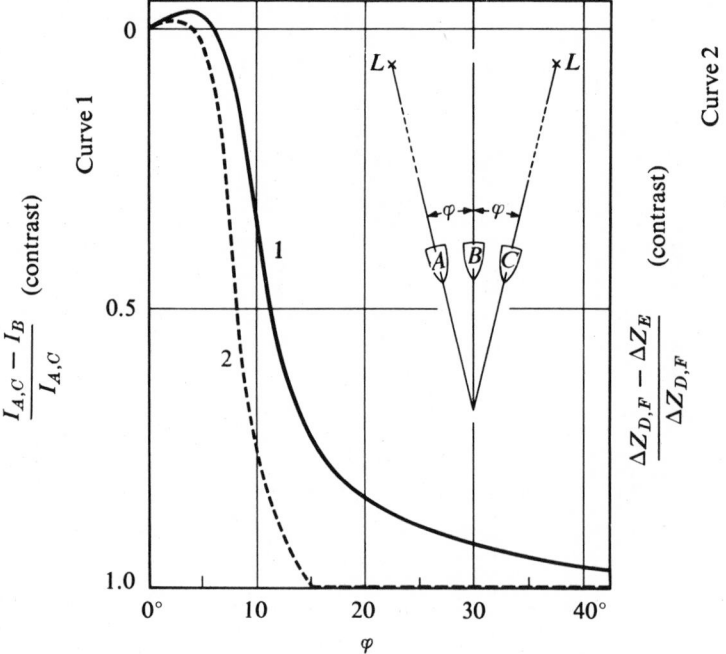

FIGURE 4. Calculated contrast in light intensity distributions at the ommatidial level (Curve 1) and at the level of optic nerve excitation (Curve 2) for various axial angles, φ, between three neighboring ommatidia in a row (O_A, O_B, O_C). The definitions of contrast used are indicated on the left and right ordinates for Curves 1 and 2 respectively. The insert shows the relation of the ommatidia to the two point sources of stimulating light located at a distance on the axes of O_A and O_B. I_A, I_B, and I_C are light intensities received by O_A, O_B, and O_C respectively (I_A, I_C are assumed to be nearly equal because of symmetry); Z_D, Z_E, and Z_F are optic nerve fiber spike frequencies for three units in Figure 6. (Redrawn from Reichardt.[41])

the retina and the postretinal optic tract so that the visual data ultimately available to the central nervous system (CNS) will be the sum total of the interactions between the optical, neurosensory, and nervous components involved. The following section will demonstrate that the *Limulus* eye does in fact possess a nervous integrating mechanism which corrects the deleterious effect of the overlap in visual fields.

C. *Neurology of* Limulus *Compound Eyes*

In recent years the neurophysiology and histology of xiphosuran lateral eyes have been intensively studied.[7,14–19,33–39,52] Structurally these organs have been known for a long time to consist of ommatidia whose retinal components consist of clusters of about 8–10 retinular cells, each of which contributes a sector (rhabdomere) to a central light-absorbing structure, the rhabdom. Axially the rhabdomeres enclose the distal process of a bipolar cell (the eccentric cell) whose soma is located away from the retinular axis (Figures 2 and 3 in reference[52]).

Proximally the retinular cells and the eccentric cell continue as axons. These form the elongated optic nerve which runs without synapsing[46] to the CNS. Directly below the ommatidia a fibrous network of collaterals connects the optic nerve axons with one another, probably via synapses terminating on retinular cells. Illumination of an ommatidium induces a generator potential in the eccentric cell whose steady state amplitude varies with the logarithm of the light intensity. Spikes are apparently limited to the eccentric cell axon and their frequency is linearly dependent on generator potential amplitude with 15 spikes per sec corresponding to a potential of about 20 mv. No spike generation or conduction has been demonstrated in the retinular cells or their axons.

D. *A Model for Imaging Intensity Patterns*

These results make possible a quantitative model for the transformation by the *Limulus* eye of an environmental intensity distribution into a retinal pattern of generator potentials and spike frequencies in the optic nerve. For this purpose consider a linear array of n-ommatidia and a corresponding one-dimensional intensity distribution consisting of distant point sources located one on the axis of each ommatidium.

1. *Intensity and excitation patterns.* If x_i is the intensity of an individual light source, where $i = 1, 2, \ldots k \ldots n$, this produces in O_i a light intensity $\alpha_{ii}x_i$. The overlap coefficient α_{ii} allows for the geometry and dioptrics of the individual ommatidium. However, because of the overlap in visual fields, more than one point source illuminates O_i. Hence source k adds $\alpha_{ik}x_k$, source $k + 1$ adds $\alpha_{i,k+1}x_{k+1}$, and so on. The degree of overlap of visual fields is described by the coefficients α_{ik} so that the light intensity in O_i is

$$\sum_{k=1}^{n} \alpha_{ik}x_k$$

which is general for all ommatidia in the linear array.

Since a logarithmic relation exists between light intensity and generator potential

$$\ln \sum_{k=1}^{n} \alpha_{ik}x_k = a_i y_i \tag{3a}$$

where y_i is the generator potential in the eccentric cell of O_i and the coefficient a_i accounts for light absorption in the rhabdom and conversion of absorbed light energy into generator potentials in the same ommatidium.

If $x_{\min}$ is the intensity of the weakest point source of light, the linear intensity distribution can be ascribed to a fixed component ($x_{\min}$) and a superimposed variable component (Δx_k). From Equation (3a) the spatially constant component of the generator potentials will be

$$\ln \sum_{k=1}^{n} \alpha_{ik} x_{\min} = \ln \left\{ x_{\min} \sum_{k=1}^{n} \alpha_{ik} \right\} = a_i y_{i\,\min} \qquad i = 1, 2 \ldots n \tag{3b}$$

The $y_{i\,\min}$ depend only on α_{ik} since $x_{\min}$ is spatially constant and not dependent on k.

2. *The imaging process.* In a second equation the influence of deviations in stimulus intensity, Δx_k, on changes of generator potential, Δy_k, can be given as a first approximation by the total differential of Equation (3a)

$$\frac{\sum_{k=1}^{n} \alpha_{ik} \Delta x_k}{x_{\min} \sum_{k=1}^{n} \alpha_{ik}} = a_i \Delta y_i \qquad i = 1, 2 \ldots n \tag{3c}$$

This shows that the spatial changes in generator potential depend linearly on the spatial deviations in light intensity. The validity of this approximation depends on the left-hand side of Equation (3c) being less than one. This requirement will be better fulfilled the smaller the difference, $x_{\max} - x_{\min}$, and the greater the overlap of visual fields, α_{ik}.

If a new coefficient α'_{ik} is defined as

$$\alpha_{ik} / a_i x_{\min} \sum_{k=1}^{n} \alpha_{ik}$$

Equation (3c) simplifies to

$$\sum_{k=1}^{n} \alpha'_{ik} \Delta x_k = \Delta y_i \qquad i = 1, 2 \ldots n \tag{3d}$$

This equation is unaffected if the intensities x_i are all changed by a factor N because $x_{\min}$ and Δx_k both are altered by the same factor N. Hence the latter has no effect on the relation of Δx_k to Δy_i in Equations (3c) or (3d).

3. *Matrix restatement.* If Δx_k and Δy_i are assumed to be components of the vectors x and y respectively, and A' designates the matrix of coefficients α_{ik}, then the set of equations (3d) may be abbreviated to

$$A'x = y \tag{3e}$$

which may be interpreted as follows. The proposed model of the *Limulus* eye linearly transforms spatial changes in light intensity to spatial changes in generator potentials. The coefficients of the transformation matrix are determined essentially by the overlap of ommatidial visual fields.

An important question in this model of imaging in the *Limulus* eye is whether more than one environmental intensity distribution can give rise to the same retinal generator potential distribution. If so, part of the environmental visual information is lost because of the field overlap; if not, then the sense organ merely transforms the information without losing any. In the case of the present model an answer to this question may be mathematically deduced from Equation (3e) which describes the relation between the distributions x and y.

A reversible one-to-one correspondence between x and y exists if the determinant of the coefficients differs from zero. This condition is necessary and sufficient although ambiguities appear if this determinant disappears. The average angular sensitivity distribution for single receptors (Figure 3) shows that the determinant of the overlap coefficients in fact is not zero. Hence the overlap of visual fields in neighboring ommatidia does not produce any loss in optical information.

E. *Inhibitory Interactions*

The next feature of the visual pathway which affects the processing of information is the inhibitory influence which excitation in one axon of the optic tract has on neighboring axons. This process of interaction is not strictly localized to neighboring elements but extends to larger groups of ommatidia as well. Apparently it is restricted to axons of the eccentric cells.[16,17,37] To extend our model to these levels, first consider the interaction between two ommatidia, O_i and O_k.

1. *Inhibition coefficients and spike frequency.* If these ommatidia are illuminated, and no interaction occurs, their generator potentials, y_i, y_k give rise to spike frequencies z_i, z_k in the corresponding eccentric cell axons. With interaction, however, $z_i z_k$ are dependent on $y_i y_k$ through a coupled set of equations valid within certain boundary conditions.

$$\beta_{ii} z_i = y_i - y_{ii}^* - \beta_{ik}(z_k - z_{ik}^*)$$
$$\beta_{kk} z_k = y_k - y_{kk}^* - \beta_{ki}(z_i - z_{ki}^*)$$

(4)

The coefficients β_{ii} and β_{kk} take into account the linear transformation of generator potentials into spike frequencies, while the inhibitory coefficients β_{ik}, β_{ki} are always positive and less than one. They are dependent on the interommatidial distance between O_i and O_k; they decrease as it increases.

Frequency threshold values are designated by y_{ii}^* and y_{kk}^* whose magnitudes increase with distance between O_i and O_k. Since negative nerve impulse frequencies do not exist, z and z^* are always positive. Equations (4) indicate that the impulse frequencies in neighboring ommatidia influence each other reciprocally. This is true only when $z_i \geq z_{ki}^*$ and $z_k \geq z_{ik}^*$, but not when $z_i < z_{ki}^*$ and $z_k < z_{ik}^*$. Hence the inhibitory coefficients have to be set to zero within this range. Similarly if y_i, y_k are so strongly inhibited as to be lower than the potential threshold y_{ii}^*, y_{kk}^*, then the coefficients β_{ii}, β_{kk} have to be set to zero within that range.

Since these reciprocal interactions are not restricted to two ommatidia but extend over a considerable area, a set of coupled equations different from Equations (4) needs to be used for the general case, namely,

$$y_i - y_{ii}^* = \beta_{ii} z_i + \sum_{\substack{k=1 \\ k \neq 1}}^{n} \beta_{ik}(z_k - z_{ik}^*) \qquad i = 1, 2 \ldots n$$

(5a)

and corresponding boundary conditions to those for Equations (4) must hold for y_i, z_k, y_{ii}^*, z_{ik}^*, and β_{ik}.

The effects of this sort of reciprocal inhibition on the excitation distribution in the visual pathway depend on the relations of the stimulus intensities to the excitatory and inhibitory thresholds of the system.[41] Only one of a number of possible cases will be considered here. This is the situation in which the light intensity at the retinal level is sufficiently high so that all the eccentric cell axons are excited, inhibition extends through the whole linear array of ommatidia, and the threshold frequencies z_{ik}^* can be neglected in comparison with the spike frequencies z_k. This is the case if $y_i \gg y_{ii}^*$, $z_k \gg z_{ik}^*$, and therefore all $\beta_{ik} > 0$, where $i, k = 1, 2 \ldots n$.

In this instance, Equation (5a) can be approximated by

$$y_i = \sum_{k=1}^{n} \beta_{ik} z_k \qquad i = 1, 2 \ldots n \tag{5b}$$

For $|i - k| \leq 3$, this equation is a good approximation to the inhibitory interaction observed in *Limulus*. However, this approximation is also applicable for greater values of $|i - k|$ because the relevant inhibitory coefficients are very small.

2. *Stimulus intensity and spike frequency.* To indicate the relation between stimulus intensity distribution, x_i, and impulse frequency distribution in the optic nerve, z_k, only the spatial changes in intensity, Δx_i and Δz_k, are important. From Equation (5b) we know that

$$\Delta y_i = \sum_{k=1}^{n} \beta_{ik} \Delta z_k \qquad i = 1, 2 \ldots n \tag{5c}$$

If now B is the matrix of the coefficients β_{ik}, and Δy_i and Δz_k are respectively the components of the vectors y and z, Equation (5c) may be written

$$y = Bz \tag{6}$$

and from Equation (3e)

$$Bz = A'x \tag{7a}$$

Since the inhibitory interactions in the *Limulus* eye have been shown to be stable,[37] the real parts of the eigenvalues of the B-matrix must all be greater than zero. This means that the determinant of the inhibition coefficients is not zero, and therefore that Equation (7a) can be solved for z. To do so the equation is multiplied by the inverse matrix B^{-1} yielding the imaging equation

$$z = B^{-1}A'x \tag{7b}$$

since $B^{-1}B = I$, the unit matrix. In the case under discussion, the lateral interactions in *Limulus* are in effect a nervous mechanism for the solution of Equation (7a).

3. *Effect on resolution.* The relationship of all this to the processing of visual information in the *Limulus* eye depends on the coefficients allowing for visual field overlap, α'_{ik}, and the inhibition coefficients, β_{ik}. The most interesting situation from a theoretical point of view is that one where $\alpha'_{ik} = \beta_{ik}$ for all i, k. Then $A' = B$, and Equation (7b) reduces to $z = x$. When this is true, the optic nerve excitation pattern directly reproduces the stimulus intensity distribution despite the existing overlap of ommatidial visual fields. On this basis the optical resolution of such an apposition eye is solely determined by the angle φ between neighboring ommatidial axes.

In this hypothetical case, then, lateral inhibition in the neurosensory system can replace a lens in front of the receptor mosaic, or, as in the present instance, it can correct the existing dioptric apparatus.

4. *Estimating the coefficients.* For the *Limulus* eye the degree of correction provided depends on the magnitude and spatial distributions of the inhibition coefficients β_{ik}. In general the strength of mutual inhibition between ommatidia decreases monotonically with the distance separating them.[37] The mean mutual inhibition between the two ommatidia 1 mm apart was found in one case to be 16%. However, a mathematical relationship between β and separation of ommatidia cannot as yet be given.*

However, some data of Ratliff and Hartline[37] on patterns of excitation in the *Limulus*

---

* Experiments on this subject and new theoretical investigations have now been carried out: Kirschfeld, K., and Reichardt, W., 1964. *Kybernetik* **2**: 43–61.

eye allow the order of magnitude of the inhibition coefficients to be estimated. Their basic experimental problem was to determine how a stimulus intensity pattern consisting of a single step function was transformed into a pattern of spike frequencies in optic nerve fibers. If all but one ommatidium was masked, the passage of the stimulus past this point reproduced the intensity change of the step function directly in the impulse frequencies of the corresponding eccentric cell axon (Figure 5, Curve 1.) However, if the response of this same axon was recorded with the whole eye uncovered, the resulting response was strikingly different due to inhibitory interactions (Curve 2). In essence, the eye's response boundary between dark and light areas was proved not to be a sharp step like the stimulus, and the effect of lateral inhibition as well as a physiological basis for simultaneous contrast was made evident in the neighboring distribution of excitation.

From these data, inhibition coefficients can be computed for the ommatidial chain in our model ($O_A - O_H$, Figure 5). Numerically these will differ from the coefficients for a row of ommatidia in the actual eye since the model substitutes a one-dimensional linear array of units for the receptor plane. To make appropriate calculations, we consider an intensity step from I_2 to I_1, with $I_2 > I_1$ projected on an eight-unit row of ommatidia so that it falls between O_D and O_E (Figure 5).

For convenience we set $I_2 = I_0 + \Delta I_2$, and $I_1 = I_0 + \Delta I_1$. Thus the components of x in Equation (7b) are $\Delta x_1 = \Delta x_2 = \Delta x_3 = \Delta x_4 = \Delta I_2$ and $\Delta x_5 = \Delta x_6 = \Delta x_7 = \Delta x_8 = \Delta I_1$. Since the intensity step was sharply focused on the receptor plane, the main diagonal elements of the overlap matrix A' (Equation 7b) are one, and all the other elements are

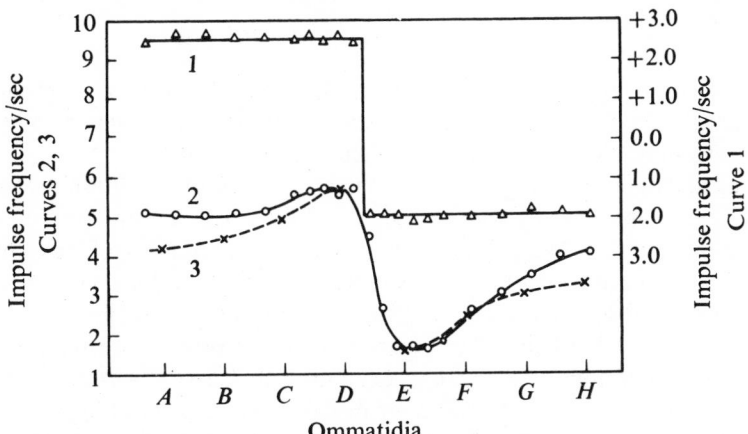

FIGURE 5. Effect of a light intensity step-function on the response of a *Limulus* ommatidium. In Curve 1 the frequency of eccentric cell discharge (right ordinate), relative to a reference frequency evoked by control illumination of the same facet, was plotted for a single ommatidium exposed to different positions of the step-function while all other ommatidia were covered over. Under this condition no lateral inhibition of the responding unit existed. In Curve 2 the frequency of discharge (left ordinate), again relative to a control level, was plotted under similar conditions except that the mask was removed. Hence all ommatidia were uncovered and lateral inhibition was fully operative. Therefore, the differences between Curves 2 and 1 are due to the effects of lateral inhibition. For these two curves, taken from Ratliff and Hartline,[37] the abscissa represents an extent of cornea about 1.5 mm long with the responding element in its center. In Curve 3 the outputs of an analog computer model of this system, consisting of a row of eight ommatidia, were plotted as volts (left ordinate) against an abscissa representing positions of the eight facets corresponding to $O_A - O_H$ (Redrawn from Reichardt.[41])

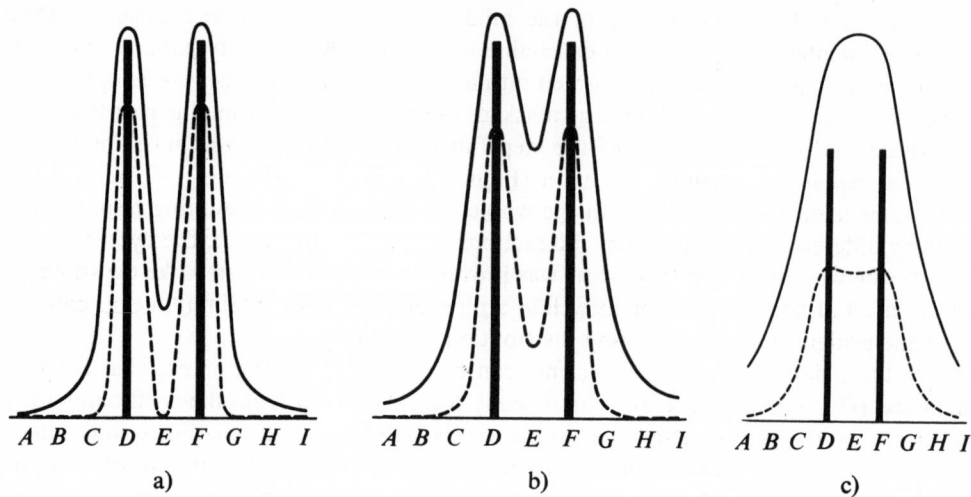

FIGURE 6. Effects of overlap coefficients and inhibition coefficients on the response of a 9-omma-
tidium ($O_A - O_I$) linear model in which two distant point sources are located on the axes of O_D and
O_F. The black bars represent the intensity distribution occurring when there was no overlap in
visual fields. The solid curves are the calculated intensity distributions at the ommatidial level
when there was field overlap, and the broken line shows the calculated axon frequency response
under the same conditions. Note the compensating effects of lateral inhibition for the resolution
losses in the dioptric system. The angle, φ, between ommatidial axes was 15° in a), 10° in b), 5° in
c). (Redrawn from Reichardt.[41])

zero. Hence Equation (7b) reduces to $z = B^{-1}x$. The components of x are given and those
of z are available from Figure 5, Curve 2; consequently we have a set of eight equations
with 64 unknown inhibition coefficients, the elements of matrix B.

The experimental data show in general that the magnitudes of inhibition coefficients vary
symmetrically and monotonically with distance, and for small areas are not dependent on
any particular ommatidia. These conditions mean that the number of unknowns in our
set of equations is reduced to eight because the B-matrix is symmetrical and the elements in
the diagonals are equal to each other. Precise symmetry of the distribution of inhibition
coefficients would imply that Curve 2 in Figure 5 should be precisely antisymmetric. Since
this is not the case, an antisymmetric approximation to Curve 2 was computed with an
analog model having a symmetric coefficient distribution. The resulting curve, given as
Curve 3, was computed to correspond with the maximum and minimum of Curve 2 and to
maintain the same differences in excitation between the first and last ommatidia in the chain.
This approximated response distribution yields inhibition coefficients of 0.3 between
neighboring ommatidia in the linear model, 0.2 for two units separated by one other,
0.1 for next-but-two separation, and zero for greater distances. These approximate values
of the inhibition coefficients permit the B-matrix to be plotted.

The numerical values of the overlap coefficients of the A'-matrix can be calculated from
the average angular sensitivity curve for a single ommatidium (Figure 3), provided that
the axial angles between ommatidia φ are assumed.

5. *Solving the imaging equation.* Now the image equation (7b) can be solved for various
values of φ since we know x, A, and B. In this way both the effects of overlapping fields
and their correction by lateral inhibition can be calculated (Figure 6). Obviously for a

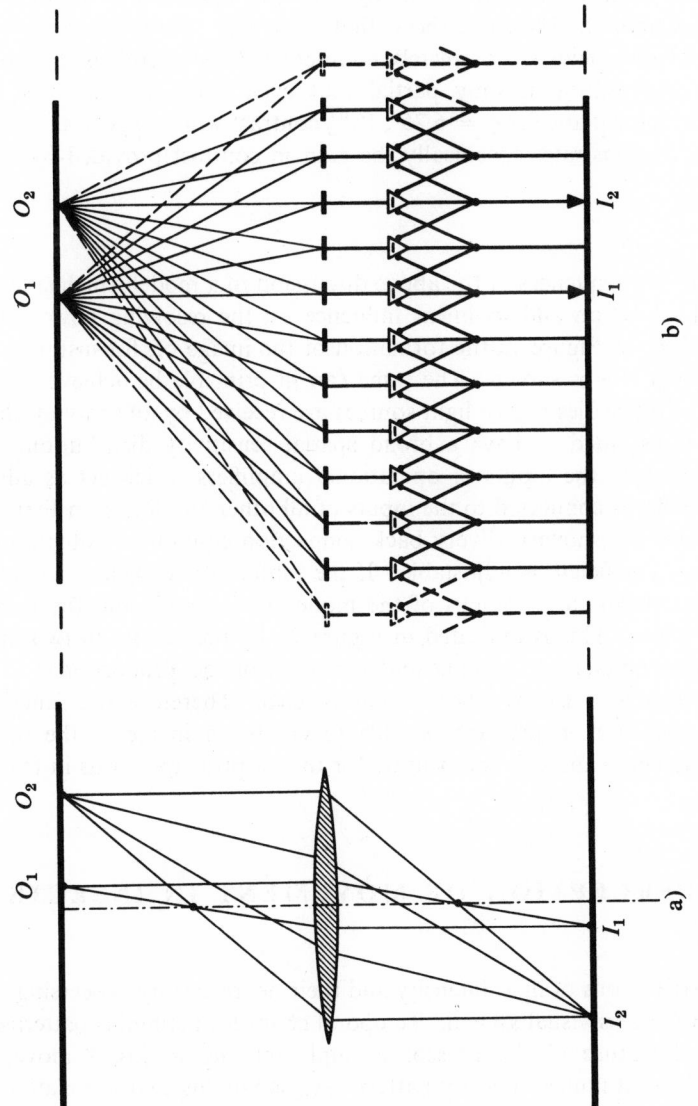

FIGURE 7. Image formation a) by a lens, and b) in a compound eye by the principle of lateral inhibition. O_1, O_2 are two light points in object space, and I_1, I_2 are the two corresponding image points. (Redrawn from Reichardt.[42])

fixed stimulus intensity pattern and for given degrees of overlap and reciprocal inhibition, the optical resolution will be inversely related to φ.

These calculations permit the effective contrast at the eccentric cell axon level to be compared with the optical contrast at the ommatidial level (Figure 4, Curve 1). To do this, changes in excitation of O_E relative to O_D, O_F must be computed and the quotient $(\Delta z_{DF} - \Delta z_E)/\Delta z_{DF}$, which is a measure of contrast in the optic nerve, plotted as a function of φ (Figure 4, Curve 2). The curve shows that when $\varphi > 15°$ (and hence contrast $> 77\%$) the overlap of visual fields is completely counteracted by lateral inhibition, for smaller axial angles compensation is only partial, but even when contrast has been completely lost at the receptor plane for $\varphi = 6.25°$, 10% contrast will reappear at the axon level. This comparison demonstrates specifically the gain in contrast provided by lateral inhibition.

F. Conclusion

We can summarize the consequences of the above discussion in a model which simulates the principle of neural inhibition and its linear influence on the resolving power of the apposition eye of *Limulus*. In Figure 7a the formation of the image of, for instance, two point sources of light by a lens is shown. The same can in principle be achieved by the model in Figure 7b. The intensities of two light sources are received by an array of photocells. Each photocell is assumed to have a broad spatial sensitivity distribution. The outputs of the photocells feed the inputs of operational amplifiers which act as adders. The output of each amplifier is connected to the inputs of all other amplifiers (in Figure 7b only neighbor connections are shown). Every back connection contains a potentiometer with which the inhibitory coefficient is adjustable. If the inhibitory coefficients equal the overlap coefficients, the optical surroundings of the model are imaged onto the outputs of the operational amplifiers. This is indicated in Figure 7b by the arrows in two of the output lines. Only these units have outputs and carry a voltage proportional to the intensities of the light sources. Every other output is zero. Therefore the functional mechanism of lateral inhibition in principle is able to create an image of the optical surroundings in the optic nerve and can compensate for the dioptric apparatus in front of the receptor mosaic.

III. VISUAL PERCEPTION OF MOVEMENT IN INSECTS

A. Introduction

Only static spatial distributions of light intensity and their neurosensory processing were considered above in the *Limulus* visual system. Temporal changes in stimulus patterns are an important additional feature of the present example relating to insect movement perception. In this case the stimulus intensity pattern Δx_{ik} is moving and not stationary. This analysis is based on quantitative experiments conducted by Hassenstein[20-23] on the optomotor responses of the beetle *Chlorophanus viridis*.

Many animals respond to displacements of extensive parts of their optical surroundings by moving the eyes, head, or whole body in a direction following the stimulus. However, the *Chlorophanus* data have proved to be outstanding both in demonstrating important features of optokinetic responses[5b,8b] and in stimulating extensive theoretical work on the nature of movement perception, of which this is a review.[20-27,40,42,44,47]

B. Optomotor Response Measurements

1. *Method.*   In a typical optomotor experiment the animal is placed in a hollow cylinder lined with perpendicular black and white stripes. When the cylinder rotates, the animal tends to turn with the movement so that the observed displacement of the surroundings is reduced. Organism and moving pattern together form a feedback loop.

In the Hassenstein technique, *Chlorophanus* is held fixed in the axis of the cylinder (Figure 8). This opens the feedback loop and prevents movements of the animal from changing its position relative to the stimulus. The optomotor turning tendency is measured quantitatively by allowing the beetle to "walk" along a light-weight spherical maze which it holds with its legs. This globe is so constructed (Figure 8) that the insect continually reaches Y-shaped branches in its path along the maze. These obviously force a series of right-left choices which have been shown to provide a sensitive measure of its movement-induced turning tendency.

The intensity of the optomotor reaction has been measured by the ratio

$$R = \frac{W - A}{W + A}$$

where W is the number of choices with the stripe movement, and A is the number against. Statistical considerations have shown that R represents a linear measure for the strength

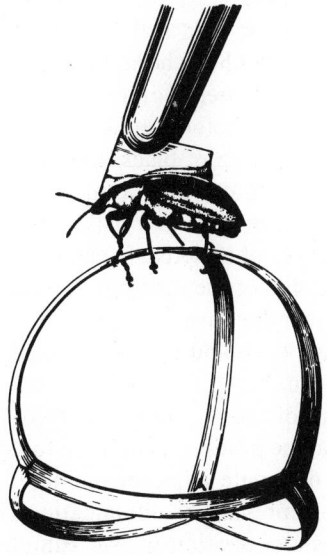

FIGURE 8. Hassenstein technique for quantitative measurement of optomotor responses in the beetle *Chlorophanus viridis*. The insect's head and neck are fixed, and the dorsal surface is glued to a piece of cardboard held in fine forceps. By its legs it holds a light (30 mg) straw spherical maze with four Y-shaped intersections. The beetle tends spontaneously to "walk" along the paths of the sphere, thereby rotating the latter. As a result a continual series of right or left turns have to be made at the Y-intersections. If there is no turning tendency, right and left choices will be equally common; if there is some optokinetic turning reaction, the proportion of turns in the two directions has proved a sensitive quantitative measure of this reaction's intensity. For such testing, the insect and the spherical maze are suspended in the axis of a striped test cylinder (Figure 9). (Redrawn from Hassenstein.[20])

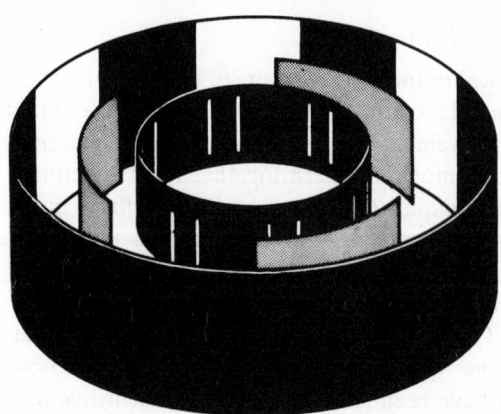

FIGURE 9. Arrangement for generating series of light changes to act as optomotor stimuli for a *Chlorophanus* suspended in the center. The black and white outer cylinder and the slotted inner cylinder are fixed, while the middle cylinder consisting of three gray screens separated by three equal gaps (60° each) can be rotated at various speeds. The leading and trailing edges of the moving screens set up for the test animal an alternating sequence of light changes visible through the slots. (Redrawn from Hassenstein.[22])

of the turning tendency if R does not exceed 0.7.[21-23] Hence measurements of the reaction have been limited to the range $-0.7 < R < +0.7$.

Many different series of light stimuli have been provided *Chlorophanus* in this setup. In one case (Figure 9) the stimulating system comprised three cylinders of which only the middle one, consisting of three gray sectors separated by wide openings, was rotatable. The outer stationary cylinder is made up of black and white stripes and the inner one has pairs of narrow perpendicular slits so cut that from the beetle's axial position the background of each slit consists of either a white or a black field. Rotation of the gray cylinder causes the leading and trailing edges of its screening components to generate an alternating sequence of light changes in the slits of the innermost cylinder.

If light changes from darker to lighter are designated by a plus sign (+), and those from lighter to darker by a minus sign (−), and the slits labeled X, Y, Z, the arrangement in Figure 9 produces sequences + in X, − in Y, + in Z, or − in X, + in Y, and − in Z, and so on. With other spacing of stripes, slits, and screens, programs involving nearly any sequence of light changes can be produced and used for stimulation of the beetle's eyes.

If O_A, O_B, O_C are used to designate adjacent ommatidia in a horizontal row in the compound eye, and if again + represents an illumination change from darker to lighter, the formula $S^{++}(t_1, t_2)$ describes a succession of two stimuli in adjacent ommatidia. The first is received by O_A at time t_1, the second in O_B at time t_2. The reaction of the animal to this stimulation S_{AB}^{++} is represented by R_{AB}^{++}.

2. *Summary of results.* From the results of a large number of experiments, the following general conclusions may be drawn about the stimulation of optomotor reactions in *Chlorophanus*. This brief summary of the experimental work will provide the necessary background for understanding the theoretical analysis of the movement perception system presented below.

1) A sequence of two stimuli in adjacent ommatidia is the most elementary succession of light changes capable of releasing an optomotor response.

2) In generating optomotor responses, the stimulus received by one ommatidium can interact only with the stimulus received by the immediately adjacent ommatidia and those once removed. No physiological interaction for movement perception exists between ommatidia separated by more than one unstimulated unit.

3) Maximum reaction is elicited when stimuli in neighboring ommatidia are separated by about 0.25 sec. The strength of reaction decreases with both longer and shorter $t_2 - t_1$. The maximum interval Δt, producing small reactions, is somewhat more than 10 sec and is undoubtedly due to the interaction of the aftereffect of one stimulus with the initial effect of a following one.

4) The combined stimulus S_{AB}^{++} leads to the reaction $+R_{AB}^{++}$ where the first $+$ indicates that the turning direction follows the direction of stimulus successions.

5) The sequence of dark stimuli S_{AB}^{--} produces $+R_{AB}^{--}$ and $R_{AB}^{--} = R_{AB}^{++}$.

6) Successions of stimuli in adjacent ommatidia produce the reaction $R_{A\,B\,C\,D}^{+++}{}_{:::}$. This response equals the sum of all the partial reactions invoked. Thus $R_{A\,B\,C\,D}^{++++}{}_{:::} = R_{A\,B}^{++} + R_{B\,C}^{++} + R_{C\,D}^{++}\ldots + R_{A\,C}^{++} + R_{B\,D}^{++} + R_{C\,E}^{++}\ldots$.

7) Stimulation with alternating light sequences S_{AB}^{+-} or S_{AB}^{-+} leads to reactions opposite to the direction of stimulus successions. Thus $R_{AB}^{+-} = R_{AB}^{-+} = -R_{AB}^{++} = -R_{AB}^{--}$, where the first $-$ indicates turning in the direction opposite the stripes. The results reported here and in Item 5) show that the relation between stimulus input and reaction output is in accordance with algebraic sign multiplication.

TABLE 1

	S_A^+	S_A^-
S_B^+	$+R$	$-R$
S_B^-	$-R$	$+R$

8) The intensity of optomotor responses depends not only on the speed of the moving patterns but also on absolute changes of light intensity making up the stimulus pattern. Thus when different shades of gray, whose sum was kept constant, were alternated in a series of tests with constant time intervals, the reaction was found to be a quadratic function of stimulus intensities (Figure 10). Since R is proportional to $-x(1 - x)$, the stimuli received in adjacent ommatidia (when O_A received x, O_B received $-[1 - x]$) appear to have been multiplied together.

In this regard, this item as well as 5) and 7) all show that there must be a physiological mechanism in the *Chlorophanus* CNS which links sensory input to motor output by a process working in accordance with the mathematical operation of multiplication.

C. *The Model*

1. *General features.* On the basis of these general experimental conclusions concerning the properties of the *Chlorophanus* optomotor system, we have designed a minimum mathematical model.[24,26,40,42,44] This model (Figure 11) does in fact account for the functional properties of the physiological system; it also permits the prediction of reactions to various stimulus patterns not previously tested.[47]

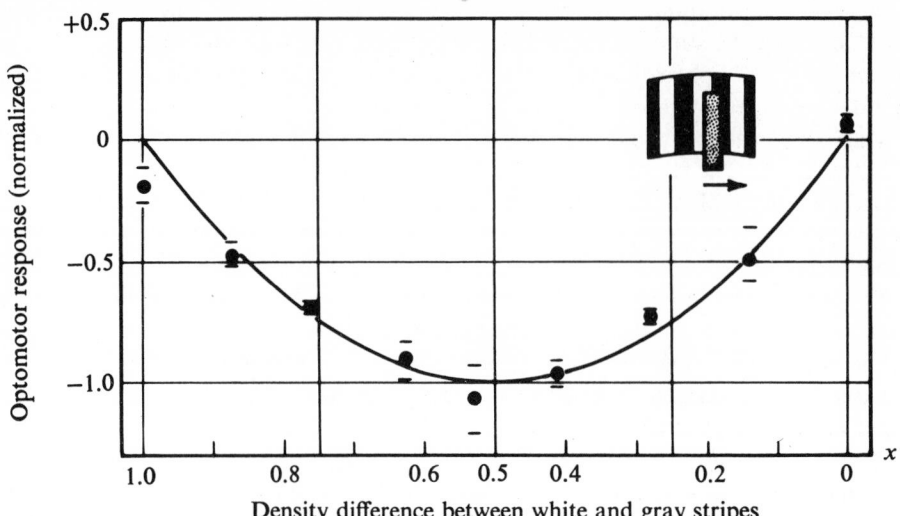

FIGURE 10. Optomotor responses of *Chlorophanus* to gray stripes of density x moving in front of a fixed cylinder of black and white stripes of contrast 1.0. A third, inner cylinder had slits spaced at the same angular distance as the stripe period of the outer cylinder (Figure 9). The observed turning tendencies to gray stripes of various densities are shown as the black circles, and the extreme values by short horizontal bars. The fitted curve is for the quadratic equation $-aR = x(1-x)$, with $a = 0.25$, so that the maximum response (R) was -1.0. (Redrawn from Hassenstein.[23])

The model consists of two information channels with cross connections and a common output to the motor system (Figure 11). Its light-sensitive receptors A and B represent two adjacent ommatidia which provide the minimum detector requirement for optomotor reactions. The two input elements transform the space and time coordinates of the stimulus, say the shift of a light pattern L from Receptor A to Receptor B, into the time functions L_A, L_B. The original stimulus value L covers a range of $0 < L \le L_{max}$ and may be either a patterned or a random stochastic variable. The resulting time functions L_A, L_B are considered to be the sum of an average intensity C and a fluctuating light component $G(t)$.

$$L_A = C + G(t) \qquad L_B = C + G(t - \Delta t) \tag{8}$$

where t is time and Δt (dependent on the axial angle φ between the two channels and the rotation speed w of the striped drum) is the time interval between the reception of a stimulus element by A and its reception by B. Thus G is defined so that its average value is zero.

The time functions L_A and L_B are transformed in the model by a succession of direct and cross-connected components comprising linear filters (D, F, and H), multipliers (M), and time averaging low pass filter elements (S). Since optomotor reactions are evoked equally well by left-to-right and right-to-left movements, the model must be symmetrical. Hence the characteristics of the corresponding components in the channels of the model are the same: $D_A = D_B = D$, etc.

The M and S elements process the transformed time functions $L_{AF}^* L_{BH}^*$ to the time average $\overline{L_{AF}^* L_{BH}^*}$, and $L_{BF}^* L_{AH}^*$ to the average $\overline{L_{BF}^* L_{AH}^*}$. Since multiplication and time averaging of two time functions is called first order correlation (for example, in Wiener[53]), these parts of the model may be considered correlator units. The output of one of these correlators is subtracted from that of the other in the last model component which controls the response R of the animal's motor system (Figure 11).

Since experimental data show that the filters D, F, and H are linear, their outputs for any arbitrary input $F(t)$ may be expressed as convolution integrals.† On this basis the inputs L_{AF}^*, L_{BH}^*, L_{BF}^*, L_{AH}^* of the multipliers can be derived from the original time functions L_A and L_B, along with the weighting functions of the filters (for example, in Laning and Battin[31]) in the direct channels W_{DF} and of those in the cross channels W_{DH}. Multiplying these appropriately, specifying the relevant correlation function, and subtracting the

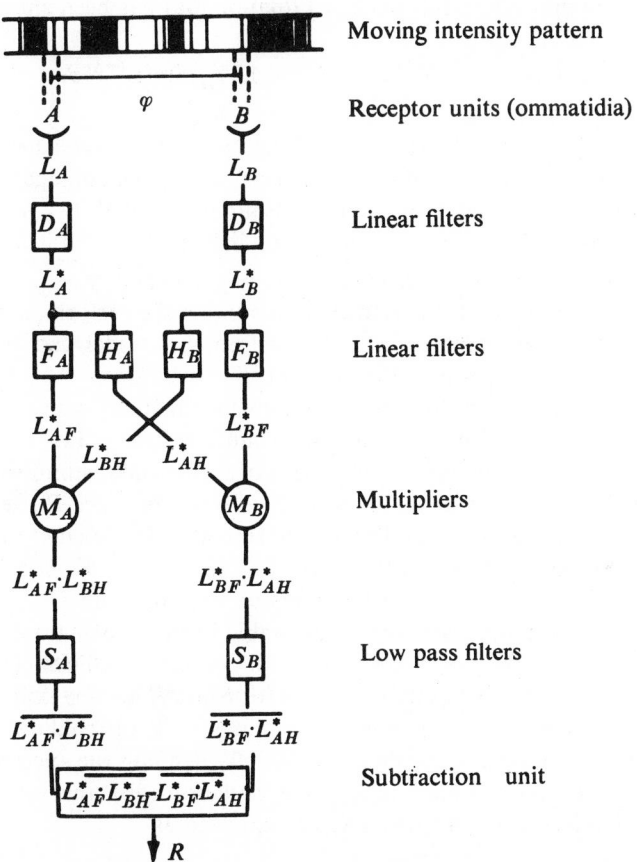

FIGURE 11.   Minimal model for optomotor movement perception in *Chlorophanus*. This consists of two direct and cross-connected information channels starting with a pair of receptor units A and B, followed by three filter stages (with differing but relatively short time constants) D, F, and H which feed into multiplier components M, followed by filters S with very long, averaging time constants whose outputs are finally subtracted in the last component, giving rise to the opto-kinetic response R. The time functions representing the transformed stimulus light intensity sequence at various stages in the system are symbolized by L_A, L_{BF}^*, L_{AH}^*, etc. Note that this circuit diagram is not at all intended as a literal representation of neural pathways. (Redrawn from Reichardt and Varjú.[44])

† For details of the following derivations see Reichardt[40] and Reichardt and Varjú.[44]

output of the two channels, the response of the whole model system may be expressed in the time domain as

$$R = \int_{\eta=0}^{+\infty} W_{DF}(\eta)\,d\eta \int_{\xi=0}^{+\infty} W_{DH}(\xi)\Phi_{GG}(\eta - \xi - \Delta t)\,d\xi$$

$$- \int_{\eta=0}^{+\infty} W_{DH}(\eta)\,d\eta \int_{\xi=0}^{+\infty} W_{DF}(\xi)\Phi_{GG}(\eta - \xi - \Delta t)\,d\xi \quad (9a)$$

Here Φ_{GG} designates the autocorrelation function of the light intensity fluctuations $G(t)$, and η and ξ are integration variables of the convolution integrals.

In the frequency domain the equivalent of Equation (9a) has been shown to be

$$R = \frac{1}{2}\int_{-\infty}^{\infty} Y_D Y_D^*[Y_F Y_H^* - Y_F^* Y_H]S(\omega)e^{iw\,\Delta t}\,d\omega \quad (9b)$$

where Y_D, Y_F, and Y_H are transfer functions of the subscript filters related to the weighting functions of the time domain by Fourier transforms; Y^* is the conjugated complex of Y; $S(\omega)$ is the spectral density of $G(t)$ and makes a Fourier pair with $\Phi_{GG}(\xi)$; ω is related to the period (in degrees) λ of a sinusoidal stimulating light pattern and its angular velocity w by the following: $\omega = (2\pi/\lambda)w$; i designates the imaginary unit $\sqrt{-1}$.

Thus Equations (9a) and (9b) describe in alternative ways the performance of the proposed model for optomotor movement perception. Before the model can be experimentally tested, it is first necessary to evaluate the filter transfer functions.

2. *Filter transformations.* To determine the transfer functions explicitly some response characteristics of the *Chlorophanus* visual system must be used. For this purpose data[23] on the relation between the velocity of movement of a sinusoidal stimulus pattern and the optomotor response R are appropriate (Figure 12). In this instance R rises to a maximum as movement velocity increases, then falls again to zero at high velocities in a curve which is symmetrical on a semilog plot. From these results Y_F, Y_H, and Y_D can be expressed in a form permitting the time constants τ of the filters to be estimated.

Because the filters in question are linear and stable in time, their transfer functions can be described with linear differential equations with constant coefficients. Analysis of the data in Figure 12 show that input-output relations for F and H may be expressed by ordinary first-order equations, whereas D responds in accordance with a partial differential equation such as that describing one-dimensional diffusion. By defining the spectral density of the sinusoidal component $G(t)$ and then integrating Equation (9b), the values of Y may be obtained. In the Laplace domain these may be expressed as

$$Y_F = \frac{\pm b_{0F}}{a_{0F} + p} \quad Y_H = \frac{\pm b_{0H}}{a_{0H} + p} \quad Y_D = \pm b_{0D}\sqrt{p}\,e^{-\sqrt{b_{1D}p}} \quad (10)$$

where p represents the variable of the Laplace transform. From these and the response curve the time constants can be calculated as

$$\tau_F = \frac{1}{a_{0F}} = 1.6\ \text{sec} \quad \tau_H = \frac{1}{a_{0H}} = 0.03\ \text{sec} \quad \tau_D = b_{1D} \leq 10^{-4}\ \text{sec} \quad (11)$$

Using this solution of Equation (9b) and Equations (10), the calculated response curve in Figure 12 was obtained.

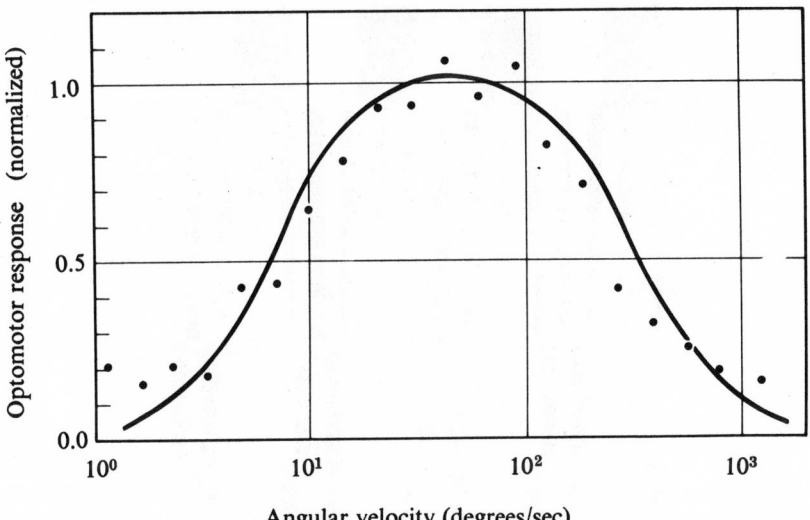

FIGURE 12. Optomotor response of *Chlorophanus* to various speeds w of the stimulus cylinder bearing a sinusoidal pattern with a period of $\lambda = 4.7\varphi = 66°$ shown by the filled circles.[23] Curve calculated from the general model (Figure 11). Maxima on the ordinate adjusted to $+1.0$. (Redrawn from Reichardt and Varjú.[44])

So far experimental results have been used to induce the minimal properties of a quantitative mathematical model relating stimulus input to optomotor output. The model itself must now be tested for its predictive power for new experimental results on *Chlorophanus*.

D. Testing the Model

1. *Periodic stimuli.* If the $G(t)$ function is determined for any arbitrary stimulus pattern, the optomotor reaction to this pattern moving at various speeds may be predicted from Equations (9a) or (9b), and (10). Then new experiments can be performed to test this prediction. An even more rigorous test of the model can be obtained by decomposing the one-dimensional light patterns and the time function $G(t)$ into their Fourier components. Since these Fourier elements can only interact with each other in the correlator units and since correlator outputs are known not to be influenced by phase shifts between sinusoids in their inputs, all stimulus patterns differing from each other only in the phase relations of their Fourier components should produce the same optomotor responses over the full range of effective movement velocities.

To test this predicted property of the beetle CNS, two stimulus patterns which could be superimposed were chosen to consist of vertical alternating black and white stripes with periods of 22.5° and 90° (Figures 13a, 13b). These were put together in two ways:[47] 1) contour edges of the 90° pattern were placed in the middle of two contour edges of the 22.5° pattern (Figure 13c); or 2) contour edges were directly superimposed without any phase shift (Figure 13d). These two patterns (Figures 13c and 13d) therefore differ by 90° in the phase of the shorter period pattern. Yet experimental measurements of R show that such phase difference has no effect on the reaction curve (Figure 14). Therefore *Chlorophanus* is phase-blind in its optomotor responses.

FIGURE 13.   Periodic optomotor cylinder patterns to test effect of the phase of Fourier components on *R*. Patterns *a* (90° period) and *b* (22.5° period) were superimposed so that vertical contours of *a* fall halfway between the vertical contours of *b* (Figure 13c), or so that the vertical contours of *a* and *b* coincided (Figure 13d). Figure 13e was obtained from *d* by interchanging two black and white stripes per period. Note that, in superimposing, black + black = black, white + white = white, and black + white = gray. (From Reichardt.[42])

The validity of this conclusion has been tested by interchanging a pair of black and white stripes in each period of Figure 13d to obtain Figure 13e. This slight alteration of pattern markedly affects the responses because the interchange of stripes changes not only the phase relationships but also the amplitude distribution of the Fourier components. These responses to movement of patterns in Figures 13c, d, and e agree well with the curves predicted from the mathematical model. Therefore we conclude that the model in Figure 11 effectively describes the movement perception functions of the beetle's CNS with respect to its optomotor behavior in the presence of periodic light stimuli.

2. *Stochastic stimuli.*   The stimuli tested so far, being periodic, are quite different from the more random distributions of light points normally experienced by the beetle in nature. An important question in this regard is whether optokinetic reactions require patterns with figural qualities which are thus ordered, or whether such responses are obtainable from completely random patterns which are visual noise functions (Figure 15) containing contrast but no order or figurative character.

Answers to this question predicted from the model (Figure 11) have perforce been based on two assumptions which can be realized in an experiment only approximately. These are that, 1) the width of the component stripes is infinitely small, and that 2) the stripe sequence does not recur periodically, which is inevitable when a cylindrical stimulus is used. Comparisons of the actual[21,23] and predicted responses (Figure 16) to random sequences of 7° and 1° stripe width (Figure 15) show that for cylinder speeds up to about 60°/sec there was fair agreement for the 7° stripes and reasonably good agreement for the 1° stripes.

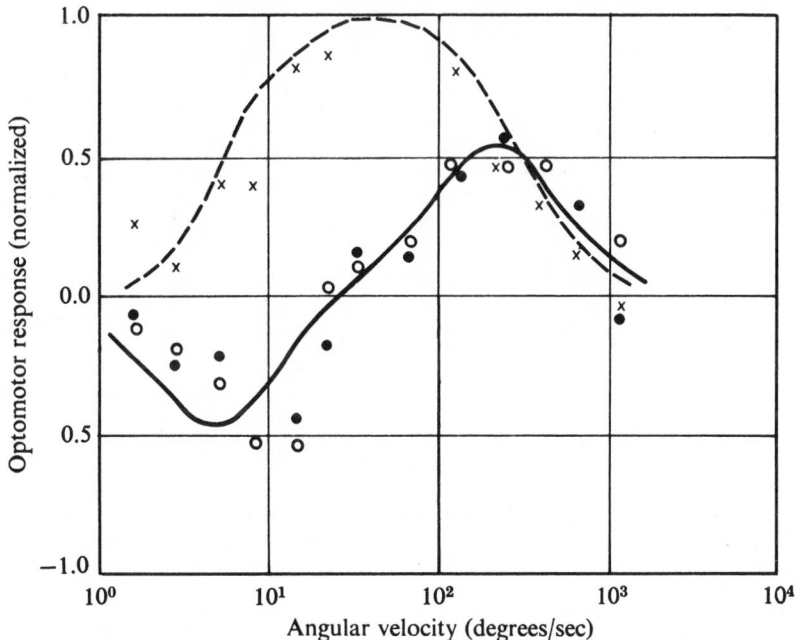

FIGURE 14. Optomotor responses of *Chlorophanus* to different angular velocities of the patterns in Figure 13c (open circles), Figure 13d (filled circles), and Figure 13e (*x*'s).[23] The two curves were predictions derived from the minimal model for optomotor perception (Figure 11).[47] (Redrawn from Reichardt.[42])

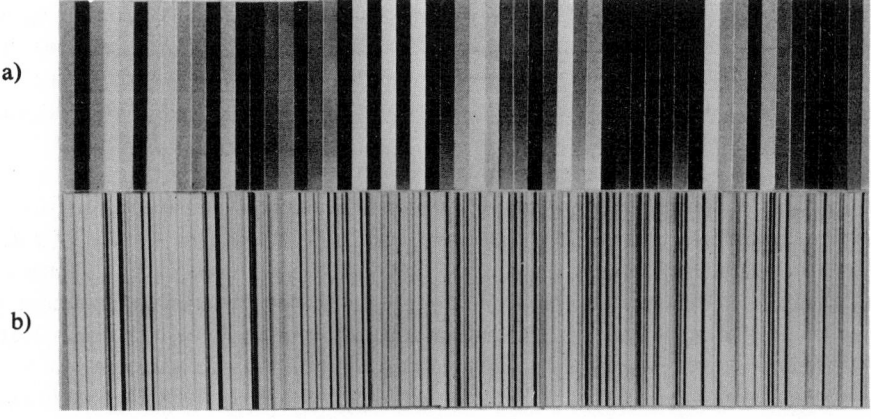

FIGURE 15. Random patterns of stripes (visual noise) for optomotor test cylinders. Order of stripes selected by throwing dice. a) 7° stripe width; b) 1° stripe width. (From Reichardt.)[42]

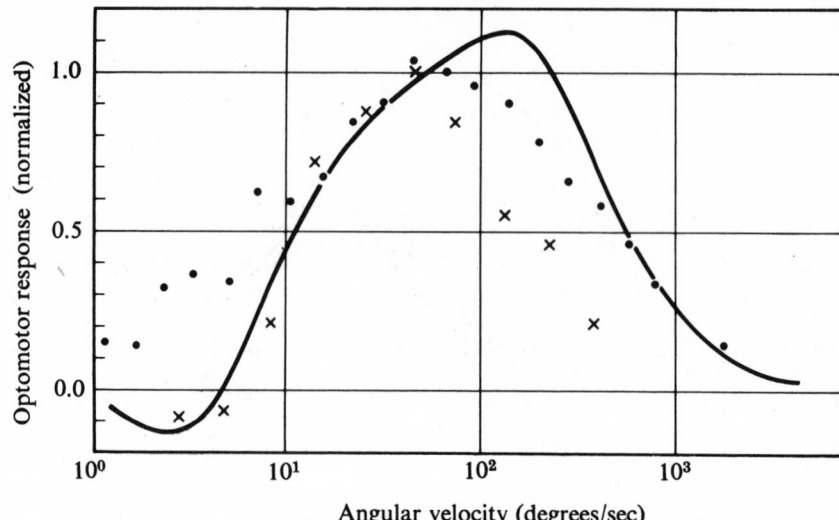

FIGURE 16. Optomotor reactions of *Chlorophanus* to random stripe patterns moving at different velocities. Filled circles, 7° stripe width; *x*'s, 1° stripe width. The predicted curve was derived from the minimal model (Figure 11), assuming $\varphi = 14°$. (Redrawn from Reichardt and Varjú.[44])

Above 60°/sec the periodicity of the cylindrical pattern begins to exert a significant effect on *R*. Note also that for the 1° random pattern slow movements gave turning against the pattern movement both in observations and in predictions. This phenomenon has been shown to be the result of the transmission characteristics of the *D* filters.

The fact that a moving random stimulus can elicit optokinetic reactions in *Chlorophanus* can be qualitatively accounted for by the minimal mathematical model. The first crucial question obviously is whether or not the random signals received by *A* and *B* are still random when they reach the inputs of the mixing components. If the effects in Channel *A* of a particular point in the pattern moving from left to right have been completely dissipated in *D*, *F*, and *H*,* by the time the same stimulus point reaches Channel *B* then the four possible light sequences (dark-light, light-dark, dark-dark, light-light) will be equally common entering the multiplier.

If, on the other hand, the aftereffects of the signal in Channel *A* last as long or longer than Δt then the sequences light-light and dark-dark will begin to constitute more than 50% of those entering M_A while those entering M_B will continue to be equal for the four possibilities since the $\tau_H \ll \tau_F$. Since the persistence of the aftereffect in *F* which determines the predominance of coincidence messages decreases with time, the quantitative excess on the *A* side is a function of the relative velocity of the moving random pattern.

These influences on the input to the correlator stages give rise in their output to a net outflow of positive signals on the *A* side for left-right movement and on the *B* side for right-left movement. The strength of this signal flow depends on the velocity of the moving pattern.

In this way the *Chlorophanus* eye and its minimal model for optokinetic perception can measure seen movements independently of figural components in the moving patterns.

---

* Since τ_F is 50× greater than τ_H and several 1000× greater than τ_D, the aftereffects of a signal in *F* will be the important factor here.

Since the information processing involved is analogous to algebraic multiplication and averaging which is classified as first order correlation, correlation has been demonstrated to be an evaluation principle in the CNS of *Chlorophanus*.

E. Conclusion

From this review on visual perception of movement in *Chlorophanus* the following conclusions can be drawn. 1) A sequence of stimuli in two ommatidia is the most elementary succession of light changes capable of releasing an optomotor response. 2) The stimulus received by one ommatidium can interact only with the stimulus received by the immediately adjacent ommatidia and those once removed. 3) No physiological interaction for movement perception has been observed between ommatidia separated by more than one unstimulated ommatidium. 4) Stimuli received by the ommatidia are linearly transformed into responses in the nervous system. 5) After transformation the signals interact with each other in accordance with a first-order correlation process. 6) The partial responses formed by the interaction process between adjacent and adjacent-once-removed ommatidia add up to the total reaction. 7) The optomotor response of *Chlorophanus* can be described as a transformed autocorrelation function of the brightness fluctuations of the optical surroundings. 8) The main consequence of this evaluation principle is that the optomotor responses are invariant to phase shifts of Fourier components which synthesize brightness distributions. 9) Reactions are elicited not only by periodic or redundant brightness patterns but also by stochastic patterns.

IV. SUMMARY AND DISCUSSION

In this chapter on nervous processing of sensory information, the application of systems theoretical methods to the analysis of sensory mechanisms is demonstrated with two specific examples.

The first part of the chapter deals with nervous inhibition in the lateral eye of the horseshoe crab *Limulus*. The resolving power of apposition eyes in insects is discussed on the basis of diffraction theory. It is shown that diffraction does not play an important role in the *Limulus* eye. In spite of this, the visual fields of neighboring ommatidia overlap strongly. A mathematical relation is given which describes the dependence of the eccentric cell generator potential distribution on the brightness distribution in the surroundings. This relation takes into account the overlap of the visual fields as well as the logarithmic relation between light intensity and generator potential.

On the basis of Hartline and Ratliff's reports[16,37] on lateral inhibition in the *Limulus* eye, it is shown that this process corrects the overlap and therefore increases the resolving power of the eye. Neither the overlap of ommatidial visual fields nor the nervous process of lateral inhibition destroys information. Therefore the functional mechanism of lateral inhibition is in principle able to create an image of the optical surroundings in the optic nerve.

The theoretical investigations so far are limited to the steady state case whereas the dynamics of the lateral interaction are not yet understood. Future research will undoubtedly be directed toward the solution of this problem and might establish the basis of a complete mathematical theory of lateral inhibition in *Limulus*.

In the second part of the chapter an analysis of optomotor responses in the beetle *Chlorophanus* is presented. In this insect's apposition eye only neighboring and neighboring-once-removed ommatidia interact. The partial reactions produced by these processes add up to the total responses. In all such interactions the information received from the optical surroundings is linearly transformed, and the transformed signals interact with each other in accordance with a first-order correlation process. Therefore the optomotor response is invariant to phase transformations of the Fourier components which describe the brightness distribution of the optical surroundings.

Comparing the analyses in *Limulus* and in *Chlorophanus* from the systems theoretical point of view, their basic difference can be easily seen. In *Limulus*, optical information received by the receptors is transformed into signals in the optic nerve fibers without loss of information. Consequently, at the level of the *Limulus* retina neither filtering nor perceptual processes take place. The situation is quite different for the optomotor reactions in *Chlorophanus*. Here the perceptive processes consist in the correlation of sensory signals. Thereby *Chlorophanus* is able to measure relative optic movements; however, this ability is accompanied by a loss of sensory information which is not regained in the optomotor response. Therefore the investigation of invariance of the response to classes of transformations in the surroundings can be considered as a key to the neural principles involved in the quantitative response studied.

REFERENCES

1. Barlow, H. B. 1952. The size of ommatidia in apposition eyes. *J. Exptl. Biol.* **29:** 667–674.
2. Barlow, H. B. 1953. Summation and inhibition in the frog's retina. *J. Physiol. (London)* **119:** 69–88.
3. Barlow, H. B., FitzHugh, R., and Kuffler, S. W. 1957. Change of organization in the receptive fields of the cat's retina during dark adaptation. *J. Physiol. (London)* **137:** 338–354.
4. Baumgärtner, H. 1928. Der Formensinn und die Sehschärfe der Bienen. *Z. Vergleich. Physiol.* **7:** 56–143.
5a. Cohen, M. J., and Dijkgraaf, S. 1961. Mechanoreception. *In:* "The Physiology of Crustacea" (T. H. Waterman, ed.), Vol. II, pp. 65–108. Academic, New York.
5b. Fermi, G., and Reichardt, W. 1963. Optomotorische Reaktionen der Fliege Musca domestica. *Kybernetik* **2:** 15–28.
6. Florey, E., ed. 1962. "Nervous Inhibition." 490 pp. Pergamon, Oxford.
7. Fuortes, M. G. F. 1958. Electric activity of cells in the eye of *Limulus*. *Am. J. Ophthalmol.* **46:** 210–223.
8a. Galambos, R., and Davis, H. 1944. Inhibition of activity in single auditory nerve fibers by acoustic stimulation. *J. Neurophysiol.* **7:** 287–303.
8b. Götz, K. G. 1964. Optomotorische Untersuchung des visuellen Systems einiger Augenmutanten der Fruchtfliege Drosophila. *Kybernetik* **2:** 77–92.
9. Granit, R. 1947. "Sensory Mechanisms of the Retina," 412 pp. Oxford Univ. Press, London.
10. Granit, R. 1952. Aspects of excitation and inhibition in the retina. *Proc. Roy. Soc. (London)* **B 140:** 191–199.
11. Granit, R. 1955. "Receptors and Sensory Perception," 369 pp. Yale Univ. Press, New Haven.
12. Hartline, H. K. 1939. Excitation and inhibition of the "off" response in vertebrate optic nerve fibers. (Abstract) *Am. J. Physiol.* **126:** 527.
13. Hartline, H. K. 1940. The receptive fields of optic nerve fibers. *Am. J. Physiol.* **130:** 690–699.
14. Hartline, H. K. 1959. Receptor mechanisms and the integration of sensory information in the eye. *Rev. Mod. Phys.* **31:** 515–523.

15. Hartline, H. K., and McDonald, P. R. 1947. Light and dark adaptation of single photoreceptor elements in the eye of *Limulus. J. Cellular Comp. Physiol.* **30:** 225–253.
16. Hartline, H. K., and Ratliff, F. 1957. Inhibitory interaction of receptor units in the eye of *Limulus. J. Gen. Physiol.* **40:** 357–376.
17. Hartline, H. K., and Ratliff, F. 1958. Spatial summation of inhibitory influences in the eye of *Limulus*, and the mutual interaction of receptor units. *J. Gen. Physiol.* **41:** 1049–1066.
18. Hartline, H. K., Wagner, H. G., and MacNichol, E. F. 1952. The peripheral origin of nervous activity in the visual system. *Cold Spring Harbor Symp. Quant. Biol.* **17:** 125–141.
19. Hartline, H. K., Wagner, H. G., and Ratliff, F. 1956. Inhibition in the eye of *Limulus. J. Gen. Physiol.* **39:** 651–673.
20. Hassenstein, B. 1951. Ommatidienraster und afferente Bewegungs-Integration. *Z. Vergleich. Physiol.* **33:** 301–326.
21. Hassenstein, B. 1958a. Die Stärke von optokinetischen Reaktionen auf verschiedene Mustergeschwindigkeiten. *Z. Naturforsch.* **13b:** 1–6.
22. Hassenstein, B. 1958b. Über die Wahrnehmung der Bewegung von Figuren und unregelmässigen Helligkeitsmustern. *Z. Vergleich. Physiol.* **40:** 556–592.
23. Hassenstein, B. 1959. Optokinetische Wirksamkeit bewegter periodischer Muster. *Z. Naturforsch.* **14b:** 659–674.
24. Hassenstein, B., and Reichardt, W. 1953. Der Schluss von Reiz-Reaktions-Funktionen auf Systemstrukturen. *Z. Naturforsch.* **8b:** 518–524.
25. Hassenstein, B., and Reichardt, W. 1956a. Functional structure of a mechanism of perception of optical movement. *Proc. Intern. Congr. Cybernetics (Namur)* **1:** 797–801.
26. Hassenstein, B., and Reichardt, W. 1956b. Systemtheoretische Analyse der Zeit-, Reihenfolgen- und Vorzeichenauswertung bei der Bewegungsperzeption des Rüsselkäfers *Chlorophanus. Z. Naturforsch.* **11b:** 513–524.
27. Hassenstein, B., and Reichardt, W. 1959. Wie sehen Insekten Bewegungen? *Die Umschau* **10:** 302–305.
28. Hecht, S., and Wolf, E. 1929. The visual acuity of the honey bee. *J. Gen. Physiol.* **12:** 727–760.
29. Jung, R. 1953. "Handbuch der Inneren Medizin," Vol. 5, Part 1, 181 pp. Springer, Berlin.
30. Kuffler, S. W. 1953. Discharge patterns and functional organization of mammalian retina. *J. Neurophysiol.* **16:** 37–68.
31. Laning, I. H., and Battin, R. H. 1956. "Random Processes in Automatic Control," 194 pp. McGraw-Hill, New York.
32. Mach, E. 1865. Über die Wirkung der räumlichen Verteilung des Lichtreizes aus die Netzhaut, I. *Sitzber. Math. Naturw. Kl. Wien* **52:** 303–322.
33. MacNichol, E. F., Jr. 1956. Visual receptors as biological transducers. Molecular structure and functional activity of nerve cells. *Am. Inst. Biol. Sci. Publ.* **No. 1:** 34–53.
34. MacNichol, E. F., Jr. 1958. Subthreshold excitatory processes in the eye of *Limulus. Exptl. Cell Res., Suppl.* **5:** 411–425.
35. Miller, W. H. 1957. Morphology of the ommatidia of the compound eye of *Limulus. J. Biophys. Biochem. Cytol.* **3:** 421–428.
36. Miller, W. H. 1958. Fine structure of some invertebrate photoreceptors. *Ann. N.Y. Acad. Sci.* **74:** 204–209.
37. Ratliff, F., and Hartline, H. K. 1959. The responses of *Limulus* optic nerve fibers to patterns of illumination on the receptor mosaic. *J. Gen. Physiol.* **42:** 1241–1255.
38. Ratliff, F., Miller, W. H., and Hartline, H. K. 1958. Neural interaction in the eye and the integration of receptor activity. *Ann. N.Y. Acad. Sci.* **74:** 210–222.
39. Ratliff, F., and Mueller, C. G. 1957. Synthesis of "On-Off" and "Off" responses in a visual-neural system. *Science* **126:** 840–841.
40. Reichardt, W. 1957. Autokorrelationsauswertung als Funktionsprinzip des Zentralnervensystems. *Z. Naturforsch.* **12b:** 447–457.

41. Reichardt, W. 1961. Über das optische Auflösungsvermögen der Facettenaugen von *Limulus*. *Kybernetik* **1:** 57–69.

42. Reichardt, W. 1962. Nervous integration in the facet eye. *Biophys. J.* **2** (2, Suppl.): 121–143.

43. Reichardt, W., and MacGinitie, G. E. 1962. Zur Theorie der lateralen Inhibition. *Kybernetik.* **1:** 155–165.

44. Reichardt, W., and Varjú, D. 1959. Übertragungseigenschaften im Auswertesystem für das Bewegungssehen. *Z. Naturforsch.* **14b:** 674–689.

45. Roberts, E., ed. 1960. "Inhibition in the Nervous System and Gamma-Aminobutyric Acid," 591 pp. Pergamon, Oxford.

46. Tomita, T. 1956. The nature of action potentials in the lateral eye of the horseshoe crab as revealed by simultaneous intra- and extracellular recording. *Japan. J. Physiol.* **6:** 327–340.

47. Varjú, D. 1959. Optomotorische Reaktionen auf die Bewegung periodischer Helligkeitsmuster. *Z. Naturforsch.* **14b:** 724–735.

48. von Békésy, G. 1928. Zur Theorie des Hörens. Die Schwingungsform der Basilarmembran. *Physik. Z.* **29:** 793–810.

49. von Békésy, G. 1958. Funneling in the nervous system and its role in loudness and sensation intensity on the skin. *J. Acoust. Soc. Am.* **30:** 399–412.

50. Waterman, T. H. 1954a. Directional sensitivity of single ommatidia in the compound eye of *Limulus*. *Proc. Natl. Acad. Sci. U.S.* **40:** 252–257.

51. Waterman, T. H. 1954b. Relative growth and the compound eye in Xiphosura. *J. Morphol.* **95:** 125–158.

52. Waterman, T. H., and Wiersma, C. A. G. 1954. The functional relation between retinal cells and optic nerve in *Limulus*. *J. Exptl. Zool.* **126:** 59–85.

53. Wiener, N. 1949. "Extrapolation, Interpolation, and Smoothing of Stationary Time Series," 163 pp. M.I.T. Press, Wiley, New York.

[15]

GENETIC CONSEQUENCES OF NATURAL SELECTION

Richard Levins

I. INTRODUCTION

The disciplines of population genetics and population ecology have developed largely independently of each other. Despite the use of similar mathematical techniques, they have been concerned with different sorts of problems and have used models with very different assumptions. Population genetics is concerned primarily with changes in gene frequency and the maintenance of genetic heterogeneity within populations. Most work in this area has assumed a constant environment, a fixed or irrelevant population size, constant systems of mating, and of course a single species at a time.

Population ecology, on the other hand, has generally assumed a uniform population whose size and age distribution might change with time, but not its genetic make-up. Thus ecological models considered demographic equilibrium without evolutionary change. Finally, the ecologists studied multi-species systems which influence each other's abundance but not each other's genetic properties.

Clearly, evolutionary biology requires a much closer integration of its genetic and ecological aspects. But here we immediately get into serious technical difficulties. An equation which is at all realistic in representing such systems must include many different kinds of terms, some of which will be random variables. Such equations may be completely insoluble analytically. Furthermore, they often depend on constants which are themselves so extremely difficult to measure that numerical solutions are not available.

Another difficulty is that even when the solutions of these complex equations are known, they may not suggest any biologically meaningful interpretation. Thus the solution of a system of simultaneous equations will be the ratio of two determinants, the over-all significance of which is not obvious, but each of which is a sum of the products of constants which themselves have biological meaning even if they are not readily measured.

These difficulties occur in many situations where we attempt to analyze the properties of a macrosystem in terms of the properties and dynamics of complexly related subsystems. In attempting to overcome such difficulties there are several approaches that may be taken.

1) Research into the mathematical properties of stochastic differential and difference equations may eventually provide better techniques for handling the models formally.

2) The fact that a complicated expression has no obvious biological meaning may be treated as a limitation of our own intuition rather than of the objective situation. Thus we

371

might choose to define the determinant of such a system as a property of the macrosystem under study. Eventually it may acquire the same sort of intuitive meaning that the physicist sees in the Hamiltonian of a mechanical system. Then our theory can be framed directly in terms of the macrolevel entity and can proceed to study how it affects the properties of the whole system, and how it is determined by the constants of the subsystems. Any differential equation of the form

$$\frac{dx}{dt} = f(x)$$

reaches an equilibrium value at which $\int f(x)\, dx$ is a maximum or minimum. Thus the integral acquires a certain significance on the macrolevel, and the process may be said to move in such a direction as to maximize that integral.

3) Many microlevel terms may combine directly into macrolevel constants so that their individual identification becomes unnecessary. Thus the frequencies of genes, the relations of dominance and epistasis on many loci, and their phenotypic effects enter into the equations for natural selection only by way of the genetic variance which can itself be estimated directly.

4) The equations need not be solved explicitly at all, but used for determining inequalities. Then what is important is not the root of the equation, but the way in which the root is affected by various factors. Thus the expected amount of polymorphism in a species will be shown below to increase with the heterogeneity of the species' environment and decrease with the tolerance of the individual member of the species. It is far easier to estimate relative rank of species for either property than to measure the heterogeneity or tolerance accurately themselves. But then the prediction of the theory is also less precise. The test of the theory will depend on the analysis of information for many groups of species. For instance, the environment of weeds from generation to generation is more variable than is the environment of forest trees. Therefore we can predict that weeds as a whole will be more polymorphic than the forest trees as a group in the same region.

The principle of natural selection is the link which permits us to go from the microlevel of genes and chromosomes to the macroproperties of multi-species systems. The present chapter deals with the methods and outcome of such genetic and evolutionary integration. For further background on the problem, references[1,5–13,15] may be consulted. The integration of population ecology and evolution is the subject of the next chapter (Chapter 16).

II. THE CYBERNETICS OF A MENDELIAN POPULATION

Recent interest in cybernetics and systems research has led to analogies between biological and engineering systems, with emphasis on the collection and storage of information and on autoregulation. From the point of view of population genetics, a population is an aggregate of essentially similar kinds of units. The properties of the whole population are all statistics of the properties of individual members. Thus there are the mean and variance of metric traits, the frequencies of genes, and the average fitness of the population. Each individual contributes to the population in the same way, as part of an average, and even though the individuals may interact with each other, the effect of the interactions can be expressed in terms of the frequencies of different types within the population.

The population is changing in time as a result of natural selection and other evolutionary forces, so that the array of gene frequencies at any given time contains information about past environments. For example, in a situation in which there is no dominance or mutation and where the rate of change is low, the gene frequency x changes in accordance with the equation

$$\frac{dx}{dt} = sx(1 - x)$$

where s is an environmentally determined selection coefficient; s can be considered as a random variable with its own statistical properties. The equation can be solved to give

$$x = \frac{x_0}{1 - x_0} \exp \int_0^t s(\gamma) \, d\gamma \left/ \left(1 + \frac{x_0}{1 - x_0} \exp \int_0^t s(\gamma) \, d\gamma \right) \right.$$

Hence the gene frequency represents information about the past environment, giving equal weight to each environment of the past.

Mutation can be introduced into the model, giving an equation of the form

$$\frac{dx}{dt} = sx(1 - x) - Ux + V(1 - x)$$

where U and V are the mutation rates in opposite directions. The effect of mutation is that the gene frequency still depends on the past environments, but no longer giving all of them equal weight. As will be seen below, mutation reduces the dependence of gene frequency on the environments of the remote past and therefore increases the relative dependence on recent environments. This means that environmental information is stored in a different way. Therefore it is incorrect to regard mutation simply as an information-destroying process analogous to noise in a circuit.

In the engineer's cybernetic model there is a memory unit which stores information, elements which process the incoming signal to produce some output which does not destroy the information, and which can be measured against some criterion of value. In the Mendelian population there is no memory unit separate from the output. The output of a population is its fitness, which depends on the array of genes and genotypes. Therefore the output is a transformation of the environments of the past, and there is no separate memory unit. In the process, some information is lost. For example, there is no direct transfer of environmental information from parent to offspring as in the Lamarckian model.

Thus the various factors of evolution such as mutation, migration, and drift can be regarded as filters of information, and we can ask how the optimum performance of the system depends on each of these and on the nature of the input signal.

III. FITNESS AND NATURAL SELECTION

In order to build a theory of evolutionary ecology on the population and system level, we would like to be able to say, with Darwin, that from among a set of alternative types within a population, selection will establish the "best" or most fit in some sense. It should not be necessary to know the exact physiological basis for this fitness. For example, it may not always be true that animals in a colder climate will be larger, but we would like to be able to say that they are better cold-adapted. This is important because in most cases the ecologist is unable to examine the population's genetic system. Therefore the first question is, to what extent is it true that natural selection increases fitness?

A.   The Basic Genetic Model

The first important work in this direction is associated with the names of Sewall Wright[16–18] and R. A. Fisher[3,4] who used different notation but arrived at the same result. In Wright's terminology, let the relative rates of reproduction of the three genotypes at a single locus with two alleles be w_{11}, w_{12}, w_{22}, respectively. Then the average fitness $\overline{W}$ is given by

$$\overline{W} = w_{11}x^2 + 2w_{12}x(1 - x) + w_{22}(1 - x)^2$$

and the rate of change in the frequency x is

$$\frac{\Delta x}{\Delta t} = \frac{\frac{1}{2}x(1 - x)}{\overline{W}} \frac{\partial \overline{W}}{\partial x}$$

The rate of change will be zero when x is zero or one, and also when

$$\frac{\partial \overline{W}}{\partial x} = [w_{11} + w_{22} - w_{12}]x - [w_{22} - w_{12}]$$

is zero, provided x lies between zero and one. That will be the case only when the heterozygote is superior or inferior to both homozygotes. The former case gives a stable equilibrium, the latter an unstable equilibrium. Therefore if the heterozygote is superior, natural selection will not produce a population uniformly showing the optimal characteristics, but one in which $\overline{W}$ is maximum, subject to the restriction of the Hardy-Weinberg law. The "fitness" which is maximized is a relative optimum.

Several consequences emerge from a consideration of a single locus. First, if M is a metric character which is genetically determined, and S is the optimal value of M, selection will change the population toward the gene frequency at which the average M is S, and the rate of change will be proportional both to the additive genetic variance and the deviation of M from S. Second, the intensity of selection slows down as the gene frequency approaches its optimal equilibrium value. As M approaches S, selection for this character is weakened and therefore any other selection pressures which are operating with respect to other aspects of the environment become relatively more important and can stop selection. However, in this simple model, and in extensions of it to many alleles and many loci, selection changes the population toward an equilibrium state which maximizes $\overline{W}$.

If we want to go beyond these simple models, several qualifying statements are necessary. These come from a variable environment, from a possible dependence of the w_{ij}'s on the proportions of the different genotypes, and from the correlation of responses to selection.

B.   Fitness in a Variable Environment

In a variable environment the Wright-Fisher theory holds only in the sense that the population changes toward the state that would maximize $\overline{W}$ in the present environment. Whether or not this increases $\overline{W}$ depends on whether the environment of the next generation is similar to that of the present. Suppose, for example, that an organism has one winter and one summer generation per year. In the summer, natural selection increases the proportion of summer-adapted types so that this generation produces offspring better adapted to summer conditions, but which have to grow up in winter. The winter generation similarly undergoes selection for winter adaptedness, but its offspring face the summer. The responding population always lags behind the environment, and the over-all effect is to reduce fitness.

In order for the response to selection to improve fitness, there must be a sufficiently high correlation between the environments of successive generations. In one model, in which the fitness declines as the square of the deviation of the phenotype from the optimum phenotype for the given environment, the minimum correlation between successive environments for selection to improve fitness is about 0.8 or 0.9. But the exact threshold obviously depends on details of the model.

If selection is taking place in a variable environment, there is no equilibrium gene frequency. However, there is an average gene frequency, and we could ask whether natural selection results in an average gene frequency which is optimal in the average environment. But this is not generally true either. To illustrate this, consider a single locus with a heterotic lethal. The heterozygote is taken to have fitness 1, and the other homozygote $1 - s$, where s is a measure of selection against the viable homozygote. If s were constant, this would give an equilibrium at

$$x = \frac{s}{1 + s}$$

where x is the frequency of the lethal allele. When s is a random variable, for simplicity assumed to have no autocorrelation, the rate of change of x is given by

$$\frac{dx}{dt} = \tfrac{1}{2}x(1 - x)[s - (1 + s)x]$$

Taking the expected value of both sides of the equation we get

$$E\left(\frac{dx}{dt}\right) = \tfrac{1}{2}\bar{x}(1 - \bar{x})[\bar{s} - (1 + \bar{s})\bar{x}] + (\bar{s} - 1)\sigma_x^2 + (\bar{s} + 1)\mu_3$$

which is the rate of change of the mean gene frequency. E is the expected value, that is, average; σ_x^2 is the variance of x; and μ_3 is skewness, the third moment about the mean. If the average gene frequency were $\frac{\bar{s}}{1 + \bar{s}}$, then when this value is substituted in the above equation $\frac{d\bar{x}}{dt}$ would equal zero. But

$$\left.\frac{d\bar{x}}{dt}\right|_{\bar{x}=\bar{s}/(1+\bar{s})} = (\bar{s} - 1)\sigma_x^2 + (\bar{s} + 1)\mu_3$$

which is always negative for small values of $\bar{s}$. This means that the average gene frequency is below that which maximizes the $\overline{W}$.

This introduces another significance for mutation. Whereas in a constant environment the only effect of mutation is to displace the gene frequency from its optimum, thus producing a mutational load, in a fluctuating environment mutation toward a heterotic lethal can increase $\overline{W}$ toward its optimal value. Hence a lethal mutation can increase fitness.

C. *Frequency-Dependent Selection*

A second qualification to the idea that natural selection necessarily increases fitness occurs in frequency-dependent selection. The following arbitrary example illustrates this.

Genotype	Frequency	Fitness
AA	x^2	$1 - x$
Aa	$2x(1 - x)$	$(1 - s)(1 - x)$
aa	$(1 - x)^2$	$(1 - 2s)(1 - x)$

Here the first genotype is always superior to the other homozygote, with the heterozygote intermediate. Therefore selection always increases x. As the frequency of x increases toward one, the fitness of the whole population approaches zero. Therefore natural selection can select a population to extinction.

D. Correlated Responses

It has been the experience of animal breeders especially that when one tries to improve egg production, meat quality, disease resistance, and a number of other characteristics simultaneously, progress is much less than expected. The reason for this is that the same genes which affect one of these traits also affect the others, and not necessarily in the same direction. Dickerson[2] showed that if selection is acting on N characters simultaneously, an average negative correlation of $-1/N$ between the effects of the same gene on two characters is sufficient to stop completely progress under selection. He called this phenomenon genetic slippage.

E. The General Case

The result of the foregoing discussion is that intrapopulation selection does not always maximize fitness, or even $\overline{W}$, which is one restricted definition of fitness. The outcome of selection will depend on the specific genetic system operating. However, a given phenotype can be produced by many different genetic systems, and the genetic systems are themselves subject to selection. Therefore, even where we cannot make a precise statement with respect to a particular character in a particular species, we are on somewhat better ground when we attempt to generalize about systems of species.

For example, we can say that most species which inhabit a transect from north to south (in the northern hemisphere) will be larger in the northern part of their range because there is a selective advantage to large size there. In particular cases, selection may not result in increased size. But in comparing large faunas this size cline may be expected. As a result of this argument, we feel justified in making statements on the ecological level only by using large groups of species at a time, comparing whole floras or faunas. Our working hypothesis is not that optimal systems will be established, but that groups of species will differ among themselves in the same directions in which their optima differ. It is on this level that the rest of the theory will be developed.

IV. THE FITNESS SET MODEL

A. The Many-Niche Case

Assume that for each phenotype in the population there is a fitness which can be measured in each of a set of different environments. The fitness reaches a maximum in some particular environment in which this phenotype is optimal, and decreases as the optimal and actual phenotypes diverge. The rate at which fitness decreases with deviation from the optimum depends on the homeostatic properties of the genotype in question, so that fitness can be expressed by

$$W = W\left(\frac{S - y}{H}\right)$$

where y is the phenotype, S the optimum, and H the measure of homeostasis, the tolerance for nonoptimal conditions. W is a symmetric, positive function with a peak at $S = y$.

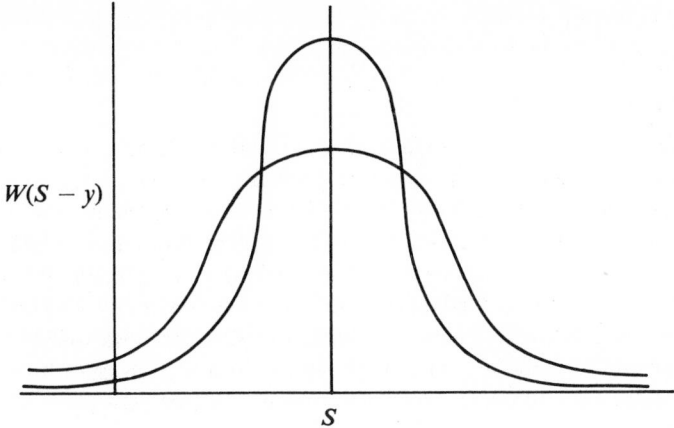

FIGURE 1. Fitness as a function of environment for specialized and generalized organisms.

Since the expression is symmetric in S and y, we can graph the function in two ways that are equivalent. With the ordinate equal to W, we can allow the abscissa to represent units of environment. Then the curve in Figure 1 shows the fitness of a given phenotype over a range of environments. Or we can allow the abscissa to be units of phenotype, and the same curve shows the fitness of all phenotypes in a given environment. In the first case, the peak is the optimal environment for a given phenotype; in the second, the optimum phenotype for a given environment.

B. The Two-Niche Case

For convenience the model will now be restricted to two environments (or niches), and the fitness of a given phenotype can be plotted along two axes which represent fitness in niches 1 and 2, respectively. Such a diagram shows that there will be some phenotypes better in one environment, some better in the other. The whole array of fitness points can be called the fitness set. Then we can ask, what phenotype or combination of phenotypes is optimal for the population under different criteria of optimality?

An important distinction arises, depending on whether the fitness set is convex or concave on its upper right-hand boundary. Since it is assumed that the fitness of a given phenotype depends only on that phenotype and the environment, the fitness point representing a mixed population of two phenotypes lies on the straight line joining their fitness points. If the fitness set is convex, this will lie inside the set. Hence when the fitness set is convex, every polymorphic population has a fitness point which is also the fitness point of some monomorphic population. In contrast, when the fitness set is concave, a polymorphic population can have a fitness point lying outside the set. In fact, all points on the upper right-hand boundary of the fitness set for all populations now represent polymorphic populations, except for the end points. Thus it is possible for the optimum population to be polymorphic.

It can be shown that, when S_1 and S_2 are the optima in niches 1 and 2 respectively, the fitness set will be convex when $\dfrac{|S_2 - S_1|}{H}$ is small, and concave when $\dfrac{|S_2 - S_1|}{H}$ is large. The exact threshold value depends on the form of W. Thus when the optima in the two niches are very different compared to the level of homeostasis, the fitness set is concave and the optimum population may be polymorphic.

C. The Heterogeneous Environment

Whether in fact the optimum is polymorphic or not depends on one further consideration. Given the fitness of different phenotypes or populations in two environments separately, how can they be combined to make an over-all evaluation of the fitness of the population in the heterogeneous environment? Many different criteria of fitness can be established. However, it seems reasonable that in each case the fitness in the mixed environment should be an increasing function of the fitnesses in the two niches separately, and be of a form which reflects the way in which the two niches are distributed in time and space.

1. *Niches constant.* Suppose first that the environment is constant in time and always consists of the same two niches in fixed proportions. In that case the rate of expansion of the population into new territory will be equal to the average fitness, $pW_1 + (1 - p)W_2$, where the W's are fitnesses in the two niches and p is the proportion of niche 1. The optimum population is the one which is represented by the fitness point that maximizes the above expression. It can be found immediately from a consideration of the family of straight lines that

$$pW_1 + (1 - p)W_2 = k$$

for all values of k. Some of these lines do not touch the fitness set at all, some cut across it, and the line with the greatest value of k that touches the fitness set is tangent to it. In Figure 2 the fitness set and point of maximum fitness are shown for the convex and concave fitness sets. The graph shows that on a convex fitness set the point of tangency lies along the boundary between the points representing specialization to the two niches. The optimal population will be monomorphic, and of a phenotype that has intermediate fitness in both niches.

In contrast, on a concave fitness set the line $pW_1 + (1 - p)W_2 = k$ touches the fitness set at either end point. This means that the optimum population is specialized to one of the two niches and is monomorphic.

2. *Niches varying.* The proportion of niche 1, p, can be allowed to vary along a geographic gradient. Then the changes in the optimum population as p changes indicate the

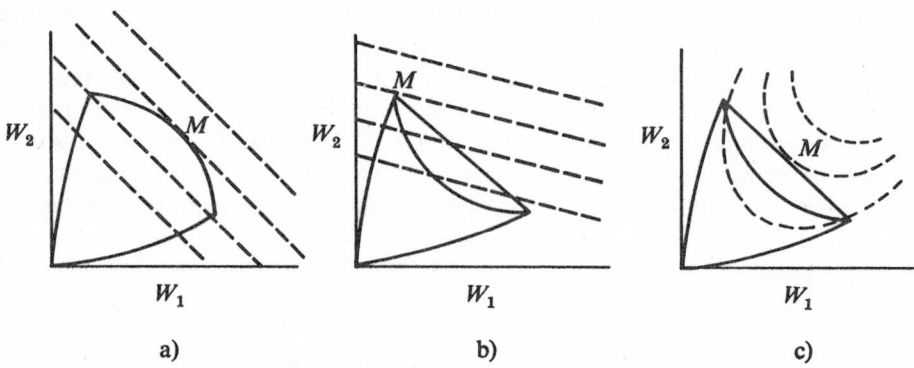

FIGURE 2. Optima on the fitness set. Linear adaptive function (broken line) maximized on: a) convex fitness set, and b) concave fitness set. c) Maximization of $A(W_1, W_2) = W_1^p W_2^{1-p}$ on concave fitness set. (From Levins.[9])

optimum pattern in space. On a convex fitness set, the optimum phenotype varies in a continuous way with p. Thus along a geographic gradient in p there should be a continuous cline in phenotype, with local populations essentially monomorphic. In contrast, on a concave fitness set the optimum will be specialized to one of the niches as long as it is sufficiently abundant, and then changes abruptly to the phenotype specialized in the other niche. Hence the optimal geographic pattern is a series of discrete, monomorphic races.

3. *Threshold variation.* The same diagram can be interpreted in yet another way. Suppose there is some clue from the environment as to the proportion of niches. For example, suppose that the environment may be either hot or cold, and that the length of day, as an indicator of the season, affects the probabilities of the winter and summer environments. Then p in our equation can be replaced by p_e, which means the probability of niche 1, given environment e. On a convex fitness set, the optimum phenotype changes continuously with p_e. Therefore the optimum developmental system is one in which phenotype varies continuously with some environmental factor. In contrast, on a concave fitness set there is a threshold effect. The optimal phenotype remains constant until the environment reaches some threshold value at which all individuals now have the opposite phenotype. This is the mechanism which is observed in the control of diapause in insects, or the formation of melanin in the Himalayan rabbit, where different parts of the body have different thresholds.

Now let the environment consist entirely of niche 1 with probability p, or of niche 2 with probability $1 - p$. The rate of increase can now be expressed by $W_1^p W_2^{1-p}$. The optimum is now that point on the fitness set which maximizes this new expression, which gives rise to a family of curves that look like hyperbolas. On a convex fitness set this does not change the results of the previous discussion, but on a concave fitness the hyperbolas can be tangent to points on the line joining the two specialized phenotypes, and represent polymorphic populations. As p changes, the whole family of hyperbolas rotates and the point of tangency moves along the line representing polymorphic populations. Thus along a geographic gradient one expects to find changing proportions of the same two phenotypes.

Interpreted in terms of development, the result is that on a concave fitness set the same developmental system should produce a mixture of phenotypes in proportions which vary with the environment. The determination of winged or wingless aphids seems to be a mechanism of this type.[14]

4. *Résumé.* Thus we can summarize the results of this model, which admits only static populations having a constant array of phenotype frequencies and no response to selection, as follows: 1) When the two niches are not very different compared to the range of tolerance of the species, optimal populations will be generalized and monomorphic, geographic gradients will show continuous clines, and the developmental system will produce phenotypes that vary continuously with the environment. 2) When the niches are very different compared to the environmental tolerance, and when they both occur in fixed proportions, the optimal populations will be specialized and monomorphic, the geographic gradient will show discrete races, and the developmental system will have threshold switch mechanisms. 3) When the niches are very different compared to the tolerance and their relative abundance fluctuates greatly in time, the optimum population will be polymorphic, the geographic gradient will show a cline in the proportions of the same forms, and development may show a stochastic switch mechanism.

V. OPTIMAL GENETIC SYSTEMS

A. *Phenotypic Diversity*

When we allow the population not only to be polymorphic but also to be changing in time, the genetic system must be specified more completely. Consider the following model:

Genotype	Frequency	Phenotype	Fitness
AA	x^2	a	$1 - \dfrac{1}{H}(s - a)^2$
AA$'$	$2x(1 - x)$	0	$1 - s^2/H$
A$'$A$'$	$(1 - x)^2$	$-a$	$1 - \dfrac{1}{H}(s + a)^2$

Then the fitness of the whole population is given by

$$\overline{W} = 1 - \frac{1}{H}\{(s - a)^2 x^2 + 2s^2 x(1 - x) + (s + a)^2(1 - x)^2\}$$

The constant a is a measure of phenotypic diversity at the locus in question. If a equals zero, the locus effectively disappears. The first question then is, what is the optimal value for a? If the optimum is defined as greatest average W, we can take the expected value of the above expression and maximize it as a function of a. The problem can be simplified somewhat by taking a symmetric situation where s is taken to be zero, so that $\bar{x} = \frac{1}{2}$ (or, mean $x = \frac{1}{2}$). Then the expected average fitness is

$$E(\overline{W}) = 1 - \frac{1}{H}\left\{\sigma_s^2 + \frac{a^2}{2} + 2a^2\sigma_x^2 - 4a \text{ cov }(s, x)\right\}$$

Thus the average fitness is reduced because of heterogeneity in the population at any time, and by the variance of the gene frequency; it may be increased by the covariance. Unfortunately I have not been able to evaluate cov (s, x) in a general way, but it can be estimated for very small a. Here

$$\text{cov }(s, x) \sim \frac{2a}{H}\alpha\sigma_s^2(\tfrac{1}{4} - \sigma_x^2)$$

so that the expected value of $\overline{W}$ is

$$E(\overline{W}) = 1 - \frac{1}{H}\left\{\sigma_s^2 + a^2\left[\tfrac{1}{2} + 2\sigma_x^2 - \frac{8}{H}\alpha\sigma_s^2(\tfrac{1}{4} - \sigma_x^2)\right]\right\}$$

where the correlation between $s(t)$ and $s(t - h)$ is $e^{-h/\alpha}$. When the coefficient of a^2 is positive, the optimum value of a is greater than zero. Hence, heterogeneity at the A locus improves fitness.

To find the optimum values of a, a computer was necessary. A random variable s was generated having the desired statistical properties, the equation for change in gene frequency was iterated, and the average W calculated. In each case, selection was allowed to run for 100 generations and repeated ten times by means of different random environments. The average W was thus calculated for values of a until a maximum was reached. For an environmental variance of 0.1 and autocorrelations of 0.5, 0.8, and 0.9 respectively, the optimal values for a were found to be 0.0, 0.06, and 0.12. The optimum a is zero for autocorrelations below about 0.8, and increases with autocorrelation and variance of the environment.

B. *Effects of Mutation*

The average value of W can be affected by mutation in several ways. In the previous model, which was symmetric, the mean gene frequency was the optimum mean, so that if mutation changes the mean at all, the effect will be detrimental. This is not necessarily the case in asymmetric models, as discussed above.

Secondly, mutation affects the variance of gene frequency. In the symmetric model, with mutation equal in both directions, the mean is unchanged and variance reduced, thus increasing fitness. Therefore, in symmetric models mutation was beneficial.

Finally, mutation increases the correlation between the environment and the gene frequency. An explicit expression for this effect is not available, but its qualitative aspect is made more apparent by consideration of a linear system which no longer represents any particular genetic situation. Suppose

$$\frac{dx}{dt} = s - \lambda x$$

where λ is analogous to mutation rate. Then

$$x = x_0 + \int_0^t e^{-\lambda(t-\gamma)} s(\gamma) \, d\gamma$$

For λ equal to zero, x is the integral of all past environments; whereas as λ increases, the effects of the remote past are increasingly damped. In the nonlinear equations of genetics the same thing happens, and mutation increases the correlation between s and x. Although the correlation increases, the variance of x decreases, so that the covariance first increases and then decreases. In Table 1 the effect of mutation rate on fitness and some of its components are shown for autocorrelation of 0.9 and variance of environment 0.1.

The table indicates that for this model the optimum mutation rate is several orders of magnitude greater than the mutation rates actually found in nature. There are two possible explanations for this discrepancy. First, the model was deliberately made symmetric, thus precluding the effects of mutation on the mean. In the one asymmetric model that was investigated, in which there was a heterotic lethal, the optimum mutation rates were of the order of 10^{-5} or 10^{-4}. The second explanation involves polygenic systems. It was found that if the phenotypic effect a at one locus was replaced by $a/2$ at each of two loci, the optimum mutation rate per locus was approximately halved. Thus the optima which are found by this approach are optimal not per locus, but per unit of phenotypic variance. For systems involving about 100 loci, the optima would correspond to those which are observed. Thus the analysis to date does not yet permit prediction, but does elucidate the adaptive significance of mutation.

C. *Migration*

Migration, which involves the exchange of genes between two populations, opposes differential selection and retards their divergence. This may improve or reduce the fitness

TABLE 1

Fitness and its components as functions of phenotype and mutation

Model	a	u	$\overline{W}$	Factors reducing $\overline{W}$		COV	COR
				VARM	VAPHE		
1	0.06	0*	0.926457	0.000206	0.001430	−0.000113	−0.031
		10^{-4}	0.926454	0.000204	0.001434	−0.000101	−0.028
		5×10^{-3}	0.926257	0.000150	0.001576	+0.000159	+0.100
	0.12	0*	0.927946	0.001731	0.004625	0.000471	+0.045
		5×10^{-3}	0.928417	0.001380	0.005537	0.001750	+0.187
		$7 \times 10^{-3}*$	0.928448	0.001300	0.005733	0.002068	+0.228
		10^{-2}	0.928391	0.001197	0.005956	0.002419	+0.277
	0.24	0	0.919426	0.011168	0.015001	0.004656	+0.175
		4×10^{-3}	0.923455	0.010195	0.019229	0.008270	+0.325
		8×10^{-3}	0.924590	0.009365	0.020762	0.009484	+0.389
		$16 \times 10^{-3}*$	0.925193	0.007995	0.022557	0.010549	+0.468
		20×10^{-3}	0.925146	0.007429	0.023167	0.010788	+0.497
2	0.10	0	0.999745	—	—	−0.000254	−0.082
		0.010	1.000098			+0.000103	+0.033
		0.040	1.000925			+0.000950	+0.341
		0.086*	1.001257			+0.001317	+0.616
		0.088	1.001256			+0.001318	+0.623
		0.090	1.001255			+0.001317	+0.630

Model 1: $W = 1 - (s - \text{PHENOTYPE})^2$, $\sigma_s^2 = 0.1$, autocorrelation of $s = 0.9$
Model 2: Periodic environment, half period 20 generations, s alternates between $+0.33$ and -0.33
$\qquad W = 1 + s \times \text{PHENOTYPE}$
$\qquad a$ = additive phenotype effect
$\qquad u$ = mutation rate, equal in both directions
VARM = variance of mean phenotype
VAPHE = average phenotypic variance within population
$\qquad$COV = covariance of s and mean phenotype
$\qquad$COR = correlation of s and mean phenotype
$\qquad$* = optimum mutation rate for each a

of the populations, depending on the statistical pattern of the environment in space and time.

Suppose that the environments of the two populations are constant and different. Then the exchange of genes between them displaces each gene frequency from its optimum and reduces fitness. This is the familiar swamping effect.

Now consider an opposite situation, in which the average environments of the two populations are equal, but they fluctuate independently. Then the effect of migration is to damp the response to selection in each population. We have seen above that a response to selection is not advantageous unless the environment has a high autocorrelation. Thus migration increases fitness by preventing the population from responding to fortuitous fluctuations of the environment. However, it might also prevent response to long-term environmental change and retard adaptation were it not for the fact that environmental changes that are of long duration are also more widespread. Therefore, the fluctuations in the two regions will tend to be in phase with respect to long-term trends and independent with respect to short-range events. Thus migration provides additional "information" about the kind of environmental change which is occurring, and increases fitness by permitting response mainly to those of high autocorrelation.

From the above it can be concluded that the optimum level of gene flow between populations will be greatest where the spatial gradient of the environment is small compared to the variance in time within a locality, whereas the optimum for migration will be least when the spatial gradients are steep and temporal variances small.

One additional aspect of migration must be noted. When the genetic heterogeneity within and among populations is based on epistatic interactions among many loci, recombination between populations often results in F_2 breakdown. Therefore migration will be especially harmful when such systems are important. But it was shown in the previous discussion that a stable polymorphism, a genetic heterogeneity that does not respond readily to selection, will be optimal when the environment fluctuates in time with low autocorrelation, and where the individual homeostasis is small compared to the environmental differences. In such a situation, strongly epistatic systems are expected. Thus in such groups gene flow among local populations will be especially harmful and isolating mechanisms would have a selective advantage. This may be the mechanism at work in the formation of sibling species and subspecies in the *willistoni* group of *Drosophila*.

VI. MULTI-SPECIES SYSTEMS

In community ecology, a major question relates to the conditions of coexistence of species. The rate of change of each species x_i in each niche k is given by an equation of the form

$$\frac{dx_{i,k}}{dt} = R_{i,k}x_{i,k}\left[N_k - x_{i,k} - \sum_{j \neq i}\alpha_{ijk}x_{jk}\right] + \text{Net Migration},$$

where $R_{i,k}$ is the rate of increase in an open environment, N_k is the carrying capacity of the environment in niche k, and the term in brackets shows the density effects of the same and the other species. The α_{ijk} are coefficients of interaction, the effects of species j on species i in niche k. For the study of equilibrium values it is not too important that $R_{i,k}$ might also have to include x if the interaction is not adequately expressed by the linear term. The first question is, what are the conditions for equilibrium?

There are several possibilities. First, if $R_{i,k}$ is greater than zero, so that the species can sustain itself in niche k without immigration, and if all the α_{ijk}'s are less than 1.0, so that the inhibiting effect of another species is less than the effect of individuals of the same species, a stable equilibrium is possible. Second, even if these conditions are not met, equilibrium is possible provided there is sufficient immigration.

However, this refers only to demographic, not evolutionary, equilibrium. The ecologist ordinarily treats $R_{i,k}$, α_{ijk}, and the rates of migration as constants. But these are all biological properties of the species concerned, and hence subject to change under natural selection. Therefore the question is not merely, will this set of species with these constants reach demographic equilibrium, but will evolution change these constants in a way that preserves or destroys the equilibrium? In what follows, the evolutionary pressures on the ecological "constants" are examined.

A. The Evolution of R

The constants $R_{i,k}$ are the logarithms of the corresponding $W_{i,k}$, the average number of offspring of species i in niche k. We could ask, over what range of environments will R be positive (or W greater than 1.0)? The plot of W against environment in Figure 1 is a single peaked curve which can be tall and narrow, or short and broad. If the restriction is established that $\int W(s)\, ds = 1$, it becomes possible to ask how a fixed amount of reproductive potential should be spread over the niches in such a way as to maximize R. Thus the problem is to maximize $\int \log W(s)P(s)\, ds$, where $P(s)$ is the probability distribution of the environment, and can be continuous or discrete (in the latter case the integral is replaced by summation).

The solution to this problem, which plays an important role in information theory, is that $W(s)$ should be proportional to $P(s)$. Thus when the environment is more variable the optimal adaptive system has a broader tolerance and a lower peak (less specialized). This result is essentially the same as that obtained in the fitness set model, except that it does not separate the tolerance into individual flexibility and polymorphism.

B. Niche Selection

However, the variance of the environment refers not to the meteorological environment, but to the effective environment which members of the species actually experience. This will be grossly related to the meteorological environment, and also to niche selectivity. Niche selectivity enters into the equations for equilibrium directly, through its influence on net migration between niches, and indirectly through its influence on R.[9b]

At first glance it would seem desirable for an organism to have the greatest possible niche selectivity and always to move to its preferred niche. However, this is not so, as can be seen by the following argument. Suppose an insect is inseminated and goes forth to find an oviposition site. It has a limited period of time available. If it finds the preferred niche, in which R is maximal, it will accept it and stay there. But suppose it finds a niche which is not as good. If it oviposits there, the possibility of finding the preferred niche is sacrificed. If it does not oviposit but continues searching for the preferred niche, it runs the risk of not finding any niche at all, within the limit of the available time.

A reasonable decision function would be for the insect to seek the preferred niche initially, but to become less exacting as time runs out. If the fitness in the preferred niche is W_p and in the less preferred niche is W_L, it is advantageous to accept the less preferred niche when $pW_p = W_L$, that is, when the risk of finding no niche at all $(1 - p)$ is sufficiently great so that the average fitness attached to continued searching no longer exceeds fitness in the less preferred niche. This point will be reached sooner if W_L is greater, that is, if the environmental tolerance is greater. In Figure 3 the evolutionary relationships among some of these factors is shown. An arrow indicates a positive effect; a line terminating in a circle indicates a negative effect.

Thus, a large effective variance of the environment increases the optimal tolerance and reduces optimal niche selectivity by increasing the probability of not finding the preferred niche. High tolerance reduces optimal niche selectivity. Niche selectivity reduces the effective environmental variance. Competition reduces both the optimal tolerance and niche selectivity, whereas high population density reduces niche selectivity to allow spillover. The diagram shows the way in which the various factors affect the direction of natural selection on the other factors. However, it cannot directly predict the results in a given case since the genetic system involved has not been specified.

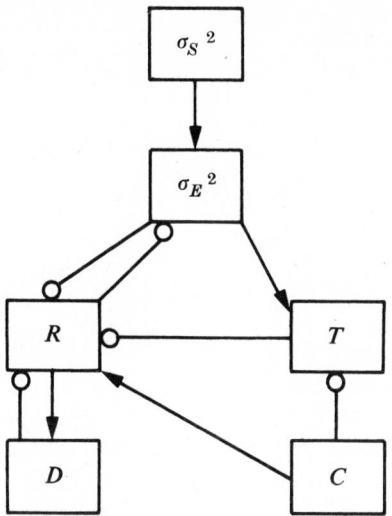

FIGURE 3. Interaction of evolutionary pressures. σ_S^2, environmental variance; σ_E^2, effective environmental variance; C, competition; T, tolerance; R, niche selection; D, population density. $\rightarrow$ indicates enhancing effect; $-\!\!\circ$ indicates reducing effect.

C. *Matrix Representation of an Ecosystem*

A set of interacting species in a single niche have their equilibria defined by the set of equations

$$x_i + \sum_{i \neq j} \alpha_{ij} x_j = 1$$

or in the matrix notation, $AX = I$. It appears as if the structure of the matrix can be used to describe the community, and that certain matrix properties will change as the community evolves. For purposes of illustration some simplifying assumptions will be made. Let the α_{ij} be independent statistically, except that α_{ij} may be correlated with α_{ji}. For instance, in competitive relations both will be positive, whereas in prey-predator pairs they will have opposite signs. Further, assume that the expected value of each α_{ij} is zero. Define D_n as the value of the determinant of order n, D_{n-1}^i as the determinant of order $n - 1$ formed by striking out the ith row and column, et cetera.

When a new community is formed by random immigration, the assumption of independent α_{ij} holds. The determinant of the whole system can be expanded by minors, and the expected values taken. Then it can be shown that

$$E(D_n) = E(D_{n-1}) - (n - 1) \operatorname{cov}(\alpha_{ij}, \alpha_{ji}) E(D_{n-2})$$

From this it follows that the average value of D_n becomes negative as n increases, whenever the covariance term is positive. But since a positive determinant is necessary for the stability of the equilibrium, the model places an upper limit on the average number of species as a function of the symmetry of interactions.

For each i, the expected relative abundance is

$$x_i \sim [E(D_{n-1}) - (n - 1)E(\alpha_{ij})E(D_{n-2}) - \sum \operatorname{cov}(\alpha_{ij} D_{n-2}^{ij})]/D_n$$

where the covariance term is initially zero. In the course of subsequent evolution, selection will reduce the α_{ij}'s, the sensitivity of a species to competition. This is the familiar character displacement. However, the strength of selection is strongest for those α_{ij}'s whose D_{n-2}^{ij} is greatest. Thus selection will result in the development of negative correlations between the α_{ij}'s and their cofactors.

This is a special case of a matrix property which changes under selection. The stability of such a system will also change, as will the probability that a new species can successfully enter. The hierarchical structure of the community enters through the covariance term cov $(\alpha_{ij}, \alpha_{ji})$. The heterogeneity of the community enters through the variance of the α_{ij}'s, and the model can also be adjusted to allow for size differences. No doubt the evolutionary maturity of a community will be measurable eventually through its matrix properties which in turn may be deduced from the distributions of relative abundance.

VII. CONCLUSION

The patterns of adapted biological systems are the result of natural selection. The relative roles of individual flexibility, polymorphism, and geographic differentiation, the contributions to fitness of mutation, migration, additive and epistatic genetic effects, and the evolution of specialization, niche selection, and community composition, all depend on the statistical structure of the environment in space and time. But each mode of adaptation affects the evolution of the others, so that the analytic framework must deal with many complexities simultaneously.

By sacrificing precise numerical prediction and working with inequalities it is possible to begin analyzing these complex interactions and to make testable predictions about the large-scale patterns in nature.

REFERENCES

1. da Cunha, A. B., and Dobzhansky, T. 1954. A further study of chromosomal polymorphism in *Drosophila willistoni* in its relation to the environment. *Evolution* 8: 119–134.
2. Dickerson, G. E. 1955. Genetic slippage in response to selection for multiple objectives. *Cold Spring Harbor Symp. Quant. Biol.* 20: 213–224.
3. Fisher, R. A. 1930. "The Genetical Theory of Natural Selection," 272 pp. Clarendon, Oxford.
4. Fisher, R. A. 1934. Randomization and an old enigma of card play. *Math. Gazette* 18: 294–297.
5. Kimura, M. 1956. A model of a genetic system which leads to closer linkage by natural selection. *Evolution* 10: 278–287.
6. Kimura, M. 1961. Natural selection as the process of accumulating genetic information in adaptive evolution. *Genetical Research* 2: 127–140.
7. King, J. C. 1961. Inbreeding, heterosis, and information theory. *Am. Naturalist* 95: 345–364.
8. Levins, R. 1961. Mendelian species as adaptive systems. *General Systems* 6: 33–39.
9a. Levins, R. 1962. Theory of fitness in a heterogeneous environment. I. The fitness set and adaptive function. *Am. Naturalist* 96: 361–373.
9b. Levins, R. 1963. Theory of fitness in heterogeneous environments. II. Developmental flexibility and niche selection. *Am. Naturalist* 97: 75–90.
10. Lewontin, R. C. 1955. The effects of population density and composition on viability in *D. melanogaster. Evolution* 9: 27–41.
11. Lewontin, R. C. 1957. The adaptation of populations to varying environments. *Cold Spring Harbor Symp. Quant. Biol.* 22: 395–408.

12. Lewontin, R. C. 1961. Evolution and the theory of games. *J. Theoret. Biol.* **1:** 382–403.
13. Luce, R. D., and Raiffa, H. 1957. "Games and Decisions," 507 pp. Wiley, New York.
14. Shull, A. F. 1929. Determination of types of individuals in aphids, rotifers, and Cladocera. *Biol. Rev. Cambridge Phil. Soc.* **4:** 218–248.
15. Watt, K. E. F. 1962. Use of mathematics in population ecology. *Ann. Rev. Entomol.* **7:** 243–260.
16. Wright, S. 1931. Evolution in Mendelian populations. *Genetics* **16:** 97–159.
17. Wright, S. 1949. Adaptation and selection. *In:* "Genetics, Paleontology and Evolution," (G. L. Jepsen, G. G. Simpson, and E. Mayr, eds.), pp. 365–389. Princeton Univ. Press, Princeton.
18. Wright, S. 1955. Classification of the factors of evolution. *Cold Spring Harbor Symp. Quant. Biol.* **20:** 16–24.

[16]

ECOLOGICAL CONSEQUENCES OF NATURAL SELECTION

Robert H. Mac Arthur

I. INTRODUCTION

Why is a viceroy butterfly orange? The cell biologist might answer, "Because it has orange pigment, or the gene for it." The population biologist would answer, "Because only those viceroy ancestors who, by being orange and thus resembling the distasteful monarch butterfly, deceived the predators and were able to leave descendants." Neither answer is more correct, or more fundamental. However, the population biologist prefers his answer because, he is convinced, the viceroy does not care what orange pigment it contains, or what biochemical pathway leads to orange color, so long as it continues to resemble the monarch butterfly. And this belief allows the population biologist to predict correctly,[1] that in regions where the monarch is largely replaced by the distasteful queen butterfly which is brown, the viceroy, to mimic it, will be browner.

The principal difference between the two answers to our initial question is one of strategy as opposed to mechanism. The cell biologist is giving the machinery by which that particular viceroy became orange, and the population biologist is giving the strategy by which the viceroy population manages to persist in the world. The predictions the population biologist is interested in making are usually based on the assumption that organisms have acquired a good strategy by natural selection. Thus it would be a good strategy for the viceroy to be browner where the mimic species is browner, and the correctness of this prediction reinforces our belief that good strategies are the outcome of natural selection.

But good strategies are sometimes ambiguous. Altruism, for instance, when practiced on strangers, may help preserve a species. However, a gene which causes it will almost always suffer within its local population at the expense of the selfish, nonaltruistic allele. We will return to this later; for the time being, we will only be concerned with predictions of strategies which benefit individual and society alike.

But what makes us sure that natural selection can ever achieve these good strategies? Random genetic changes might overcome adaptively directed ones; enough time might not have elapsed for the adaptation to be completed; mutations for the best strategy might even theoretically be lacking. We need not worry too much about these possibilities, because there is good evidence that evolution does in fact lead to some predictable state. This evidence is convergence.

If the marsupial "mole" and the true moles are so similar in spite of their different ancestries, surely we can conclude that the similarity is due to the requirements of the mole's underground life and is thus more or less unaffected by drift, lack of sufficient time and, even to some extent, of the spectrum of available mutations. We thus conclude that prediction is possible; if we understood the difficulties of the environment and were wise enough to predict which tools would allow an organism best to cope with these difficulties, predictions would be easy. We can, however, go only a little way at present.

Is there any phenotypic trait which always changes in a predictable way through the action of natural selection? We might answer, "Yes, any trait which allows its bearers to leave more descendants." But, although the current rate of leaving descendants can be measured (and we will call it "fitness"), the number of descendants remaining one hundred years hence, say, is not measurable now and hence is not a phenotypic trait. Fisher[2] and Kimura[3] have shown that, when conditions remain constant so that current fitness does determine the number of descendants at future times, then natural selection always increases the fitness and, in fact, changes the population composition so that, subject to certain restrictions, the increase in fitness is a maximum. (See also Chapter 15.)

However, if conditions do not remain constant, fitness does not necessarily increase. What, then, does? We can proceed a little further[7] by assuming that the environmental changes are in the population density itself. Then the fitness of each genotype falls with population density and is zero for some density K, depending on the genotype. Then, the K values replace the fitnesses as the variables controlling natural selection, and the mean value of K usually increases. More generally, if the genotypes have different effects on the renewal of the limiting resource, then the density of the limiting resource necessary to maintain the population at a constant level always decreases. But even this rule fails to hold if the utilization of the resource is not conservative, for example, if one competitor pollutes the resource so that it is unpalatable to the other.

In general, it does not seem possible yet to name a phenotypic (or measurable) trait which always increases, unless we are willing to make assumptions about the uniformity, or at least the degree of regularity[5] (see Chapter 15), of the environment. Let us then assume that the environment continually maintains its same course. There will be occasional storms and other catastrophes, but we shall assume these are constant in frequency.

II. PREDICTING LIFE-HISTORIES

A. The Cost of Reproduction

Since birth rates, death rates, and other life-history phenomena have the most obvious influence on fitness, K and the like, their control by natural selection will be considered first. Clutch size and sex ratio are phenotypic traits to which fitness can easily be assigned; hence they are predictable as outcomes of natural selection. By assuming that genes vary clutch size and sex ratio *independently*, Fisher[2] (see also Kolman[4]) and Lack[5] were able to give accounts of the action of selection on these factors. Here we shall allow genes to vary both clutch size and sex ratio separately or *simultaneously* and will show that natural selection will lead to that clutch size and sex ratio which maximizes the product of the number of male offspring times the number of female offspring. To see this, let us make a log-log plot of the possible family compositions of children which existing genes will allow (Figure 1). The virtues of the logarithmic plot will appear below.

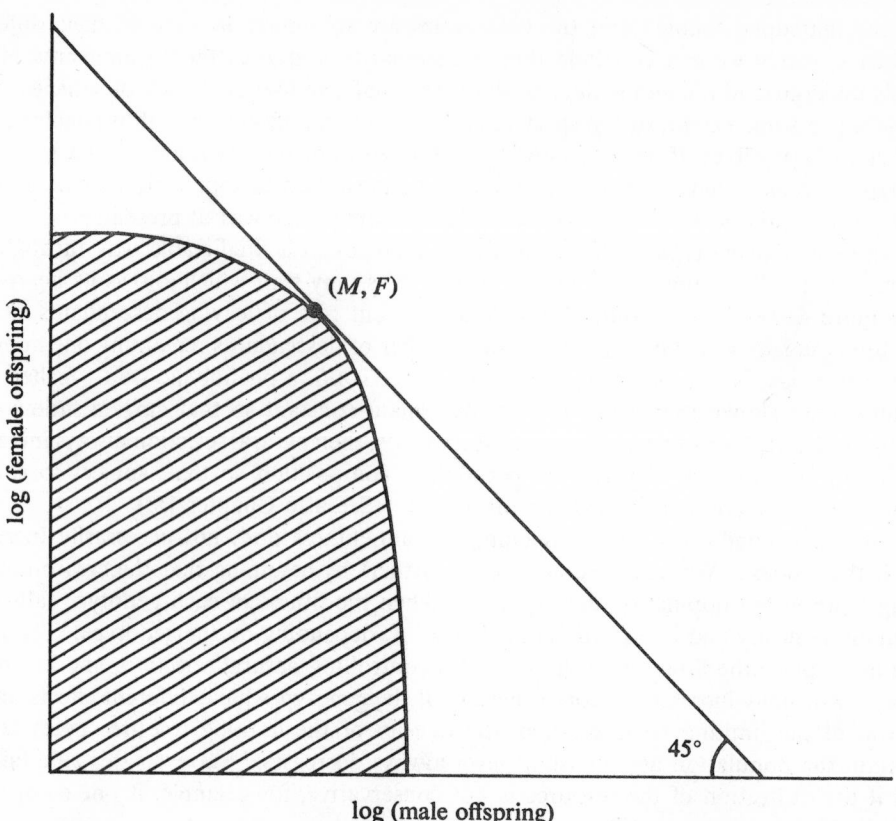

FIGURE 1.   Graphic model for determining the action of natural selection when clutch size or sex ratio or both together may vary under genic control. The possible family compositions (numbers of male and female offspring) permitted by a given genotype are plotted as the shaded area. The optimal strategy is the point (M, F) at which the line log males + log females = constant is tangent to the shaded area.

In the graph all the shaded family compositions will be possible, but that one favored by natural selection will clearly be somewhere along the boundary of the shaded area. Consider any autosomal gene influencing family size or sex ratio. Half of the genes in the population at this locus came from female parents and half from male parents. Hence, from the grandparent's viewpoint, the set of all their sons will contribute equally to the set of all their daughters, and precisely one half of the genes at this locus will be expected to have come from the grandparent generation by way of sons and the remaining half by way of daughters.

Hence if one grandparent has a gene a influencing either sex ratio or family size, or both together, the proportion of the second generation of their descendants which will have the gene is given by C_a:

$$C_a = \frac{1}{2}\frac{M_a}{M_a + M_r} + \frac{1}{2}\frac{F_a}{F_a + F_r}$$

where M_a is the number of males reared to reproducing age by the grandparent with the *a* gene and M_r those reared by the rest of the grandparents. F_a and F_r are the corresponding numbers of females. Natural selection thus maximizes C_a. Taking the first differential,

$$-dC_a = \frac{1}{2} \frac{M_r}{(M_a + M_r)^2} dM_a + \frac{1}{2} \frac{F_r}{(F_a + F_r)^2} dF_a$$

and since $dC_a = 0$ when M_a and F_a are adjusted for a maximum contribution,

$$\frac{M_r}{(M_a + M_r)^2} dM_a = - \frac{F_r}{(F_a + F_r)^2} dF_a \qquad (1)$$

Let us now inquire what the best equilibrium strategy for the whole population is. In other words, what are the optimal values of M_a, F_a when the ratio $\dfrac{M_r}{F_r} = \dfrac{M_a}{F_a}$, so that all the population is using the same sex ratio? In this case $M_r = kM_a$ and $F_r = kF_a$ where the k's are equal. Substituting these in Equation (1),

$$\frac{dM_a}{M_a} = - \frac{dF_a}{F_a} \quad \text{or} \quad \frac{d \log M_a}{d \log F_a} = -1$$

This is the differential equation of a line of slope -1 in a log-log plot. Thus in Figure 1, C_a will be maximized where the line of slope -1 is tangent to the shaded area. But this is the point in the shaded area whose coordinates (M, F) have the largest value of $\log M + \log F = \log (MF)$. And where $\log (MF)$ is maximal, so is MF.

Hence we have proved that natural selection will favor that family composition (M, F) which maximizes $M \times F$. In this argument M and F, and also Figure 1, are calculated by counting males and females at the end of the period of parental care, if any, or at the onset of reproduction. But this was just to take a specific example; a similar graph could have been plotted for any age and the M's and F's calculated for that age.

If the genes affect the age at which the mother gives birth (so that generations are no longer synchronized), then the M's and F's and the coordinates of the graph must be replaced by the reproductive value of males and females as defined by Fisher.[2] In this case maximizing $M \times F$ will involve the simultaneous selection of sex ratio, clutch size, and age at reproduction. This model can be extended to any other factor influencing the reproductive values of the offspring.

B. *Geographic Distribution*

It is simple to extend this kind of analysis to include the action of natural selection on geographic distribution. Each species, in each area of the earth, can expect a certain inevitable mortality due to the hazards of migration, unpredictable climate and its effects on food and shelter, and so on. And, as already discussed, each species will acquire as large an effective birth rate as possible. Where this birth rate exceeds the inevitable mortality, the species will persist (Figure 2) and increase until an additional density-dependent mortality balances the excess births.

Where inevitable mortality exceeds the birth rate the species cannot persist and, by continuity, where the species reaches the edge of its geographic distribution (in the figure, at points *A* and *B*), it will have a birth rate just equaling its inevitable mortality. As might be expected, high latitudes with their more severe climate often produce higher inevitable mortality, and consequently, at the northern edges of species ranges they usually have higher birth rates than at the southern edges.

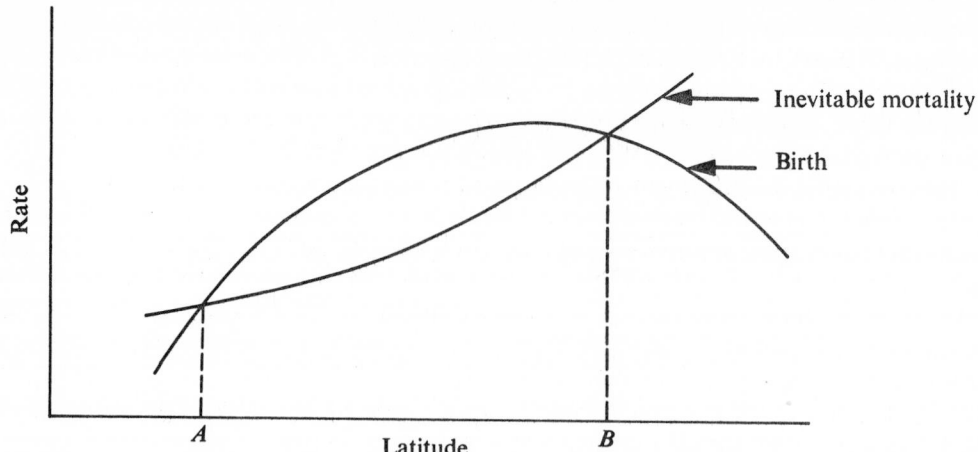

FIGURE 2.   Diagram representing the birth and inevitable death rates of a given animal species as functions of latitude. Between latitude *A* and latitude *B* the species will persist. Notice that, at the edge of the species' range with higher inevitable mortality (*B*), the birth rate must also be higher, and that raising the inevitable mortality will move *B* to the left.

The result of this would be of interest in understanding the number of species that breed in each latitude. For, if too many species settled in high latitudes, and each became correspondingly more specialized, the inevitable mortality rate would rise (because of the climate they would more often stray from the new, more specialized preferences) and the edges of the species ranges would then be forced further toward the tropics, thus reducing again the number of species.

C.   Senescence

A great many other aspects of life history can be predicted as outcomes of natural selection.[6] No more will be discussed in detail here, but the account of senescence, due to Medawar,[10] must be briefly mentioned. Senescence is the increased likelihood, accompanying postreproductive age especially, of succumbing to the hazards of life. Many of these hazards are diseases to which organisms can have different degrees of hereditary resistance. Any hereditary postponement of their time of onset will be favored by natural selection, so long as the disease occurs during reproductive age.

There is no selective advantage to postponing a prereproductive or postreproductive disease, except in certain social situations. The strength of selection for postponement diminishes with age as the reproductive value of the individual dies away. However, Medawar's claim that postponement would be favored only after the peak of reproductive value seems unfounded; this would only be true for diseases which became hereditary after the age of onset, that is, harmful mutations.

III.   NATURAL SELECTION

A.   The Principle of Equal Opportunity

Imagine the following sequence of events. Many species of animals invade a new and varied living area and each is faced with choosing the most suitable habitat and food for itself. But this most suitable habitat depends upon possible competitors. Each species attempts to move into that area for which it is best suited, but some are forced out by competition. Those forced out then try to occupy the habitat which is inherently second best for them. Again some are forced out by competition and these attempt to colonize their third choice, and so on, until every species is undisputed in its habitat.

This process is optimal in the following sense: when each species has found an undisputed habitat, no two could jointly better their lot by exchanging habitats. For, in this case, each would have tried and been evicted from the other's habitat by a species at least as well suited, which species, in turn, can be no better than the one which finally settled there. Thus each species would be outcompeted in its new habitat by the species with which it was about to exchange, and so each could not be bettered by the switch. The above argument assumes that a species outcompeting another makes better use of the habitat, but this is not quite universally true. It is usual enough, however, that the species occupying a particular habitat soon would become essentially sedentary and little more shifting about would be expected.

When the shifting had subsided and our hypothetical multiple invasion had reached a steady state, some habitats would have many species (utilizing different aspects of the environment and so not competing) and some habitats would have few species. What would determine the number of species in each habitat? In general, we can state that this must be dependent on some principle of equal opportunity for further colonization. For if some area presented an ideal opportunity in contrast with others which were packed with species, each barely able to persist, some of the species would benefit by moving into the area with the opportunity. Thus, when shifting had subsided, there would be some property of the over-all system, difficult to measure, which would be equalized.

B. Applications

This hypothetical principle is of interest only if we can measure opportunity or make some other biological statement about it. We can.

1. *Levels of bird speciation.* For birds, at least,[8] we can measure a property of the habitat which allows us to predict the number of species present. In fact, if we define three layers of vegetation, one of ground cover from zero to about 0.6 m above the ground, a second of bushes and understory from 0.6 to about 8 m, and the third of canopy above 8 m, then the number of bird species in American habitats is controlled with astonishing accuracy by the proportions of the total foliage area lying in each of the layers.

When the layers have equal proportions of the total foliage, the number of bird species is greatest; this prediction is virtually independent of the diversity of plant species. Now, if the hypothesis of equal opportunity is valid, the opportunity, locally, is proportional to this measure. There are two other kinds of use we can make of this hypothesis of equal opportunity for further colonization, discussed below.

2. *Island colonization.* Island faunas are often impoverished. For such habitats, opportunity involves not only the structure of the habitat, but also the chances of recolonization if the species should die out. If equal opportunity obtains, the number of species that should be supported by otherwise equal islands of varying distances from sources of colonization can be predicted (Figure 3). Before the shuffling has ceased, the remote islands will have fewer than this prediction. The descending curves represent the rates of immigration of new species not already on the island, the lower rates of immigration of course being those to the more remote islands. The ascending curve is the rate of extinction of species on the islands, assumed equal.

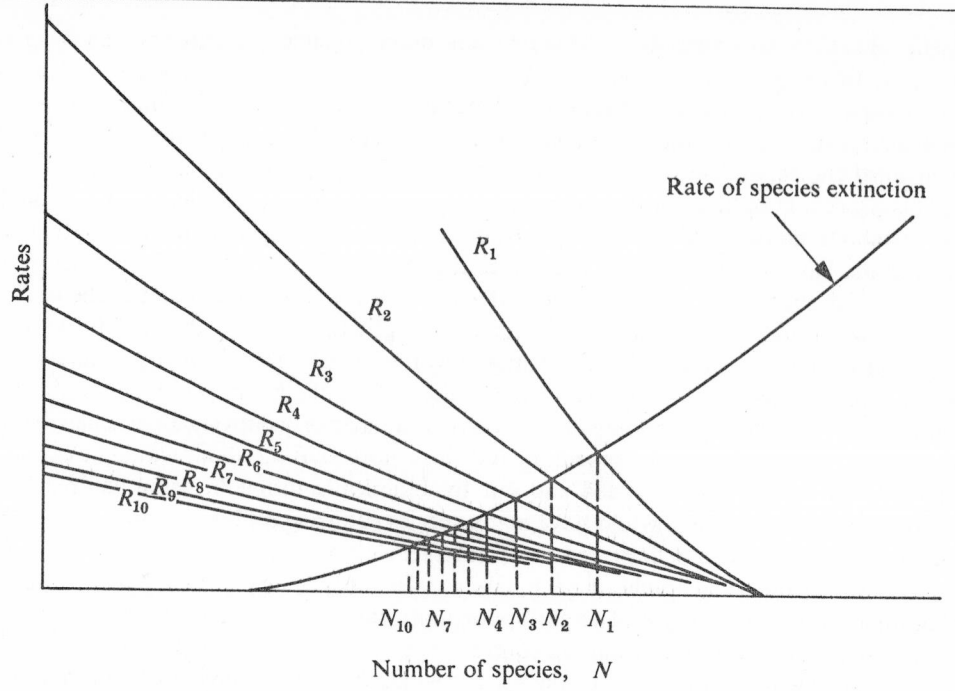

Rate of species extinction

R_1

R_2

R_3

R_4

R_5

R_6

R_7

R_8

R_9

R_{10}

Rates

N_{10} N_7 N_4 N_3 N_2 N_1

Number of species, N

FIGURE 3.   The set of curves R_1 to R_{10} graphs the relations between the number of species already present (N) and the rates of immigration of new species onto islands lying 1 to 10 units of distance from the source of colonization. The extinction curve indicates the number of species dying out in a unit of time as a function of N. The corresponding equilibrium numbers of species on the various islands are shown by N_1 to N_{10}.

For obvious reasons, both immigration and extinction curves are functions of the number of species present. Where the curves intersect, new species are colonizing precisely as fast as old ones are dying out, and there will be an equilibrium number of species at this point. Similarly, we could draw a family of extinction curves representing islands of different area, different climate, or different rates of extinction for other reasons. This kind of graph allows us to predict the differences between islands in terms of the number of species to be expected on each.[9]

3. *Tropical diversity*. A less likely application of the principle of equal opportunity utilizes this rule to explain the well-known high species diversity in tropical areas. For, if there is equal opportunity for further colonization in tropical and temperate habitats of approximately the same structure, then the greater number of species in the tropical area must depress the opportunity there by precisely the same amount as do the less predictable climate and higher mortality in temperate regions. Thus, if the principle holds, a relation between effects of species diversity, environmental hazards, and opportunity would be expected.

In fact, Figure 4, or one like it, will be appropriate. For, if all species had equal chances of becoming extinct, then the chances of any given one dying out would be $1/N$ times the expected number of species dying out, which is the slope of the straight line in Figure 4. Thus, with species extinction curves as in the figure, N_1 and N_2 would be sample numbers of species determined by the principle of equal opportunity. (If the last species to arrive is the most likely to die, equal opportunity would produce N_1 and N_2 at points of equal slope on the mortality curves.)

As shown in the figure, a fairly small difference in extinction rates between tropical and temperate areas could account for a large difference in the numbers of species expected on the basis of equal opportunity. However, there are many who claim, with some evidence, that tropical and temperate habitats do not have equal opportunity. Rather, they believe that the tropics have some sort of a head start in the process of speciation and that species are still gradually moving out from the tropics to settle temperate regions. If this proves generally true, then equal opportunity will have to be rejected as an explanation of tropical diversity, but it will in all probability still apply locally.

4. *Predator-prey relations.* Finally, let us discuss the intricate subject of the effect of natural selection on predator-prey interactions. The basic nature of these interactions can be demonstrated in a graph where the coordinates are the predator and prey population densities (Figure 5). Time is not a coordinate; its effect will be introduced later with arrows, indicating the direction in which the state will change. On the figure, the areas (sets of situations) which lead to predator increase are stippled. The situations which cause a prey increase are hatched.

Basically, the shapes of the shaded areas are determined as follows. The predators can increase only when the prey density exceeds some number; this number is, in an instantaneous model, relatively independent of the predator population density. The prey can increase only when they are common relative to the predators, and, at the same time, are not so numerous that they exhaust their own food supply. Now, in the region which is both

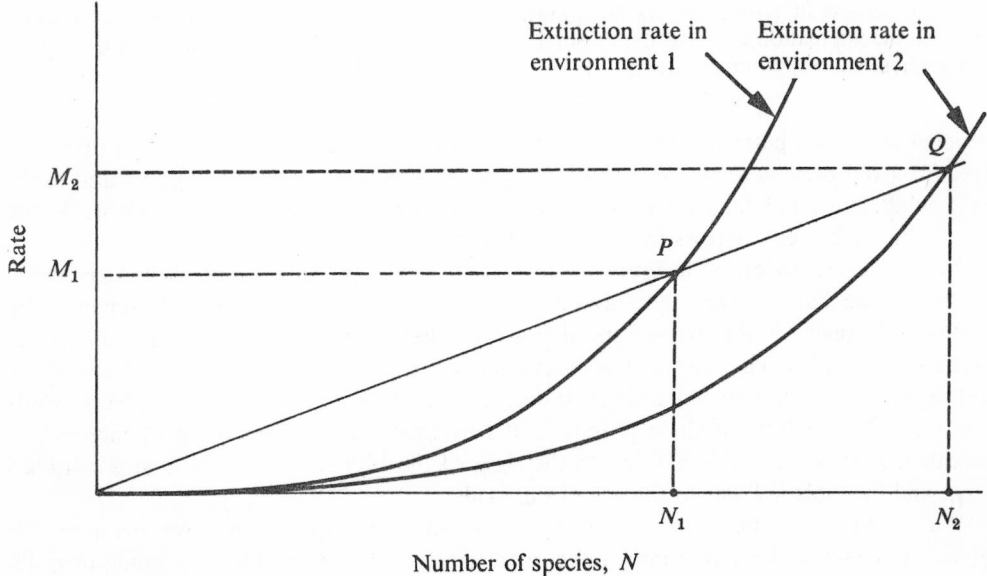

FIGURE 4. Sample extinction rates in two different environments are plotted as functions of the number of species present, N. By similar triangles, $M_1/N_1 = M_2/N_2$, provided Q lies on the straight line from the origin passing through P. Since M_i/N_i is the expected rate of extinction of any randomly chosen species in the area with N_i species, then in each environment the species all have, on the average, equal chance of dying out; i.e., the areas offer equal opportunity for further colonization.

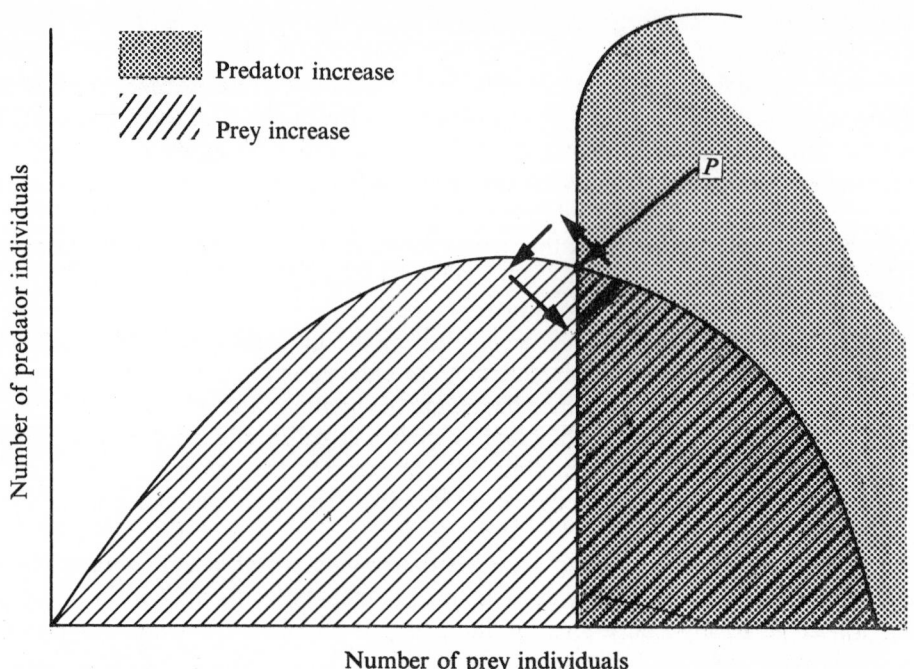

FIGURE 5. Interrelations between numbers of prey and predators in a given environment. The zones of increase of typical species are shown superimposed. The arrows indicate the direction in which the population composition must change in the four quadrants determined by the shaded zones whose envelopes intersect at *P*.

stippled and cross-hatched, the arrows must go up and to the right, indicating that both predators and prey increase. Where stippling alone is present, arrows will go up and to the left; where cross-hatching alone is present, arrows will go down and to the right; where no shading is present, arrows will go down and to the left.

Putting the arrows onto the figure, we see that they spiral around the point of intersection, *P*. Hence we have proved that predator-prey interactions inevitably are oscillatory in nature. However, if the arrows spiral inwards, then a stable, stationary population of predators and prey will exist and no oscillations need be witnessed. If the arrows spiral outwards, the oscillations will always be detectable and the situation will be at least locally unstable. An analysis of these graphs in the neighborhood of the point of intersection reveals that they are stable if *P* lies to the right of the highest point of the cross-hatched area, and unstable if *P* lies to the left of this point.

We are now in a position to consider the effect of natural selection on one aspect of predator behavior. For, as pointed out earlier, natural selection will favor a predator genotype which can maintain itself on fewer prey individuals, thus moving the stippled area to the left. If we can assume that the shape of the cross-hatched area does not change with the genotype composition of the predator population, then we can conclude that natural selection produces more unstable predator-prey interactions.

This, however, is the starting point of a theory of group selection because the really unstable communities will perish, taking all the local population of the unstable genotype with them. If the recolonizers are more likely to be of the stable type, then group selection will be operating. The investigation of group selection, the situations in which it could operate, and the role it has played is one of the most promising aspects of population biology.

IV. SUMMARY

1) We can name no phenotypic trait which always increases under the action of natural selection, but the number of individuals maintained by a unit of available resource is the trait which most often increases.

2) Life-history phenomena such as sex ratio, clutch size, and geographic distribution can be partially understood as outcomes of natural selection.

3) To the extent that there has been enough time for species to adjust their habitats and distributions until all shifting has subsided, an equal opportunity for further colonization will obtain and can account for the numbers of species found in different habitats. Some examples of the necessary calculations are given.

4) Ordinary natural selection often favors increasing instability of predator-prey interactions, but group selection may prevent this from eliminating stably oscillating types.

REFERENCES

1. Brower, J. V. Z. 1958. Experimental studies of mimicry in some North American butterflies. *Evolution* **12**: 32–47.
2. Fisher, R. A. 1958. "The Genetical Theory of Natural Selection," 2nd rev. ed., 291 pp. Dover, New York.
3. Kimura, M. 1958. On the change of population fitness by natural selection. *Heredity* **12**: 145–167.
4. Kolman, W. 1961. The mechanism of natural selection for the sex ratio. *Am. Naturalist* **95**: 373–377.
5. Lack, D. 1954. "The Natural Regulation of Animal Numbers," 343 pp. Clarendon, Oxford.
6. Mac Arthur, R. H. 1961. Population effects of natural selection, *Am. Naturalist* **95**: 195–199.
7. Mac Arthur, R. H. 1962. Some generalized theorems of natural selection. *Proc. Natl. Acad. Sci. U.S.* **48**: 1893–1897.
8. Mac Arthur, R. H., and Mac Arthur, J. W. 1961. On bird species diversity. *Ecology* **42**: 594–598.
9. Mac Arthur, R. H., and Wilson, E. O. 1963. An equilibrium theory of insular zoogeography. *Evolution* **17**: 373–387.
10. Medawar, P. B. 1957. "The Uniqueness of the Individual," 191 pp. Basic Books, New York.

[17]

CODA

Talbot H. Waterman

I. INTRODUCTION

When a man ceases to be creative, he becomes an anachronism. His emotional and intellectual life is reduced to a dim preoccupation with past perceptions rather than being an ever renascent expression of present insights or challenging prophecies of the future. This is true not only of the feelings and thoughts of an individual but also of their social communicative counterparts, commonly recognized as art and science. The essence of the creative act lies in its perceptive keenness and its expressive power. Fresh relationships and new elements are its substance. Yet its success is measured somehow by evaluating the balance established between the accepted, classic, regular, coherent, and expected components of the thing created (be it a painting, a quartet, or a scientific hypothesis) and those which are unconventional, modern, exceptional, isolated, and unforeseen.

Such value judgments now seem largely intuitive, as indeed does the process of creation itself. Nevertheless we have dared to suggest that some serious reconsideration of the methodology of biology could provide a stimulus to the whole field's development into a more balanced and rewarding branch of science. Specifically it has been proposed that the deliberate cultivation by biologists of a more theoretical and mathematical approach to their work might well give rise to a disproportionately great advance in the power and interest of their results. To support this notion we have enlisted the combined talents of the contributors who have written this volume.

In this concluding section can our suggestion be said to have been justified? Can the varied and even disparate parts of the book be shown to comprise an intelligible as well as helpful series of signposts from which to steer future courses of action? The following summary attempts to answer these questions.

II. PHYSICAL THEORY

It is belaboring the obvious to claim that the methodology of molecular biology pays off. Both in principle and in fact the use of physical theory for the explanation of life phenomena in terms of underlying mechanisms has been a richly rewarding procedure. The basic biochemical unity of living systems and their organizational distinction from the nonliving lead directly to the molecular level.[12] In this regard, the origin of life, as well as its unique functional and structural features, all depend on the special properties of essential polymeric macromolecules (Chapter 5). The secondary and tertiary structure of these units, in the first instance proteins and nucleic acids, along with their specific aggregation into particles or other fine structures of various sorts like membranes, fibers, and viruses, are of crucial biological importance.

All of development and evolution depends on the self-reproduction of the nucleic acids and, through their mediation, on the precise synthesis of enzymes and coenzymes. Such complex, precisely balanced systems must have gone through a long process of molecular and systems evolution since the origin of life.

In the earliest phases of this development, whether it took place on earth or extraterrestrially, chance properties of particular elements, constituting part of L. J. Henderson's fitness of the environment,[18,19] had important determinant effects on the nature of living things. The appearance of exactly self-duplicating information-storing molecules and the isolation of organisms were critical subsequent steps. In the latter process the development of molecular sheets to form partitioning membranes seems a key evolutionary advance. This would be essential to formation of the first cells and thus the first discrete living being. Then the striking structural uniformity of cilia and flagella, of striated muscle fibers and of centrosomes, would suggest the early fixation of a precise basic pattern for a number of the organelles of cells.

Although major emphasis recently has been centered about the relation of detailed molecular structure to biological function, it is abundantly clear that other aspects of physical and chemical theory have had rewarding applications. For example, the examination of the thermodynamic and chemical kinetic nature of living systems has been a matter for experiment and analysis since Lavoisier's time. In recent years the application of quantitative reaction rate theory derived ultimately from statistical mechanics has illuminated the problem of enzyme mechanisms and greatly increased our understanding of the metabolic flow of energy (Chapter 4).

Thus experimental data on light output in bioluminescent reactions as affected by temperature, pressure, and various inhibitors have been analyzed by such methods. By using the thermodynamic form of the absolute rate theory as a model, good agreement can be obtained in a number of cases between prediction and observation; at the same time some significant conclusions can be drawn about the number of molecules involved in a particular reaction or about the nature of the intermediate activated complex in the process.

Similarly, several problems important in protein synthesis can be treated quantitatively with reaction rate theory, for instance, enzyme specificity, stereochemical mechanisms, and errors in transmitting the genetic code. Statistical errors in this last category may be thought of as somatic mutations. From this point of view the kinetic results of enzyme specificity may have a considerable, but as yet largely unexplored, influence on the rates of evolution.

Important applications can also be derived from reaction rate theory for the analysis of membrane transfer. The standard physical treatment of diffusion and permeability can be modified by incorporating thermodynamic state functions so that a powerful model is available for prediction and testing. Significantly, such analysis is valid not only for equilibrium systems but also in open systems near equilibrium where irreversible thermodynamics is required.[4] Parallel treatment is also appropriate and fruitful in the study of coupled reactions such as those normally occurring in metabolic systems (for instance, Chapter 13). In all these cases the free energy of activation determines the rate of the component steps while the entropy of activation provides clues to the specific mechanism involved.

In the study of biological membranes, marked progress has likewise been derived from the application of basic principles of electricity and communications engineering to the crucial functions of these living structures, particularly in excitation and conduction (Chapter 6). This field has in fact been one of the most fruitful in the recent history of biology, both in the relative elegance of its theoretical treatment and in the extent and sophistication of its experimental data which have been intimately linked together with theory, as indeed they must be in a mature science (Chapters 1 and 12, also references[6,9]).

One fundamental property of most cells is that their membrane conductance increases during activity although their electrical capacity remains effectively constant. Strong overshoot of the action potential beyond the resting potential shows the spike to be an actively generated process, while the demonstration of nonlinear properties in the dynamic responses of such systems has greatly increased the difficulties of their experimental study or effective theoretical treatment. However, satisfactory quantitative measurements of the relations between membrane voltage and membrane current are possible with the use of voltage clamp techniques. These stabilize the axon membrane area being investigated in such a way that an ordinary differential equation, rather than an intractable partial differential one, can be used to model the results.

From this platform the remarkably successful Hodgkin-Huxley axon model (consisting of empirically derived equations and an hypothesized ionic mechanism) quantitatively accounts for many of the membrane's resting and active properties specifically in terms of its conductances to sodium and potassium ions. The latter are, of course, intimately related to the special elementary properties of the alkali metals (Chapter 5) and to the molecular structure of membranes as well as to the kinetics of membrane permeability and transport (Chapter 4). Evidence is at hand that these phenomena are not parochial to the squid giant axon from which they were first experimentally derived but are of quite broad generality, at least in principle. The relations between membrane structure and permeability, in addition to that between metabolism and transport, are far from being adequately understood even though they have long been a major challenge to biologists (Chapter 6; see also reference[1]).

Although the applications of physical theory to biology so far considered in this summary have dealt with phenomena largely on the molecular or ionic level, this is by no means a limitation of the approach. The topic of the mechanics of the mammalian cochlea (Chapter 7) may serve as proof of this. The explanatory principles relevant here are the physics of vibration and hydraulics. The inner ear structure whose function is to be understood, comprises the basilar membrane which is a complex mechanical oscillator, coupled to the fluid which fills the cochlear cavity. Although the structure of the cochlea is complicated and impossible of adequate study in a living man, experiments prove that its mechanics can be reduced to those of the basilar membrane alone and that with adequate care the cochlea of a cadaver vibrates just like a normal living one.

Direct observations on the effect of point deformation of the basilar membrane clearly demonstrate that of the four hypotheses put forward for cochlear mechanism only one can be valid, namely that vibrations transmitted to the cochlea via the oval window give rise to patterns of traveling waves in the basilar membrane. In turn, these determine the patterns of stimulation in the organ of Corti which is the actual mechanoreceptor of hearing. Direct microscopic observation of light reflections from the cochlear membrane not only confirms the traveling wave theory but also, from vibration phase and amplitude data, provides a dynamic analysis of the membrane's behavior.

In this way the vibration amplitude maxima can be shown to move up and down the cochlea with frequency, being nearest the apex for low frequencies and nearest the oval window for high. Fascinatingly enough, the mechanical properties of this system are remarkably stable to changes in dimensions or shape of the canals and to loading or cutting of the membrane itself. Models which produce traveling waves showing a number of parallels to cochlear behavior can be made with a series of vibrating reeds or swinging pendulums having different periods and coupled together in some suitable wày. In general, energy flows through these systems from the stiffer components to the more compliant ones.

In the cochlea, how these basilar membrane vibration patterns deform the hair cells in the organ of Corti and how these deformations in turn give rise to the primary sensory responses, generator potentials, and ultimately auditory neuron spikes is still largely speculative. It is already clear, however, that lateral inhibition and temporal interactions have important effects here as they do in other sensory systems (Chapter 14).

III. STATISTICAL ANALYSIS AND COMPUTERS

Although most biologists use at least a minimum of statistics in their data analysis, the simultaneous quantitative treatment of a number of interdependent variables or systems by the techniques of multivariate analysis is not yet widespread despite their power and appropriateness to many biological issues (Chapter 8; also reference[16]). The central problem here may be considered to be the discrimination between different complex biological systems or populations.[8,14,15] Its solution can be obtained by determining the positions of these systems in n-dimensional space and calculating an appropriate quantitative measure of the differences separating them (for instance, the generalized distance or the angles between vectors).

This is one approach being used in the development of numerical taxonomy (Chapter 9; see also reference[17]); the same kind of analysis is equally relevant to the study of relative growth and development as well as to the study of evolution. In the last case multivariate analysis provides clues to the linkage between assemblages of characters which are acted on by natural selection essentially as units; the further exploitation of such potential evidence for mechanisms should be rewarding. In simpler cases multivariate statistical methods essentially confirm the conclusions reached with traditional techniques. However, despite the fact that their reasonably sophisticated use is just beginning, the newer procedures are already able to move strongly into more difficult problems where the older methods fail.

Computers are particularly suited for dealing with the complex interrelated systems that characterize biology. However, even though the development and the widespread application of these instruments have been practically explosive in the past ten to fifteen years, a relatively small percentage (perhaps only about 1%) of total computer time has been devoted even recently to basic research in biology (Chapter 10).

Analog computers can carry out a variety of mathematical operations for which the number being handled is converted, for example, to a voltage which can then be operated on electronically as required. Addition, subtraction, multiplication, division, and integration are possible, and the output appears with time as the independent variable and a voltage on the ordinate as the dependent variable. In the case of a general purpose differential analyzer, this final output would be the solution of a differential equation input. Where a series of differential equations represents the dynamic properties of some functional structure like the circulatory system, an analog computer can act as an equation solver predicting its performance.

In contrast, digital computers handle numbers as numbers and are capable of extremely rapid arithmetical operations. Furthermore, their sequencing, decision-making, iteration, and instruction-changing capabilities are of even greater importance. For convenience in programming, special computer languages (for example, FORTRAN and ALGOL) are ordinarily used but must first be fed into a compiler which issues instructions meaningful to the main instrument. Of the large range of powerful computer applications, programs which aid in establishing amino acid sequences in proteins from biochemical experiments, in recognizing, counting, and measuring the chromosomes of histological preparations, and in various aspects of medical diagnosis, may be cited.

An important digital computer method, the so-called Monte Carlo technique, should be particularly mentioned since it permits the indeterminacy of quantum biochemical events[13] or other stochastic processes to be accounted for in programming (Chapter 11). Where reactants or enzymes occur in a fixed or bound state as in the case of the electron transfer system, this may be a necessary feature of any satisfactory treatment. The Monte Carlo method can also deal effectively with reactions which occur in solution and obey the mass law. Other useful digital computer programs for modeling biochemical systems are simulations of radioactivity in reaction components, and of the effects of compartmentation on complex processes.

One of the most complicated systems to be thoroughly studied with digital computers is glycolysis in the Ehrlich mouse ascites tumor cell, for which a 22-equation simplified model was programmed (Chapters 11 and 13). If all the components known to be important in the real system were included, several hundred differential equations, notably in excess of the then available computer capacity, would be required. In such biochemical modeling, hypotheses concerning poorly known or as yet experimentally unapproachable relationships can be tested by experiments carried out with the computer itself.

Programs based on differential equations like the law of mass action obviously are not restricted in their use to the study of biochemical systems. They can also be applied in ecology, an analogy particularly obvious from the application of the law of mass action to ecological systems by Volterra and others (Chapters 2 and 11). More or less complex models reflecting competition and many other ecological phenomena can be programmed (Chapter 16). In pelagic regions of the sea one might expect the ecosystem to approach a chemical system rather closely in its behavior. However, such modeling is not yet feasible because of lack of adequate biological oceanographic data, not in this case because of lack of suitable programs and computers. Nevertheless, a variety of parametric and nonparametric analyses are beginning to be applied to the general study of plankton.[2,5,20]

Curiously enough, the cost of computer time usually limits the modeling problems which now can be tackled in practice by this means; nevertheless it seems likely that when the speed and expense problems are properly solved, computer modeling will emerge as a widespread, powerful method in biology, provided that enough biologists are interested in it and are capable of using it.

IV. SYSTEMS THEORY

For any science such as biology which deals with complex, interconnected entities, systems theory is an approach of great general importance (Chapters 1, 2, and 12). It deals formally with organization and hence is useful over a broad range of applications.[7] Thus the mechanism of the homeostatic regulation of blood pressure in the brain of a giraffe would be a relevant specific case while the general concept of black boxes and white boxes, as well as their interrelations, underlies the whole of natural science.

The much-cited black box represents any empirical system under study, chosen for reasons of scientific strategy or convenience. It has an input and an output which can be measured. By observation or experiment it is found to operate according to some rule which may be probabilistic or analytical and which associates output with input. This whole concept is a useful one because it isolates components (of greater or lesser complexity themselves) in a system too complicated to be analyzed otherwise and characterizes in a simple, direct way their essential contributions to the whole organization's behavior.

Hence a biological black box is merely a symbol for the functions of some component of interest. It is nothing metaphysical, incapable of scientific study, but merely a useful, reasonably isolatable unit. This may range, for example in the case of metabolic energy flow, all the way from an ecosystem embracing the world ocean whose caloric output and input are estimated, down to a specific molecular step in glycolysis where coupling of oxidation and phosphorylation is the relevant datum.

Although the contents of a black box are not known, the usual purpose of isolating it as a unit is to discover or hypothesize what they are. To do this the black box is tentatively replaced in the over-all system by a white box whose contents are known and have in fact been deliberately chosen so that its input-output relations will be the same as those observed for the black box it represents. The white box therefore is a model or hypothesis or explanation of how the black box works. It is inherent in the nature of science that, at a minimum, a circular pathway must interconnect the black and white boxes.

Upon starting with empirical data (behavior of the black box) one must induce generalizations, hypotheses, or laws from these (the contents of the white box) and then close the circle by returning again to the data plane to check on their predictability, extensibility, and other metaphysically desirable requisites of scientific constructs.[11] Such new data may in turn require minor or major alterations in the white box whose effect must then be tested on the empirical level, and so on.

Of course in the long run the pathways followed must be more complex than this. Ultimately, as wide a range of data and constructs as possible should be interconnected since coherence and generality are necessary attributes of a well-developed area of science. Nevertheless the circularity here emphasized between the two kinds of boxes is fundamental.

On the basis of such ideas a unified concept of systems analysis can be developed to demonstrate an inherent similarity in the main theories of organization: cybernetics, decision and detection theory, game theory, and communication theory (Chapter 12). In all these cases the system whose behavior is to be analyzed is treated as a white box receiving inputs from and delivering outputs to its surroundings.

Then within the system three types of components are hypothesized. Two of these are in effect black boxes at the next more detailed level within the whole system. These are 1) sensors and effectors which receive inputs from the environment or other components and produce outputs which influence the environment or other components, as well as 2) computer-like elements which generate the laws or strategies by which the system works. A third type of component, the motivator, establishes the reference level needed in regulation; the origin of such criteria is not explained by systems theory and hence is a weakness in it.

The method of systems analysis consists basically of assembling within a white box a number of these components connected together so that the over-all behavior of the model system parallels in significant ways that of the empirical one under study. Important general features of systems models of this kind are their ability to detect differences between their actual output to the environment and the predetermined level set by the motivators, as well as their capacity for minimizing such differences by feedback loops.

Used with proper understanding and precautions, the various kinds of systems analysis can provide powerful tools for biological research. For example, an interesting model can be derived for the nucleic acid-mediated induction of specific enzyme synthesis in cells; the model in question shows striking organizational similarity to the general scheme of systems analysis outlined above. In this particular case the genes would probably be simulated by motivator components.

For dealing with the various inputs and outputs considered in systems analysis, it is often convenient to use the terminology of information and communication theory. The messages transmitted over these conceptual networks may be referred to as information and the latter defined specifically as the average number of binary choices required to select a given message from the whole set available. So defined, the over-all information input to biological systems is enormous while their capacity to handle information is much more modest.

Consequently, living beings are organized at many levels on the Principle of Signatures, according to which only one or a few of the many features of a given complex unit are used as information. The ethologists' sign stimuli and active sites on enzymes would be examples. By such selection of the small fraction of the total input which is of adaptive importance, the amount of information which must be processed and give rise to appropriate effector outputs is kept within the system's channel capacity. Another important feature of the information handling activity of the nervous system is its capability of maintaining a high degree of accuracy, despite noise and a lack of precision in individual components of the circuit.[3]

Sequential analysis of the biochemical steps in metabolism is an important goal in understanding metabolic control mechanisms (Chapter 13). Conceptually the system can be modeled by a sort of directional graph with feedback loops. Knowledge essential to its analysis may be obtained by studying the effects of transients on the time course of reactions within the system. Hence quantitative data on the rate changes in nucleotide phosphorylation and cytochrome oxidation after muscle contraction or after substrate addition to a suspension of starved cells, can provide important clues to over-all organization of the metabolic mechanism (Chapter 11). Distinction between cytoplasmic and mitochondrial phases as well as determination of respiratory rates can provide additional evidence for the importance of compartmentation and feedback in this system.

A systems analytical approach to the functioning of the nervous system permits important properties of this crucial integrating mechanism to be deduced either from detailed electrophysiological and physiological optical data or from appropriate quantitative behavioral data on the whole organism. For example, the underlying mechanisms determining visual acuity and movement perception in the compound eye of arthropods can be hypothesized from data originating in these two ways (Chapter 14).

In the lateral eye of the horseshoe crab *Limulus*, a quantitative model can be devised which accounts for the observed acuity of this sensory system. Appropriate analysis of the optical properties of ommatidia and their effective aperture demonstrates that, at this level, marked overlap of the visual fields of neighboring units produces a low-resolution system.

However, the physiologically useful acuity depends in addition on the processing and central registration of the basic optic information. Hence the retinal phenomena of lateral inhibition may counteract the coarseness of the optical resolution so that neurological "focusing" will improve the over-all system's performance, a sensory mechanism which apparently has quite general importance (Chapter 7).

The available data for the *Limulus* eye permit the development of a simplified but rigorous model of its image formation on the basis of these optical and neurological interactions. Provided with estimated overlap coefficients and inhibition coefficients, this model predicts that for ommatidial axial angles of 15° or more, lateral inhibition could completely compensate for the effects of optical overlap. With smaller interommatidial separations the compensation would be partial.

From the behavioral side, a minimal mathematical model of sensory processing in insect visual tracts can be developed from the good data available on optomotor responses to movement of vertical stripes in the field of vision. This model comprises two information transmitting channels with cross connections leading from adjacent receptor units to a motor output. Three pairs of transfer functions are involved in the minimal model, and these must be evaluated to test it. Data on the quantitative responses to different velocities of a sinusoidal input can be utilized for this purpose.

Confirmation of predictions made from the minimal model on the real system provides reassuring support for the model's validity. Consequently, a linearly transformed auto-correlation function of the brightness variations in the visual field may be considered as the basis for optomotor output responses observed. This measures relative optic movement but, unlike the *Limulus* acuity mechanism, does involve irretrievable loss of information in the channels concerned.

Comparable systems analytical methods may be fruitfully extended to the level of populations considered both from genetic (Chapter 15) and from ecological (Chapter 16) points of view. In the first instance the cybernetic model must link together the molecular events of gene action with the large-scale properties of organisms and populations. The input of the system at any given moment is the pattern of gene frequencies inherited from the past while the output is population fitness which is the expression of another array of gene frequencies and genotypes. Differences between past and present genotypes are due to mutation, migration, and drift, while natural selection is the Darwinian basis for fitness.

Analogous measures of fitness in terms of reproductive rates for different genotypes have been independently derived for simple systems by Sewall Wright and R. A. Fisher. For more naturalistic treatment, environmental variability, interactions of genetic influences on several characters, and the fact that natural selection does not necessarily increase fitness (see also Chapter 16) have to be taken into account. To deal with these effectively, one needs to consider large faunas and floras at once and to assume that even though optimal systems may not evolve, the relations between species groups as they actually exist will be similar in kind to those between their optima.

With models of this sort the properties of various kinds of evolving populations may be predicted by computer simulation of the system. Effects of polymorphism, niche diversity, competition, and other potentially important features may be evaluated by this means. Matrix representation of the multispecies case may provide helpful insight into the importance of particular parameters or in any effort to assess the evolutionary maturity of a population.

Clearly it is a short step from systems analysis of population behavior based on such genetic models (Chapter 15) to comparable analysis of examples where the primary emphasis falls on the ecological aspects of the system (Chapter 16). In this case fitness may be considered as an inverse function of population density, usually being highest at low densities and falling to zero at some higher density, K. With such a model, numerous aspects of life history such as birth and death rates, sex ratios, cost of reproduction, geographical distribution, and senescence can be explained as outcomes of natural selection.

In considering the invasion of a heterogeneous territory previously not inhabited by a particular group of organisms, there is some property of the system which may be called opportunity for maintained existence. As all the niches are entered, competed for, and ultimately occupied in a quasi-steady state condition, this opportunity tends to be equalized in all parts of the system. In several diverse cases of bird distribution, for example, this opportunity can be measured and given some biological meaning. Thus, in island colonization the opportunity comprises both habitat structure and access for immigration (defined in terms of distance from a source of invasion). Other suggestive applications of the principle of equal opportunity can be made to habitat levels in vegetation, speciation in the tropics, and prey-predator interactions.

V. CONCLUSION

The power and range of the work reported in the body of this book (and reviewed above) provide strong support for our contention that almost every phase of biology can benefit greatly from appropriate use of theoretical and quantitative methods. For those who already work in this manner, or are at least now convinced of its efficacy, our basic point needs no further emphasis even though much remains to be done in all parts of the field to realize adequately the values of the approach.

For those who have not yet used such methods or who remain unconvinced that they could be of much help to them, important educational problems remain. Clearly biologists who would like to follow and extend the strategies here outlined must learn the essential techniques and see to it that their students are properly trained to use them. This means that mathematics, statistics, systems theory, computer techniques, physical chemistry, and other theoretical and quantitative methods must have a greater place in the education of all biologists.

Of course this cannot happen on an effective scale without further evolution of proper training programs. Undergraduate and graduate curricula must be devised with a variety of alternative approaches to these areas. These are difficult enough to plan for students, who already have enormous areas of knowledge competing for their understanding, but such planning is particularly hard for the mature biologist whose early training was deficient in some essential respects. Provided the latter has sufficient motivation, advanced training courses, senior post-doctoral fellowships, and collaboration with experts in the relevant interdisciplinary methods are important opportunities which must be made increasingly available.[10] However, the crucial problem of motivation is a subtle one for which there is no short-cut solution.

From the point of view taken in Chapter 1, that revolution in biology should come both from within and from without, much of the book may seem lopsided. In it we have mainly emphasized the powerful gains which can be made in all of biology when a more conceptual and quantitative approach is used. Yet it can also be strongly argued that equally great advances in biology would ensue if the theoretical biologists, biometricians, biomedical engineers, biophysicists, and systems analysts who work on biological systems were more adequately acquainted with the living systems which they wish to analyze and model.

Here again we are faced with major educational and motivational problems like those mentioned above. Researchers and students alike must have strong foundations in the whole field of biology from the molecular to the population level before they are likely to make their deserved contributions to progress. If this point is granted, and it seems inevitable that it must be, there can remain no doubt that the soundest course for biology is to develop into a truly interdisciplinary field in which really adequate techniques, knowledge, and insight are brought to bear on its major problems. More important problems for mankind would be hard to cite.

REFERENCES

1. Agin, D. 1963. Some comments on the Hodgkin-Huxley equations. *J. Theoret. Biol.* **5:** 161–170.
2. Cassie, R. M. 1963. Multivariate analysis in the interpretation of numerical plankton data. *New Zealand J. Sci.* **6:** 36–59.
3. Cowan, J. D. 1963. The engineering approach to the problem of biological integration. *In:* "Nerve, Brain and Memory Models" (N. Wiener and J. P. Schadé, eds.), pp. 22–29. Elsevier, Amsterdam.
4. Dainty, J., and Ginzburg, B. Z. 1963. Irreversible thermodynamics and frictional models of membrane processes with particular reference to the cell membrane. *J. Theoret. Biol.* **5:** 256–265.
5. Fager, E. W., and McGowan, J. A. 1963. Zooplankton species groups in the North Pacific. *Science* **140:** 453–460.
6. Finkelstein, A., and Mauro, A. 1963. Equivalent circuits as related to ionic systems. *Biophys. J.* **3:** 215–237.
7. Grodins, F. S. 1963. "Control Theory and Biological Systems," 205 pp. Columbia Univ. Press, New York.
8. Harman, H. H. 1960. "Modern Factor Analysis," 469 pp. Univ. Chicago Press, Chicago.
9. Hoyt, R. C. 1963. The squid giant axon, mathematical models. *Biophys. J.* **3:** 399–431.
10. Lucas, H. L., ed. 1962. "The Cullowhee Conference on Training in Biomathematics," 390 pp. Typing Service, Raleigh, N.C.
11. Margenau, H. 1961. "Open Vistas," 256 pp. Yale Univ. Press, New Haven.
12. Netter, H. 1959. "Theoretische Biochemie," 816 pp. Springer, Berlin.
13. Pullman, B., and Pullman, A. 1963. "Quantum Biochemistry," 867 pp. Interscience, New York.
14. Quenouille, M. H. 1952. "Associated Measurements," 242 pp. Butterworths, London.
15. Rao, C. R. 1952. "Advanced Statistical Methods in Biometric Research," 390 pp. Wiley, New York.
16. Seal, H. L. 1964. "Multivariate Statistical Analysis for Biologists," 207 pp. Methuen, London.
17. Sokal, R. R. 1962. Variation and co-variation of characters of alate *Pemphigus populi-transversus* in Eastern North America. *Evolution* **16:** 227–245.
18. Wald, G. 1962. Life in the second and third periods; or why phosphorus and sulfur for high-energy bonds? *In:* "Horizons in Biochemistry" (M. Kasha and B. Pullman, eds.), pp. 127–142. Academic, New York.
19. Waterman, T. H. 1961. Comparative physiology. *In:* "The Physiology of Crustacea" (T. H. Waterman, ed.), Vol. II, pp. 521–593. Academic, New York.
20. Williamson, M. H. 1961. An ecological survey of a Scottish herring fishery. Pt. IV: Changes in the plankton during the period 1949 to 1959. *Bull. Marine Ecol.* **5:** 207–229.

AUTHOR INDEX*

---

* Reference numbers in parentheses are citations for which the author's name does not appear in the text. Italic page numbers indicate the location of actual bibliographic entries.

SUBJECT INDEX

ABOUT THE EDITORS

Harold J. Morowitz is an Associate Professor of Molecular Biology and Biophysics at Yale University. He received his B.A., M.S., and Ph.D. from Yale, where he held an Atomic Energy Commission Predoctoral Fellowship from 1949 to 1951, and is a member of Phi Beta Kappa and Sigma Xi. Dr. Morowitz then worked as a physicist for the National Bureau of Standards, and as a biophysicist for the National Heart Institute before returning to Yale in 1955. He is a member of the Biophysical Society, the American Chemical Society, the American Association for the Advancement of Science, and a Fellow of the New York Academy of Sciences.

Talbot H. Waterman is a Professor of Biology at Yale. A *magna cum laude* graduate of Harvard University, Dr. Waterman is a member of Phi Beta Kappa and Sigma Xi, and was elected a Junior Fellow of the Society of Fellows. After earning the degrees of M.A. and Ph.D. at Harvard and working as a Research Associate of its Psycho-Acoustic Laboratory, Dr. Waterman became a Staff Member of the Radiation Laboratory at MIT until he joined the Department of Zoology at Yale in 1946. His present major interests within the field of biology are visual physiology, spatial orientation, and submarine polarized light. A Guggenheim Fellow (at the Australian National University) from 1962–1963, he is on the Executive Committee of the American Society of Zoologists, a Trustee of the Bermuda Biological Station, and a Sigma Xi National Lecturer for 1964. Dr. Waterman has published many scientific papers, and was editor of a two-volume work on *The Physiology of Crustacea*.

THIS BOOK WAS SET

IN TIMES ROMAN TYPE BY

THE UNIVERSITIES PRESS.

IT WAS DESIGNED BY THE STAFF OF

BLAISDELL PUBLISHING COMPANY.